nutrition
FOR LIVING

nutrition
FOR LIVING

Janet L. Christian
Janet L. Greger
University of Wisconsin, Madison

with the assistance of Susan A. Nitzke
on Part Six

The Benjamin/Cummings Publishing Company, Inc.

Menlo Park, California ● Reading, Massachusetts ● Don Mills, Ontario ● Wokingham, U.K.
Amsterdam ● Sydney ● Singapore ● Tokyo ● Mexico City ● Bogota ● Santiago ● San Juan

Sponsoring Editor   Jane Reece Gillen

Developmental Editor   Amy Satran

Production Coordinator   Pat Waldo

Interior and Cover Designer   Michael Rogondino

Photo Researchers   Tobi Zausner and Monica Suder

Illustrators   George Omura, Cathleen Jackson Miller, and Mary Burkhardt

Layout Artist   Brenn-Lea Pearson

Copy Editor   Carol Dondrea

Library of Congress Cataloging in Publication Data

Christian, Janet L.
   Nutrition for living.

   Bibliography: p.
   Includes index.
      1. Nutrition. I. Greger, Janet L. II. Title.
QP141.C548   1984   613.2   84-22971
ISBN 0-8053-2000-8

ABCDEFGHIJ-RN-898765

The Benjamin/Cummings Publishing Company, Inc.
2727 Sand Hill Road
Menlo Park, California 94025

Brief Contents

Detailed Contents

PART ONE You Are What You Eat **1**

FRONTIER ■ FRONTIER ■ FRONTIER ■ FRONTIER ■ FRONTIER

Discussions of subjects on the frontier of nutrition science are integrated within the text, but are set off by a vertical color band running along the edge of the page. These subjects, which are often controversial, are listed at the bottom of the Detailed Contents on the pages that follow.

FRONTIER ▪ FRONTIER ▪ FRONTIER ▪ FRONTIER ▪ FRONTIER

FRONTIER ■ FRONTIER ■ FRONTIER ■ FRONTIER ■ FRONTIER

FRONTIER ▪ FRONTIER ▪ FRONTIER ▪ FRONTIER ▪ FRONTIER

FRONTIER ■ FRONTIER ■ FRONTIER ■ FRONTIER ■ FRONTIER

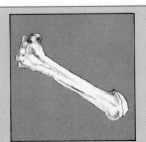

FRONTIER ■ FRONTIER ■ FRONTIER ■ FRONTIER ■ FRONTIER

FRONTIER ■ FRONTIER ■ FRONTIER ■ FRONTIER ■ FRONTIER

FRONTIER ▪ FRONTIER ▪ FRONTIER ▪ FRONTIER ▪ FRONTIER

FRONTIER ▪ FRONTIER ▪ FRONTIER ▪ FRONTIER ▪ FRONTIER

Preface

Are you

- an instructor of a college introductory nutrition course for nonmajors?
- a student who wants nutrition information for your own use, rather than for a nutrition career?
- a student who has little or no college science background?
- an agency or business representative who must frequently answer questions consumers have about nutrition?

If you answered "yes" to any of the above questions, this book may be a match for your textbook needs. Our goal in writing the book was to present the science of nutrition in a lively and personal way. We wanted to help people focus on their own eating practices, and to help them evaluate those habits alongside guidelines for eating that support good health. We are eager to share in this book what nutrition can accomplish, and we will be equally straightforward about its limitations.

Features of This Book

These are the reasons we think this book deserves your attention:

1. Instructors and students helped to develop this book

Before a single word was put on paper, the publisher conducted a mail survey of nutrition instructors to learn in detail about their textbook needs. They also brought together discussion groups of educators in different parts of the country to learn how they envisioned an ideal text. After a preliminary outline had been prepared, and as the chapters were written, the publisher sought critical feedback from instructors on the developing manuscript. Last but not least, the comments and questions of our own students over the years have had a major influence on the topics we chose to cover and how we present the material. The result, we believe, reflects the current needs and preferences of instructors and students nationwide.

2. We have tried to make the text appealing, accessible to the beginning student, and a useful learning tool

We have tried to write with a clear, friendly style and to provide the background necessary for understanding; for example, the basic anatomy and physiology needed to understand digestion is presented in Chapter 3. We have been especially careful to define terms accurately and plainly. Key terms are highlighted in color where they first appear and are defined in a margin glossary immediately adjacent. To emphasize the main message of each section of text, major headings are in sentence form. For preview or review, these headings are listed at the opening of each chapter, and a more detailed outline for the entire book appears in the Detailed Contents (page vii). End-of-chapter summaries review key terms and concepts in a clear, concise form. The reader who wants to pursue certain topics further will find up-to-date references listed at the end of each chapter; citations within the text are given in a "name and date" format.

3. We relate nutrition to the student's life circumstances

For the study of personal nutrition to be useful, students must be able to see how the principles apply to them and the foods they typically eat. In sections called "Slices of Life," we cite examples, both ordinary and extraordinary, that help to bring out the relevance of the information just presented. To make the information even more personal, after the discussion of each nutrient class is a section on self-assessment, which guides the reader through an appropriate nutritional assessment technique.

4. "Frontier" sections highlight nutrition topics still under study

Given the dynamic nature of nutrition today, many questions currently being asked about the effects of nutrition on health do not yet have definitive answers. Discussions of these topics on the frontier of nutrition science are integrated within the text, but are set off by a vertical color band running along the edge of the page. Within these sections, we present the different points of view on the topics covered and describe the recent research studies. Our aim is to provide readers with the basis for forming their own opinions and making their own nutrition decisions. Our hope is that, after reading this book, they will be able to evaluate critically new nutrition information that reaches them through the public media.

5. We offer materials most other texts don't have

A food guide called the Sound Approach to Nutritious Eating (SANE), developed by the authors specifically for this book, builds on the strengths of existing food plans and offers additional easy-to-use information on the fat, sodium, and sugar content of many common foods. We explain in detail how it can be used for both diet assessment and planning (see pages 38–47). An additional tool for assessment and planning is the Appendices section at the back of the book, which includes not only the standard food composition tables but also a number of tables not often found in introductory nutrition texts. These new tables cover zinc, sodium, folacin, vitamin B-6, vitamin B-12, cholesterol, and dietary fiber for a list of selected foods, with the serving sizes converted to common household units.

Also notable in this text are chapters on eating disorders (anorexia and bulimia); the effects of food processing on nutrients; and other substances in food, such as microorganisms, naturally occurring toxicants, and additives.

Topic Capsules (pages xxiii–xxxiii) give overviews of eight topics that are dealt with in several chapters. For example, nutritional needs of the athlete are discussed in the chapters on water, carbohydrates, energy, protein, vitamins, and minerals. To get an overview of the topic, readers can turn to a sentence outline that brings together the key facts and puts them in perspective, along with page references to the text treatment. A margin symbol specific to that topic (e.g., a whistle for athletics) identifies the appropriate paragraphs where they appear in the text. Similar outlines are given for dental health, vegetarian diets, food labeling, atherosclerosis and coronary heart disease, cancer, alcohol, and international nutritional concerns.

Organization of the Book

The scope of this book ranges from discussions of the individual nutrients to a thorough treatment of life-cycle nutrition issues. An introductory section, Part One, sets the stage for these topics by describing how we know that nutrition is important to health, by explaining and illustrating how nutritional status can be assessed, and by reviewing the basic anatomy and physiology of the gastrointestinal system.

Part Two presents the "macronutrients," the substances needed in large quantities by the body for raw materials and energy production. Following an opening chapter on water comes the chapter on "Energy Sources and Uses." We feel that the relatively early position of the energy chapter provides useful background for the next chapters and also allows for early discussion of weight control issues, if desired. The next three chapters—on carbohydrates, lipids, and proteins—make up most of the unit. These nutrient chapters (like the later ones on vitamins and minerals) discuss nutrient functions, distribution in the body, dietary sources, recommended levels of intake, health effects of deficiencies or excesses, evaluation of one's own status, and just enough about chemical structures to make all of that understandable.

Part Three discusses eating behaviors, which provides a change of pace and an opportunity to apply the technical material in Part Two. It starts with a chapter on factors that influence food consumption, "Why You Eat What You Do." In the next chapter, a favorite student topic—how to bring about changes in body weight—is thoroughly discussed, in the light of new thoughts on what constitutes ideal body weight. Anorexia nervosa and bulimia are covered in a separate short chapter on eating disorders.

Part Four returns to the nutrients, with a comprehensive, up-to-date discussion of vitamins and minerals, the "micronutrients." Part Five, *A Taste of Food Science*, speaks to the worries many people have about whether our food supply is offering fewer nutrients and more hazards than it did in "the good old days." To this end, effects of food processing on nutrients, additives, naturally occurring toxicants, and microorganisms in food are discussed.

The final unit, *Nutrition through Your Life*, explains how the levels of need for nutrients change as we grow older. Each phase of life has its own social as well as physiological challenges that involve nutrition. Examples of topics covered include introduction of solid food to infants, special needs of females during adolescence, and nutrition and arthritis. Social programs such as child feeding and nutrition programs for the elderly are also mentioned here.

How should this book be used? Although it is logical to take up the nutrient chapters before those on the life cycle, the other topics can be taken in almost any sequence. For example, Chapter 9 ("Why You Eat What You Do") could be discussed at any time, and the weight control chapter, Chapter 10, could be covered elsewhere in the course. Similarly, the food science chapters of Part Five could easily be relocated as a unit or used singly. We think that the book is sufficiently flexible to meet the restrictions of almost any course calendar and the preferences of any instructor. Furthermore, we believe that it will continue to serve as a useful reference after the course is over.

Supplementary Materials

A complete package of supplementary materials accompanies this text.

- A Student Study Guide by Dr. Bernice Stewart is available through campus bookstores. For each chapter in the text, the Study Guide provides an overview, learning objectives (keyed to pages in the text), a detailed chapter outline, a list of new terms, a programmed self-test, a sample exam, and answers to the sample exam. It also includes blank copies of all the nutrition self-assessment forms in the text, with instructions for their use.

- An Instructor's Guide by Dr. Stewart will be supplied by the publisher to each course instructor who adopts the text. It includes an extensive test bank, a guide to audiovisual materials, and blank copies of all the self-assessment forms in the text, with instructions for their use.

- A Transparency Set, consisting of 50 two-color overhead transparencies, will be available to qualified adopters of the text.

Acknowledgments

In writing this book, help has come in many different forms and from many different corners. We appreciate the inputs of the many colleagues who shared their knowledge and perspectives in different ways. Special recognition goes to Dian Gans, who efficiently located references and helped evaluate materials and prepare tables; and to Susan Nitzke, who brought her impressive resources and positive attitude to the first draft of the "Nutrition Through Your Life" section. The helpfulness of the campus librarians, particularly at the Middleton and Steenbock libraries, made all of our jobs easier.

For their very direct roles in transforming this effort into a book, we thank the exceptional team at Benjamin/Cummings. Special appreciation goes to Sponsoring Editor Jane Gillen and to Developmental Editor Amy Satran for the encouragement, judgment, and skills they gave to us and this project. Also special thanks to the outstanding free-lance professionals who worked on this book—especially Production Coordinator Pat Waldo, who was a model of resourcefulness, efficiency, and cheerfulness while birthing several creative works at once.

We also acknowledge the many careful reviewers and consultants who scrutinized this book in various stages of its development; they are listed below. In addition, we thank the many teachers of introductory nutrition courses who responded to mail and telephone surveys regarding their vision of an ideal text. If your opinions were not tapped, we hope that your colleagues in the field represented your viewpoints. If after using this book you would like to suggest some modifications, please share them with the publishers: your comments will influence the second edition.

Finally, we both warmly thank our families and friends for their personal support and understanding while we took time out from other aspects of living to write this book.

Janet L. Christian
Janet L. Greger

Reviewers and Consultants

Andrea Arguitt, Oklahoma State University
Nancy Betts, University of Nebraska
Wen Chiu, Shoreline Community College
Maxine Cochran, William Penn College
Dorothy Coltrin, De Anza College
Marie Cross, University of Kansas
Lael Cutler, Northeastern University
Marjorie Dibble, Syracuse University
Susan Dougherty, Monroe Community College
Bessie Fick, Auburn University
B.L. Frye, University of Texas
Yolanda Gutierrez, University of San Francisco
Amy Ireson, College of San Mateo
Charlotte Juntunen, University of Minnesota, Duluth
Joan Karkeck, University of Washington
Janet King, University of California, Berkeley
Sondra King, Northern Illinois University
Bo Lonnerdal, University of California, Davis
Sharleen Matter, University of Louisville
Sally McGill, Cañada College
Glen McNeil, Arizona State University
Barbara Mitchell, University of Houston
Elizabeth Mills, Central Michigan University

Susan Nitzke, University of Wisconsin, Madison
Mary Ann Page, Dixie College
Ellen Parham, Northern Illinois University
Ellyn Satter, Jackson Clinic, Madison
Barbara Schneeman, University of California, Davis
Charles Seiger, Atlantic Community College
Jean Skinner, University of Tennessee
Katherine Staples, North Dakota State University
Bernice Stewart, Prince George's Community College
Jon Story, Purdue University
Susan Strahs, California State University, Long Beach
Kathryn Sucher, San Jose State University
Barry Swanson, Washington State University
Steve Taylor, University of Wisconsin, Madison
Mary Ann Thompson,
  Waubonsee Community College
Linda Vaughan, Arizona State University
Jane Voichick, University of Wisconsin
Kathy Watson, Arizona Western College
Margaret West, Chicago State University
Billie Wood, Daytona Beach Community College
Margaret Younathan, Louisiana State University

Topic Capsules

Each of the following Topic Capsules pertains to a subject that is treated, as appropriate, in several chapters in the book. Each capsule is an outline of all major points made on the topic through the book.

Nutrition for the Athlete

The whistle symbol is used in the text margin where these points regarding nutrition for the athlete are presented. The term "athlete," as used in this text, applies to a person who trains for several hours daily to improve strength, agility, and/or stamina.

■ Although the need for some B vitamins increases slightly with high energy intakes, food sources can supply them; supplements are not needed.   **317**

■ Needs for most minerals are not significantly greater for the athlete, although there are a few concerns.

    1.   Iron status may warrant some concern for athletes with short-term "sports anemia" and for anemic female athletes; dietary treatment is often successful.   **351**

    2.   Mineral losses in sweat do not usually need replacement unless water losses are substantial.   **343**

An athletic activity can be influenced by what is consumed a few hours before it.

■ The pre-event meal should be at least three hours before intense competition.   **57, 66**

■ Large amounts of sugary foods or beverages shortly before exercising may have negative effects.   **128, 130**

■ Ingestion of caffeine before exercising may prolong endurance.   **407**

Extreme and/or rapid weight loss has negative effects for anybody, but there are some special concerns for athletes.

■ In women, low body fatness may lead to cessation of menstruation.   **230**

■ In wrestlers who use extreme measures to "make weight," performance may be negatively affected.   **245, 476**

Vegetarian Diets

The carrot symbol is used in the text margin where these points regarding vegetarianism are presented.

Pages

Vegetarianism is an eating style that relies primarily on foods of plant origin; people who practice it are called vegetarians. There are many types of vegetarianism.

180

Although vegetarian diets that include milk and eggs can be adequate if well chosen, vegetarian diets based only on plant foods (*vegan* diets) are more likely to be low in nutrients and/or contain factors that decrease bioavailability of nutrients, particularly minerals.

■ Vegan diets may call for attentiveness to certain nutrients.

1. They may be improved by complementing proteins, especially for pregnant women and young children. **180**

2. They may require supplementation or deliberate intake of food containing vitamin B-12, vitamin D, and/or riboflavin. **301, 312**

3. They may require emphasis on foods that are good sources of the minerals calcium, iron, and zinc due to bioavailability considerations. **331**

■ Vegetarian diets for young children (p. 469), pregnant women (p. 435), and lactating women (p. 446) must be planned with special care because of the particular vulnerability of these groups to inadequate nutrition. **469, 435, 446**

■ Food guides can help vegetarians achieve nutritional adequacy. **48**

U.S. subgroups that practice vegetarianism tend to have certain health characteristics.

■ Vegetarians tend to weigh less than a matched group of omnivores (people who eat foods from *all* sources). **249**

■ Vegetarians tend to have lower serum cholesterol and blood pressure levels than omnivores. **160**

■ Groups of vegetarians have less heart disease (p. 139) and cancer (p. 165) than the general population; however, other lifestyle factors may be involved. **139, 165**

■ Vegetarians are less likely to experience constipation than the general population. **136**

Food Labeling

The can symbol is used in the text margin where nutritional aspects of food labeling are presented.

              Pages

The ingredient list on a food label tells what is in the product.

■ Ingredients must be listed in order of occurrence by weight, from the heaviest to the lightest.   **119**

■ Foods for which there is a standard of identity in the Code of Federal Regulation do not require an ingredient list.   **414**

A nutrition label (headed "NUTRITION INFORMATION") provides quantitative information about nutrients in one serving of the product.

■ Nutrition labels appear on a wide variety of food products, although they are only mandatory if nutrients have been added or if a nutritional claim is made about the product.   **14**

■ The top section of a nutrition label identifies serving size, number of servings in the whole container, kcalories per serving, and grams of protein, carbohydrate, and fat per serving.   **93**

■ The lower section of a nutrition label identifies what percentage of the U.S. RDA is present per serving of food.

   1.   The U.S. RDA (U.S. Recommended Daily Allowances) is a standard derived from the RDA (Recommended Dietary Allowances) that includes the needs of almost all healthy people.   **13**

   2.   The nutrients that *must* be included are protein (p. 181), vitamin A, vitamin C, thiamin, riboflavin, niacin, calcium, and iron. Sodium is included as of July, 1985.   **181, 320**

   3.   The nutrients that *may* be included (any or all) are vitamin D, vitamin E, vitamin B-6, folacin, biotin, pantothenic acid, vitamin B-12, phosphorus, iodine, magnesium, zinc, and copper.   **320**

   4.   You can calculate approximate amounts of micronutrients in labeled food products.   **320**

Atherosclerosis and Coronary Heart Disease

The heart symbol is used in the text margin at the start of each discussion of atherosclerosis and/or coronary heart disease. The primary discussion falls on pages 158–163.

Pages

Atherosclerosis is a condition in which certain materials gradually accumulate in the lining of blood vessels, narrowing and hardening them. It often results in serious health problems such as stroke or cerebrovascular accident (CVA), heart attack or myocardial infarction (MI), or coronary heart disease (CHD).   **158, 159, 492**

CHD occurs with greater frequency in association with certain *risk factors*.

■ Clinical findings help identify risk.   **160**

   1. High blood pressure   **160**

   2. Abnormal blood lipids   **161**

      High total blood cholesterol

      High LDL (low density lipoprotein) cholesterol and low HDL (high density lipoprotein) cholesterol

   3. Abnormal electrocardiogram (measurement of the electrical activity of the heart)

   4. Diabetes

■ Certain living habits put a person at higher risk.

   1. Smoking   **160**

   2. Excess energy intake (obesity)   **160, 228**

   3. Excess fat consumption, perhaps   **161**

   4. Physical inactivity   **160**

■ Some uncontrollable factors increase risk, such as being male, aging, and having a family history of atherosclerosis.   **160**

Several interventions may be useful for lowering high blood pressure.

■ Achieve and maintain body weight within a desirable range.   **342**

■ Regulate intake of certain electrolytes.   **342**

■ Take medication, if indicated and as prescribed.

Several interventions have been suggested for lowering high total blood cholesterol. (Not all experts agree with these recommendations.)

■ Achieve and maintain body weight within a desirable range.   **162**

■ Limit total dietary fat to 30–35% of kcaloric intake, and limit saturated fat and dietary cholesterol. (There is considerable disagreement on these points.)   **161, 167**

■ Other modifications that have been found helpful by some researchers are increasing certain types of fiber and moderate consumption of alcohol.   **138, 504**

■ Take medication, if indicated and as prescribed.

Experts are not in complete agreement whether the general population should be advised to change their diets as a preventive measure.   **163**

Cancer

The cancer symbol is used in the text margin at the start of each discussion relating to cancer. Much of this information occurs on pages 163 through 166.

■ Reduce intake of dietary fat to 30% of kcalories.

■ Increase the consumption of fruits, vegetables, and whole grain products.

■ Be moderate in consumption of salt-cured, smoked, and charcoal-broiled foods.

■ Be moderate in consumption of alcoholic beverages.

Although the weight of evidence suggests that what we eat during our lifetime strongly influences the probability of developing certain kinds of cancer, ". . . it is not now possible, and may never be possible, to specify a diet that would protect everyone against all forms of cancer" (Committee on Diet, Nutrition, and Cancer, 1982).

Alcohol

The wineglass symbol is used in the text margin at the start of each discussion regarding alcohol. Much of this information occurs on pages 501 through 504.

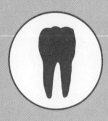

Dental Health

The tooth symbol is used in the text margin at the start of each discussion regarding dental health. Much of this information occurs on pages 133–135.

International Nutrition Concerns

The globe symbol is used in the text margin where these points regarding international nutrition concerns are presented.

Pages

Food production capacity is dependent on availability of basic production resources and advanced technology. Nutrition problems in developing countries are complex, with agricultural conditions, transportation, size of population, national politics, economics, and religious and ethnic factors all influencing per capita availability of food.

205–211

The typical distributions of kcalories in diets in developing and developed countries differ considerably from each other.

210

■ Carbohydrate often accounts for well over 50% of kcalories in developing countries but less than that in developed countries.

139, 210

■ Fat may sometimes be below the recommended intake levels in developing countries, whereas it is often too high in many developed countries.

167, 210

■ Protein intakes are sometimes too low in the developing countries, and often occur in conjunction with adequate energy intake; whereas in the developed countries, protein intakes are usually generous.

190

The major nutritional problems in developing countries are protein energy malnutrition (PEM) (p. 190), and deficiencies of iron (p. 350), vitamin A (p. 288), and iodine (p. 352). Also seen are multiple vitamin deficiencies (p. 294), and deficiencies of zinc (p. 353) and selenium (p. 355).

190
350, 288
352
294, 353,
355

Breast feeding is encouraged in the developing countries because it usually provides nutritional, immunological, and sanitary advantages, and because infants and young children are the most drastically affected by inadequate nutrition. However, seriously malnourished mothers may produce an inadequate supply of milk.

439, 444

440

Foods in developing countries often contain substances that decrease the bioavailability of nutrients (p. 331, 353), and/or may be toxic (p. 412), particularly to malnourished individuals.

331, 353
412

PART ONE

YOU ARE WHAT YOU EAT

1

How Food Affects You

IN THIS CHAPTER: The Human Body Is Made of Elements That Must Be Obtained Mainly from Essential Nutrients ▪ Nutrients Are Used for Three Basic Purposes ▪ Inadequate and Excessive Intakes of Nutrients Are Both Unhealthy ▪ The Effects of Nutrition Occur over Various Time Periods ▪ Different Types of Studies Document the Effects of Nutrition ▪ Good Nutrition Studies Require Careful Work

This is likely to be your first organized study of the science of nutrition.

Nevertheless, you have encountered a great deal of nutrition information already. Throughout your life, you have been gathering your own unique assortment of ideas and feelings about food and nutrition—simply by being a consumer, by participating in family, ethnic, and regional traditions, and by being exposed to advertising and information in the media. You have undoubtedly become convinced from such an ongoing blizzard of ideas (whether they are right or wrong) that food and nutrition are important to health and well-being.

We agree.

nutrition—the interactions between food and a living organism

Nutrition is of such broad influence that it is defined as all the interactions between food and a living organism. Therefore, it involves physiological and biochemical processes, but is also affected by a myriad of psychological, social, economic, and technological factors (American Dietetic Association, 1983).

Nutrition is so important that anthropologists who study the food habits of groups of people say that a society's patterns of choosing, obtaining, preparing, and serving their characteristic foods have a major influence in shaping their culture. Certainly, our food-related activities help to define us and our relationships to each other.

We will deal with such matters in various places throughout the book. But here, to begin, we are focusing on the importance of food for another reason—the nutrients it contains.

nutrient—a substance in food that is used by the body for normal growth, reproduction, and maintenance of health

A nutrient is a substance in food that is used by the body for normal growth, reproduction, and maintenance of health. Nutrients are the basic materials from which the body is constructed and by which it is fueled and regulated.

Unfortunately, people do not instinctively eat foods that contain the nutrients they need, although some other animals may. Human beings not only can—but must—choose foods from a varied banquet of possibilities. We in North America have an especially wide selection, and each one of us has the responsibility for selecting foods that will provide adequate nourishment.

Finding out which foods are the most beneficial to eat is a challenge (Figure 1.1). If you have relied on the print and electronic media for nutrition information, you have probably found some contradictory views. How can you know which are true? For example, you can read different points of view on whether nutrition affects your moods or your ability to think. Or you may hear different suggestions about how the athlete should eat to enhance his or her performance. How can you sort out which information is valid and applicable to you?

We intend to speak to such concerns as the book proceeds. The way the information in this book may differ from some of what you find elsewhere is that we base our material on careful scientific investigation. Because

Figure 1.1 Nutrition ideas come from varied sources.
What any individual knows about nutrition has been accumulated
from different sources and is of variable quality. Some sources of
information are much better than others, and we intend for the
information in this book, which is based on scientific research, to
help you sort out nutrition facts from wishful thinking or misleading pitches.

research is time-consuming and expensive, there are still many gaps in
the knowledge base; we will point out the limits of what is known.

We must also point out the limits of what nutrition can accomplish.
Right at the start, we acknowledge that nutrition, although it is needed
for achieving and maintaining health, cannot by itself guarantee well-
being. Other factors that influence health are the amount of exercise and
sleep people get, whether they protect themselves from environmental and
psychological stresses, whether they get good medical help when they need
it, and what their general attitude is about life. Important as these other
aspects of living are, though, we will leave a discussion of such topics for
experts in those fields.

This chapter explains more fully why nutrition is important. It describes
what types of nutrients are needed by the body and what general roles
they play. It points out the dangers of either deficiencies or excesses of
nutrients, gives standards of recommended amounts for intake, and comments on how long it takes for nutrient effects to be noticed. The chapter
concludes with a discussion of the kinds of studies that can provide valid
information about nutrition.

The Human Body Is Made of Elements That Must Be Obtained Mainly from Essential Nutrients

It is possible to learn what substances are important for maintaining the
body by analyzing what it contains.

Chemical Elements in the Human Body

The basic components of which all things on the earth are constructed are
the 103 elements, the most fundamental chemical substances known. When
the body is analyzed, 27 of these substances are usually identified, although

many more are likely to be found in minute amounts if extremely sensitive testing methods are used.

Oxygen accounts for 65% of the body's weight, carbon for 18%, hydrogen for 10%, and nitrogen for 3%. The remaining 4% of the body's weight is contributed by all the other elements together.

Some elements can be used by the body only when they are consumed in chemically combined form (compounds). For example, hydrogen does nothing useful for the body if it is available in uncombined form as a gas, but the body readily makes use of various compounds that are made with it. If hydrogen is combined with oxygen, carbon, and other elements into specific structures such as water, carbohydrates, fats, proteins, and vitamins, the body can incorporate the hydrogen. Therefore, the body's need is not for the hydrogen per se, but rather for certain compounds that contain it.

The Essential Nutrients

essential nutrients—specific substances that must be taken into the body preformed and in sufficient quantities to meet the body's needs

Humans require close to 50 specific substances that must be taken into the body preformed and in sufficient quantities to meet the body's needs; these are called essential or indispensable nutrients. The nutrients are distinguished from thousands of nonessential substances that are found in food in that the nonessentials either can be produced within the body or are not needed by it.

The nutrients are grouped into six classes: water, carbohydrates, lipids (commonly called fats), proteins, vitamins, and minerals. Table 1.1 shows which elements they contain.

The classes of nutrients needed in the largest amounts are water, carbohydrates, lipids, and proteins; for this reason they are called macronutrients. Vitamins and minerals, which are needed in very small amounts, are micronutrients. Some minerals are required in such minuscule amounts that they are called trace minerals.

Nutrients Are Used for Three Basic Purposes

Nutrients have three functions in the body: (1) They form body structures, (2) they provide energy, and (3) they serve as regulators of body processes.

Structure

The cliche "You are what you eat" succinctly expresses the truth: the materials of which you are composed are made up of nutrients that you—or your mother when she was pregnant with you—consumed and biochemically reconstructed into your unique body substances.

This is not to say that you can completely determine what you become by what you eat. The limits of your body's physical potential are determined by your genetic makeup; the degree to which you achieve that potential is influenced substantially by nutrition (Figure 1.2).

For example, if your genes (the materials that determine hereditary

Table 1.1 Classes of Essential Nutrients and Their Elemental Components

Water	Carbohydrates	Lipids	Proteins	Vitamins	Minerals
Oxygen	Oxygen	Oxygen	Oxygen	Oxygen	22 separate mineral elements
Hydrogen	Hydrogen	Hydrogen	Hydrogen	Hydrogen	
	Carbon	Carbon	Carbon	Carbon	
			Nitrogen	Nitrogen[a]	
			Sulfur[a]	Sulfur[a]	
				Cobalt[a]	

[a]Found in some but not all members of the class.

characteristics) contain instructions for developing unusually long bones, you have a chance of being taller than others whose genes do not carry that information. But if you receive far less than the level of nutrients you should have as you grow, your chances for basketball stardom may be dimmed.

Similarly, if a baby is very seriously deprived of adequate nutrients during periods of rapid brain growth both before and after birth, brain size may be smaller than normal. For the body to be able to generate the full extent of well-organized tissues, organs, and systems for which it has the potential, it must have the appropriate level of raw materials to work with.

The nutrient classes that contribute in a major way to body structure are water, proteins, lipids, and minerals.

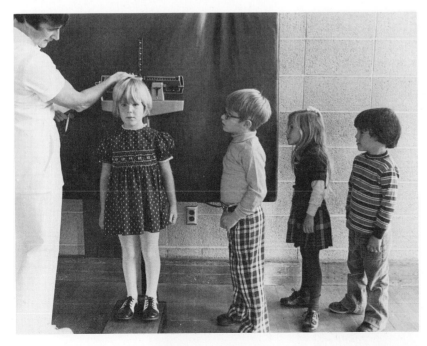

Figure 1.2 You are what you eat . . . within limits. Although what you eat can influence your body development, genetic factors set limits on your body's structural characteristics.

Energy

Another vital function of nutrients is to provide energy. Without energy production, life ceases.

Energy is measured in a unit of heat called the kilocalorie, which will be abbreviated in this book as kcalorie or kcal. (The term *calorie* is in popular use, although this is not technically correct, since a small calorie is only 1/1,000 as large as a kcalorie.) Most adults use between 1500 and 3000 kcalories in a day.

Carbohydrates, lipids, and proteins are nutrients that provide energy. These nutrients are available both from food or from your own body stores of these substances, as we will explain more thoroughly in Chapter 5 (on energy).

The energy nutrients do not provide equal numbers of kcalories. Carbohydrates and proteins each have the potential to produce four kcalories per gram, and fat produces nine. Alcohol, which is variously classified as a nutrient or a drug, furnishes 7 kcalories per gram.

In some situations, there are important implications to what proportion of kcalories come from one energy nutrient as compared with another. For example, if you are pushing yourself to perform a demanding physical activity such as running or cross-country skiing for hours at a time, you may benefit from having consumed more carbohydrate and less fat in the couple of days before the event (Figure 1.3). This process—called carbohydrate loading—will be discussed more thoroughly in Chapter 6 (on carbohydrates).

Regulation

The third important function that nutrients perform is regulation of body processes. The biochemical reactions that take place in a living system, which are cumulatively called metabolism, do not occur in random fashion; they are intricately controlled. Proteins, vitamins, and minerals are the chief nutrient regulators.

Kilocalorie (kcalorie, kcal)— the amount of heat needed to raise the temperature of one kilogram of water one degree Celsius; a measure of energy

metabolism—the biochemical reactions that take place in a living organism

Figure 1.3 Endurance and nutrition. The ability of this woman to endure the rigors of intense physical competition is influenced by genetics, training, motivation, and nutrition.

For example, many of the vitamins participate in the series of reactions that are needed to generate energy, although they themselves are not energy sources. If the vitamins are missing or inadequate, the body will not be as efficient a producer of energy.

Certain essential minerals such as sodium and potassium help regulate how water is distributed in the body; protein also performs this function.

Phosphorous and chloride influence the acidity or alkalinity (the opposite of acidity) of various body substances. This function is critical because a balance between acidity and alkalinity must be maintained in the body; departure from this balance in the blood can result in death. However, these mechanisms normally work so well that even though we take in foods and produce body substances of widely varying acidity and alkalinity, the balance in the blood is maintained.

Inadequate and Excessive Intakes of Nutrients Are Both Unhealthy

There is a beneficial range of intake for any nutrient; to go either below or above that range is usually undesirable, as shown in Figure 1.4. Both undernutrition and overnutrition are forms of malnutrition.

malnutrition—poor nutritional status resulting from intakes either above or below the beneficial range

Consequences of Inadequate Intake of Nutrients

If all or some of the nutrients are totally missing, the body will stop growing, fail to thrive, be incapable of reproduction, and eventually die. On the other hand, if all of the nutrients are present but are generally available in less-than-adequate amounts, the obvious consequences will be less severe: limited growth is the likely result, at least in children. The effect in adults is likely to be low body weight and poor work capacity.

If just one nutrient is restricted to low levels while the others are adequate, a more specific effect is likely to be apparent. For example, if your body did not get enough vitamin A over a period of years, you might begin to have difficulty with visual acuity at night (night blindness). Worse than that, eye damage (so serious as to eventually cause permanent blindness) could result in some situations. Although it would be unusual to see

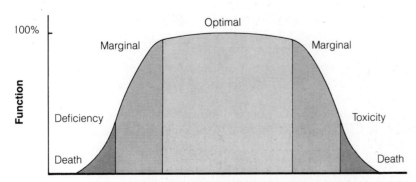

Figure 1.4 Effect of level of intake of an essential nutrient. Either too little or too much of an essential nutrient can interfere with growth and health. (Adapted from Mertz, W. 1983. The significance of trace elements for health. *Nutrition Today* 18(no.5):27. Reproduced with permission of *Nutrition Today* Magazine, P.O. Box 1829, Annapolis, Maryland 21404.)

Figure 1.5 Nutritional supplements: boon or bane?
Although concentrated nutritional supplements are useful in some circumstances, they also carry the potential for harm.

this severe a vitamin A deficiency in people in the developed countries, it is not unusual in the developing countries, which provide thousands of examples.

The chapters that deal with the nutrients will point out the consequences of severe, prolonged, inadequate intake for each nutrient.

Consequences of Excessive Intake of Nutrients

Just as getting too little of a nutrient has damaging effects, a consistent and substantial overdose of a nutrient will have negative consequences as well. If vitamin A is consumed in much higher-than-recommended amounts for a period of many months, toxicity symptoms including headache, nausea, and vomiting can occur. These high doses can result in elevated pressure of the fluid surrounding the central nervous system, sometimes causing the condition to be mistaken for a brain tumor. [See Chapter 12 (on vitamins).]

The dangers of excess nutrient intake have become more apparent in recent years. Now that concentrated nutrients can be formulated inexpensively in the laboratory as pills, powders, or liquids, overdosing is possible if people use such products inappropriately (Figure 1.5). Although nutrient toxicities have resulted once in a great while from a person eating too much food that is high in a particular nutrient, nutrient overdoses are caused much more often by the indiscriminate use of nutritional supplements.

An example of the danger of supplement overdose involves vitamin B-6, a nutrient formerly thought to be safe at high levels of intake. Now it is known that when vitamin B-6 is consumed for long periods of time in amounts a thousand or more times the recommended intake, it can cause nerve problems that make both large and small muscle control difficult. One report describes people who were no longer able to walk unassisted, and office workers whose typing abilities were impaired. [See Chapter 12 (on vitamins).]

This is not to say that using vitamin supplements is always dangerous: there are situations in which they are very beneficial if used properly, as in pregnancy. In Chapter 12, we provide information on situations in which supplementation may be appropriate.

Standards of Adequate Intake

How can a person know how much of the nutrients to consume daily? Several helpful standards will be discussed in this section.

The Recommended Dietary Allowances (RDAs). The results of research on the quantities of nutrients needed daily for human health have been summarized in a publication called *Recommended Dietary Allowances.* About every five years, the findings from recent studies are reviewed, and daily nutrient intake recommendations are updated. This process is undertaken by a group of leading nutritional scientists who comprise the Recommended Dietary Allowances Committee, which is part of the Food and Nutrition Board of the National Research Council, National Academy of Sciences. A table of the 1980 RDAs is inside the back cover and in Appendix A.

In Canada, a process similar to the development of the RDAs is undertaken by the Department of National Health and Welfare when they prepare the *Recommended Nutrient Intakes for Canadians.* The 1983 edition is in Appendix B.

Note that nutrients are measured in metric units; conversion factors for metric values and U.S. measures are shown in Appendix C. The macronutrients are expressed as gram (g) amounts; there are about 30 grams in an ounce. Most micronutrients are quantified in milligrams (mg); a mg is a thousandth of a gram. The recommended intakes for some vitamins and minerals are so small that they are given in micrograms (μg); a μg is a millionth of a gram.

Research has shown that a person's actual level of need for any given nutrient can be influenced by sex, body size, growth, and reproductive status. Therefore, separate recommendations are made for various subgroups, defined by sex, age, pregnancy, and lactation.

There is also variability among individuals within any given subgroup. Figure 1.6 represents the typical distribution of people's needs for a nutrient.

Recommended Dietary Allowances (RDAs)—daily nutrient intake recommendations established by the Food and Nutrition Board of the National Research Council, National Academy of Sciences

gram (g)—metric unit of measure convenient for expressing macronutrient needs; 30 g = 1 ounce

milligram (mg), microgram (μg)—respectively, one-thousandth and one-millionth of a gram; used for expressing micronutrient needs

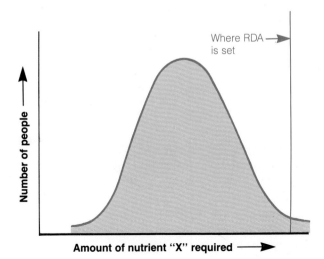

Figure 1.6 Variability in requirements of different people for a nutrient.
The shaded area shows how many people are likely to need the hypothetical nutrient "X" at the various levels along the horizontal axis. Note that *the RDA recommendation for intake is higher than almost all of the people's actual needs.*

When the committee establishes a recommended nutrient level, it usually makes it high enough to include the needs of 97.5% of the people in that group. In addition, the recommendations are generous enough to allow for some loss of the nutrient as it makes its way through the body. For example, the RDA allows for losses such as those that occur during absorption or conversion from one chemical form to another, when some of the nutrient's activity may be decreased.

The one set of values that the RDA committee does not set high enough to meet the needs of almost all of the people in the category is energy: These recommendations have been established at an average level of need for each age group in order not to encourage overconsumption.

A factor that has not been taken into account in the RDAs is the effect of illness or injury, which raise the body's need for nutrients. Keep in mind that the RDAs apply to healthy people only.

Scientific judgment also plays a role in establishing the recommended levels of intake. This is why nutritional scientists rather than statisticians comprise the committee. Further, it explains why the recommended levels of intake vary slightly from one country to another.

In the 1980 version of the RDAs, several nutrients were added to the table that had not appeared in prior editions. These new additions are presented as "estimated safe and adequate daily dietary intakes," reflecting that considerable uncertainty remains about what levels are most beneficial. Even with these recent additions, there are still some nutrients missing from the table. Future research and revisions of the RDAs will fill those gaps.

The U.S. Recommended Daily Allowances (U.S. RDA). Many food products have nutrition information on their labels that refers to the "U.S. RDA." (Figure 1.7). The U.S. RDA is different from the Recommended Dietary

U.S. Recommended Daily Allowance (U.S. RDA)—standard designed for use in nutrition labeling; gives relative levels of nutrients in a serving of food, expressed as a percentage of a standard that includes the needs of almost all healthy people

Figure 1.7 The U.S. RDA. The U.S. RDA is a standard that was developed for use on food product labels to provide information about nutrient content and to allow comparisons between products.

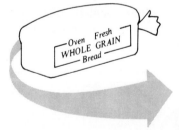

Nutritional information per serving

Serving size, slices	2
Servings per container	8
Calories	150
Protein, grams	5
Carbohydrate, grams	30
Fat, gram	1

Percentage of U.S. Recommended Daily Allowances (U.S. RDA)

Protein	8
Vitamin A	*
Vitamin C	*
Thiamin	15
Riboflavin	8
Niacin	15
Calcium	2
Iron	10

* Contains less than 2% of the U.S. RDA of these nutrients.

Allowances, although it was derived from them. Rather, it is a standard that was designed for use in nutrition labeling that applies to healthy people of various ages.

Table 1.2 shows the U.S. RDA. This standard was developed so that people would be able to see at a glance what relative levels of nutrients a serving of food contains, expressed as a percentage of the standard. The U.S. RDA standards were set to include the highest recommended level of intake for most nutrients on the RDA table for anybody from four years old through adulthood, except pregnant and lactating women.

Therefore, if a nutrition label states that a serving of canned corn provides 6% of the U.S. RDA for riboflavin, it means that four-year-olds

Table 1.2 The U.S. Recommended Daily Allowance (U.S. RDA) as a Derivative of the Recommended Dietary Allowance (RDA)

Nutrient	RDA for adult man (1968)	RDA for adult woman (1968)	U.S. RDA for 4-year-olds through adults
Nutrients that *must* appear on the label			
protein (higher quality) (g)[a]	—	—	45
protein (lower quality) (q)[a]	65	55	65
vitamin A (IU)	5000	4000	5000
vitamin C (ascorbic acid) (mg)	60	55	60
thiamin (vitamin B-1) (mg)	1.4	1.0	1.5
riboflavin (vitamin B-2) (mg)	1.7	1.5	1.7
niacin (mg)	18	13	20
calcium (g)	0.8	0.8	1.0
iron (mg)	10	18	18
Nutrients that *may* appear on the label			
vitamin D (IU)	—	—	400
vitamin E (IU)	30	25	30
vitamin B-6 (mg)	2.0	2.0	2.0
folic acid (folacin) (mg)	0.4	0.4	0.4
vitamin B-12 (μg)	6	6	6
phosphorus (g)	0.8	0.8	1.0
iodine (μg)	120	100	150
magnesium (mg)	350	300	400
zinc (mg)	—	—	15
copper (mg)	—	—	2
biotin (mg)	—	—	0.3
pantothenic acid (mg)	—	—	10

The U.S. RDA was developed to be the standard for nutrition labeling. Based on the 1968 RDA (which was in use at that time), the U.S. RDA usually incorporates the highest RDA for each nutrient.

[a]Proteins found in food vary in their usefulness to humans. If a particular protein is very good for meeting people's needs, it is called a "high-quality protein," and the 45-gram standard is used. If the protein is of lower quality, the 65-gram standard is used.

through adults, except pregnant and lactating women, will get *at least* 6% of their RDA for riboflavin from a serving. The nutrition label must specify what serving size was analyzed; note that it may vary from one product to another.

U.S. RDAs can also be used to compare nutrient values between products. For example, labels show that a one-cup serving of canned peas provides approximately 10% of the U.S. RDA of protein, whereas canned carrots provide about 2%. On the other hand, the carrots have 600% of the U.S. RDA for vitamin A, and the peas have 15%.

Nutrition labeling is required on foods that have had nutrients added to them, or whose labeling or advertising make a nutritional claim. Many processors voluntarily provide this information for other products as well.

The Effects of Nutrition Occur over Various Time Periods

There is tremendous variety in how long it takes for a nutrient—or the absence of a nutrient—to have an obvious effect on the body.

Short-Range Effects of Nutrition

Some effects of nutrition begin to take place within minutes or hours after a food or beverage is consumed. The way your body responds to your drinking something sugary, such as a carbonated beverage or lemonade, is an example of an almost immediate effect. If you consume the drink on an empty stomach, some of the sugar will appear in the bloodstream within minutes, and from there the sugar will move into your cells. You may even note that you feel more energetic as a result. But probably within an hour, depending on how much sugar you consumed and on how active you were during the hour, you may feel hungry and tired.

Another example of rapid nutritional cause and effect is the impact that being without water makes. A person who does not have access to drinking water will become thirsty and progressively more dehydrated—leading to headache, dizziness, confusion, and eventually unconsciousness and death, all within a few days. But if water becomes available soon enough, drinking it can quickly and dramatically reverse the symptoms of deprivation.

Intermediate-Range Effects of Nutrition

Some nutritional effects take weeks or months to manifest themselves. For example, if a person quits eating foods or drinking beverages that are sources of vitamin C, in a couple of months he may notice that his gums bleed slightly when he brushes his teeth. The connection between low levels of vitamin C and the bleeding gums can be demonstrated by watching the gum condition improve in the days after vitamin C is put back into the diet. Generally, vitamin deficiencies and excesses fit into this category of effects that take an intermediate amount of time to become evident.

Surplus kcalories show another intermediate-range effect: if a person regularly takes in excesses of the energy nutrients, in weeks or months those accumulated kcalories will become apparent as extra body fat.

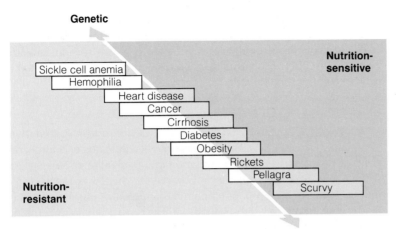

Figure 1.8 The influence of nutrition on some health conditions. Health conditions vary in the extent to which nutrition can influence them. You can estimate the relative effectiveness of nutrition in modifying these diseases if they already exist by noting how much of the bar is to the right of the line. (Adapted from Olson, R. E. 1978. Clinical nutrition—where human ecology and internal medicine meet. *Nutrition Today* 13(no.4):18–28. Reproduced with permission of *Nutrition Today* Magazine, P.O. Box 1829, Annapolis, Maryland 21404.)

Long-Range Effects of Nutrition

Some noticeable effects of nutrition are delayed longer than months. Links have been established, for example, between nutrition and the development of health problems such as heart disease and cancer which take years—even decades—to become apparent. Because so much time intervenes and so many circumstances other than diet apparently come into play in the development of these conditions, it is a great challenge to identify positively how nutrition affects them.

When there are many factors that influence the development of a disease, it is referred to as multifactorial. Other factors that may be involved are inborn predisposition (genetically controlled likelihood of developing the disease), stress, detrimental substances in the environment, and level of exercise.

multifactorial—having many contributing factors or causes

If nutrition is only partly responsible for a condition, then nutrition can be looked to for only one aspect of prevention. For example, if you have a strong genetic tendency to develop hypertension (high blood pressure), even if you do all the right nutritional things to try to prevent yourself from developing it, you probably will develop hypertension anyway. In the meantime, however, you may at least delay its onset through your choice of diet. Similarly, if you do get one of these conditions, diet can furnish only part of the treatment or control for it. Figure 1.8 illustrates the extent to which nutritional intervention is thought to be able to change the rate or course of certain diseases once they are in progress.

Different Types of Studies Document the Effects of Nutrition

We have emphasized that the information in this book is based on scientific research. In this section we will describe the types of experiments considered valid so that you can start to evaluate for yourself various claims about the effects of nutrition.

The majority of useful nutrition research involves either epidemiological or metabolic studies. (Human metabolic studies are sometimes called clinical studies.) We will describe them in this section. In addition, we will mention two types of "evidence" that should *not* be relied on as the basis of nutrition knowledge.

Epidemiological Studies

Epidemiology is the study of disease as it occurs within populations. In epidemiological studies, scientists assess the health status of a large, defined group of people, such as the population of a particular country or region. At the same time, the researchers observe the dietary patterns and other lifestyle features of the population. The people are not asked to change their diets in any way: the scientists simply record what is normally consumed. Then the researchers observe other populations that have different diets, recording their health status as well. They note which health factors exist side by side with which diets.

For example, physicians practicing in Africa noticed that natives who ate high fiber diets rarely developed appendicitis, bowel cancer, or heart disease, but frequently contracted infectious diseases.

On the other hand, Europeans living there had a different experience: they developed appendicitis, bowel cancer, and heart disease more commonly than the natives did, but had much lower rates of infectious diseases. Their diets were different, too: they contained less fiber than those of the Africans.

It is tempting to conclude that the level of fiber in the diets was responsible for the type of health problems these two groups of people experienced. However, the coexistence of two conditions does not prove that either causes the other. Even if there is a cause-effect relationship, other factors are also usually involved in the disease process. In this example, in addition to the different levels of fiber, the diets of the two groups also varied in levels of fat, protein, and other substances. Moreover, the activity levels and overall lifestyles of the two groups differed markedly.

The observations that come from epidemiological studies such as these nonetheless have great value, because they can raise important questions for further research. Scientists may form a hypothesis (theory) to try to explain what nutritional factors led to certain health consequences, which can then be tested by using other kinds of research methods. For example, many hypotheses regarding the relationship between fiber intake and health have been sparked by the epidemiological study just mentioned. We will discuss some of that research later.

Metabolic Studies

Studies that involve a detailed examination of what effects occur when controlled levels of nutrients or other food substances are given to human subjects or laboratory animals are called metabolic studies.

Metabolic Studies Involving Laboratory Animals. For animal studies, researchers design a set of diets in which the levels of the nutrient(s) or other food substances being studied are varied from one phase of the

epidemiological studies—assessments of the health status of a large, defined group of people

metabolic studies—detailed assessments of the effects that occur when controlled levels of nutrients are given to humans or animals

experiment to another or from one animal to another, while all other nutrient intakes are kept constant throughout. The researchers want to find out whether changes in the amount of the test substance(s) cause changes in the animals' body chemistry or in substances excreted in urine or feces (solid waste).

Animal metabolic studies have several advantages over human metabolic studies. First of all, because the animals are caged, there is no possibility that they will consume other than the designated diet. Also, it might be possible to feed the animals more extreme levels of nutrients than would be ethical to use on humans; seeing these effects may help scientists to forecast what might happen in people. Finally, since animals are usually sacrificed (killed) at the end of a study, a great deal of detailed information can be gained from postmortem examinations and chemical analysis of tissues.

If the objective of an animal metabolic study is to yield information that could eventually contribute to human nutrition knowledge, it is important to select a type of animal for the study that uses the test nutrient(s) in a way similar to the way people do. For example, vitamin C is an essential nutrient for humans, but rats do not need it in their diets because their own bodies produce it. Therefore, the guinea pig, which does require vitamin C, is a better choice for vitamin C research.

Animal studies yield a wealth of detailed information about *animal* nutrition. How much *human* nutrition information they provide depends on how carefully the study was designed, and on appropriate interpretation of the results.

BOGUS! Animal Single Food Experiments BOGUS! From time to time, studies are done in which test animals are fed just one human food—such as a certain cereal—throughout a study; the effects on the animals' condition are recorded as the study progresses. Invariably, the health of animals deteriorates when they are fed only one food. This is predictable, since no single food meets all the nutritional needs of either laboratory animals or humans. Even foods that make many valuable nutritional contributions to a normal diet are not nutritionally adequate by themselves (Hegsted, 1975).

Nonetheless, reports periodically circulate that one food is "better" than another because the rats who ate it lived longer than those who ate something else. Such reports are specious. Although they appear persuasive, they are not relevant to animals—or people—who normally eat a variety of foods.

Metabolic (Clinical) Studies Involving Humans. In human metabolic (clinical) studies, as in experiments with laboratory animals, careful chemical analyses are done. A major difference, however, is that in human studies the substances analyzed are unlikely to go beyond blood, urine, and feces. On the other hand, physical measurements such as blood pressure may be collected as well.

The scope of human metabolic or clinical studies may vary considerably. A study may involve as few as 8–12 subjects for a month or two, or it may involve up to thousands of subjects for years, depending on the objectives of the study.

In the larger studies, fewer types of data are collected, often at widely spaced intervals. The participants in smaller, shorter human studies are monitored daily for various biochemical changes, and their food intake is rigidly controlled; therefore, subjects must be able and willing to tolerate food restriction for several weeks. Compliance is usually encouraged by paying the subjects for their cooperation.

Studies of this sort are sometimes used to establish levels of nutrient requirement by finding out how much of a nutrient the subject must get to stay "in balance"—that is, to have an intake of the nutrient equal to the need for the nutrient.

When researchers who conduct metabolic or clinical studies publish their results, they are careful to explain under what circumstances the findings were obtained. It is possible that the results might not have been the same if a different test diet or other conditions had been used.

Sometimes it is important to keep those involved in nutrition research from knowing who is receiving the test substance or during which phase of the study it is being administered. To accomplish this, a placebo (which is a food or pill made to look, taste, and smell like the test substance but without its activity) is given when the experimental treatment is not. Such studies are described as "blind."

In single-blind studies, only the subjects are kept unaware of whether the test substance is being administered. This is done for studies in which the subjects' expectations might influence test results. For example, if a study is being done to test the effect of caffeine on blood pressure, subjects should not know whether they received the caffeine or not, since blood pressure can be modified by psychological factors. The subjects' expectations may cause their blood pressures to rise or fall, which would confound the effects of the caffeine.

In double-blind studies, neither the subjects nor the researchers working directly with the subjects know who is receiving the test substance; this eliminates the likelihood of bias on the part of the researchers as well. For example, if a test were being done on whether vitamin E supplements ease respiratory problems, and the person on the listening end of the stethoscope knew which subjects had received the vitamin, she might "hear" the person's breathing a little differently depending on her expectation. (Of course, somebody in charge of the study has to know who got what—but the information is not revealed until the study is over.)

In general, double-blind studies are more likely than single-blind studies to be regarded as scientifically valid.

BOGUS! Personal Testimony or Anecdotal Reporting BOGUS!

Another type of "evidence" that you will see used at times to try to prove that a nutrient has a particular effect is personal testimony or anecdotal reporting. It is not scientifically sound. It usually consists of a poorly documented description of an individual's experience, rather than a controlled study. For example, an article might say, "Mrs. Jones was troubled for

placebo—a food or pill superficially identical to a substance being tested, but without its activity

blind studies—studies in which only the subjects (single-blind) or both the subjects and researchers working directly with them (double-blind) do not know who is receiving the test substance

As the alarm rings, Tom awakens with the realization that this is going to be an unusual day: it is *day one* of a metabolic study regarding the mineral zinc, for which he has agreed to be a subject. He recalls the recent chain of events that led to his signing up: seeing the ad for subjects on a campus bulletin board, interviewing with the major professor and the graduate students who comprise the research team, and being examined by the project's physician.

He shuts off the alarm and stretches, thinking about the ways in which his life will be different for the 51 days of the study. He will still live in his apartment, but he will get everything he eats and drinks from the kitchen of the research unit: fifty-one identical-looking and -tasting breakfasts, 51 identical lunches, and 51 identical dinners. Even the water he drinks must be from the study, since it must be distilled to get rid of the naturally occurring traces of minerals that would interfere with the study results.

He steps into the bathroom, realizing that even this activity will be different during the study. He will have to collect all body wastes in the containers given to the subjects.

During the weeks of the study, Tom learns a great deal about himself, including his real relationship to food. At first he doesn't mind the repetitious menus and being restricted from eating other foods, but after about two weeks he realizes that he has the "blahs." He's tired of eating the same three meals a day—every day of the week—in the same place, and he'd like to leave town for a weekend. But the research team is depending on him to complete the study, and he wants to earn the full payment. Besides, he has come to enjoy the company of the other subjects and the "TLC" he gets from the researchers.

Finally, with just days to go, everybody is "counting down" the last meals, and anticipating the party that will be held at the end of the study . . . with different food!

After that, a gradual return to normalcy.

many months by waking frequently during the night, which left her exhausted the next day. Then she started supplementing her diet with nutrient 'X'; within a week she was sleeping soundly all night, feeling refreshed and energetic the next morning and throughout the day. Nutrient 'X' has improved Mrs. Jones' vitality 100%."

This sort of recitation of one person's experience can be interesting and is often dramatic, but cannot be used to claim anything except that

Mrs. Jones now sleeps better. It would be overextending the conclusions that can be drawn from the facts given to say that Mrs. Jones—or anybody else, for that matter—can improve her sleep by taking nutrient "X." To discover whether nutrient "X" has anything to do with people's sleep patterns, a double-blind study involving many people with similar sleep disturbances would need to be conducted.

Personal testimony is sometimes given by celebrities who are deservedly respected for work in their own fields, but who have little understanding of the science of nutrition. When these individuals promote various dietary products and services, you have no guarantee that the product is either safe or effective.

Personal testimony or anecdotal evidence is sometimes used to try to prove that nutrition can affect people's moods. Such claims are almost impossible to counter with the results of scientific studies: well-controlled experiments on this topic have thus far been very difficult to construct. It's not easy to measure a person's mood objectively, because there are no good numerical standards that the researcher can apply to emotional changes observed in the subject. And if the subject is asked to describe the nature or extent of mood changes being experienced, the researcher cannot evaluate whether the subject is exaggerating or underplaying the changes. Because there is almost no respected research in this area, the hucksters have gleefully moved in to fill the vacuum.

Don't take personal testimony seriously: although it may be engrossing, it does not constitute proof of nutritional effects.

Good Nutrition Studies Require Careful Work

Selecting the appropriate type of research method is not by itself enough to guarantee the validity of a study. Other factors are also characteristic of good work.

Time Demands of Thorough Studies

Considerable time and effort are required to design, fund, operate, analyze, and publish valid nutrition studies. With all the steps involved, it may take anywhere from two to five years for a "short" study, from the time a researcher conceives the idea for an experiment until the findings have been published. Studies in which the test period runs for several years take much longer in total.

Qualifications of Researchers

Ideally, researchers working in human nutrition should have earned advanced degrees in human nutrition, medicine, or biochemistry from universities of good reputation. Unfortunately, some "PhD" diplomas in nutrition are available by mail-order for a price and without authentic scientific training. This means that the consumer cannot automatically trust a person who claims to hold a degree.

Reputation of Journals

A careful scientist will also be particular about having his or her research published in respected journals. Those that are *refereed* are more likely to contain accurate information, because articles submitted to them are carefully critiqued by other experts in the field before they can be published. A list of refereed publications that carry nutrition research and review articles is given in Appendix D. Journals that do not use a rigorous review process are more likely to contain errors in study procedures and/or conclusions.

Reproducibility of Results

Even after publication the work is not immediately accepted. Only after thorough discussion by fellow scientists, and replication (repeating) of the same study elsewhere with similar results, does the new information become a part of mainstream thinking within the nutrition community.

Why is all of this important to know? We hope that it will help you to understand the difference in quality and reliability between science-based information and wishful thinking. It can also help you appreciate that since judgment is needed to interpret scientific data and to relate the results of studies to each other, there can be legitimate disagreement among scientists about the practical implications of study findings. The lively debates currently taking place on many nutrition issues attest that nutrition is a dynamic and healthy field of inquiry.

You can be confident that the information in this book is based on scientific experiment. For issues that are on the frontier and are therefore still open to debate, we will present the various points of view currently being aired, so you can make a tentative decision that will serve you until more conclusive evidence is available.

SUMMARY

■ Nutrition is the sum of all the interactions between an organism and the food it consumes. Foods contain nutrients and other substances, and each of us is responsible for selecting foods that will provide us with adequate nourishment. We are constantly bombarded with information about what we should or should not eat, and learning to evaluate this information wisely is an important goal.

■ The human body is composed of elements that must be obtained primarily from nutrients. Some of these elements can be used by the body only if they are chemically combined with others. In our diets we require about 50 specific substances, called essential nutrients, which can be grouped into six classes: water, carbohydrates, lipids, proteins, vitamins, and minerals. The first four classes are macronutrients; vitamins and minerals are micronutrients.

■ Nutrients are used for three basic purposes. (1) They form body structures (such as bones and blood). (2) They provide energy, which is measured in kilocalories. (3) They help to regulate the body's biochemical reactions, collectively called metabolism.

■ Both inadequate and excessive intakes of nutrients are unhealthy, and both result in malnutrition. The effects of malnutrition can be general or specific, depending on which nutrients and what level of deficiency or excess are involved.

■ Standards of adequate intake called the Recommended Dietary Allowances (RDAs) have been established by the Food and Nutrition Board of the National Research Council, National Academy of Sciences. Since many factors influence nutritional needs, the recommendations vary for people of different sexes, ages, and reproductive statuses. The U.S. Recommended Daily Allowances (U.S. RDAs) are derived from the RDAs and have been designed for use in food labeling. They give the relative levels of nutrients in a serving of food, expressed as a percentage of a standard that includes the needs of almost all healthy people.

■ The effects of nutrition occur in various time frames, taking anywhere from a few minutes to many years to become apparent. Some of the long-range effects of nutrition are now thought to be among the factors involved in certain diseases of multifactorial origin.

■ Epidemiological studies address the health status of large groups of people, whereas metabolic studies usually involve more detailed assessments of the effects that occur when controlled levels of nutrients are given to humans or animals. Single- and double-blind studies and the use of placebos help to remove some of the possible sources of bias created by human expectations and other psychological factors. Experiments using animals must be designed and interpreted with care if they are to yield any meaningful information about human nutrition. Animal single food experiments and anecdotal evidence do *not* provide valid support for nutritional claims.

■ Validated scientific studies are most likely to be conducted by qualified researchers, published in refereed journals and replicated by other scientists before the conclusions become generally accepted. Good studies take years to complete, and since their interpretation requires judgment, there can be legitimate disagreement among experts about what the findings mean. These debates often spark future research that may eventually lead to clearer answers.

REFERENCES

American Dietetic Association. 1983. Conceptual framework for the profession of dietetics. *ADA Courier* 22(no. 1).

Committee for the Revision of the Dietary Standard for Canada. 1983. *Recommended Nutrient Intakes for Canadians.* Ottawa: Minister of Supply & Services Canada.

Doyle, R. P. 1983. *The medical wars: Why the doctors disagree.* New York: William Morrow and Company, Inc.

Hegsted, D. M. 1975. Sole foods and some not so scientific experiments. In *The nutrition crisis: A reader*, ed. T. P. Labuza. New York: West Publishing Co.

Mertz, W. 1983. The significance of trace elements for health. *Nutrition Today* 18(no.5):27.

National Nutrition Consortium, Inc. with R. M. Deutsch. 1975. *Nutrition labeling: How it can work for you.* Bethesda, MD: National Nutrition Consortium, Inc.

National Research Council, National Academy of Sciences (NAS). 1980. *Recommended dietary allowances.* Washington, DC: NAS.

Olson, R. E. 1978. Clinical nutrition—where human ecology and internal medicine meet. *Nutrition Today* 13(no.4):18–28.

2

Rating Yourself Nutritionally

IN THIS CHAPTER: The Body Responds Differently to Varying Nutrient Levels • Body-based Measures of Nutritional Status Have Limitations for Ordinary Use • Diet Analysis Is Ordinarily More Useful for Estimating Nutritional Status

How can you tell whether you are getting the right amounts of the essential nutrients to meet your needs? What kind of clues can alert you to inadequate or excessive intakes, or reassure you that your consumption is on target?

There are many suggestions in the popular press about what conditions are caused by malnutrition. Are they accurate? For example, when you are continually tired, does this mean you have iron-deficiency anemia? If you have cracks at the corners of your mouth, are you vitamin deficient? If your skin has taken on a yellowish cast, could it be from eating too many carrots? Such questions will be answered in this chapter as various methods of rating yourself nutritionally——called nutritional assessment techniques—are discussed.

Before discussing those techniques, however, we will describe what happens in the body when a person consumes a nutrient at levels that deviate from the amount the person actually needs. This information is important background for understanding nutritional assessment.

The Body Responds Differently to Varying Nutrient Levels

Nobody gets exactly the amounts of nutrients that are needed each day. All of us typically deviate somewhat from optimal levels.

Alternate Underconsumption and Overconsumption

Usually, a person alternates between brief periods of moderate underconsumption and overconsumption of nutrients. This is normal and does not damage health.

For example, if cheese sandwiches and milk have been the mainstay of your lunches recently, your intake of calcium may have been above what you need, since cheese and milk contain generous amounts of that mineral. If you change your menu to peanut butter sandwiches and fruit juice for a few days, your intake may be less than your body needs, since those foods are not as calcium-rich.

Such short-term deviations can be handled easily by a healthy person, since the body stores at least some of the surplus nutrients it receives, and makes use of them later when intake is not as high. Even the nutrients that are the least storable or stable in the body, such as vitamin C and the B vitamins, won't be completely depleted as a result of just a couple of days of low intake.

Long-Term Underconsumption

Sometimes a person consistently *under*consumes a particular nutrient or group of nutrients for weeks or months at a time. The body's initial response is to mobilize the stored nutrient and circulate it via the bloodstream to where it is needed, as it does in the case of a temporary shortage. But when the inadequate intake continues, there is eventually a decrease in the level of the nutrient in the body's tissues, blood, and urine, along with a drop in the amount of related chemical compounds (metabolites) that are created from the nutrient during normal body processes. There is no consistent order in which these events will occur, since it varies from one nutrient to another.

When the blood levels have been very low for a time, some of the body's functions and structures begin to change, and the person starts to look and feel unhealthy. Death can result from severe, prolonged deficiency of certain essential nutrients.

Long-Term Overconsumption

Now for a look at what happens when a person consistently *over*consumes a nutrient for a long period of time. Each nutrient has a slightly different ceiling, or saturation point, for storage in the body. Generally, only small amounts of nutrients that are soluble in water can be stored; large excesses of water-soluble substances or their metabolites are usually filtered out by the kidneys into the urine.

Originally it was thought that as long as such excesses were excreted, they would cause no problems; more recent evidence, however, indicates that there are circumstances in which large excesses of water-soluble nutrients can have undesired effects on the body. For example, vitamin B-6 in repeated, large doses may cause nervous system malfunction in some people.

Some substances, notably the fat-soluble vitamins A and D, can accumulate to much higher levels than the water-soluble nutrients can. If overconsumed for long periods, these substances can eventually increase in tissues to a toxic (damaging) level that causes a person to look and feel sick. Some serious permanent effects have occurred from such overdosing.

To summarize the effects of long-term malnutrition: deficiencies or excesses influence the levels of nutrients and their metabolites in tissues, blood, and/or urine before they affect a person's appearance or sense of well-being. The entire process may take anywhere from months to several years, depending on the specific nutrient(s) involved.

Even with what is known about the effects of malnutrition, it is not easy to get an exact and comprehensive evaluation of what nutrients are present in the body at a given time. Two general types of methods are used to assess nutritional status. With the first type, the body itself is evaluated to determine what level of a given nutrient or its metabolites are present. With the second type, the diet is examined: the amounts of nutrients consumed are compared to a standard for adequate intake. Since you can use the dietary techniques by yourself without professional help or special equipment, these are the methods we will emphasize throughout the book.

Body-based Measures of Nutritional Status Have Limitations for Ordinary Use

biochemical tests—chemical analyses of body substances such as blood or urine

anthropometric tests—external measurements of the body such as height, weight, and skinfold thickness

In the following sections, body-based means of measuring nutritional status are discussed; those that yield more specific data are mentioned first, and those that furnish less precise information later. Generally, biochemical tests, or chemical analyses of such body substances as blood and urine, are the most specific; anthropometric tests, or external body measures, are next best (height/weight data and skinfold thicknesses); and appearance and sense of well-being are the least specific.

Blood Test

The blood test is a technique for professional use only. The skin and an underlying blood vessel are pierced to collect a blood sample, which is analyzed to determine whether certain nutrients and their metabolites are within normal ranges. Even though this technique shows what levels of nutritional substances are circulating, it does not necessarily indicate how much is present elsewhere in the body.

Abnormal levels of nutrients in the blood do not always mean that something is wrong with the person's diet: an illness could be the real culprit, causing the nutrients to be handled in an abnormal way. For example, a high level of blood sugar (glucose) could mean that a person has recently consumed a large amount of sugar, or it might mean that the individual's body is incapable of handling even a moderate sugar intake in a normal way, due to a disease such as diabetes mellitus.

Because blood tests are also very helpful for diagnosing and monitoring disease conditions, they have become a fairly routine part of general health checkups and hospitalizations, as well as nutritional status surveys. It is surprising how many people (adults as well as children!) resist this procedure, but the wealth of information it yields to aid in a person's health care makes it extremely valuable.

Urine Test

Chemical analysis of urine also involves skilled laboratory procedures. Like blood tests, urine tests can reveal whether the levels of some nutrients and/or their metabolites are within normal ranges, giving clues to nutritional status or the presence of disease. This technique is commonly used in general health checkups, hospitalizations, and nutritional status surveys.

Height and Weight

Measurements of height and weight have some value for nutritional assessment. Remember that although growth is influenced by your intake, genetics sets the limit on how tall you potentially can become. Nutrition helps determine how far you grow toward that limit.

In children, measures of both height and weight can provide a rough evaluation of general nutritional status, particularly of energy intake and output. In adults, weight changes testify either to *fluctuation in body fat content* due to recent kcalorie consumption and expenditure, or *fluctuation in muscle mass* due to variations in physical effort, or both.

Height/weight tables are the standards to which an individual's measurements are compared. Their limitations will be discussed in Chapter 10 (on body fatness).

Skinfold Thickness

Judgments about past energy intake and expenditure can also be made when an experienced professional measures the thickness of the skin and underlying fat layer at various body sites using a special caliper (Figure 2.1). If many more kcalories have been eaten than expended over a period of time, the fat layer will be thicker than before. Conversely, if a person used more energy than was consumed during past weeks or months, the fat layer will be measureably thinner.

Tables based on large numbers of people have been developed to show typical fat thicknesses at various body sites. Any individual's measurements can be compared to the tables to determine body fatness relative to the reference group.

Such measurements are useful for assessing changes in fatness. Chapter 10 describes why it is difficult to make accurate determinations of absolute levels or percentages of body fat by using this method.

Appearance

Changes in   eans of assessing
nutritio   gns that often
accom

                                                         ment, you

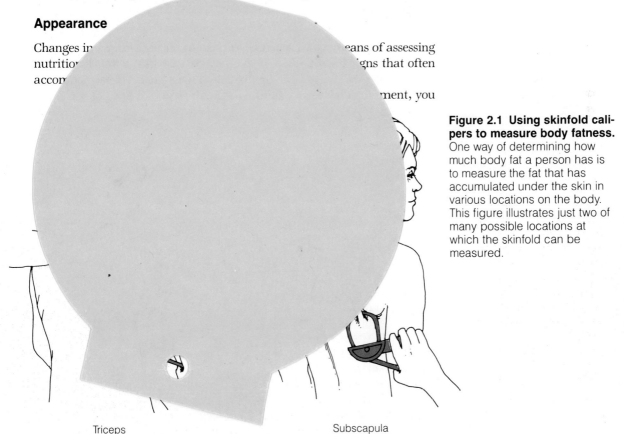

Triceps   Subscapula

Figure 2.1 Using skinfold calipers to measure body fatness. One way of determining how much body fat a person has is to measure the fat that has accumulated under the skin in various locations on the body. This figure illustrates just two of many possible locations at which the skinfold can be measured.

Table 2.1 A Few Signs of Nutritional Problems . . . or Something Else?

Noticeable sign	Possible nutrient involvement(s)	Possible other explanation(s)
Change in hair color	Deficiency of protein or copper	Sun-bleaching
		Chemical bleach or dye
Dry, scaling skin	Deficiency of vitamin A, zinc, or essential fatty acid	Chapping from cold or wind
		Sunburn
	Excess of vitamin A	Chemical irritation, e.g., detergents
Increased yellow pigmentation of skin	Excess of carotene, a compound that becomes vitamin A (harmless)	Liver disease (serious health problem)
Swollen, bleeding gums	Deficiency of vitamin C	Poor dental hygiene
		Particular medication
Swelling of feet and ankles due to fluid retention (edema)	Deficiency of thiamin or protein	Pregnancy
		Hot weather
		Standing for long periods
		Some medications
		Cardiovascular problems
		Kidney disease
Cracks in lips and at corners of mouth (cheilosis)	Deficiency of riboflavin or multiple B vitamins	Cold, windy weather
		Repeated wetting or rubbing of lips
		Viral infections
Obesity	Excessive kcalorie intake in relation to energy output	Possible hormone imbalance in rare cases

Obvious physical changes occur only after a long period of deficient or excessive intake. They are not a particularly accurate way of identifying malnutrition, partly because the signs may have had other causes. This table gives some examples to demonstrate the point.

Some data drawn from Weinsier, R. L., and C. E. Butterworth. 1981. *Handbook of clinical nutrition*. St. Louis: The C. V. Mosby Company.

might think that this would be a good method of assessment to use for yourself. However, this is a rather inexact method, and even trained health professionals do not always identify malnutrition or its cause correctly when using it.

There is another reason that assessing appearance is not very useful: few people in the United States, especially in the young adult population, experience malnutrition severe enough to result in obvious external changes. If you have one of the signs, it has more likely resulted from some other cause than a nutritional one. Notice the alternate explanations for some external symptoms in Table 2.1.

North Americans who might be undernourished enough to show such signs are the elderly and the chronically (persistently) ill, including alcoholics. Developing countries offer many more examples of obvious undernutrition than our area of the world does.

One type of obvious overnutrition that is commonly seen in North America is obesity. Cases of overnutrition of specific nutrients, on the other hand, are more unusual but do occur.

Despite the weaknesses of the technique, it has this usefulness: these signs can signal to health care professionals that a nutrition problem may exist, and that more specific tests should be done.

Sense of Well-Being

Sometimes a person is aware of changes in the way he or she feels or functions.

Like changes in appearance, these self-reports are of limited value because they are very subjective and could be the result of circumstances other than nutrition-related ones. For example, tiredness could result from prolonged inadequate iron or kcalorie intake, or from nonnutritional factors such as too little sleep, mental depression, or other illness. Increased frequency of minor health problems (e.g., colds, digestive upsets) may also relate to poor nutritional status.

No matter what the cause may be, you should report such observations to your doctor so that professional evaluation can be done, a diagnosis made, and appropriate care begun.

BOGUS! Hair Analysis BOGUS!

Some enterprising pseudoscientists market a service of analyzing hair samples to see what nutrients they contain. They report their findings as evidence of nutritional status. However, this technique is not reliable for assessment of most nutrients.

Biochemistry experts say that although it certainly is possible to analyze the amounts of various minerals present in hair, there are currently few standards as to what values are normal. Furthermore, the composition of hair does not accurately reflect the current composition of other body tissues. In addition, products that come in contact with hair can change its chemical composition: shampoos, bleaches, dyes, solutions used for permanents, and even the water supply can remove or add chemicals to hair (Hambidge, 1982).

Hair analysis has very limited valid use. It can sometimes help in identifying mineral poisoning (for example, lead), and in comparing the status of various population groups in regard to certain minerals.

Diet Analysis Is Ordinarily More Useful for Estimating Nutritional Status

A thorough nutritional assessment includes not only techniques that focus on the body, as just discussed, but also on dietary evaluation. This involves analyzing a person's intake and comparing it to a predetermined standard for adequacy. Because of its convenience, we will emphasize diet analysis in this text for people who have no apparent health problems.

Describing Your Diet

To analyze your diet, you first need to describe your intake. Several methods can be used.

Twenty-four-Hour Recall. Look at your watch; what time is it? Think back to what you were doing 24 hours ago. From that point forward, list everything you consumed (foods, beverages, and supplements). That process is a 24-hour recall. A common alternative is to use all of yesterday as your recall period.

Now ask yourself whether that list is representative of your eating; it may or may not be. After all, people's diets vary considerably from day to day. For example, you probably don't eat the same way on weekends as on weekdays; you may have eaten unusual items or amounts that day; or you may eat differently during one season than another. The more typical the diet you analyze, the more useful the information can be to you.

Remembering what you ate may be a challenge, especially when you try to recall details, such as the mayonnaise on the sandwich, or the butter in which the egg was fried. But such details are important, since they can influence the results substantially, especially in regard to kcalories.

Another task is to estimate correctly the amounts you consumed. Estimating serving sizes accurately takes practice. You may need to measure several food items to establish a mental image of various food volumes.

Food Records. A way to avoid forgetting what you consume is to record what you take in as a day goes along. This technique may tempt you to change your eating habits to reflect what you think you *ought* to eat instead of the way you usually *do* eat.

You can get a more accurate picture of what you eat by keeping records for many consecutive days. Experts in diet analysis have suggested various minimal time periods for achieving reasonable accuracy, such as a week or a month. Although it seems that any length of time has its limitations, generally longer recording periods provide a more accurate picture of typical nutrient intake.

Daily Food Summary. Another approach is to generalize about how often you eat various types of foods. Using a list of common categories of food such as the one in Figure 2.2, record how many times a day (or week) you are likely to consume such foods.

Dietitians and nutritionists often use this technique when working with patients as an aid in understanding a person's eating habits. It is a helpful prelude to diet counseling: if the dietitian thoroughly understands a person's typical eating style, she can offer suggestions to make the transition to a modified diet easier. Of course, the accuracy of this method depends on a person's ability to make generalizations about what he eats and to summarize that information for a particular time frame.

Analyzing Your Diet

Once the diet has been described using one of the preceding methods, there are several approaches to analyzing it. We will consider the use of food composition tables, food group plans, and various other dietary guidelines.

Do you include the following in your diet? Check **yes** or **no.** If **yes,** indicate how much you consume of the item per day; if you use it less often, use the last column to indicate how much you consume per week.

Food	Yes or No	Amount daily	If not daily, amount weekly
1. Milk or cheese	[✓] Yes [ ] No	2 oz. cheese	
2. Meat, fish, poultry	[✓] Yes [ ] No	3 oz.	
3. Eggs	[✓] Yes [ ] No		1–2
4. Nuts and seeds	[✓] Yes [ ] No	½ cup	
5. Legumes (cooked dried peas and beans)	[ ] Yes [✓] No		
6. Vegetables	[✓] Yes [ ] No	3 servings	
7. Fruits	[✓] Yes [ ] No	½ c. o.j. and 2 pieces fruit	
8. Bread, potatoes, rice, cereals, other starches	[✓] Yes [ ] No	1 oz. dry cereal ½ c. potato 2 sl. bread	
9. Potato or corn chips or other fried snacks	[✓] Yes [ ] No		small bag from vending machine 2–3 times/week
10. Butter, margarine, or other fats	[✓] Yes [ ] No	2–3 t.	
11. Desserts and sweet baked goods	[✓] Yes [ ] No	1	
12. Coffee, tea, or decaf	[ ] Yes [✓] No		
13. Alcoholic beverages	[✓] Yes [ ] No		6 12-oz. cans beer
14. Carbonated beverages (regular, not diet)	[ ] Yes [✓] No		
15. Sugar—added to food at the table	[ ] Yes [✓] No		
16. Salt—added to food at the table	[ ] Yes [✓] No		

Figure 2.2 Daily food summary.
Adapted from American Dietetic Association. 1981. *Handbook of clinical dietetics.* New Haven: Yale University Press.

Food Composition Tables. Thousands of foods have been analyzed in laboratories to discover what nutrients they contain. These findings are available in various publications and computer data bases. The U.S. Department of Agriculture (USDA) has been the leader in the United States in assembling food composition information. The table in Appendix E was reproduced largely from USDA Home and Garden Bulletin Number 72, and provides nutrient information for over 700 items.

Other USDA publications are even more extensive: a series of tables called *Agricultural Handbook 8* that is now under revision will contain more than 4000 entries. Another recognized comprehensive food composition data source is *Bowes and Church's Food Values of Portions Commonly Used* (now authored by Pennington and Church).

Notice that only 17 nutrients are given in the table in Appendix E, even though there are about 50 essential nutrients. Because costly time, skill, and equipment are required to do analyses for all of the nutrients in these foods, additions to the government tables occur only gradually. However, other research facilities such as universities and independent laboratories have published the results of specific testing they have done. Some of these data for additional nutrients are found in Appendices I through L. Nutrient analyses for many fast foods are found in Appendix F.

Following are the steps in doing a diet analysis using a food composition table; Figure 2.3 shows an example and suggests a form.

1. Look up the items in your diet on a food composition table, and record the amounts of nutrients in them. You will have to adjust the nutrient values for different serving sizes. (If you drank $\frac{1}{2}$ cup of milk but the table gives the values for 1 cup, you will need to divide all values in half before you record them.)

2. After you have entered all of the items, calculate the sum for each nutrient.

3. Enter the RDA (see inside back cover) for your sex, age, and reproductive status on the line below the sums.

4. Compare the sums to your RDAs. How far apart are they? Calculate what percentage of your RDA you obtained for each nutrient by dividing the sum for a given nutrient by your RDA for it. Multiply your answer by 100 to get the percentage (move the decimal point two spaces to the right). If you took in less than your RDA for a nutrient, the percentage will be less than 100; if you took in more, the percentage will be over 100.

What do the percentages mean? You have to think back to how the Recommended Dietary Allowances are derived to appreciate their significance. Since most healthy people's nutrient needs are actually below the levels recommended by the RDA, you might very well be able to meet your need for a particular nutrient with an intake of less than 100% of the RDA. Some experts in nutritional assessment judge a diet to be generally acceptable if it contains at least 70% of all nutrients, although experts are not unanimous on this point. (Remember, we're talking only about healthy people here; people who are ill may have higher nutrient needs.)

What is the guideline for an *upper* limit? There is no standard percentage of the RDA at which an excess amount of a nutrient begins to cause problems. For one nutrient, an intake of 500% (five times the RDA)

Item	Amount	Protein (g)	Fat (g)	Carbo-hydrate (g)	Calcium (mg)	Iron (mg)	Vitamin A (IU)	Thiamin (mg)	Vitamin C (mg)
Egg bagel	1	6	2	28			30	.14	0
Jelly	1 J.	0	0	13	9	1.2	0	0	1
7-Up	12 oz.	0	0	36	4	0.3	0	0	0
McDonald's Cheeseburgers	2	32	26	62	0	0	744	.48	3
Potato chips	2 oz.	3	24	30	316	5.8	0	.12	9
McDonald's Cookies	small box	4	11	45	24	1.2	47	.28	1
Cola drink	12 oz.	0	0	37	10	1.4	0	0	0
Pork chop	3 oz.	21	28	0	0	0	0	.83	0
Baked potato	1 avg.	4	0	33	11	3.0	0	.15	31
Frozen peas	½ c.	4	0	10	14	1.1	480	.22	11
Butter	2 t.	0	8	0	15	1.5	288	0	0
Iceberg lettuce	2 c.	0	0	4	2	0	360	.06	6
French dressing	2 J.	0	12	6	22	0.6	0	0	0
2% milk	½ c.	4	3	6	4	0.2	250	.05	1
Graham crackers	2 sq.	1	1	10	147	0	0	.02	0
					6	0.5			
Totals		79	115	320	584	16.8	2199	2.35	63
Your RDA		44			800	18.0	4000	1.1	60
% of your RDA		180			73	93	55	214	105

Figure 2.3 Diet analysis using food composition data. This diet analysis of a food intake record was done by a 20-year-old woman. For vitamin A, use the number from the RDA table in this text that represents International Units (IUs), since that is the type of unit the food composition tables use to describe vitamin A quantities. Do not use the value for Retinol Equivalents (REs), since they are not comparable to the food composition table values.

could lead to difficulties if continued for months at a time. For another, there may be no more negative effect from megadoses (often defined as ten times the RDA or more).

megadoses—doses of a nutrient ten times the RDA or more

This disparity makes it difficult to set a limit that can be generally applied. It is important to remember that *more is not better; there is no known advantage for a healthy person to consume more than 100% of the RDA.*

You now have a means of determining your approximate nutritional status for a number of nutrients. This method lends itself very well to computerization. Nutrient data bases and diet analysis software are being used increasingly in research, health care, and nutrition education, thereby saving much time that would otherwise have been spent in hand calculation.

Two notes of caution need to be sounded about computerized diet analysis. One is that there is considerable variation in the quality of the available software. The second is that even if the software is sophisticated, the reports the system produces can only be as good as the diet record or recall it was given to analyze.

Another type of diet evaluation is faster to use than analyzing food composition data, although it sacrifices much detail; this is using the food group plans. Such plans are convenient both for evaluating past intakes and for planning future consumption.

Food Group Plans. The food group plans pay less attention to what specific foods were eaten, and more to the general type of products that were consumed. This is a workable approach because related foods often have similar nutrient values. For example, the grains rice, wheat, and oats are significant sources of carbohydrate, iron, and the B vitamin thiamin (although the amounts of the nutrients are not identical from one grain to another). Given this similarity in the composition of the foods, if a person eats several servings of grain per day, he can be confident that he will have an appreciable intake of those nutrients (Table 2.2).

Given the nutritional characteristics of each group, it is then possible to construct an eating plan that contains close to RDA levels of nutrients by recommending how many servings from each group should be eaten daily. Using this type of plan, you can evaluate whether a person's consumption has been generally satisfactory without directly calculating how many milligrams of iron or thiamin or any other nutrient were in it.

Many food group plans have been developed over the last four decades to help people evaluate and plan their diets. These plans have used as many as ten to as few as four groups. Each plan has had its enthusiasts and detractors: not one plan has satisfied everybody. Here we will briefly describe the food group plans that have been in use recently.

The *Basic Four Food Guide* is easy to remember and use because of its small number of groups. Introduced by the USDA in 1956, the plan recommends that people eat at least the stated minimum numbers of servings of fruits and vegetables, milk and milk products, meats and meat substitutes, and grain products every day to provide the foundation for an adequate diet.

Although using the Basic Four does not guarantee that you will get RDA levels of nutrients, you are likely to come close much of the time for many nutrients, especially if you eat more than the minimum recommendations. This plan emphasizes the importance of eating a variety of foods within each group, rather than repeatedly eating the same items.

The foods in each group vary in their **nutrient density**; that is, they contain variable levels of nutrients for the number of kcalories they provide. If a food has a low or moderate kcalorie value and is loaded with nutrients, such as broccoli, it is said to have a very high nutrient density. But if a food has many kcalories and low levels of nutrients, such as sugar-

nutrient density—a term used to describe whether a food is a good source of nutrient(s) relative to the kcalories it contains

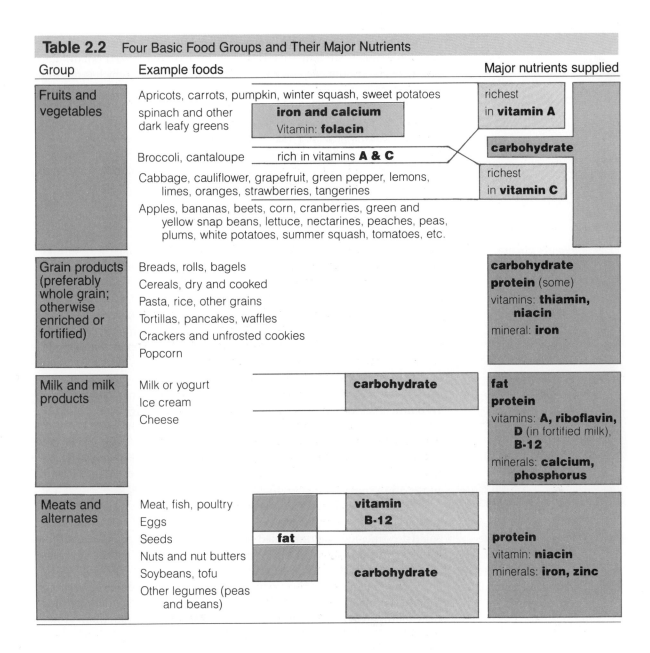

Table 2.2 Four Basic Food Groups and Their Major Nutrients

Group	Example foods	Major nutrients supplied
Fruits and vegetables	Apricots, carrots, pumpkin, winter squash, sweet potatoes	richest in **vitamin A**
	spinach and other dark leafy greens — **iron and calcium** Vitamin: **folacin**	**carbohydrate**
	Broccoli, cantaloupe — rich in vitamins **A & C**	
	Cabbage, cauliflower, grapefruit, green pepper, lemons, limes, oranges, strawberries, tangerines	richest in **vitamin C**
	Apples, bananas, beets, corn, cranberries, green and yellow snap beans, lettuce, nectarines, peaches, peas, plums, white potatoes, summer squash, tomatoes, etc.	
Grain products (preferably whole grain; otherwise enriched or fortified)	Breads, rolls, bagels	**carbohydrate**
	Cereals, dry and cooked	**protein** (some)
	Pasta, rice, other grains	vitamins: **thiamin, niacin**
	Tortillas, pancakes, waffles	mineral: **iron**
	Crackers and unfrosted cookies	
	Popcorn	
Milk and milk products	Milk or yogurt	**fat**
	Ice cream — **carbohydrate**	**protein**
	Cheese	vitamins: **A, riboflavin, D** (in fortified milk), **B-12**
		minerals: **calcium, phosphorus**
Meats and alternates	Meat, fish, poultry	**vitamin B-12**
	Eggs	**fat**
	Seeds	**protein**
	Nuts and nut butters — **carbohydrate**	vitamin: **niacin**
	Soybeans, tofu	minerals: **iron, zinc**
	Other legumes (peas and beans)	

sweetened gelatin dessert, it is of low nutrient density (known as "junk food").

People who are critical of the Basic Four plan point out that it does not give any guidance about consumption of many low-nutrient-density foods and beverages that people commonly eat and that are not included in the food groups—such as fats, sugary foods, and alcoholic beverages. Furthermore, there is a related issue: how do you categorize foods that are made from Basic Four items but have had so much fat and/or sugar added during processing that their nutrient density has dropped dramatically?

For example, 100-kcalories-worth of potato chips contain only one-seventh as much vitamin C as 100-kcalories-worth of baked potato, and only half the amount of many other nutrients (except fat, which is higher). Therefore potato chips have a much lower nutrient density overall than baked potatoes have. Should potato chips still be considered a serving of vegetable?

Vegetarians may also take issue with the Basic Four food plan. For those who choose to avoid milk and its products, a food plan that recommends those foods is not relevant. They object to a plan that assumes that everybody eats all kinds of foods.

Despite such criticisms, the Basic Four Food Guide has been widely used for decades, and has taught many people how to evaluate and improve their diets.

The Canadian Ministry of Health and Welfare makes very similar recommendations in *Canada's Food Guide*. These guidelines are found in Appendix B.

In 1979, USDA replaced the Basic Four Food Guide with the *Hassle-Free Guide to a Better Diet*, which reiterates the recommendations of the familiar Basic Four. However, it then adds a fifth group that includes foods high in fats, sugar, and alcohol, and suggests moderation in consumption of those items.

Critics of this plan are concerned that people may misconstrue the purpose of the fifth group and think that the foods it includes are being recommended for regular *consumption* rather than *restriction*.

Another attempt at improving the Basic Four was the *Modified Basic Four*, proposed in 1978 by nutrition researcher Janet King and her colleagues at the University of California at Berkeley. It recommended changes that would be more likely to bring the levels of nutrients in diets to 100% of the adult male RDA.

This plan increased some serving sizes and suggested daily consumption of legumes and nuts, as well as some vegetable oil (for example, in salad dressings). It recommended exclusive use of whole grains rather than refined cereal products, in order to ensure the intake of certain nutrients that are lost during refining of grain.

This system's detractors point out that not all adults need 100% of the adult male RDA. Furthermore, foods chosen using this plan will furnish about 2200 kcalories per day, which is more energy than many American adults—especially women—need.

Other Dietary Recommendations. In the late 1970s and early 1980s, a barrage of dietary recommendations was issued by various governmental bodies besides USDA. They reflected the growing popular commitment to self-responsibility for health, and reinforced the importance of getting enough of the needed nutrients. These recommendations also addressed concerns regarding consumption of fat, sugar, sodium (a mineral found in salt and other compounds), and alcohol. They pointed out that high intakes of these substances increase some people's risk of heart and blood vessel diseases, cancer, stroke, diabetes, cirrhosis, and dental decay. (There will be more about the potential relationship between these dietary factors and diseases in later chapters.) These reports also had important political ramifications, since any significant changes in diet would have repercussions on agricultural systems and the food processing industry as well.

The first of these was *Dietary Goals for the United States*, a report of the Senate Select Committee on Nutrition and Human Needs, which was published and revised in 1977. It asserted that American eating patterns are a critical public health concern. It recommended specific reductions in fats, refined and processed sugars, cholesterol, and salt, and suggested adjusting kcalorie intake to achieve desirable body weight.

Heated debate followed the release of the report, with some experts questioning whether there were adequate scientific data to substantiate that the specific levels of nutrients recommended could actually prevent or delay the stated diseases. Antagonists maintained that diets with such restrictions were unnecessary for the population as a whole. They contended that such diets should be prescribed only on a case-by-case basis, if an individual's family medical history put the person at risk for those health problems. Others said that the recommendations were difficult to translate into diets that people would eat.

Then, in 1980, the USDA and the Department of Health and Human Services (formerly Health, Education, and Welfare) jointly produced *Nutrition and Your Health: Dietary Guidelines for Americans*. These recommendations took into account the earlier Dietary Goals and the voluminous comments that had been sparked by them. Although both publications reflected concern about many of the same substances, the Guidelines were less specific in their recommendations than the Goals had been.

These are the key points of the Guidelines:

1. Eat a variety of foods daily.

2. Maintain ideal weight.

3. Avoid too much fat, saturated fat, and cholesterol.

4. Eat foods with adequate starch and fiber.

5. Avoid too much sugar.

6. Avoid too much sodium.

7. If you drink alcohol, do so in moderation.

Other reports making dietary recommendations at about the same time were *Healthy People: The Surgeon General's Report on Health Promotion and Disease Prevention*, which was issued in 1979; and *Toward Healthful Diets*, a 1980 paper from the Food and Nutrition Board of the National Academy of Sciences. In general, these reports agreed with the others on the importance of variety in the diet, on regulation of kcalorie intake to achieve best weight, and on moderation in salt consumption. They reflected some differences of opinion as to who would benefit from restriction of sugar and fats.

A Synthesized Approach: The Sound Approach to Nutritious Eating (SANE). The SANE guide was developed by the authors of this book to build on the strengths of the previously mentioned guidelines and add other useful information. It enables you to check your diet not only for whether you have been getting enough of the essential nutrients, but also to see whether you consume many foods that are high in fat, sugar, salt, and alcohol. You can use it equally well for planning what you *intend* to eat.

The SANE guide begins with the same major groupings of foods that are found in the venerable Basic Four and the Hassle-Free Guide (Figures 2.4–2.7). There is also a boxed listing showing the number of servings per day that are recommended as minimums for an adult. For the milk products group, different intakes for various ages are recommended.

These box listings make additional important qualifying statements. For fruits and vegetables, note that within the four servings recommended for each day, one good source of vitamin A and one of vitamin C should be included. (Table 2.2 identifies these.)

Also note that for the four servings of grain products that are recommended, you are encouraged to use whole grain foods as much as possible; enriched and fortified products are second best. Refined, unenriched, and unfortified products aren't even accepted as members of the group. (The effects on nutritional value of the processes that create such products will be discussed in Chapter 14.)

For meats and alternates, make use of some plant sources every week, even if you like meat well enough to eat it as your only choice from that group. The plant sources are richer in certain nutrients such as magnesium (a mineral) and folacin (a B vitamin) than the meats are.

The other box in the middle of each food group page lists serving sizes for some representative foods within each group. For foods that are not on the list but seem very similar to others that are found there, you can assume the same serving size.

At the bottom of each food group page are vertical lines (rulers) labeled "fat," "sodium," and "added sugar." They can help you get an idea about how much of these substances are in some representative foods in each group.

The bottom of each ruler represents zero, with values increasing as you ascend. Some foods from the group are placed along each ruler, showing the relative content of fat, sodium, and added sugar. For the sake of comparison, a specific amount of pure fat, salt, or sugar is also indicated along the ruler. If you want to reduce the amounts of fat, sodium, and added sugar in your diet, you can do so by eating more foods from nearer the bottom of the rulers, and fewer foods from higher up.

Figure 2.8 shows how you can count combination foods such as casseroles or sandwiches when you use this system: mentally separate the foods into their components, identify which groups the ingredients belong to, and decide what part of a serving each represents. Some common examples are shown. Using these as guidelines, you can estimate other combination foods in your diet for yourself.

Figure 2.4

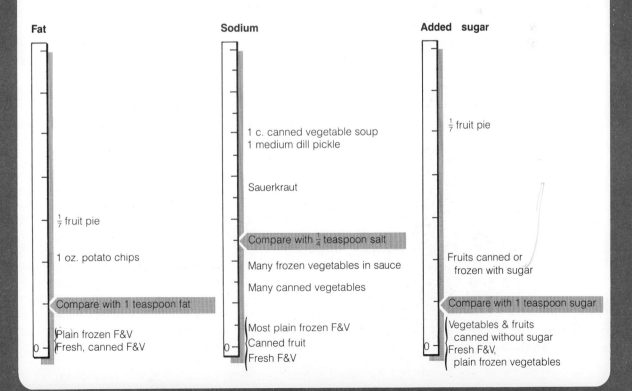

Fruits and Vegetables

At least 4 servings daily including
1 good source of vitamin A
1 good source of vitamin C
(see Table 2.2)

Each of these is a serving
$\frac{1}{2}$ cup fresh, frozen, or canned solid product
1 medium-sized piece of fruit, e.g., apple, orange, banana
$\frac{1}{2}$ cup fresh, frozen, or canned juice
1 cup raw leafy vegetable
2 tablespoons dried fruit or vegetable

How much fat, sodium, and added sugar are likely to be found in fruit and vegetable (F & V) products?
(When no serving size is specified, assume that the serving size stated above applies.)

Fat

$\frac{1}{7}$ fruit pie

1 oz. potato chips

Compare with 1 teaspoon fat

Plain frozen F&V
Fresh, canned F&V

Sodium

1 c. canned vegetable soup
1 medium dill pickle

Sauerkraut

Compare with $\frac{1}{4}$ teaspoon salt

Many frozen vegetables in sauce

Many canned vegetables

Most plain frozen F&V
Canned fruit
Fresh F&V

Added sugar

$\frac{1}{7}$ fruit pie

Fruits canned or
frozen with sugar

Compare with 1 teaspoon sugar

Vegetables & fruits
canned without sugar
Fresh F&V,
plain frozen vegetables

Figure 2.5

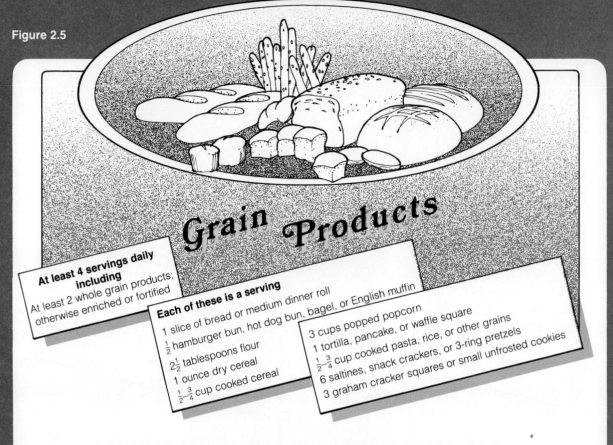

Grain Products

At least 4 servings daily including
At least 2 whole grain products; otherwise enriched or fortified

Each of these is a serving
1 slice of bread or medium dinner roll
½ hamburger bun, hot dog bun, bagel, or English muffin
2½ tablespoons flour
1 ounce dry cereal
½–¾ cup cooked cereal

3 cups popped popcorn
1 tortilla, pancake, or waffle square
½–¾ cup cooked pasta, rice, or other grains
6 saltines, snack crackers, or 3-ring pretzels
3 graham cracker squares or small unfrosted cookies

How much fat, sodium, and added sugar are likely to be found in grain products?
(When no serving size is specified, assume that the serving size stated above applies.)

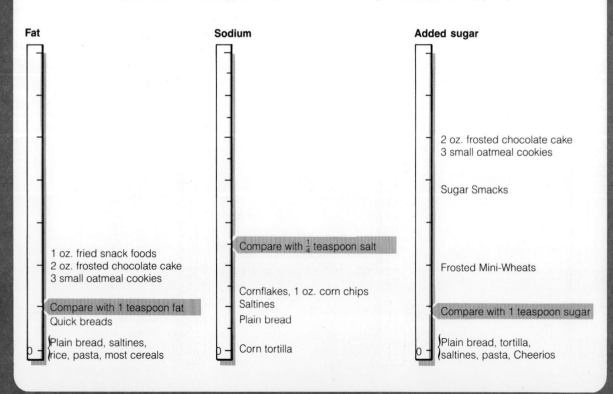

Fat

1 oz. fried snack foods
2 oz. frosted chocolate cake
3 small oatmeal cookies

Compare with 1 teaspoon fat
Quick breads

}Plain bread, saltines,
rice, pasta, most cereals

Sodium

Compare with ¼ teaspoon salt

Cornflakes, 1 oz. corn chips
Saltines
Plain bread

Corn tortilla

Added sugar

2 oz. frosted chocolate cake
3 small oatmeal cookies

Sugar Smacks

Frosted Mini-Wheats

Compare with 1 teaspoon sugar

}Plain bread, tortilla,
saltines, pasta, Cheerios

Figure 2.6

Milk and Milk Products

At least 2 servings (adults)

4 (teens)
3 (children, 9–12 years)
2–3 (children under 9)

Each of these is a serving

1 cup milk or yogurt
$1\frac{1}{3}$ ounces hard cheese
2 ounces processed cheese food
2 cups cottage cheese
1 cup sauces or puddings made with milk
$1\frac{1}{2}$ cups ice cream

How much fat, sodium, and added sugar are likely to be found in milk and milk products?
(When no serving size is specified, assume that the serving size stated above applies.)

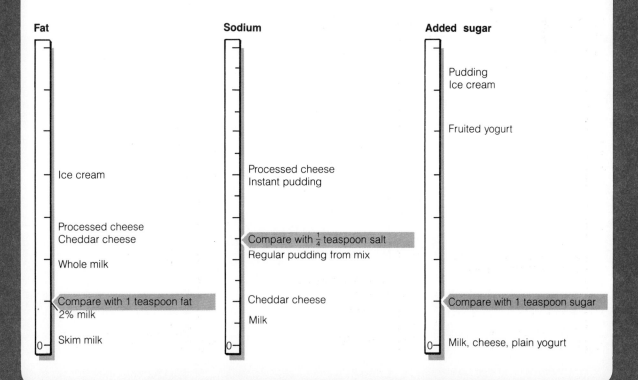

Fat

Ice cream

Processed cheese
Cheddar cheese

Whole milk

Compare with 1 teaspoon fat
2% milk

Skim milk

0

Sodium

Processed cheese
Instant pudding

Compare with $\frac{1}{4}$ teaspoon salt

Regular pudding from mix

Cheddar cheese

Milk

0

Added sugar

Pudding
Ice cream

Fruited yogurt

Compare with 1 teaspoon sugar

Milk, cheese, plain yogurt

0

Figure 2.7

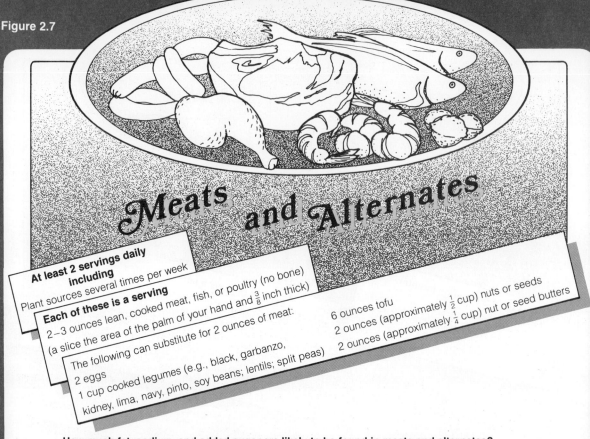

Meats and Alternates

At least 2 servings daily including
Plant sources several times per week

Each of these is a serving
2–3 ounces lean, cooked meat, fish, or poultry (no bone)
(a slice the area of the palm of your hand and $\frac{3}{8}$ inch thick)

The following can substitute for 2 ounces of meat:
2 eggs
1 cup cooked legumes (e.g., black, garbanzo, kidney, lima, navy, pinto, soy beans; lentils; split peas)

6 ounces tofu
2 ounces (approximately $\frac{1}{2}$ cup) nuts or seeds
2 ounces (approximately $\frac{1}{4}$ cup) nut or seed butters

How much fat, sodium, and added sugar are likely to be found in meats and alternates?
(When no serving size is specified, assume that the serving size stated above applies.)

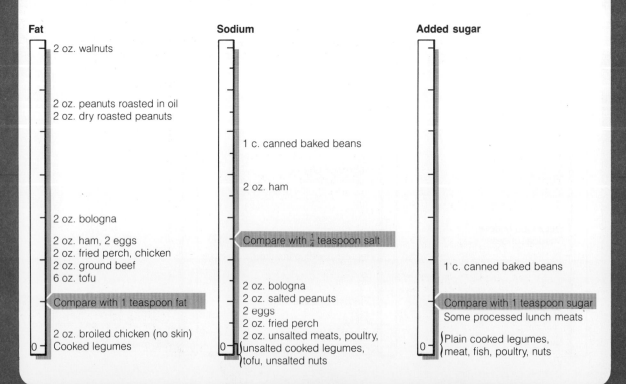

Fat
- 2 oz. walnuts
- 2 oz. peanuts roasted in oil
- 2 oz. dry roasted peanuts
- 2 oz. bologna
- 2 oz. ham, 2 eggs
- 2 oz. fried perch, chicken
- 2 oz. ground beef
- 6 oz. tofu
- Compare with 1 teaspoon fat
- 2 oz. broiled chicken (no skin)
- Cooked legumes

Sodium
- 1 c. canned baked beans
- 2 oz. ham
- Compare with $\frac{1}{4}$ teaspoon salt
- 2 oz. bologna
- 2 oz. salted peanuts
- 2 eggs
- 2 oz. fried perch
- 2 oz. unsalted meats, poultry, unsalted cooked legumes, tofu, unsalted nuts

Added sugar
- 1 c. canned baked beans
- Compare with 1 teaspoon sugar
- Some processed lunch meats
- Plain cooked legumes, meat, fish, poultry, nuts

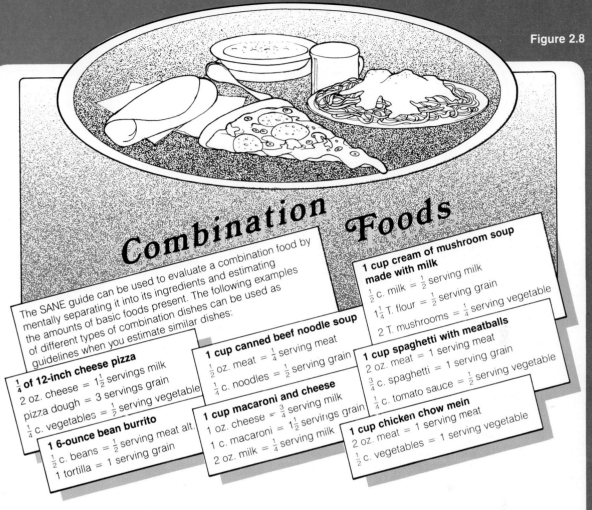

Figure 2.8

Combination Foods

The SANE guide can be used to evaluate a combination food by mentally separating it into its ingredients and estimating the amounts of basic foods present. The following examples of different types of combination dishes can be used as guidelines when you estimate similar dishes:

$\frac{1}{4}$ of 12-inch cheese pizza
2 oz. cheese = $1\frac{1}{2}$ servings milk
pizza dough = 3 servings grain
$\frac{1}{4}$ c. vegetables = $\frac{1}{2}$ serving vegetable

1 6-ounce bean burrito
$\frac{1}{2}$ c. beans = $\frac{1}{2}$ serving meat alt.
1 tortilla = 1 serving grain

1 cup canned beef noodle soup
$\frac{1}{2}$ oz. meat = $\frac{1}{4}$ serving meat
$\frac{1}{4}$ c. noodles = $\frac{1}{2}$ serving grain

1 cup macaroni and cheese
1 oz. cheese = $\frac{3}{4}$ serving milk
1 c. macaroni = $1\frac{1}{2}$ servings grain
2 oz. milk = $\frac{1}{4}$ serving milk

1 cup cream of mushroom soup made with milk
$\frac{1}{2}$ c. milk = $\frac{1}{2}$ serving milk
$1\frac{1}{4}$ T. flour = $\frac{1}{2}$ serving grain
2 T. mushrooms = $\frac{1}{4}$ serving vegetable

1 cup spaghetti with meatballs
2 oz. meat = 1 serving meat
$\frac{3}{4}$ c. spaghetti = 1 serving grain
$\frac{1}{4}$ c. tomato sauce = $\frac{1}{2}$ serving vegetable

1 cup chicken chow mein
2 oz. meat = 1 serving meat
$\frac{1}{2}$ c. vegetables = 1 serving vegetable

How much fat, sodium, and added sugar are likely to be found in combination foods?
(When no serving size is specified, assume that the serving size stated above applies.)

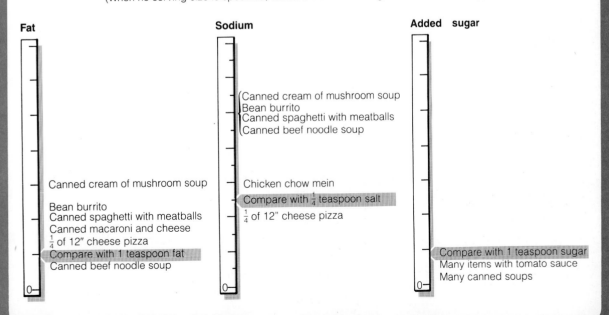

Fat
- Canned cream of mushroom soup
- Bean burrito
- Canned spaghetti with meatballs
- Canned macaroni and cheese
- $\frac{1}{4}$ of 12" cheese pizza
- Compare with 1 teaspoon fat
- Canned beef noodle soup

Sodium
- Canned cream of mushroom soup
- Bean burrito
- Canned spaghetti with meatballs
- Canned beef noodle soup
- Chicken chow mein
- Compare with $\frac{1}{4}$ teaspoon salt
- $\frac{1}{4}$ of 12" cheese pizza

Added sugar
- Compare with 1 teaspoon sugar
- Many items with tomato sauce
- Many canned soups

Figure 2.9

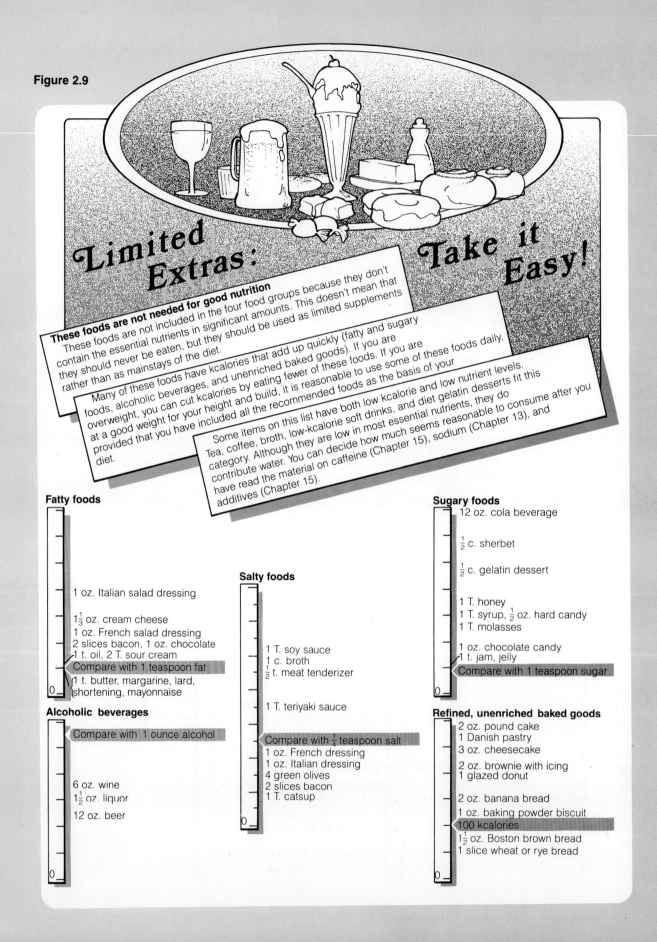

Limited Extras: Take it Easy!

These foods are not needed for good nutrition

These foods are not included in the four food groups because they don't contain the essential nutrients in significant amounts. This doesn't mean that they should never be eaten, but they should be used as limited supplements rather than as mainstays of the diet.

Many of these foods have kcalories that add up quickly (fatty and sugary foods, alcoholic beverages, and unenriched baked goods). If you are overweight, you can cut kcalories by eating fewer of these foods. If you are at a good weight for your height and build, it is reasonable to use some of these foods daily, provided that you have included all the recommended foods as the basis of your diet.

Some items on this list have both low kcalorie and low nutrient levels. Tea, coffee, broth, low-kcalorie soft drinks, and diet gelatin desserts fit this category. Although they are low in most essential nutrients, they do contribute water. You can decide how much seems reasonable to consume after you have read the material on caffeine (Chapter 15), sodium (Chapter 13), and additives (Chapter 15).

Fatty foods

1 oz. Italian salad dressing

$1\frac{1}{3}$ oz. cream cheese
1 oz. French salad dressing
2 slices bacon, 1 oz. chocolate
1 t. oil, 2 T. sour cream
Compare with 1 teaspoon fat
1 t. butter, margarine, lard, shortening, mayonnaise

Alcoholic beverages

Compare with 1 ounce alcohol

6 oz. wine
$1\frac{1}{2}$ oz. liquor
12 oz. beer

Salty foods

1 T. soy sauce
1 c. broth
$\frac{1}{2}$ t. meat tenderizer

1 T. teriyaki sauce

Compare with $\frac{1}{4}$ teaspoon salt
1 oz. French dressing
1 oz. Italian dressing
4 green olives
2 slices bacon
1 T. catsup

Sugary foods

12 oz. cola beverage

$\frac{1}{2}$ c. sherbet

$\frac{1}{2}$ c. gelatin dessert

1 T. honey
1 T. syrup, $\frac{1}{2}$ oz. hard candy
1 T. molasses

1 oz. chocolate candy
1 t. jam, jelly
Compare with 1 teaspoon sugar

Refined, unenriched baked goods

2 oz. pound cake
1 Danish pastry
3 oz. cheesecake

2 oz. brownie with icing
1 glazed donut

2 oz. banana bread
1 oz. baking powder biscuit
100 kcalories
$1\frac{1}{2}$ oz. Boston brown bread
1 slice wheat or rye bread

Figure 2.9 deals with the limited extras. These are consumables that do not belong to any of the basic food groups, usually because of their very low nutrient densities. Nonetheless, it is reasonable to use a few servings per day if your weight allows you to eat more food than the SANE guide suggests. (If you still need more food after that, choose more items from the basic groups.)

These are the limited extras:

■ High fat foods: butter, cream, sour cream, cream cheese, bacon, lard and other solid shortenings, cooking oil, oil-based salad dressings, mayonnaise, margarine

■ High sugar foods: white, brown, or raw sugar; honey; syrup; molasses; jam or jelly; soft drinks; gelatin desserts; other sweet desserts

■ Refined, unenriched, or unfortified grain products: breads, crackers, cereals, cookies, cakes, or fried snack foods that are not made from whole, enriched, or fortified grains

■ Alcoholic beverages (avoid during pregnancy): beer, wine, hard liquor, liqueur

■ Foods that are low in both kcalories and essential nutrients: coffee, tea, broth, some artificially sweetened products such as soft drinks and gelatin desserts, condiments

limited extras—foods that do not belong to any of the basic food groups; they are not recommended for consumption, but can be eaten in moderation by well-nourished people for whom being overweight is not a concern

Evaluating Your Diet Using the SANE Guide. When you use this plan to evaluate a menu, use a form such as the one shown in Figure 2.10.

These are the steps for using it:

1. For an entire day, record all the foods and beverages you consume, along with the amounts of each. For items that are combinations, list the components separately. (See the example in Figure 2.10.)

2. Using the information in Figures 2.4 – 2.8, decide which groups each food belongs to (if any), and how much of a serving your intake represents. Record it in the appropriate columns. For food items that do not fit into any of the four groups, put an "x" in the column for limited extras.

3. Add up each column to get subtotals for fruits and vegetables and group totals for all groups.

4. Fill in the standards for the four food groups that are appropriate for you; standards according to age and reproductive status are given in Table 2.3. The adult standard applies to both adults and full-grown teenagers, that is, teens who have not added any height for a year or more. Standards for athletes, some vegetarians, and people who want to eat as inexpensively as possible are shown in Table 2.4.

5. Compare your intake to the standards. Look only for shortages in your diet; record them on the bottom line. If you are consistently low in

Indicate number of servings that each food represents								
Food or beverage	Amount eaten	Fruits and vegetables				Grain products	Milk and milk products	Meat and alternates	Limited extras
		A	C	Other	Total				
Dry cereal (enriched)	1½ oz.					1½			
Whole milk	½ c.						½		
Strawberry Pop Tart (enriched)	1					1			
Hot dog	1								
Bun (not enriched)	1								X
Frankfurter	1							½	
Catsup	1 T.								X
French fries	20 pcs.			2					
Orange	1 med.		1						
7-Up	12 oz.								X
Cube steak	6 oz.							2	
Mushrooms	¼ c.			½					
Baked potato	1 med.			1					
Butter	1 T.								X
Whole milk	1 c.						1		
Beer	12 oz.								X
Coke	24 oz.								X
Subtotals		0 +	1 +	3½ =	4½				
Group totals					4½	2½	1½	2½	6
Standards		1	1		4	4	2	2	
Shortages		1	1		0	1½	½	0	

Table 2.3 SANE Guide for Various Ages and Reproductive Statuses

	Include at least this many servings daily				
	Child 1/2–9 years	*Child 9–12 years*	*Teen*[a]	*Adult*[a]	*Pregnant or lactating*
Fruits and vegetables	[b]				
Vitamin A rich	1	1	1	1	1
Vitamin C rich	1	1	1	1	2
Others to make a group total of . . .	4	4	4	4	5
Grain products (preferably whole grain; otherwise enriched or fortified)	4[c]	4	4	4	4 or more for adequate weight gain
Milk and milk products	2–3	3	4	2	4[e]
Meats and alternates	2[d]	2	2	2	3

[a]Here, define "teen" as a person who has added height in the past year and is at least 12 years old; an "adult" has not added height in that time.

[b]For preschool children, serving size is 1 tablespoon per year of age.

[c]Give smaller servings, depending on age.

[d]For preschool children, serving size is half of the standard serving.

[e]For pregnant teenagers, increase to 5 servings.

your intake of foods from certain groups, you are probably getting less than you need of that group's major nutrients.

If you find that you have consumed more than the standard numbers of servings, do not assume that you have eaten too much. Remember, the standards are minimums, not maximums. Most people need to eat more than the standards recommend. They are smart to eat additional foods from the basic groups, rather than consuming large amounts of the limited extras.

On the other hand, if you are overly fat, you would be wise to see which columns register high. First look at how many fatty and sugary limited extras you consumed; cutting down on your intake of these foods is the best way of cutting kcalories without sacrificing important nutrients. Then check the basic foods columns. If your intake is much above the standards, you could further reduce kcalories by gradually bringing your intake down closer to the standards; don't drop below them, though, or you will shortchange yourself on essential nutrients. You can also replace some of the foods in each group that are higher in fat and sugar with other group members that have lower levels, as shown along the rulers. (Weight reduction will be dealt with more thoroughly in Chapter 10.)

◀

Figure 2.10 One-day diet analysis using the SANE guide.
This illustration is based on a one-day food record of a 21-year-old man.

Table 2.4 Food Guides for Other Groups

Include at least this many servings daily

	Athletes[a]		Adult vegetarians[b]		Adults with limited budget[e]
	Teen	Adult	Who use milk	Who use only plant foods	
Fruits and vegetables	Fruits/vegetables: 1 vitamin A 1 vitamin C Others to make group total of 4		Fruits: 1–4, including 1 raw vitamin C Vegetables: 3, including 1 or more dark leafy green	Fruits: 1–4, including 1 raw vitamin C Vegetables: 4, including 2 or more dark leafy greens	Fruits/vegetables: 1 vitamin A 1 vitamin C Others to make group total of 4
Grain products	4–12 or more as needed for energy		Whole grain yeast bread: 3 slices Other grains: 2	Whole grain yeast bread: 4 slices Other grains: 3–5	9—12
Milk and milk products	4	2	2	0	$1\frac{1}{2}$
Meats and alternates	2		Legumes: 1 serving Nuts or seeds: $\frac{1}{2}$ serving	Nuts or seeds: 1 serving $\{$ Fortified soybean milk: 2 cups Legumes: $\frac{1}{3}$ cup or $\{$ Legumes: $1\frac{1}{4}$ cup Good sources of vitamin B-12[c] and calcium[d]	2

[a]Reference: Smith, N. 1976. *Diet for sport.* Palo Alto: Bull Publishing Company.

[b]Reference: Robertson, L., C. Flanders, and B. Godfrey. 1976. *Laurel's kitchen,* pages 69 and 322. Berkeley: Nilgiri Press.

[c]Good sources of vitamin B-12: fortified soy milk, fortified nutritional yeast, vitamin supplement (Robertson, 1976).

[d]Good sources of calcium: fortified soy milk, some leafy greens, sunflower seeds, unhulled sesame seeds, blackstrap molasses (Robertson, 1976).

[e]Adapted from Consumer Nutrition Division. 1983. *The thrifty food plan, 1983.* Hyattsville, MD: Human Nutrition Information Service, United States Department of Agriculture.

What other use can you make of the fat, sodium, and added sugar rulers at the bottom of the food group pages? They can simply help you to become familiar with which foods are relatively high or low in those substances. You will find both high and low levels of fat, sodium, and sugar among the basic group foods as well as among the limited extras. In general, though, notice that the more processing a food has experienced, the more likely it is to have gained in fat, sodium, and/or sugar.

You can postpone forming opinions about whether you should reduce your intake of these items until after you have received more information from later chapters about what is known regarding their impact on health.

SUMMARY

■ Most of us alternately overconsume and under-consume moderate amounts of the nutrients we need. This is normal and does not damage health. Long-term over- or underconsumption, however, can have many negative effects.

■ There are several body-based means of measuring nutritional status. Biochemical tests involving the chemical analysis of blood or urine require special equipment to perform, but yield relatively specific information. Anthropometric measurements of height, weight, or skinfold thickness are easier to make but reveal less about nutritional status. Changes in appearance or sense of well-being may be related to nutritional status, or to another cause entirely.

■ For most healthy people, diet analysis is more useful and practical than body-based measurements for estimating nutritional status. Methods of diet analysis include doing a 24-hour recall, keeping a food record, filling out a daily food summary, and analyzing your intake using food composition tables.

■ Food group plans focus less on what specific foods were eaten and more on the general types of products consumed. Many such plans have been developed over the last four decades. The Basic Four Food Guide, Canada's Food Guide, the Hassle-Free Guide to a Better Diet, the Modified Basic Four, and the Dietary Goals and subsequent Dietary Guidelines all have both merits and drawbacks.

■ The authors of this book have devised a guide called The Sound Approach to Nutritious Eating (SANE), which builds on the strengths of the existing guidelines and also provides useful information on the amount of fat, sodium, and sugar in many foods. It begins with the groupings of the Basic Four and the Hassle-Free Guide, and identifies a fifth group called limited extras. The limited extras are foods of low nutrient density that are not recommended items, although they can be eaten in moderation by well-nourished people for whom being overweight is not a concern.

REFERENCES

American Dietetic Association. 1981. *Handbook of clinical dietetics.* New Haven: Yale University Press.

Consumer Nutrition Division. 1983. *The thrifty food plan. 1983.* Hyattsville, MD: Human Nutrition Information Service, United States Department of Agriculture.

Food and Nutrition Board. 1980. *Toward healthful diets.* Washington, DC: National Research Council, National Academy of Sciences.

Getchell, B. 1979. *Physical fitness: A way of life.* New York: John Wiley and Sons.

Hambidge, K. M. 1982. Hair analysis: Worthless for vitamins, limited for minerals. *American Journal of Clinical Nutrition* 36:943–949.

King, J. C., S. H. Cohenour, E. G. Corruiccini, and P. Schneeman. 1978. Evaluation and modification of the basic four food guide. *Journal of Nutrition Education* 10(no.1):27–29.

Pennington, J. A., and H. N. Church. 1980. *Food values of portions commonly used.* Philadelphia: J. P. Lippincott Company.

Robertson, L., C. Flanders, and B. Godfrey. 1976. *Laurel's kitchen.* Berkeley: Nilgiri Press.

Smith, N. 1976. *Diet for sport.* Palo Alto, CA: Bull Publishing Company.

U.S. Congress. Senate Select Committee on Nutrition and Human Needs. *Dietary Goals for the United States.* 95th Cong., 1st sess., February and December, 1977. Committee Print.

U.S. Department of Agriculture. 1979. *The Hassle-free guide to a better diet*. Science and Education Administration Leaflet No. 567: U.S. Government Printing Office.

U.S. Department of Agriculture. 1981. *Nutritive value of foods*. Home and Garden Bulletin No. 72: U.S. Government Printing Office.

U.S. Department of Agriculture and U.S. Department of Health and Human Services. 1980. *Nutrition and your health: Dietary guidelines for Americans*. Home and Garden Bulletin No. 232: U.S. Government Printing Office.

U.S. Department of Health, Education, and Welfare (now Department of Health and Human Services). 1979. *Healthy people: The surgeon general's report on health promotion and disease prevention*. DHEW (PHS) Publication No. 79-55071: U.S. Government Printing Office.

Weinsier, R. L., and C. E. Butterworth. 1981. *Handbook of clinical nutrition*. St. Louis: The C. V. Mosby Company.

3

Physiology for Nutrition

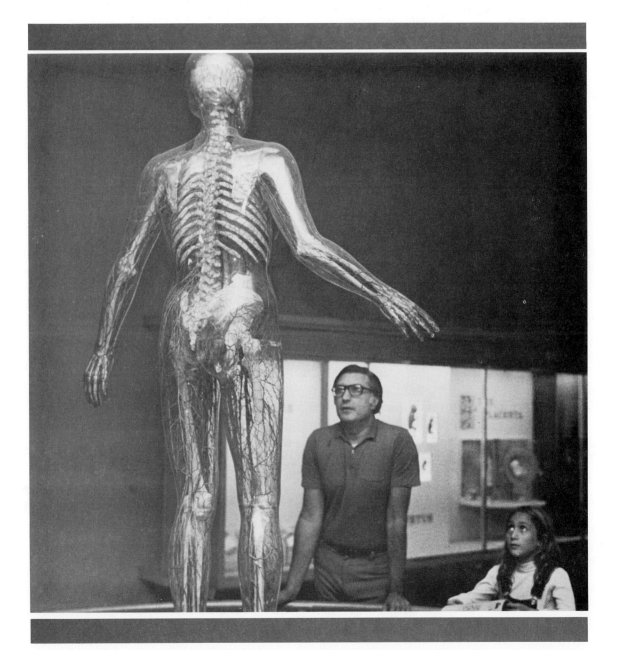

IN THIS CHAPTER: Digestion Prepares Nutrients for Absorption ▪ The Cell Is Where Nutrients Are Used ▪ Metabolism Is A Continuous, Life-sustaining, Cellular Process ▪ Circulation Delivers Nutrients Where They Are Needed ▪ Excretion of Waste Products Occurs via Several Routes

You might think that just *eating* food should guarantee that its nutrients will become an integral part of the body. Actually, though, the body must first break food apart and then get the nutrients through several screening devices before they are usable.

Because the healthy body is so efficient at doing this, we tend to take these functions for granted. It is well worth taking an appreciative look at the carefully regulated processes and structures involved in incorporating food into the body. This information can help you understand material in upcoming chapters about what particular nutrients can do for you, and about certain abnormalities that can occur in the way the body handles nutrients.

We will discuss several processes involved in the food-using activity: digestion, which prepares food to move through the screening devices; circulation, which carries nutrients and oxygen to the cells and waste products from them; metabolism, during which nutrients are used; and excretion, which transports the waste products out of the body. We will also look at the cell, the entity that ultimately uses the nutrients.

In this chapter, you will become acquainted with the basic anatomy (structure) and physiology (function) of several body systems: the digestive, circulatory, and urinary systems. We will take a more detailed look at how the body handles each of the six classes of nutrients in later chapters.

Digestion Prepares Nutrients for Absorption

digestion—the process of breaking food down into substances small enough to be absorbed

absorption—the process of taking digested substances into the body's interior

Digestion is the process of breaking food down into substances that can be absorbed. Absorption is the uptake of these substances into the body's interior.

General Characteristics of the Digestive System

Special features of the system enable it to carry out its unique tasks.

Shape. The main part of the digestive system consists of a hollow tube called the alimentary canal or gastrointestinal (GI) tract. The tube begins at the mouth and takes a turning and twisting route before it ends at the anus. Its entire length, if straightened out, would be several times your height. As you look at its structure (Figure 3.1), you can see that its various specialized sections have different diameters, from the considerable width of the stomach to the rather narrow tube of the small intestine.

alimentary canal, gastrointestinal (GI) tract—the main part of the digestive system: a hollow tube beginning at the mouth and ending at the anus

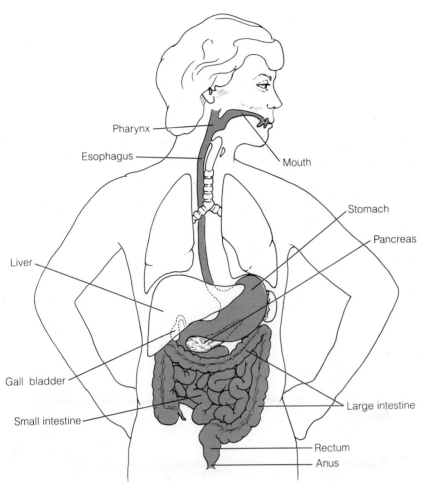

Pharynx

Esophagus

Mouth

Stomach

Pancreas

Liver

Gall bladder

Small intestine

Large intestine

Rectum

Anus

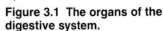

Figure 3.1 The organs of the digestive system.

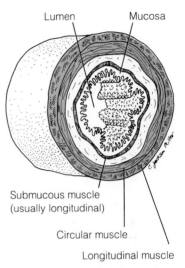

Lumen

Mucosa

Submucous muscle
(usually longitudinal)

Circular muscle

Longitudinal muscle

Figure 3.2 Cross-sectional diagram of the layers in the GI tract. Different regions of the GI tract have many similarities in structure, even though they vary considerably in the size of the lumen (central space through which food passes) and in some other characteristics. This drawing shows the features the regions have in common.

Lining. The entire tract has a lining that can be thought of as an internal skin separating the contents of the tract from the body's actual interior (Figure 3.2). (Food that is moving through the central space within the tract, called the lumen, is still technically "outside" your body.) The lining of the tract is called the mucosa; it selectively allows certain types of substances to be absorbed. An important criterion in this screening process is that the materials be particles small enough to pass through the lining.

Substances that are too large to be absorbed will simply pass through the entire length of the GI tract and exit the system. For example, if a toddler swallows a small plastic button, the button will be prevented from entering his body, and will simply pass through and exit the system within a few days. Similarly food fiber, the plant constituents that the human body is unable to digest, will not pass through the mucosa but will travel through the tract and leave the body as solid waste.

Muscles. The GI tract has many layers besides the mucosa; several of these are composed of muscles that control the progress of the contents through

lumen—the central space within which food passes through the GI tract

mucosa—the internal lining of the GI tract

the tract. Longitudinal muscles run the length of the system, and others encircle it (see Figure 3.2).

The circular muscles that occur between different areas of the tract and at the end of it are called sphincters. When a sphincter is relaxed, that part of the tube is open, and the contents can pass through. When a sphincter is contracted (constricted), the muscular ring is tightly closed, and forward movement through the tract is prevented. A contracted sphincter also prevents any GI contents from moving backward (up) in the tract.

Sphincter muscles are normally controlled automatically through stimulation by the nervous system. However, the last sphincter in the tract, the anus or anal sphincter, can be voluntarily controlled.

Secretions.   Various parts of the digestive system secrete large amounts of fluids—approximately 2 gallons per day in most people—that contain the following types of substances that assist in digestion:

1. Mucus is a slimy material produced by certain cells in the mucosa; it lubricates the tract, keeping the lining moist and allowing food to move more readily through the system, as well as coating the lining to protect it from some of the tract's harsher secretions.

2. Chemical compounds are produced that have a particular acidity or alkalinity needed for digestion.

3. Enzymes, which are proteins that speed up the rate of biochemical reactions in the body, are produced in various parts of the digestive system to help in the breakdown of food. Names of enzymes can often be recognized by their "-ase" endings—for example, prote*ase*, an enzyme that acts on protein; lip*ase*, an enzyme that acts on lipid (fat); and amy*lase*, an enzyme that acts on starch.

4. Hormones, which are chemical messengers produced in one region of the body and targeted to affect a process at some other body site, influence many aspects of digestion. Names of hormones often end in "-in" or "-ine,"—for example, epinephr*ine*, gastr*in*, secret*in*.

Transit Time.   The amount of time it takes from ingestion of a food until its solid waste leaves the system is called the transit time. Normally, transit time is from 24 to 72 hours in a healthy individual, although remnants of the residue of a given meal may remain in the system for a week or more. Factors that can influence the rate of transit, either speeding it up or slowing it down, include the content of the diet, medications, emotions, physical activity, and various illnesses. If transit time is much faster than normal, diarrhea results; if it is much slower, constipation occurs.

Maintenance.   The innermost lining of the GI tract, which directly contacts food, is renewed every two to three days. This replacement is necessary because even though there are mechanisms to protect the mucosa from damage, the digestive secretions and the movement of food through the tract cause wear and tear.

---

sphincters—circular muscles that occur between different sections of the GI tract and help to regulate the passage of materials

anus, anal sphincter—the last sphincter in the GI tract; can be voluntarily controlled

mucus—slimy material produced by the mucosa

enzymes—proteins that speed up biochemical reactions

hormones—chemical messengers produced in one region of the body and targeted to affect a process in another region

transit time—the time that elapses between ingestion of food and elimination of its solid waste from the body

Phases of Digestion and Absorption

With the general characteristics of the digestive system in mind, let's look at the sequence of steps in digestion.

Cephalic Phase: Sometimes the First Step in the Process. *Cephalic* means "pertaining to the head"; just thinking about food can initiate digestive processes. If you see food, smell it, or even hear sounds associated with it, you may sense your digestive processes beginning, even though you have not eaten anything. Your stomach may growl, and your saliva and other digestive juices may flow more copiously in anticipation.

These sensations may make you *want* to eat, but your body does not necessarily *need* food when you experience them.

The Mouth: Point of Entry. When food enters the mouth, the digestive system becomes undeniably active. With your teeth, you cut, grind, and mash food, making it easier to swallow and more accessible to the various digestive substances it will encounter along the way.

In addition, the presence of food stimulates the flow of saliva, the watery mucus produced in the mouth. Saliva not only lubricates the upper part of the GI tract, but also moistens dry foods and turns them into a cohesive wad. In addition, saliva contains the first of many enzymes involved in digestion: amylase. Amylase begins the breakdown of starch, a form of carbohydrate. Saliva functions even after food has been swallowed by rinsing the surface of the teeth, which helps prevent their decay. The amount of saliva that is produced and swallowed throughout the day totals 1 to $1\frac{1}{2}$ quarts.

The Pharynx: Origin of the Swallow. The pharynx, located just beyond the mouth, is a common pathway for both the digestive and respiratory systems. It is part of the GI tract for food and part of the airway for breathing. When it is being used for food, openings to the other portions of the airway are normally closed by muscles controlled automatically by the nervous system.

Because it contains the muscles for swallowing, the pharynx's special function in digestion is to move food along to the next region of the tract, the esophagus.

pharynx—section of the GI tract just beyond the mouth

The Esophagus: The Stomach Connection. The esophagus is a conduit between the pharynx and the stomach. Once food is in this structure, it is moved along by rhythmic waves of muscular contraction that are automatically controlled by the nervous system. This involuntary digestive muscular activity is called peristalsis; it occurs in every region of the GI tract from the pharynx to the rectum. Usually gravity, too, plays a role in helping move foods down the esophagus, but peristalsis can accomplish the task by itself if you are not in an upright position.

At the bottom of the esophagus is a sphincter that relaxes to allow food to pass into the stomach, but then closes to prevent digestive juices and food from moving back into the esophagus. Sometimes this sphincter does not stay tightly closed while food is being mixed with digestive juices

esophagus—passageway that conducts food from the pharynx to the stomach

peristalsis—rhythmic waves of involuntary muscular contraction that move food in the proper direction through the GI tract

in the stomach, and part of the stomach contents wash back up into the lower part of the esophagus. Since the stomach juices contain chemicals that are irritating to the lining of the esophagus, repeated contact causes pain that is referred to as "heartburn," although it has nothing to do with the heart. This sphincter is also open during vomiting.

The Stomach: Mixer and Reservoir. The stomach is the pouchlike enlargement in the GI tract that has the elasticity to accommodate from 1 to 2 quarts of food and fluid. Although one of its important functions is simply to hold what has been eaten until the lower portions of the tract are ready to receive and process its contents, it also has several unique roles.

- **Mixing Activity** Peristaltic contractions in the stomach are very strong. The muscles squeeze and churn the contents, mixing digestive juices with the food particles. The slushy blend that results is called chyme.
- **Secretions**   The stomach produces digestive juices that contain strong hydrochloric acid and enzymes that act on protein to begin its digestion.

chyme—slushy mixture of food and digestive juices produced in the stomach

The production of these juices is stimulated by the presence of food in the stomach. Emotions can either increase or decrease these secretions: when people feel aggressive, resentful, angry, hostile, sad, afraid, or depressed, the rate at which these substances are produced may either speed up or slow down.

Since the tissues of the stomach are composed of protein, it would seem as though they should be vulnerable to digestion by their own gastric (stomach) juices. However, under normal circumstances the tough material and tight construction of the stomach lining prevent self-digestion. Furthermore, the mucus produced there sets up a protective barrier.

ulcer—open sore in the lining of the stomach (or small intestine) produced in susceptible individuals by acidic digestive juices and/or other irritants

These fail-safe mechanisms can break down if the stomach is unusually vulnerable to stomach acid or to other known irritants such as alcohol, caffeine, black pepper, chili powder, and certain drugs (American Dietetic Association, 1981). If such irritation eventually wears deep into the lining, an ulcer results.

- **Absorption**   Little absorption takes place from the stomach. Two common substances can be absorbed without needing to be digested first—water and alcohol—and they are absorbed from this site in only small amounts. (Some drugs can also be absorbed through the stomach.)
- **Emptying**   Chyme is emptied from the stomach over a period of several hours; it is squirted from the stomach into the small intestine at intervals when the sphincter between them is relaxed.

The rate at which the stomach empties depends on a number of factors. Consistency of the material influences emptying: liquids leave the stomach more rapidly than solids do. The macronutrient composition also makes a difference: in pure form, carbohydrates empty the fastest, proteins next, and fats the most slowly. Since most consumables are mixtures of macronutrients, their emptying time depends on the relative nutrient content of each. Not surprisingly, the volume of what has been eaten is also a factor: a huge meal takes longer overall to empty than a smaller one.

Stomach emptying is actually regulated more by the small intestine than by the stomach itself, although both are involved. When chyme contacts the intestinal mucosa, hormonal messages based on the composition of the chyme are sent back to the sphincter at the lower end of the stomach; this controls when and how much chyme will be released. The nervous system also plays a role in that it prompts the opening or closing of the sphincter, depending on how distended the small intestine is, and on various chemical factors.

Emotions may affect emptying as well, either slowing or hastening it. A physician who x-rayed the stomachs of college football players found that on game days, the players' stomachs took two to four hours longer to empty, presumably because of stress (Mirkin and Hoffman, 1978).

The Small Intestine: Scene of the Major Action. In a length of approximately 10 feet, your small intestine accomplishes the major work of digestion. It divides most of the carbohydrates, proteins, and fats into small

small intestine—longest section of the GI tract, performing the major work of digestion and absorption

---

According to Dr. Gabe Mirkin and M. Hoffman in *The Sportsmedicine Book,* many professional athletes learn for themselves how best to time their meals on days when they are competing.

Some former sports heroes have described their eating practices: Joe Namath never ate on game days. Neither did O.J. Simpson. Bill Russell, the former Boston Celtic superstar, had to eat at least eight hours before he played; otherwise he would "chuck it all up." Muhammad Ali preferred to eat six hours before a fight.

The Baltimore Orioles eat $4\frac{1}{2}$ hours before games, the New York Jets serve a pregame meal 5 hours before kickoff, and many hockey players eat a full meal 6 hours before game time, according to Mirkin and Hoffman.

Although the preferred timing of the pre-event meal varies from athlete to athlete, there seems to be a general agreement among sports professionals that it is not desirable to eat close to the time of intense competition. A gut distended with food is likely to be uncomfortable, especially when playing contact sports.

(Other implications of eating too soon before activity will be mentioned shortly.)

SLICE OF LIFE:
When Athletes Eat before a Game

units, and then absorbs them. It also absorbs the substances that are small enough to pass through the lining without digestion: water, vitamins, minerals, and alcohol.

■ **Secretions** In addition to the enzyme-containing digestive juices produced by the intestinal mucosa, secretions from two organs connected to the tract also pour into the intestinal lumen. The liver is a large multifunction organ that filters blood, and processes and stores various body substances. It produces bile, a solution that is stored in the gall bladder until it is needed. The function of bile is to keep fats divided into very small droplets that can be more easily digested, a process called emulsification.

The pancreas also has several functions, one of which is to produce secretions that contain alkali, which neutralizes the hydrochloric acid in the chyme. In addition, the pancreas produces various enzymes that are specific for the digestion of carbohydrate, protein, and fat.

■ **Mechanical Activity** Two kinds of muscular activity take place in the small intestine to mix and move the contents. Peristalsis, as in other areas, is evident here. In addition, circular muscles constrict at intervals, in a "sausage-link" effect. After the contents between the contracted muscles have been mixed for a time, they relax, and then other muscles constrict to form a new series of "links"; these are called segmentation contractions.

■ **Absorption** The structure of the lining of the small intestine equips it perfectly for its additional critical role of absorbing the end-products of digestion. Millions of thin, flexible fingerlike projections extend from the lining, giving the effect of a terrycloth-lined tube. Called villi, these projections waft about in the intestine, ready to absorb digested macronutrient particles, water, vitamins, and minerals.

Projecting from the villi are even smaller strands called microvilli, which enlarge surface area further (Figure 3.3.). It is estimated that this convoluted construction multiplies the intestinal surface area by 600 times what it would have been if the intestine were smooth. If the absorptive surface could be flattened out, it would measure approximately 200

bile—liquid produced in the liver and stored in the gall bladder until needed for fat digestion in the small intestine

emulsification—separation of fats into very small droplets, which aids in their digestion

pancreas—organ producing secretions that neutralize the acidity of the chyme and help to digest macronutrients

segmentation contractions—intermittent constrictions of circular muscles that produce "segments" of intestine whose contents are mixed for a time before new segments are formed

villi—thin, fingerlike projections of the intestinal mucosa that extend into the lumen, greatly increasing the surface area for absorbing nutrients

microvilli—microscopic projections from the villi that increase the intestine's absorptive surface area even further

Figure 3.3 The villi of the small intestine. The left side of this illustration represents a cross-section of the small intestine, showing how the villi project into the lumen. The right side is a magnification of two villi, showing their microvilli. These projections greatly enlarge the absorptive surface beyond what it would be if the lining were smooth.

Villus

Microvilli

square meters (Ganong, 1981), an area equivalent to the size of a tennis court! (The estimates of other physiologists vary.) After the nutrients have been absorbed, they are distributed to the body's cells via the circulation, which will be described later in this chapter.

The small intestine does a thorough job; in a healthy person it digests and absorbs macronutrients that provide 90% or more of the energy value of the consumed food. The absorption of vitamins and minerals from the small intestine is less predictable, since absorption of these nutrients is influenced by the presence of other food constituents. Water is also absorbed here, a function that is shared with the large intestine.

The Large Intestine: Absorber and Reservoir. It may seem there is nothing left for the large intestine (colon or bowel) to do, after the small intestine has played its major role. However, several important functions are performed by this section of the digestive tract.

large intestine (colon, bowel)—last major section of the GI tract, serving as a collecting chamber for solid waste, a home for bacteria, and an absorption site for water and certain minerals

- Collection   The large intestine serves as a collecting chamber for solid waste, which it holds until the feces are excreted. Of all the regions of the digestive system, food spends the longest time here, often 24 hours or more.

- Holding and Harboring of Bacteria   Because peristalsis and segmentation contractions move contents more slowly through the colon, bacteria have an opportunity to become established and to flourish (Spence, 1982).

    Bacteria act on the portions of food that have not yet been digested and absorbed by the human system. Some of the breakdown products are used by the bacteria for their own sustenance. Others are available to the person after absorption from the colon: recent research suggests that up to 10% of the kcalories a person absorbs may come via this route (McNeil, 1984).

    Another benefit of these bacteria is that they produce some vitamins during the course of their own metabolism that seem to be partially absorbed by the body. A substantial amount of vitamin K and a lesser amount of some of the B vitamins are thought to be obtained in this way.

    As bacteria metabolize food, they produce gas as one of their waste products. If the amount is small, it causes no symptoms; however, if a great deal of gas accumulates, it is emitted through the anus.

- Absorption   The colon offers the body its last chance to absorb much of the remaining water and the elements sodium and chloride. If the colon fails to do this, diarrhea results.

You have now taken a tour through the GI tract. Table 3.1 helps summarize these many processes by reviewing the regions of the canal in which the mixing, moving, and absorbing activities occur. Table 3.2 summarizes the body's digestive secretions, including where they have their effects on the macronutrients.

Table 3.1	Summary of Processes That Mix or Move the GI Contents during Digestion and Absorption
Location	Process
Mouth	Chewing
Pharynx	Swallowing
	Peristalsis
Esophagus	Peristalsis
Stomach	Peristalsis
	Absorption of small amounts of water and alcohol
Small intestine	Peristalsis
	Segmentation contractions
	Absorption of water, vitamins, minerals, alcohol, and digestion products from carbohydrates, lipids, and proteins
Large intestine	Peristalsis
	Segmentation contractions
	Absorption of water; sodium; chloride; some vitamin K, B vitamins, and bacterial breakdown products
Rectum	Peristalsis
	Defecation reflex

Table 3.2 Summary of Secreted Agents That Help Break the Macronutrients Apart in the GI Tract			
Location	Carbohydrate	Fat	Protein
Mouth	Amylase in saliva		
Stomach			Hydrochloric acid
			Protease
Small intestine	Amylase from pancreas	Bile produced by liver	Protease from pancreas
		Lipase from pancreas	
	Enzymes from mucosa that complete carbohydrate digestion	Enzymes from mucosa that complete fat digestion	Enzymes from mucosa that complete protein digestion
Large intestine	(Here bacteria carry out their own chemical processes on remaining nutrients.)		

Next we will focus on the microscopic unit that *needs* the nutrients—the cell.

The Cell Is Where Nutrients Are Used

cell—the smallest, simplest unit of living matter.

The cell is the smallest, simplest unit of living matter. It is within the cell that the most basic life processes take place, including the release of energy from nutrients.

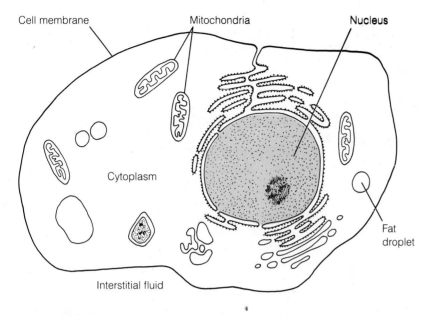

Cell membrane   Mitochondria   Nucleus

Cytoplasm

Fat droplet

Interstitial fluid

Figure 3.4 The cell. All animal and plant cells have certain structural similarities which are pictured.

The Structure of a Cell

All living animal and plant cells have certain structural and functional similarities. Figure 3.4 illustrates these:

- A thin, selectively permeable cell membrane, which encloses and protects the contents by controlling what substances come into and go out of the cell.

- A nucleus, which contains genetic information that enables new cells of the same type to form by division from the original.

- Mitochondria, small bodies within the cell in which energy production takes place.

- Various other types of small bodies that make or store protein or fat, and still others that destroy materials for which there is no further need.

- Cytoplasm, the fluid that fills the cell, and in which all the bodies just mentioned are suspended.

selectively permeable—referring to the ability of the cell membrane to exclude certain substances, and to regulate the passage of others into or out of the cell

Although a cell is microscopic, its importance cannot be overestimated. Some cells are able to survive by themselves, independent of any others; bacteria and yeasts are examples. More complex organisms—like you—consist of millions of cells that are related to each other, each with their own specialized functions.

When cells are grouped together in a more complex life form, they are seldom so tightly packed that their membranes touch each other. Rather, there are spaces between the cells called interstitial spaces, which are filled with interstitial fluid. You have seen interstitial fluid when it has

interstitial fluid—fluid that fills the spaces between cells oozed from a minor abrasion that scraped your skin, but was not deep enough to cause bleeding. This same fluid has a role to play in nutrition, which will be described soon.

Building a Body from Cells

When many cells of the same type are grouped together to perform a similar function, they are collectively referred to as a tissue. The body's tissue types are muscular, nervous, connective (for binding together and supporting body structures), and epithelial (refers to coverings and linings, such as the skin or the lining of the GI tract).

Several tissues combine to form organs, which are capable of more complex physiological processes; the stomach, for example, is an organ made up of epithelial, muscular, and nervous tissues. Several organs combine into systems, such as the digestive system, and function cooperatively to accomplish a major physiological purpose. Systems, then, unite into a total organism.

This variety and interdependence among the functions of cells make the body not only extremely complex, but also very versatile and able to adapt to different conditions.

Metabolism Is a Continuous, Life-sustaining, Cellular Process

As mentioned earlier, the chemical processes that take place in the living cell are referred to by the umbrella term *metabolism*. A regular supply of nutrients is essential for metabolism to take place.

Metabolic reactions occur all the time in every living cell. Synthesis reactions build up new substances that will become part of the body's structure or will be used to help it function; simultaneously, breakdown reactions dismantle other materials into smaller units.

Although both are occurring in all cells at the same time, synthesis and breakdown reactions may take place at different rates at different times or in different cells. During periods of growth—such as childhood, pregnancy, muscle building, healing—synthesis outstrips breakdown. At other times, such as during illness or injury, breakdown predominates.

Circulation Delivers Nutrients Where They Are Needed

The primary function of the circulatory system is to deliver to all of the body's individual cells the nutrients and oxygen they need to derive energy for living. Equally important and simultaneous roles of the circulatory system are to carry various cellular products to other sites in the body, and to carry the waste products of metabolism away from the cells for disposal.

General Characteristics of the Circulatory System

The circulatory system is a closed, continuous network of elastic blood vessels in which the body's 4- to 6-quart blood supply cycles repeatedly.

Power Source: The Heart. The heart is the pump that keeps blood moving through the circulatory system. It is composed of strong muscles that normally contract and relax 50 to 90 times per minute when the body is at rest.

The vessels that enter and leave the heart are few in number but large in size, since the body's whole blood supply is channeled through them.

Two Loops. There are two loops through which the body's blood is routed: one that circles between the heart and the lungs, and one that connects the heart to all the other parts of the body. Each circuit is powered by a different side of the heart, as shown in Figure 3.5.

Here's what happens in the circuit involving the lungs:

1. Blood is pumped from the right side of the heart to the lungs through a network of branching blood vessels.

2. In the lungs, where the vessels are especially small and permeable, the blood releases carbon dioxide (a waste product of cellular activity) to be exhaled, and takes in oxygen from the newly inhaled air.

3. The blood returns to the left side of the heart.

The following is what takes place in the circuit that serves the rest of the body:

1. Blood is pumped from the left side of the heart to all areas of the body through a network of branching blood vessels.

2. When the vessels are very small and permeable, oxygen and nutrients move out through the vessel walls, and carbon dioxide and other cellular metabolic products pass into the blood.

3. The blood returns to the right side of the heart.

This sequence is repeated with every heartbeat from before birth until death occurs.

Names of Vessels. Although the blood vessels form a continuous system, they are called by different names depending on where they are in the circuit. The large vessels that carry blood away from the heart are called arteries. They divide into many branches in order to distribute blood to different areas of the body.

After each branching, they are more numerous and smaller in diameter. Smaller arteries are called arterioles, and the very smallest versions, through which the exchange of nutrients from the blood supply and wastes from body cells finally occurs, are called capillaries. The network of tiny blood vessels that serves a given region of the body is its capillary bed.

circulatory system—closed, continuous network of blood vessels in which blood cycles repeatedly throughout the body

arteries—vessels that carry blood away from the heart

capillaries—smallest blood vessels, through which exchange of nutrients from the blood supply and wastes from body cells occurs

Figure 3.5 Schematic diagram of circulation. This drawing represents the route blood takes through the two circuits that begin and end at the heart. (Note that in anatomical drawings, the right and left sides are pictured as though you are looking at the body from the front.)

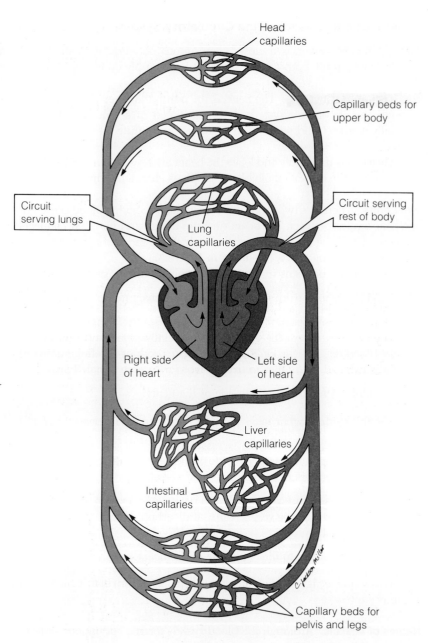

Head capillaries

Capillary beds for upper body

Circuit serving lungs

Lung capillaries

Circuit serving rest of body

Right side of heart

Left side of heart

Liver capillaries

Intestinal capillaries

Capillary beds for pelvis and legs

(You can imagine how numerous the blood vessels need to be to have a capillary close to every body cell—every cell of skin, bone, nerve, muscle, and so on. You have approximately 60,000 miles of blood vessels within you to accomplish this!)

Now to complete the circuit: blood returns toward the heart through venules. These merge to form larger veins, which funnel blood back into the heart.

veins—vessels that carry blood to the heart

How do nutrients make their entry into this system? Answering that question requires looking at the capillary bed in the part of the circuit that serves the small intestine.

The Route Taken by Nutrients Entering the Bloodstream

Recall that nutrients are absorbed into the villi in the small intestine. There are capillaries in each villus, as shown in Figure 3.6, which are ready to take up nutrients that are absorbed.

Capillaries take in mostly water-soluble nutrients. (Remaining nutrients are transported in another type of vessel, the lacteal, which will be discussed in a later section.) Many of the digested nutrients that are absorbed into the circulatory system need more modification before they can be used by the body's cells. For this reason, the venous blood leaving the small intestine goes to the liver, where such changes can be made.

The liver is the body's major metabolic clearinghouse. In the liver, many nutrients are made more suitable for circulation, energy production, or storage. Some nutrients remain in the liver; others resume their journey via the veins back to the heart.

As these veins merge with those returning from other body areas, the blood they are carrying mixes, and the nutrients are distributed through it. The dissolved nutrients keep recycling in the blood as described here and as shown in Figure 3.5: from the heart to the lungs, then back to the left side of the heart, which pumps them to all regions of the body.

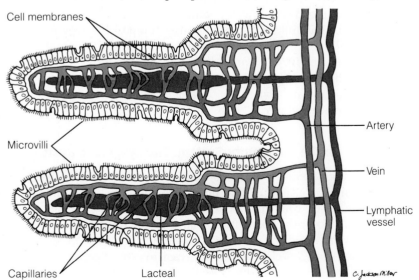

Cell membranes

Microvilli

Capillaries

Lacteal

Artery

Vein

Lymphatic vessel

Figure 3.6 The villi and their circulatory vessels. Each villus is laced with a network of fluid-carrying vessels that take in the nutrients absorbed during digestion.

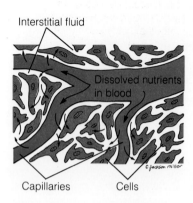

Interstitial fluid

Dissolved nutrients in blood

Capillaries   Cells

Figure 3.7 The route taken by nutrients from the capillaries to the cells. Nutrients are carried by the circulation to all regions of the body. They pass through the selectively permeable capillary walls into the interstitial fluid, and from there into the cells.

Getting the Nutrients into Cells

When nutrients are distributed via the circulation to all of your capillary beds, they are able to move through the thin selectively permeable capillary membranes into the interstitial fluid (Figure 3.7). From the interstitial fluid, the nutrients are absorbed through the individual selectively permeable cell membranes into the interior of the cells.

While they are taking in nutrients, the cells are simultaneously releasing wastes and other products of their metabolism into the interstitial fluid. Many of these products are then absorbed back into the capillaries and thereby into the general circulation. In a later section, we will describe how the body gets rid of wastes.

Distributing Blood to Various Body Regions

The volume of blood that is channeled to each of the body's various regions is determined largely by the amount of blood that is *needed* there at any given time. When the body is at rest, the heart typically directs to the abdomen about half of the total amount of blood it pumps; less than one-fourth goes to skeletal muscle (muscle that is attached to bone); and the rest is shared by the heart, brain, and skin (Ganong, 1981). This distribution is adequate to meet resting needs.

However, if a person is engaged in strenuous physical activity, as much as seven-eighths of the blood supply may be directed to the active skeletal muscles, which are in immediate need of oxygen and nutrients for energy production. Blood flow to the skin also increases, so that surplus heat can be dissipated (Guyton, 1981).

If a person has recently eaten a large meal, a greater-than-normal portion of the blood supply will be committed to the intestines, in order to pick up the nutrients that are absorbed. If you eat a large meal shortly before strenuous exercise, your skeletal muscles and GI tract will both need a greater blood supply at the same time. These increased demands cannot both be met fully and simultaneously. It is possible, therefore, that physical performance and digestion may be temporarily impaired (Stickney and VanLiere, 1974). (Eating just a *small* amount is not likely to interfere with physical performance, though.) This gives another perspective on why people are advised not to eat a large meal within three hours of intense physical activity.

A Sidekick for the Circulatory System: The Lymphatic System

The lymphatic system is a second system of vessels that serves the body; it carries lymph, a clear fluid that filters into tiny vessels from interstitial fluid. These vessels constitute a one-way network that eventually funnels lymph from all over the body into two large lymphatic vessels that empty into major veins returning to the heart (Figure 3.8).

The lymphatic vessels that serve the small intestine have an important role in nutrition, since besides collecting lymph, they also absorb and

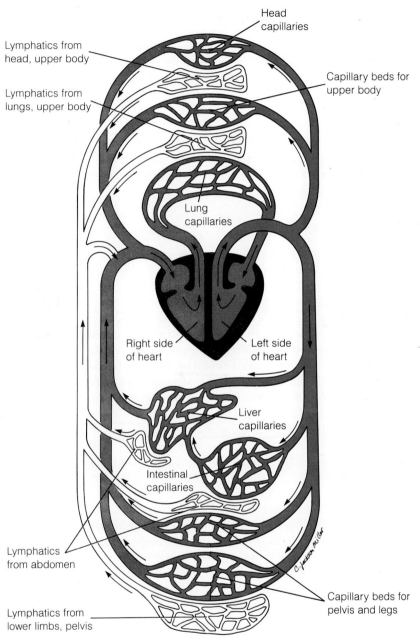

Head
capillaries

Lymphatics from
head, upper body

Lymphatics from
lungs, upper body

Capillary beds for
upper body

Lung
capillaries

Right side
of heart

Left side
of heart

Liver
capillaries

Intestinal
capillaries

Lymphatics
from abdomen

Capillary beds for
pelvis and legs

Lymphatics from
lower limbs, pelvis

**Figure 3.8 Schematic drawing
of the lymphatic system.**
This system carries lymph
(which has been filtered from
interstitial fluid) and nutrients
(which have been picked up in
the small intestine). Both enter
the bloodstream where the lymphatic system connects with
major veins near the heart.

transport some of the nutrients that the blood capillaries in the villi do
not carry. (Refer back to Figure 3.6 to see how these small lymphatic
vessels, called lacteals, fit into the total absorption scheme.) The lacteals
take in mainly fatty products of digestion and carry them through this
network, merging with larger and larger lymphatics until they join major
veins, as just described.

Excretion of Waste Products Occurs via Several Routes

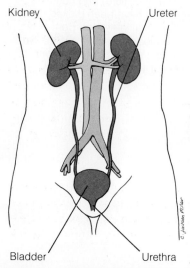

Kidney   Ureter

Bladder   Urethra

Figure 3.9 The urinary system and some neighboring structures.   The two kidneys are the body's chief organs for cleansing its internal fluids of soluble waste, and excreting surplus water and nutrients. Ureters carry the urine to the bladder for storage until it is excreted through the urethra.

urinary system—system that filters wastes out of the blood and excretes them in the urine

perspiration—loss of water from moist body surfaces by evaporation

To round out the picture of how the body uses nutrients, it is appropriate to mention the means by which the body disposes of substances for which it has no further use.

Solid Waste

As discussed in the section on the digestive system, solid waste is excreted from the body as feces. When it leaves the body, some water is also lost, since plant fiber and bacteria in the feces hold a certain amount of water and take it out with them.

Water and Soluble Waste

Several other routes are available for water and soluble substances to leave the body.

Urinary System. The greatest amount of water exits the body via the urinary system. As the body's blood supply continuously flows through the capillaries of the kidneys, much of the water and dissolved substances (solutes) in the blood passes from the capillaries into the functional units of the kidneys, which are called nephrons. The role of the nephrons is to filter waste products out of the blood. Most of the water and solutes are reabsorbed back into the bloodstream from the nephron; those that are not reabsorbed become urine. This process is under strict hormonal control to ensure that the body keeps adequate water and other substances to support its life processes.

The urine is collected and held in the urinary bladder until it is excreted (Figure 3.9).

Skin. Perspiration, the loss of water from moist body surfaces by evaporation, is another route by which water and some minerals leave the body. Although everybody loses some moisture through the skin every day, the amounts lost in this way by different people and on different days is extremely variable. [More on this in Chapter 4 (on water).]

Normally, the amount of water lost through the skin is less than half the amount lost through the kidneys.

Lungs. Along with the carbon dioxide they exhale, people also lose some water vapor through the capillaries of the lungs. The amounts lost in this way are proportional to the rate at which a person breathes. For example, when you are exercising hard, you will lose much more carbon dioxide and water by this route than you would if you were at rest. You will also lose more via the lungs when you first arrive at a high altitude, since the relative scarcity of oxygen in the air forces you to breathe more often to get enough oxygen into your body.

■ Digestion is the process of breaking food down into substances small enough to be taken into the body's interior. This intake process is called absorption.

■ The main part of the digestive system consists of a hollow tube called the alimentary canal or gastrointestinal (GI) tract. Its many specialized sections vary in diameter, but all sections have a lumen (space through which food passes) and a mucosa (inner lining). Longitudinal and circular muscles—the latter called sphincters—control the passage of material from one section of the tract to the next. Mucus, enzymes, and hormones are secreted at various points along the way to assist in digestion.

■ The amount of time food spends in the tract (transit time) is affected by diet, drugs, emotions, physical activity, and state of health.

■ Digestion and absorption have several phases, and each section of the tract has its own functions to perform. (1) Food is ground in the mouth. (2) The pharynx moves food into the esophagus, where the involuntary muscular contractions called peristalsis can then transport it to the stomach. (3) The stomach is very active in digestion, attacking food both mechanically and chemically to produce a slushy blend called chyme. (4) Digestion continues in the small intestine with the aid of secretions from other organs. The liver produces bile, which emulsifies fats (divides them into small droplets), and the pancreas produces digestive enzymes and substances that help to neutralize the acid in the chyme. Most of the absorption process also occurs in the small intestine, whose villi and microvilli project into and expose an enormous surface area to passing nutrients. (5) The large intestine collects solid waste, provides a home for bacteria, and absorbs water and some minerals.

■ The cell is the smallest, simplest unit of living matter, and is the site at which the absorbed nutrients are used. In addition to their nucleus, mitochondria, and cytoplasm, all cells are surrounded by a selectively permeable membrane that controls what substances can enter or leave it. Cells in the body are often separated by small spaces filled with interstitial fluid. Cells grouped together to perform a similar function are referred to as a tissue; tissues combine to form organs; organs that cooperate to perform a major physiological task comprise a system; and several interrelated systems make up an organism.

■ The chemical processes collectively referred to as metabolism take place at all times in every living cell. Synthesis and breakdown reactions may take place at different rates at different times or in different cells.

■ The circulatory system delivers nutrients and oxygen to all the body's cells. It is powered by the heart, which moves blood through a closed system of blood vessels. One section of the system loops between the heart and the lungs, and the other section circles between the heart and all other parts of the body. Arteries carry blood away from the heart; veins carry blood back to it; and the exchange of nutrients and wastes takes place across the walls of the smallest vessels, called capillaries. Nutrients enter the bloodstream through the capillaries of the small intestine.

■ The lymphatic system is a one-way network of vessels that carry lymph as well as some nutrients. The nutrients are picked up at the villi by small vessels called lacteals.

■ Excretion of waste products occurs via several routes. Solid waste is excreted from the body as feces. Most water leaves the body by way of the urinary system, which also has the job of filtering waste products out of the blood. Additional water is lost by perspiration, and by exhalation of water vapor from the lungs.

REFERENCES

American Dietetic Association. 1981. *Handbook of clinical dietetics*. New Haven: Yale University Press.

Ganong, W. F. 1981. *Review of medical physiology.* Los Altos, CA: LANGE Medical Publications.

Guyton, A. C. 1981. *Textbook of medical physiology.* Philadelphia: W. B. Saunders Company.

McNeil, N.I. 1984. The contribution of the large intestine to energy supplies in man. *American Journal of Clinical Nutrition* 39:338–342.

Mirkin, G., and M. Hoffman. 1978. *The sportsmedicine book*. Boston: Little, Brown and Company.

Spence, A. P. 1982. *Basic human anatomy.* Menlo Park, CA: The Benjamin/Cummings Publishing Company.

Stickney, J. C., and E. J. VanLiere. 1974. The effects of exercise upon the function of the gastrointestinal tract. In *Science and medicine in exercise and sport,* ed. W. R. Johnson and E. R. Buskirk. New York: Harper and Row, Publishers.

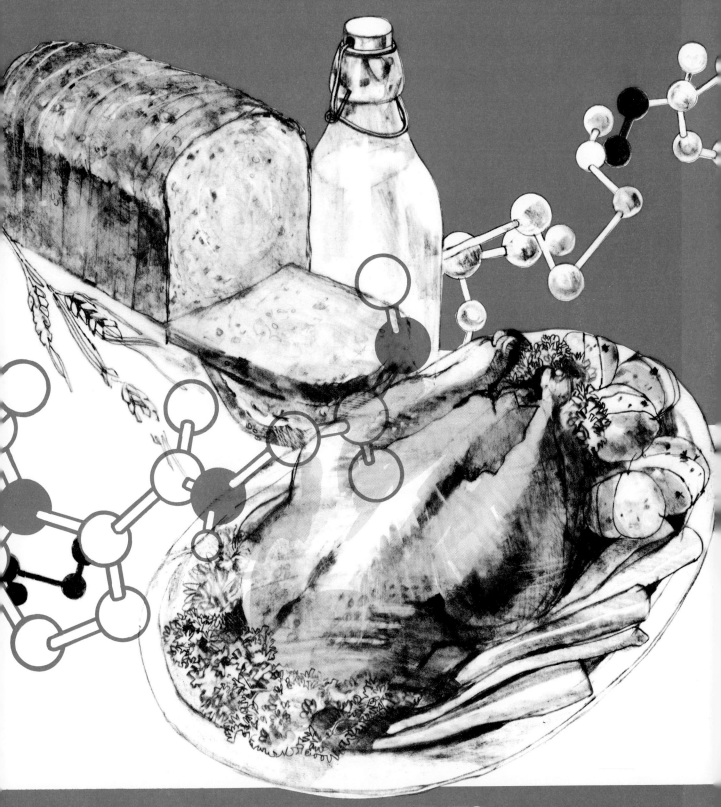

PART TWO

MACRONUTRIENTS:
BUILDING BLOCKS AND ENERGY SOURCES

4

Water: Not to be Taken for Granted

IN THIS CHAPTER: Water Is the Largest Body Constituent ▪ The Body Is Sensitive to Water Loss ▪ Water Is Lost by Four Routes ▪ Water Is Available from Three Sources ▪ Ensure Adequate Intake by Following Guidelines ▪ Water Has Structural and Regulatory Functions ▪ Distribution of Body Water Also Influences Function ▪ It Is Possible to Drink Too Much Water . . . but Unlikely

4 Water: Not to be Taken for Granted

Water. There's no doubt that we take it for granted. Maybe that's because we have such easy, inexpensive access to it almost all of the time. We seldom feel deprived of it.

But you can probably remember some occasions when you were short of water; you became thirsty and, if you didn't have any fluids handy, you probably felt quite uncomfortable—or even desperate—until you found a way to slake your thirst.

It's fortunate that we have such a drive to replace lost water, because it is crucial to our survival. We would die if we had to go without water for only a few days, whereas we can last a lot longer without other essential nutrients. Think of hunger strikers who deny themselves food but continue to take in water: many of them survive for eight to ten weeks without any intake of carbohydrates, proteins, fats, vitamins, and minerals—in progressively worsening condition, to be sure, but their existence can continue for that period if they have water. A person's hydration (water status) is that important.

hydration—referring to the presence of water

Water Is the Largest Body Constituent

You get a sense of why this substance is so important when you know how much of the body is water: water accounts for 60% of the weight of the typical adult male's body.

Every kind of tissue contains some water, although not in the same proportions: muscle tissue is almost $\frac{3}{4}$ water by weight, bones are about $\frac{1}{4}$ water, teeth about $\frac{1}{10}$ water, and fat tissue varies from $\frac{1}{5}$ to $\frac{1}{3}$ water (Figure 4.1). From this information, you can see that individuals can differ from one another in the exact percentage of body water they have, depending on the relative amounts of the different types of tissues they contain. For example, a person who has a higher-than-average proportion of body

Figure 4.1 Percentage of water in various body tissues. The percentage in most body tissues is fairly predictable, although the proportion of water in fat tissue varies.

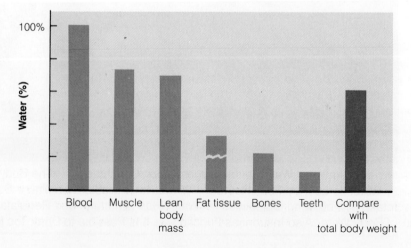

fat, which contains relatively little water, is likely to have a water content lower than 60%. This is the situation with women, even slim women, because they normally have more body fat than the average man.

Age makes a difference too: people tend to start life as more than 60% water and become drier during their first year. A newborn infant may consist of as much as 75% water, because many immature cells contain more water. As adults age past physical maturity, their percentage of body water decreases if they accumulate more fat tissue.

The Body Is Sensitive to Water Loss

With such a large amount of water within us (it has been referred to as an "internal sea"), it may seem surprising that we cannot tolerate fairly large losses before the body reacts to the decrease. But in fact, when you lose as little as 3% of your normally hydrated body weight in just hours or days due to water loss, your physical performance will be impaired (American Dietetic Association, 1980). For example, when a 150-pound person loses about $4\frac{1}{2}$ pounds of body water, performance is likely to start deteriorating. One study demonstrated the effects of a 4% water-weight loss: muscular endurance decreased by about 30% (Torranin et al., 1979).

Further losses affect mental functioning, and eventually the circulatory system loses so much fluid that it collapses. With a loss of 10–12% of body weight as water, death may occur. Table 4.1 lists symptoms that have been seen at different levels of fluid deficit.

Water Is Lost by Four Routes

Since such serious consequences result from a water deficit, let's focus on what factors cause body losses, and how water leaves the body. Keep in mind that water losses become a problem only if they are not adequately replaced.

Under normal circumstances, an adult loses 2 to 3 liters of fluid each day. More than half of that fluid is usually lost as urine, which is formed as the blood supply is continually processed through the kidneys. However, water also routinely leaves the body by several other means.

Some fluid evaporates from the skin every day simply because the cells of the skin are moister than the surrounding air. This is called an insensible loss, since we are unaware it is happening. Of course, sweating due to high environmental temperature or strenuous physical exertion is another cause of water loss via the skin. We also lose a small amount of water by exhaling, as you can see when you breathe onto a cool mirror. An even smaller amount of water leaves the system in the feces.

insensible loss—evaporation of water from the skin caused by the relative dryness of the surrounding air

The first column of Table 4.2 suggests the approximate amounts of water that are lost each day by an average adult under ordinary circumstances through these routes. But the figures can vary greatly, as the next two columns of Table 4.2 demonstrate: if the weather is hot, or if a person exercises strenuously, the amount of water lost as sweat can increase markedly. Some professional sports figures claim to have lost as much as 17

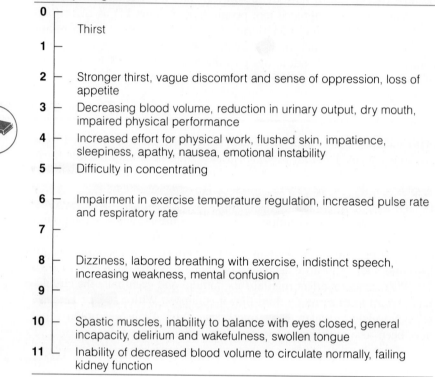

Table 4.1 Adverse Effects of Dehydration

% Body weight loss

% Body weight loss	
0	
	Thirst
1	
2	Stronger thirst, vague discomfort and sense of oppression, loss of appetite
3	Decreasing blood volume, reduction in urinary output, dry mouth, impaired physical performance
4	Increased effort for physical work, flushed skin, impatience, sleepiness, apathy, nausea, emotional instability
5	Difficulty in concentrating
6	Impairment in exercise temperature regulation, increased pulse rate and respiratory rate
7	
8	Dizziness, labored breathing with exercise, indistinct speech, increasing weakness, mental confusion
9	
10	Spastic muscles, inability to balance with eyes closed, general incapacity, delirium and wakefulness, swollen tongue
11	Inability of decreased blood volume to circulate normally, failing kidney function

Reference: Greenleaf, J. E. 1982. The body's need for fluids. In *Nutrition and athletic performance: Proceedings of the conference on nutritional determinants in athletic performance,* ed. W. Haskell, J. Scala, and J. Whittam. Palo Alto, CA: Bull Publishing Company.

pounds of fluid in basketball and football games, and one marathon runner lost 9 pounds even though he drank water every two miles (Mirkin and Hoffman, 1978)! When these huge perspiration losses occur, urinary losses decrease, which helps somewhat to conserve water in a time of shortage.

High altitudes also increase water losses: while breathing more often to try to get enough oxygen from the less dense air, a person simultaneously loses more moisture from the lungs. Very dry air increases insensible losses through skin: it has been estimated that the dry air in commercial airliners can deplete an adult of 2 pounds of fluid during a $3\frac{1}{2}$ hour flight.

Some substances in the diet promote urine loss: both alcohol and caffeine will do so, in proportion to the amounts consumed. Certain drugs called diuretics increase water loss by promoting greater urine production. Doctors frequently prescribe these medications to help patients control such conditions as high blood pressure.

Drinking any fluid beyond the level that your body needs will also increase urine production: if you "force fluids"—perhaps as part of your treatment of a viral infection—your urine output will go up in proportion

diuretics—drugs that increase water loss by promoting greater urine production

Table 4.2	Typical Routes of Loss of Water		
Source	At normal temperature (ml/day)	In hot weather (ml/day)	With prolonged, heavy exercise (ml/day)
Insensible losses:			
Skin	350	350	350
Respiration	350	250	650
Urine	1400	1200	500
Sweat	100	1400	5000
Feces	100	100	100
Totals	2300	3300	6600

Adapted from Guyton, A. C. 1981. *Textbook of medical physiology.* Philadelphia: W. B. Saunders Company.

to your intake. This, however, is really a case of getting rid of a surplus rather than taking a loss.

Water Is Available from Three Sources

The body functions best if its fluid losses are replaced promptly. You can rightly assume that beverages are a major source of water. What may be less obvious is that almost all solid foods contribute water as well. In fact, some "solid" foods have a higher weight percentage of water than some liquids. Table 4.3 demonstrates this; Appendix E gives the percentage of water in hundreds of other foods and beverages.

Table 4.3	Occurrence of Water in Some Solids and Liquids	
Food	Solids (% as water)	Liquids (% as water)
Summer squash	96	
Iceberg lettuce	96	
Tomato juice		94
Watermelon	93	
Cola beverage		90
2% milk		89
Orange juice		87
Orange	86	
Apple	84	
Vanilla milkshake		74
Cooked beef	60	
Cooked egg	50	
Cheddar cheese	37	
Bread	36	
White sugar	1	
Corn oil		0

Table 4.4   Typical Sources of Water

Source	Volume (ml/day)
Beverages	1000–1500
Solids	500–1000
Metabolic processes	250–400
Total	Approximately 2300

When average dietary intakes are evaluated for people who have not perspired noticeably, it is found that beverages usually account for only about half of the 2 to 3 liters that are taken in daily (The National Research Council, 1980). Depending on food choices, it is possible that almost that same amount of water could come from food. An additional smaller amount is derived from within the body as various metabolic processes (such as energy production) produce water from body compounds (such as macronutrients). Table 4.4 gives ranges for these daily sources.

There can be tremendous variation in daily intakes, just as there is in losses. Not only do total intake volumes vary from person to person and from day to day, but the distribution of water from solids or liquids may also vary. For example, a person who ordinarily eats generous amounts of fruits and vegetables will get a large proportion of fluids from those items, and will therefore not need to drink as much fluid as shown on the table. On the other hand, if that person is going on an extended hike, he or she will probably find it more convenient to carry foods that are drier, lighter, and less bulky; in that case, most of the needed water will have to be consumed in beverages obtained along the way.

Ensure Adequate Intake by Following Guidelines

There are several different guidelines by which you can evaluate whether your body water status is satisfactory. Since each guideline has its limitations, you need to choose the right one to match your situation.

Drink to Satisfy Thirst

Most people never give deliberate thought to how much water they should consume, since they simply drink when they are thirsty. Under normal circumstances, the thirst mechanism works very well to prompt a person to consume enough fluid—that is, provided he is not experiencing the stress of illness or prolonged and heavy sweating. In both of these latter instances, other associated discomforts seem to override the thirst mechanism.

Normally, without illness or heavy sweating, you experience thirst even before you have lost 1% of your body weight; this encourages you to replace fluids before the point at which your ability to function would start to deteriorate, as shown in Table 4.1.

New popularity for water. Water, a vital nutrient that is often taken for granted, has recently been "noticed" and given a new image.

Consume Water in Proportion to Kcaloric Expenditure

A quantified guideline for adult intake that is applicable to ordinary circumstances is that a person should consume 1 milliliter (ml) of water per kcalorie expended (National Research Council, 1980). This amounts to 1 liter (approximately 1 quart) of fluid from solids and/or liquids per 1000 kcalories used. Infants need more than adults: they should get 1.5 ml of water per kcalorie. Not only do their cells have a higher water content, but their immature kidneys also require more fluid in order to remove metabolic wastes.

This standard is inadequate to meet the body's needs during many types of illness and heavy exercise, and therefore should not be applied to those situations. People on low-calorie diets should note that the standard applies to kcalories *expended*, not to kcalories *taken in:* you should drink at least as much fluid while on a diet as you did before.

Maintain at Least a Minimal Urine Output

The volume of urine output offers another clue regarding a person's hydration. An adult should excrete *at least* 500 ml (about 2 cups) of urine per day (National Research Council, 1980). Under most circumstances in which you have produced that amount of urine, your consumption has been adequate for the excretion of toxic waste products and for maintaining normal internal functions. For the athlete, a daily urine output of at least 900 ml (about $3\frac{1}{2}$ cups) is recommended (National Research Council, 1974).

If your urine output is consistently much less than these output guidelines, you are probably taxing your kidneys by challenging them to remove metabolic wastes in too little water. Fluid intake should be increased to allow for greater urine volume.

Replace Weight of Water Lost

A good way to restore water that has been lost within a short period of time is to replace whatever weight has been lost with an equal weight of water. This is a suitable approach when you know in advance that you are likely to perspire heavily during a period of exercise, and remember to weigh yourself beforehand. An afternoon of tennis, a day of vigorous outdoor work, a long hike or run, a sport team practice session—all are candidates for this approach.

Weigh yourself (stripped) both before and after the activity; you should replace the lost weight by drinking 2 cups of water for every pound lost. Pace the drinking at whatever rate is comfortable for you, such as 1 cup every 15 minutes or so, until you have restored the whole amount.

This deliberate approach is warranted because, as mentioned earlier, your sense of thirst alone is not likely to prompt you to rehydrate completely after a period of heavy sweating. In fact, if you rely in such cases only on thirst to tell you how much fluid is needed for rehydration, you will probably take in only about half the needed amount in the first 24 hours (Saltin, 1978). It may take as long as three days to replace the fluid lost in one day of heavy sweating unless you drink more than thirst would prompt you to consume.

Successive days of such activity without deliberate replacement of water lead to progressive dehydration, which has resulted in the tragic, easily preventable deaths of some athletes. Because players often do not pay attention to their own needs in this regard, coaches should weigh their players daily. If a player has not replaced most of the fluid losses from the previous practice day, that player should be prohibited from participating again until he or she has done so.

You may have been mentally protesting during this discussion that body weight losses also reflect fat that was lost due to such strenuous activities, and therefore it should not be necessary to drink so much that the person's original weight is restored. Although it is true that fat is lost, the weight of the fat lost during any vigorous activity of a few hours' duration is very small compared to the weight of the water lost. As an extreme example, most runners of average size lose *less than a pound of body fat during a marathon* (26 miles, or several hours of running) but can easily perspire between 10 and 20 pounds of fluid during that experience. Therefore, weight loss is indeed a suitable approximate measure of water loss.

"Replace Ahead" and Replace during Heavy Sweating

Although it is semantically impossible to replace water before you lose it, in a practical sense it seems to work. Several studies have shown that a person who either *pre*hydrates and/or consumes water *during* exercise to a level that is greater than the total losses does not experience the physiological problems that are associated with dehydration (Fink, 1982).

Often, though, people cannot keep up with their losses during heavy exercise because they may sweat faster than their stomachs can accept replacement volumes. (The stomach can empty about 1 liter of fluid per hour.) Recommendations that are made for endurance physical activities, then, are compromise measures that will achieve only partial rehydration (Figure 4.2); the rest must be completed after the activity. This is a typical suggested program:

When to drink	How much to drink
Before activity	
2 hours before	2–3 cups of water
10–15 minutes before	2 cups of cold water
During activity	
every 10–15 minutes	$\frac{1}{2}$ to 1 cup of cold water

Notice that water is recommended in preference to other fluids. That is because most sugar-containing beverages such as fruit juices, sport drinks, and sugar-sweetened carbonated beverages are retained longer in the stomach than water is, delaying its usefulness (Fink, 1978). (The role of sweetened beverages in endurance activities will be discussed more thoroughly in Chapter 6, on carbohydrates).

Cold water is suggested for shortly before and during activity because it leaves the stomach faster than warmer water, making its absorption and benefits more rapid (Fink, 1978).

Figure 4.2 Replacing lost body fluids. This football player is attempting to restore water he has lost through perspiration.

Water Has Structural and Regulatory Functions

Up to this point, we have focused primarily on the penalty paid for inadequate body water. Now you will see why dehydration causes problems, as we shift attention to the roles water has in the body.

Building Material

As mentioned at the start of the chapter, water is a component of all body tissues. Within each tissue cell, water in the cytoplasm fills out the structure, giving it a characteristic shape and firmness.

Medium in Which Reactions Happen

Many biochemical reactions can take place only if the reacting compounds are dissolved in water: water is the critical biochemical solvent (liquid that can hold dissolved substances). Because this is true, virtually all body water contains solutes (dissolved substances); no body fluid is 100% water.

Many chemicals, when they are dissolved in water, dissociate (break apart) into electrically charged particles called ions or electrolytes. Certain electrolytes such as sodium and potassium have a great deal of influence on body water balance—that is, how water is distributed in the body. This will be discussed more thoroughly later in the chapter.

solvent—liquid in which substances can be dissolved

solutes—substances dissolved in water or another solvent

ions, electrolytes—particles that carry an electrical charge in solution

acid solution—one containing an excess of positively charged hydrogen ions (H^+)

basic (alkaline) solution—one containing an excess of negatively charged hydroxyl ions (OH^-)

neutral solution—one containing equal numbers of H^+ and OH^- ions

pH scale—a measure of the concentration of hydrogen ions (H^+) in solution

buffer system—a body process that helps maintain a constant pH.

hydrolysis—chemical breakdown process in which water is one of the reacting substances

When the dissociation of a solute produces an excess of positively charged hydrogen ions (H^+), the solution is usually called an acid; when dissociation produces more negatively charged hydroxyl ions (OH^-)than H^+ ions, the solution is usually a base or alkali. When there are equal numbers of H^+ and OH^- ions present, the solution is neutral. Water itself (H_2O or HOH) is an example of a neutral substance, since a small portion of its molecules dissociate into equal numbers of H^+ and OH^- ions.

The pH scale is a measure of the concentration of hydrogen ions in solution. Figure 4.3 shows a pH scale; 7 is the neutral value, with values below 7 being acidic and values above 7 being alkaline.

The body is very sensitive to changes in pH. Blood and lymph are normally maintained within a very narrow range around 7.4, just slightly basic. If the pH varies by only a few tenths of a pH unit, the normal functioning of many body systems can be interrupted. Therefore it is not surprising that your body has a number of mechanisms that help to maintain a constant pH; these are called buffer systems. Several nutrients participate in buffer systems; we will discuss them in Chapter 8 (on proteins) and Chapter 13 (on minerals).

Participant in Biochemical Reactions

There are also situations in which water itself is one of the reacting compounds. For example, in the process of digestion, when carbohydrates, fats, and proteins are broken into smaller units in preparation for absorption, water participates in the splitting process, which is called hydrolysis, by contributing its components to the new compounds.

Medium of Transport

Some body fluids that occur outside of cells have as their major function the task of carrying substances around in the body. Recall, for example, the nutrient- and waste-transporting functions of blood, lymph, and urine that were discussed in Chapter 3. Another example is water-based digestive juices, which carry enzymes to where they are needed.

Lubricant

Some body fluids serve as lubricants that enable solid materials to slide against each other. Examples are saliva, which promotes easier movement of food through the upper part of the digestive tract; tears, which allow the eyeballs to rotate smoothly in their sockets; and synovial fluid, the liquid that bathes the joints, which allows bones to move easily against each other.

Temperature Control

Another key function of water is to help control body temperature. This is important because there is a rather narrow range of temperatures in which human life processes can continue. If a person's temperature, which is normally around 98.6°F (37°C), falls below about 80°F (27°C) or rises above 108°F (42°C), death is likely to result. These values are for oral temperatures; the actual internal or core temperatures are approximately 1°F (0.6°C) higher.

Water is involved in temperature control in several ways. One property of water is that its temperature is not as influenced by changes in environmental temperatures as some other substances are. Therefore, the body maintains its normal temperature more easily with water than it would if it were filled with other fluids.

When your internal temperature begins to deviate from normal, your body puts into play a couple of water-involved mechanisms to bring it back to normal. The first of these involves the water-based blood supply. Here's how it works: if your internal temperature starts to drop because you are out in the cold, your body conserves heat by constricting (narrowing) blood vessels near the skin surface. This causes less blood to be circulated near the surface, thereby slowing blood and body heat losses.

Conversely, if you get overheated, your capillaries near the skin dilate (relax and get bigger in diameter) so that more of your blood supply can circulate nearer to the cooler surrounding air, and allow surplus heat to be lost through the skin to the environment. The flushed look of a person who has been exercising or who has a fever from illness is due to this greater than usual blood supply near the skin surface.

Perspiration is another cooling mechanism. When your core temperature rises, your sweat glands begin producing and exuding perspiration on the skin surface. The sweating itself does not cool you; it is the evaporation of the water that does. About 600 kcalories of surplus body heat are removed during the evaporation of 1 liter of perspired water (Ganong, 1981).

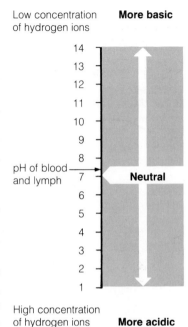

Figure 4.3 The pH scale. The measure of strength of acids and bases.

Distribution of Body Water also Influences Function

It is not enough for the right *amount* of water to be present in the body. The water must also be properly *distributed* for the body to function well. Let's see how this is accomplished.

Absorption of Water from the Gastrointestinal (GI) Tract

Water does not need to be broken down into smaller units prior to absorption. The first site in the GI tract at which it can be absorbed is the stomach. Actually, only a minute amount is taken in here, but this is notable nonetheless because so few substances can be absorbed at all from this organ.

Over 80% of water is absorbed by the villi of the small intestine. The remainder goes through to the large intestine, where the body absorbs much of what remains (Ganong, 1981).

Only about 100 ml of water per day are normally excreted with the feces. In the case of diarrhea, a much larger amount of fluid is lost due to inadequate absorption along the entire intestinal tract. This can lead to dehydration, even if intakes are normal by standards set for healthy people.

Distribution into Intracellular and Extracellular Volumes

Once absorbed, water is distributed between two general locations: inside and outside body cells. The water inside all body cells is collectively referred to as the intracellular volume or compartment; the water outside cells is called extracellular.

intracellular volume—refers to body water contained within cells
extracellular volume—refers to body water not contained within cells

Extracellular water, the smaller volume, includes the watery portion of blood (plasma), interstitial fluid and lymph, gastrointestinal fluids, fluids contained within the spinal column and eyes, tears, and the synovial fluid that lubricates the joints.

Figure 4.4 shows the normal apportionment of the approximately 42 liters of total body water into these two compartments in an average male.

Implications of Changing Volumes. It is important that adequate water volume be maintained in both of the two compartments: there are negative consequences if either one gets depleted.

If intracellular fluid is decreased, cellular metabolism including energy production may not take place efficiently. If extracellular fluid is decreased, blood volume drops; this means that less oxygen can be delivered to body cells. In addition, body temperature rises because the heat produced by metabolic processes is being absorbed by a smaller volume of fluid, which is less able to get rid of the surplus heat. This jeopardizes the functioning of the brain, the circulatory system, skeletal muscles, and virtually every other body system.

Factors Involved in Fluid Movement. To understand what can cause changes in compartment volumes, it is necessary to focus on cell membranes, which divide the intracellular and extracellular compartments.

In Chapter 3, it was mentioned that water can pass easily through the selectively permeable membranes that enclose body cells. When equal

Figure 4.4 Body fluids.
Intracellular and extracellular volumes in an average 154-pound male. (Note that total body fluid varies with body size and composition.)

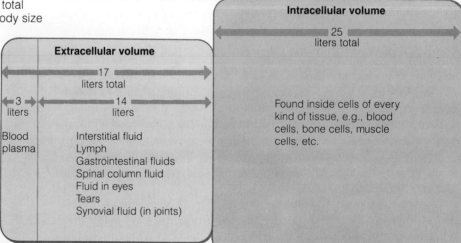

Total body fluids
42 liters

Intracellular volume
25
liters total

Found inside cells of every kind of tissue, e.g., blood cells, bone cells, muscle cells, etc.

Extracellular volume
17
liters total

3
liters

14
liters

Blood plasma

Interstitial fluid
Lymph
Gastrointestinal fluids
Spinal column fluid
Fluid in eyes
Tears
Synovial fluid (in joints)

volumes of water move through these membranes in both directions, there is no change in compartment volumes.

Sometimes, however, more water passes through in one direction than the other, resulting in changes in the volumes. To understand why this may occur, remember that there are various substances dissolved in body fluids that the selectively permeable cell membranes will not allow to pass through them. This means that some solute particles accumulate on one side of the cell membrane, resulting in a higher concentration of particles and a lower concentration of water on that side.

A basic principle of physiology is that water will move through membranes to equalize the concentration of particles in solution on the two sides. Therefore, when there is a greater concentration of water on one side of a membrane than on the other, more water will move across the membrane to the side with the lesser concentration of water. This process is called osmosis. As a result of osmosis, the volume on one side of the membrane increases, while the volume on the other decreases.

osmosis—movement of water across a selectively permeable membrane to equalize the concentration of water on each side.

Several kinds of particles in the body cannot readily pass through selectively permeable membranes. Dissolved protein is one. In a healthy, well-nourished individual, protein concentrations usually remain stable on both sides of the cell membrane. Therefore protein normally does more to *maintain* than to *change* intracellular volumes.

Other substances are more likely to produce fluid shifts. Two of these are the electrolytes potassium and sodium. The great majority of the body's potassium ions are located inside body cells, whereas the sodium ions are found mostly outside of cells. The ions are held in these respective locations because a mechanism in the cell membrane, called the sodium–potassium pump, actively transports potassium through the cell membrane into the cell but ejects sodium, segregating it in the extracellular fluid (Guyton, 1981). Therefore, if the concentration of positive ions like potassium inside the cell differs from the concentration of positive ions like sodium outside the cell, there will be a water shift in the direction of the lesser concentration of water. Figure 4.5 illustrates these principles of osmosis.

Normally, the amount of potassium and sodium in the body is regulated by the kidneys. When the total amount of either of these elements in the body becomes excessive, the kidneys allow more to be excreted. For such excretion to occur, sufficient surplus water must also be available to form the urine that will carry the surplus electrolytes out of the body.

Examples of Fluid Movement. If you eat some unusually salty food, the salt (which is a compound made of sodium and chloride) will be absorbed and will appear in your blood and interstitial fluid as sodium and chloride ions. Since the concentration of the sodium in the interstitial fluid and blood is likely to be higher than that of the positive ions like potassium inside the cell, water will move by osmosis from inside the cells to the interstitial fluid until the concentrations of the ions in the water on both sides of the membrane are equalized. Soon after this, as the excessive amounts of sodium and chloride circulate through the kidneys, the kidneys will gradually discard the surplus ions via the urine—provided you also drink enough extra water to form the additional urine.

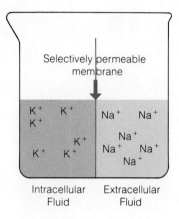 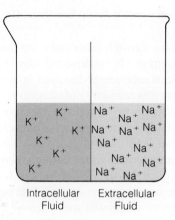 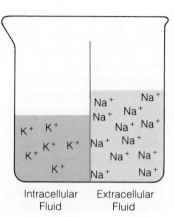

When the ions potassium (K^+) and sodium (Na^+) are equally concentrated in the intracellular and extracellular fluid, respectively, the volumes of water are equal on both sides of the selectively permeable membrane.

However, when more sodium is added to the extracellular fluid, the concentration of ions becomes higher in that compartment, making the concentration of water lower.

Water moves through the selectively permeable membrane by osmosis from the compartment where it is more concentrated to the compartment where it is less concentrated. The volumes of both compartments change in the process.

Figure 4.5 How osmosis affects fluid volumes in a simple model.

The physiological changes that occur during sweating also demonstrate fluid shifts. If you have been perspiring heavily, you have lost water from your interstitial fluid. You have also lost a small amount of sodium and chloride in the sweat, but much less than the proportion of water you lost. Therefore your remaining interstitial fluid contains a higher concentration of ions than your intracellular fluid does; this will cause water to move from both the blood plasma and the body cells into the interstitial spaces to equalize the concentration. In order for the compartments to recover from this dehydration, you will have to drink water to make up for the loss.

Time Factor. Both of the preceding examples make an important point: the body needs time to perform the processes that attempt to adjust for imbalances of water and/or electrolytes. Just as it takes time for excess electrolytes to be removed from the body, it also takes time for ingested fluid to correct dehydration by finding its way to the depleted compartments.

One study showed that even four hours after young men had drunk water to replace the 4% of body weight they had lost from sweating in a sauna, their muscular endurance was not yet back up to their original levels (Torranin et al., 1979). This fact has particular implications for wrestlers, who sometimes deliberately dehydrate themselves to make their weight classes, and then expect to be at top strength within a couple of hours after drinking some water. It doesn't work.

Figure 4.6 summarizes this discussion of the motion of water in the body.

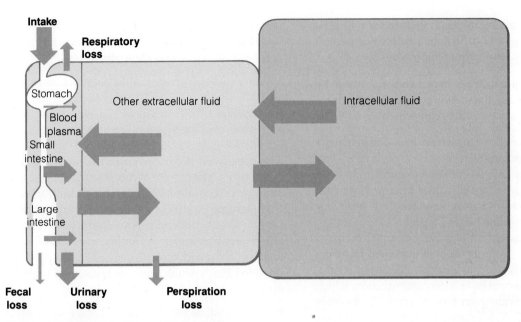

Figure 4.6 Typical motion of body fluids.
The size of the arrows represents approximate amounts of fluid
moved. (Note that volumes vary with individual circumstances.)

It Is Possible to Drink Too Much Water . . . but Unlikely

With all this emphasis on the importance of water, it would seem impossible to be able to get too much of it. Surprisingly, though, there have been reports of a few psychotic people who have actually killed themselves by an overconsumption of water (Rendell et al., 1978). Such reports help underscore the point that more—of even as critical a substance as water—is *not* necessarily better.

How much is too much? The healthy body under ordinary circumstances can cope with up to approximately $9\frac{1}{2}$ liters (about 10 quarts) of water per day (Greenleaf, 1982). It would be unusual for a person to consume even half that amount, unless she or he had experienced considerable losses previously.

SUMMARY

■ Although the average person devotes little thought to his or her hydration status, water is crucial to survival. It is the largest body constituent, accounting for roughly 60% of body weight and comprising some proportion of every tissue. If your normal body weight decreases by as little as 3% due to water loss, your performance will be impaired. Greater losses have even more serious consequences.

■ Water is lost by four routes: (1) urine excretion, (2) insensible loss and perspiration (both involving evaporation of water from the skin), (3) exhalation of water vapor, and (4) excretion in the feces. The amounts of water lost by these routes can vary considerably; for example, prolonged strenuous exercise increases water loss through perspiration.

■ Water is available from three sources: (1) beverages, (2) foods, and (in much smaller amounts) (3) the body's own metabolic processes.

■ Usually, you can meet your needs for water by drinking to satisfy thirst. However, under situations of unusual loss, deliberate replacement is advised.

■ Aside from its structural functions, one of water's most important roles is as a biochemical solvent. Many types of solutes, including charged particles called electrolytes, are dissolved in body water. An acidic solution contains an excess of positively charged hydrogen ions (H^+), and a basic solution contains an excess of negatively charged hydroxyl ions (OH^-). A solution containing equal numbers of H^+ and OH^- ions is neutral. The pH of a solution is a measure of its H^+ ion concentration, which is given on a scale from 1 (very acidic) to 14 (very basic). The body is extremely sensitive to changes in pH, and several nutrients participate in buffer systems that help maintain it at the proper level.

■ Water also participates in certain metabolic reactions such as hydrolysis (a type of breakdown reaction), acts as a transport medium and lubricant, and helps to regulate body temperature.

■ Water must be present in the right places as well as in the right amounts. It enters the body through the digestive system (mainly in the small intestine), and once absorbed makes its way to either the intracellular or extracellular compartment. Water moves between the two compartments across cell membranes. The process of movement, which results in an equal concentration of water on both sides of the membrane, is called osmosis. Given sufficient time, a healthy individual can compensate for the effects on water balance of eating an unusually salty food, or losing a great deal of water in perspiration, provided that enough water is consumed to make up for the losses.

■ As essential as water is, like all other nutrients it has a beneficial range of intake. Although it would be difficult to consume too much unintentionally, deliberate extreme overconsumption is both possible and harmful.

REFERENCES

American Dietetic Association. 1980. Nutrition and physical fitness. *Journal of the American Dietetic Association* 76:437–443.

Fink, W. J. 1982. Fluid intake for maximizing athletic performance. *Nutrition and Athletic Performance: Proceedings of the Conference on Nutritional Determinants in Athletic Performance*, ed. W. Haskell, J. Scala, and J. Whittam. Palo Alto, CA: Bull Publishing Company.

Ganong, W. F. 1981. *Review of medical physiology.* Los Altos, CA: LANGE Medical Publications.

Greenleaf, J. E. 1982. The body's need for fluids. *Nutrition and Athletic Performance: Proceedings of the Conference on Nutritional Determinants in Athletic Performance*, ed. W. Haskell, J. Scala, and J. Whittam. Palo Alto, CA: Bull Publishing Company.

Guyton, A. C. 1981. *Textbook of medical physiology.* Philadelphia: W. B. Saunders Company.

Mirkin, G., and M. Hoffman. 1978. *The sportsmedicine book.* Boston: Little, Brown and Company.

National Research Council, National Academy of Sciences. 1974. Water deprivation and performance of athletes. *Nutrition Reviews* 32(no. 10):314–315.

———. 1980. *Recommended dietary allowances.* Washington, DC: National Academy of Sciences.

Rendell, M., D. McGrane, and M. Cuesta. 1978. Fatal compulsive water drinking. *Journal of the American Medical Association* 240(no.23):2557–2559.

Saltin, B. 1978. Fluid, electrolyte, and energy losses and their replenishment in prolonged exercise. In *Nutrition, physical fitness, and health.* International series on sport sciences, volume 7, ed. J. Parizkova and V.A. Rogozkin. Baltimore: University Park Press.

Torranin, C., D. P. Smith, and R. J. Byrd. 1979. The effect of acute thermal dehydration and rapid rehydration on isometric and isotonic endurance. *The Journal of Sports Medicine and Physical Fitness* 19:1–9.

5

Energy Sources and Uses

IN THIS CHAPTER: Human Energy Is Described in Kilocalories ▪ A Food's Energy Value Depends on Its Content of Protein, Fat, and Carbohydrate ▪ Food Energy Not Needed Immediately Is Stored in the Body ▪ Stored Energy Sources Are not Equally Available for Energy Production ▪ The Proportions of Carbohydrate and Fat Used for Energy Vary with the Circumstances ▪ Energy Has Three Basic Types of Functions ▪ There Are Several Ways to Estimate Your Daily Energy Needs

Most people think of energy as the commodity they need to be vigorously active—to run with the family dog, dunk a basketball, race a bicycle, swim, bounce on a trampoline. There is no question that such activities use energy—and lots of it.

However, energy is also needed by a person sitting quietly in a rowboat waiting for the fish to bite, or sleeping in front of the TV. That is because energy is used first and foremost to carry out the basic processes that keep people alive. During an average day, the amount of energy most North Americans use for such maintenance processes is usually greater than the amount of energy they use for physical activity.

energy—the capacity to do work, measured in kcalories

Energy occurs in several forms in the body. Movement exemplifies mechanical energy. Energy that powers metabolic reactions is chemical energy. The tiny electrical impulses from nerve cells represent electrical energy. Heat produced by the body is thermal energy; most body energy ultimately takes this form.

As you know, people get their energy from food. Most people have at least a general idea of how much energy (how many kcalories) various foods provide. What they may not know is that the amount of energy available from foods depends directly on how much of the macronutrients protein, fat, and carbohydrate is in them. Alcohol also furnishes energy. Foods differ markedly in their energy values because they have different levels of these substances.

This chapter provides an overview of getting and spending energy. It is a useful introduction to Chapters 6−8, which deal separately and in greater detail with carbohydrate, fat, and protein.

Human Energy Is Described in Kilocalories

kilocalories (kcalories, kcal)—units in which energy is measured

Energy is commonly measured in units called kilocalories, which are abbreviated kcalories or kcal in this book. A kcalorie is the amount of heat required to raise the temperature of 1 kilogram of water one degree Celsius (1°C). Even energy that does not take the form of heat is described in kcalories. (The *calorie* used in the study of physics is only $\frac{1}{1000}$ as large as the *kcalorie* used here.) Energy intake and energy output are both described in kcalories: we talk about food providing a certain number of kcalories, and about various activities using a particular number of kcalories.

The metric system also quantifies energy in kilojoules. There are 4.18 kilojoules in 1 kilocalorie. However, since the kcalorie is the more familiar descriptor, we have used that term throughout this book.

Let's first discuss food and the energy it can provide.

A Food's Energy Value Depends on Its Content of Protein, Fat, and Carbohydrate

You can calculate how much energy is obtainable from a food if you know how many grams of protein, fat, carbohydrate, and/or alcohol it contains. (Water, vitamins, and minerals provide no energy, but have other valuable functions.) When you know those amounts—and we will suggest sources of that information shortly—you can calculate the energy value of each constituent by multiplying them by the following values:

- 4 kcalories per gram for protein

- 9 kcalories per gram for fat

- 4 kcalories per gram for carbohydrate

- 7 kcalories per gram for alcohol

(Scientists have found that these values are reasonable averages of the actual energy yielded in the body by these substances from various food sources.) The energy value of the whole food, then, is the sum of the kcaloric values of its constituents. Figure 5.1 shows these values for 1 cup of fruit-flavored yogurt.

Energy Nutrients That Occur in SANE Group Foods

Table 5.1 shows the levels of protein, fat, carbohydrate, and alcohol contained in some representative foods from each of the food groups of the SANE guide (Sound Approach to Nutritious Eating). You can see how widely foods vary in their composition. Even within a food group, there is sometimes considerable variation in the level of energy a given nutrient provides. For example, although fruits and vegetables generally have only small amounts of protein and fat, they vary widely in their carbohydrate content. Meats and alternates, although they have similarly high protein levels per serving, have different fat and carbohydrate contents.

In Table 5.1, the energy nutrient that is responsible for the greatest

Food *1 cup fruit flavored yogurt*			
	Protein (g)	Fat (g)	Carbohydrate (g)
Enter the composition of the food	*10*	*3*	*42*
Multipy by kcal/g of nutrient	*× 4*	*× 9*	*× 4*
to get kcal from each nutrient	*40*	*27*	*168*
Total the kcal	*40 +*	*27 +*	*168 = 235 kcal*

Figure 5.1 Calculating the energy value of a food of known composition.

Table 5.1 Energy Sources in Some Representative Foods[a]

Foods	Serving size	Protein (g)	Fat (g)	Carbohydrate (g)	Alcohol (g)
Fruits and vegetables					
Peach, fresh	1 medium	1	tr	**10**	0
Lettuce, romaine	1 cup	1	tr	**2**	0
Mashed potato with milk	$\frac{1}{2}$ cup	2	1	**14**	0
Grain products					
Bread, whole wheat	1 slice	3	1	**14**	0
Toast, whole wheat	1 slice	3	1	**14**	0
Cornflakes, plain	1 cup	2	tr	**21**	0
Cornflakes, sugared	1 cup	2	tr	**37**	0
Popcorn, air popped	3 cups	3	tr	**15**	0
Dairy products					
Milk, whole, 3.3% fat	1 cup	8	**8**	11	0
Milk, 2% fat	1 cup	8	5	**12**	0
Yogurt, plain, made from lowfat milk	1 cup	12	4	**16**	0
Meat and alternates					
Chicken, broiled	3 oz	**20**	3	0	0
Chicken, fried	3 oz	**28**	9	tr	0
Ground beef, broiled	2.9 oz	20	**17**	0	0
Peanuts, dry roasted	2 oz	16	**26**	10	0
Great northern beans, cooked	1 cup	14	1	**38**	0
Combination foods					
Cheese pizza	$\frac{1}{4}$ of 12″	12	8	**44**	0
Limited extras					
Brownie with icing	1 oz	1	5	**15**	0
Cream cheese	1 oz	2	**10**	1	0
Beer	12 oz	1	0	14	**13**
Carbonated cola drink	12 oz	0	0	**37**	0

[a]The value for the constituent that provides the largest number of kcalories is in bold print.

number of kcalories in each food is in bold print. Notice that the bold number is not always the largest gram value; since fat and alcohol furnish more kcalories per gram than carbohydrate or protein, they can be the largest contributors of energy without being the heaviest components.

Energy Nutrients Shown on Food Composition Tables

The energy nutrient contents for hundreds of other foods are shown in Appendices E and F. These appendices also give kcaloric values for each listed item. Sometimes the number of kcalories shown per serving of food will not exactly match the values you will get when you calculate them as described earlier. The discrepancy is due to the slightly different method of calculation that was used for determining the values in the appendices. The appendix values are more accurate, but your calculated values are very close, usable estimates.

Energy Nutrients Shown on Nutrition Labels

Nutrition labels are another source of information about energy nutrients in foods. At present, the only foods required to carry a nutrition label are those that make a nutrition claim (such as "low sodium") or foods to which nutrients have been added. Many other products also carry a nutrition label although it is not mandatory for them to do so.

The top part of a nutrition label must specify the number of grams of protein, carbohydrate, and fat contained in each serving of the food; the manufacturer's designation of serving size; and how many servings of product are in the whole container. The nutrition label also states the energy value per serving, rounded to the nearest 10 kcalories. Figure 5.2 shows an example.

Calculating the Percentage of Kcalories Furnished by Protein, Fat, and Carbohydrate

You can see more clearly what proportion of energy comes from a given food's protein, fat, and carbohdydrate by calculating what percentage of the food's kcalories were contributed by each nutrient.

To determine the percentages, you must first calculate the energy available from each nutrient, and find their sum, as explained earlier.

Nutrition Information (Per Serving)	
Serving size	$1\frac{1}{8}$ ounces
Number of servings	1
Calories	160
Protein	3 grams
Carbohydrate	20 grams
Fat	8 grams

Percentage of U.S. Recommended Daily Allowances (U.S. RDA)

Protein	5
Vitamin A	

Figure 5.2 Energy nutrient information found on a nutrition label. The top part of a nutrition label must supply the information shown in color on this snack-size package of tortilla chips.

Food	*4 tablespoons of peanut butter*		
	Protein (g)	Fat (g)	Carbohydrate (g)
Enter the composition of the food	16	32	12
Multipy by kcal/g of nutrient to get kcal from each nutrient	× 4 / 64	× 9 / 288	× 4 / 48
Total the kcal	64 +	288 +	48 = 400
Divide nutrient kcal by total kcal which yields a decimal fraction	÷ 400 / 0.16	÷ 400 / 0.72	÷ 400 / 0.12
Multiply by 100 to get percent	16%	72%	12%

Figure 5.3 Calculating the protein, fat and carbohydrate percentage of kcalories from a single food.

Next, divide the number of kcalories contributed by each energy nutrient in the food by the total kcaloric value of the food. Then multiply by 100 to get the percentages. Figure 5.3 gives an example of this type of calculation. If the food or beverage also contains alcohol, you need to add a column for it and include it in the calculations.

Just as it is possible to calculate the percentages of kcalories furnished by the energy nutrients in an individual food, it is also possible to do this for a whole day's intake. It is useful to be able to do this because dietary descriptions and recommendations are often expressed in such percentages. Several guidelines suggest that for adults protein should account for 10–15% of kcalories; fat, for no more than 30–35%; and carbohydrate for the remainder, or 50–60% of kcalories. The only way you can tell whether your intake corresponds to such guidelines is to evaluate intakes for several representative days. (Later chapters will discuss why some experts have recommended these ranges.)

Here's how to calculate the percentages of kcalories you derive from each energy nutrient for a day:

1. Do a 24-hour record of as typical a day as possible, using a form similar to that shown in the example in Figure 5.4. List all foods and beverages consumed. (Add a column if you also consumed alcohol.)

2. Use Appendices E and/or F to find the protein, fat, and carbohydrate contents of those foods; adjust the values to correspond to the amounts of food you consumed, and enter the values in the appropriate columns. For example, if you drank two cups of milk, and the appendix gives values for one cup, you will have to double all values as you record them.

3. Figure the sum for each column.

Food or beverage	Amount eaten	Protein (g)	Fat (g)	Carbohydrate (g)
Pork sausage	2 oz.	4	12	tr
Boiled egg	1	6	6	1
Buttermilk	1 cup	8	2	12
Fried potatoes	½ c.	2	9	23
Banana	1 med.	1	tr	26
Cracked wheat bread	1 slice	2	1	13
Butter	1 T.	tr	12	tr
Honey	1 T.	tr	0	17
Swiss cheese	2 oz.	16	16	2
Whole milk	1 cup	8	8	11
Roast beef	3 oz.	20	27	0
Baked squash	1 c.	4	1	32
Butter	1 T.	tr	12	tr
Enriched noodles	1 c.	7	2	37
Cracked wheat bread	1 slice	2	1	13
Butter	1 T.	tr	12	tr
Popcorn, oil, salt	2 c.	2	4	10
Unsweetened canned grapefruit juice	1 c.	1	tr	24
Ice cream	1 c.	5	14	32

Totals		88	139	253
Multiply by kcal/g of nutrient		× 4	× 9	× 4
to get kcal from each nutrient		352	1251	1012
Total the kcal		352 +	1251 +	1012 = 2615
Divide nutrient kcal by total kcal		÷ 2615	÷ 2615	÷ 2615
which yields a decimal fraction		0.13	0.48	0.39
Multiply by 100 to get percent		13%	48%	39%

Figure 5.4 Calculating the percentage of kcalories from protein, fat, and carbohydrate in a day's intake. (tr = trace.)

4. Continue, following the same procedure used for a single food (see Figure 5.3).

5. If you consumed an alcoholic beverage, you can determine how many kcalories the alcohol provided by subtracting the kcalories provided by the beverage's protein, fat, and carbohydrate from the total kcalories in the beverage.

Food Energy Not Needed Immediately Is Stored in the Body

Even though our *use* of energy is continuous, our energy *intake* is not. It is not necessary to eat nonstop in order to have energy, because the body can store energy for later use. However, the body does not necessarily store energy in the same form as it occurred in the food you consumed.

Fate of Dietary Carbohydrates

Sugars and starches are the major forms of dietary carbohydrates. When they are digested, absorbed, and processed by the body, their predominant product is the simple sugar glucose. Some of this glucose is used to maintain normal levels in the blood; blood glucose is one of the body's most readily available sources of energy.

After a meal, however, there is usually more glucose available than is needed for maintaining a normal blood glucose level. Some of the extra amount is used to produce glycogen, a much more complex substance composed of hundreds of glucose units linked together. Glycogen is the animal counterpart of starch; it is stored in limited amounts in the liver and skeletal muscles.

The glucose that still remains is converted into fat, a very different substance from the carbohydrate from which it originated. Once it has been converted into fat, for the most part it is not converted back into glucose.

Fate of Dietary Proteins

Food protein components are also quite versatile. If the body has an urgent need for energy that cannot be met in other ways, protein components are converted into glucose and are used for energy production. However, they are best used when reassembled into body proteins. There is a limit to how much body protein will be produced; body protein increases especially during growth and/or a deliberate muscle building program. If both of these needs have been met and there are still more protein components in the body, then they are converted into fat. Once these components have been converted into fat, they cannot be converted back into essential protein components.

glucose—a simple sugar; a common breakdown product of dietary carbohydrates and a readily available energy source

glycogen—storage form of glucose, consisting of hundreds of molecules linked together

Figure 5.5 The body's options for generating and storing energy. Since energy is essential for life, our chances of survival are increased by the body's ability to obtain energy from different dietary constituents (in boxes) and storage forms (in circles).

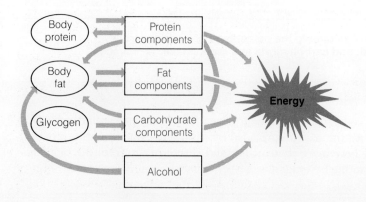

Fate of Dietary Fats

Dietary fat is the most predictable substance of the lot. Its absorbed components are used soon either for energy or for forming body fat. The body has a greater capacity for accumulating fat than for storing any other energy source.

Fate of Dietary Alcohol

If alcohol has been ingested, it is usually used quickly for energy production. The remainder is converted into fat.

Figure 5.5 summarizes these interconversions. You can see that your body is well designed for survival: a surplus of energy from any source can be converted into body fat as a hedge against future scarcity.

Stored Energy Sources Are Not Equally Available for Energy Production

Even though body protein, fat, and carbohydrate can all be used for energy, they are not usually available in equal amounts to meet typical daily needs.

Carbohydrate and Fat: The Preferred Energy Sources

Carbohydrate and fat are the two substances that the body primarily draws on for energy. As we mentioned earlier, the carbohydrate in your body usually occurs in the forms of both small molecules of glucose and the more complex carbohydrate, glycogen. You usually have only about 20 grams of glucose (less than an ounce) in your entire blood supply and interstitial fluids at a given moment.

Glycogen, which can be broken down to glucose very quickly when needed, is more generously stored. You have approximately 85 grams of glycogen in your liver (which can be used for functions anywhere in the body), and about 350 grams in the cells of various muscles (which can be used only by the muscles in which it is located). All of this carbohydrate together represents about 1800 kcalories.

Fat is much more plentiful. On the average, a man's body is approximately 15% fat by weight and a woman's body is between 20% and 25% fat. A man who weighs 154 pounds, then, will have approximately 23 pounds of body fat (almost 10,500 grams), which could yield roughly 94,500 kcalories. (Compare that to the potential kcalories available from carbohydrate.)

Table 5.2 summarizes these energy resources in the typical adult male body.

Protein: A Reserve Energy Source

Typically, protein constitutes about 15% of a man's body weight, and somewhat less of a woman's. Under ordinary circumstances, very little of that protein is used for energy. Only when the body cannot produce enough

Table 5.2 Likely Amounts of Stored Energy Sources in a Typical 70-Kilogram (154-lb) Adult Male

	Approximate grams present	Potential kcal available Calories
Carbohydrate[a]		
Glucose in blood and interstitial fluids	20	80 ⎤
Glycogen		⎬ 1820
Liver	85	340 ⎥
Skeletal muscles	350	1400 ⎦
Fat (Assuming 15% of body weight)	10,500	94,500
Protein (assuming 15% of body weight)	10,500	[b]
Total		96,320

[a]From Ganong, W. F. 1981. *A review of medical physiology.* (Page 230.) Los Altos, CA: LANGE Medical Publications.

[b]Although the body contains a substantial amount of protein, it is generally not much used for energy (see the text). If extreme and prolonged duress cause it to be used in significant amounts for energy, the body can withstand the loss of only about half of its protein before death will result. [See Guyton, A. C. 1981. *Textbook of medical physiology.* (Page 906.) Philadelphia: W. B. Saunders Company.]

energy from carbohydrate and fat to meet immediate needs does a significant amount of body protein get used for energy: it acts as a backup source of kcalories. There are only a few instances when this is likely to occur: during starvation (including starvation from extreme weight-reduction diets); during physical activities that are demanding, continuous, and last over an hour (for example, distance bicycle racing or running); and during the first couple of weeks of a rigorous athletic regimen undertaken by an untrained person (Lemon and Nagle, 1981).

The Proportions of Carbohydrate and Fat Used for Energy Vary with the Circumstances

Recall that both carbohydrate and fat are substantially drawn on for energy production, and that we use some of each at the same time. (This runs counter to the popular belief that carbohydrate is "used up first" before any fat is used.) At rest, the body uses approximately equal amounts of fat and carbohydrate (Astrand and Rodahl, 1977). However, the proportion that we use of each changes with various circumstances.

Amount of Oxygen Available in Relation to Energy Need

The amount of oxygen available affects what proportions of fat and carbohydrate will be used for energy production. This is because the production of energy from fat requires a steady supply of oxygen, while that from carbohydrate can occur with or without oxygen. To understand why this is significant, it is necessary to discuss some aspects of metabolism.

The metabolic processes that take place in body cells to produce energy are collectively referred to as biological oxidation. Biological oxidation can take place either aerobically (with air) or anaerobically (without air).

biological oxidation—energy-producing metabolic processes that take place in body cells

Aerobic Oxidation. When there is a generous amount of oxygen present, it combines chemically with energy nutrients to yield energy, water, and carbon dioxide. This process is called aerobic oxidation.

Aerobic oxidation occurs during activities (aerobic activities) that are done at less than "all out" effort. Examples of such activities are walking, jogging, swimming, dancing, bicycling, and cross-country skiing—when they are done at a pace that can be sustained for hours at a time.

aerobic—referring to the presence of oxygen

Fat is the mainstay of extended aerobic activity. Nonetheless, fat can never be used exclusively for energy production; a small amount of carbohydrate always must be involved in fat oxidation. When a person performs an aerobic activity for many hours, he or she will eventually exhaust the body's limited supply of carbohydrate and be unable to go on. This may be what long-distance runners are experiencing when they say they have "hit the wall" around the 22 mile mark (Sherman et al., 1981). Their bodies may still have fat to spare, but their stores of carbohydrate have run out; carbohydrate is the limiting factor.

[Athletes who are preparing for an endurance event of longer than $1\frac{1}{2}$ hours may store some extra carbohydrate that will allow them to continue for a while longer than they normally could. This process, called glycogen loading, will be discussed in Chapter 6 (on carbohydrates).]

Anaerobic Oxidation. If insufficient oxygen is available to produce enough energy aerobically, additional energy is produced using the anaerobic oxidative process called glycolysis.

During glycolysis, the body metabolizes glucose without oxygen. This results in the production of the metabolic product lactic acid. When lactic acid builds up in muscles that were strenuously exercised—and it does so very quickly during glycolysis—you feel fatigued (Margaria, 1972). For this reason, you can use anaerobic oxidation only for a few minutes at a time. You do not become fatigued from using up your energy nutrients; you still have ample supplies. Rather, lactic acid buildup is the cause. You recover from this fatigue gradually; lactic acid decreases when you rest.

anaerobic—referring to the absence of oxygen

glycolysis—process in which body cells metabolize glucose without oxygen

lactic acid—metabolic product of glycolysis that builds up in muscles and causes fatigue

Anaerobic activities are those done with such physical exertion that you find yourself gasping for breath after a couple of minutes of effort. Power lifting and sprints of swimming or running are examples of anaerobic activities.

Although the terms *aerobic activity* and *anaerobic activity* imply that their energy comes exclusively from *aerobic* and *anaerobic oxidation*, respectively, all activities actually involve some energy input from *both* aerobic and anaerobic oxidation. For example, when you start out for a leisurely, extended jog, you function primarily anaerobically for the first couple of minutes. During this phase, your initial rate and depth of breathing do not bring in enough oxygen to meet your energy needs totally by aerobic oxidation. By the time you have jogged for an hour, however, a very large proportion of your energy comes from aerobic oxidation.

Many activities involve alternate periods of very intense (anaerobic) and less intense (aerobic) activity. Tennis, wrestling, and basketball are examples of such activities.

Duration of Activity

The longer you spend in endurance exercise, the greater the proportion of fat you oxidize. Figure 5.6 shows this graphically. The point at which fat becomes the major energy provider varies with the type of exercise.

Environmental Temperature

Research shows that exercise in a hot environment places greater demands on carbohydrate stores. One study showed that during $1\frac{1}{4}$ hours of exercise at 42°C (106°F!), 76% greater muscle glycogen depletion occurred than occurred during similar exercise at 9°C (48°F)(Costill and Miller, 1980).

State of Training

Your state of training makes a difference in what proportions of fat and carbohydrate are used for energy production. The better your physical conditioning, the greater the proportion of fat you will use during exercise. The less-trained person uses relatively more carbohydrate.

Typical Diet Composition

The composition of your diet also makes some difference in the proportions of nutrients you use for energy. The more carbohydrate you habitually

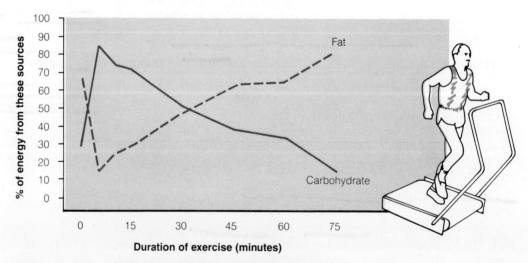

Figure 5.6 Effect of time on utilization of energy sources. In a treadmill test that lasted two hours, energy was derived from fat and carbohydrate in different porportions at different times. (Adapted from *A Scientific Approach to Distance Running*. D.L. Costill. Tafnews Press, Los Altos, CA., 1979.)

consume, the larger the fraction of carbohydrate you will use while exercising. Conversely, people who routinely consume diets with lower levels of carbohydrate will metabolically adapt to using a smaller proportion of carbohydrate. Such adaptation takes place over a period of several weeks (Horton, 1982).

Energy Has Three Basic Types of Functions

The three types of functions for which your body uses energy are basal metabolic functions, physical activity, and thermogenesis. Knowing about these functions can help you understand why there is a great deal of variation in the amount of energy used from person to person and from day to day.

Basal Metabolism and Factors That Influence It

The term basal metabolism refers collectively to the processes that must take place continuously to sustain life, such as breathing; beating of the heart; maintenance of body temperature and muscle tone; and glandular, cellular, and nervous system functioning. The number of kcalories required to maintain these basal activities for a specified unit of time is called the basal metabolic rate (BMR). BMR accounts for between 50% and 70% of a typical North American's total daily energy expenditure; most people use less energy for physical activity than for basal activity.

basal metabolism—metabolic processes that must take place continuously to sustain life

basal metabolic rate (BMR)—the number of kcalories required to maintain basal activities for a specified amount of time

A person's BMR can be determined quite exactly by measuring energy used during a period of physical, emotional, and digestive rest (Figure 5.7). But since it takes a specialized setting, equipment, and carefully controlled conditions to measure a person's BMR, most people will never have this test done. (A few may have a less exact test done, which is called resting metabolic rate or resting metabolic expenditure.)

However, it is possible to estimate BMR with reasonable accuracy for most individuals, since much is known regarding the factors that influence BMR. One important general factor is the amount of a person's lean (nonfat) body mass. Since lean tissues are the most metabolically active, anything that increases their mass is likely to increase BMR. Another general factor that raises BMR is the growth process itself. These two factors account for many of the following, more specific influences on BMR.

Body Size. A taller, larger person usually has a higher BMR than a shorter, smaller person. This reflects the different total amounts of lean tissue each body contains. There may not be much difference in BMR between a fat person and a thin person of the same height, though, because fat tissue is not very metabolically active, and therefore does not use much energy.

Age. Since people increase their mass of lean tissue as they progress from infancy through adolescence, the number of kcalories used for basal processes increases during the growth years. The growth process itself increases the BMR further: this is especially evident during the growth spurts of the toddler period and adolescence.

Figure 5.7 Test to determine basal metabolic rate (BMR). A BMR test is done under very specific conditions: in a room of comfortable temperature without distractions, and while the subject is at physical, digestive, and emotional rest. This drawing depicts one way of testing for BMR: measuring oxygen consumption and calculating energy use from it.

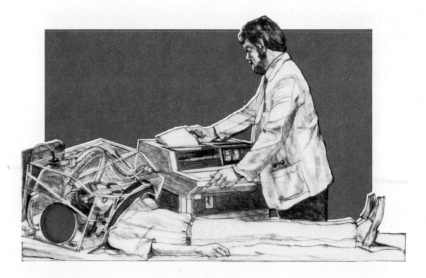

Once a person has achieved full size, lean body mass and BMR decrease gradually by anywhere from 2% to 4% per decade (NAS, 1980; Pike and Brown, 1984).

Sex. Males generally have higher BMRs than females of the same age and size. This is mainly because males usually have proportionately more lean tissue than females have. There may be hormonal influences as well (Pike and Brown, 1984).

Figure 5.8 illustrates the effects of both sex and age after physical maturity.

Health Status. A person who is physically fit has a higher BMR than one who is not. This reflects the larger muscle mass in the person who exercises regularly.

The BMR of a person who is losing weight often decreases. This helps explain why people who are on kcalorie-restricted diets lose weight more slowly after they have been dieting for a while. The BMR of a starving person may be as much as 20% lower than that of the same person when well-nourished.

Fever, on the other hand, raises BMR. For every Fahrenheit degree above normal temperature, BMR is 7% higher; for every Celsius degree of fever, there is almost a 13% increase in BMR (Pike and Brown, 1984).

Thyroid Hormone Level. The thyroid hormone thyroxin is a metabolic accelerator. Therefore, if your body produces less thyroxin than most people's, your metabolic processes will be slower, which will be reflected in a lower BMR. On the other hand, people who produce an overabundance of thyroxin have higher basal metabolic rates as a result.

If low or high thyroxin production interferes with a person's health, either situation can usually be corrected by medical intervention. Fortunately, both conditions are unusual.

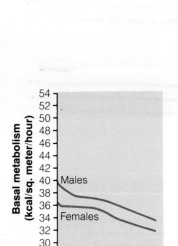

Figure 5.8 The effect of sex and age after maturity on BMR. This graph shows that males usually have a higher BMR than females. Whereas growth during the early years of life raises BMR, aging beyond maturity results in a gradual decline in the energy used for internal processes. (Adapted from Guyton, A. C. 1981. *Textbook of medical physiology.* Philadelphia: W. B. Saunders Company.)

Reproductive Status. During pregnancy, a great deal of maternal and fetal growth occurs, which raises the woman's BMR above her prepregnant level. During lactation, the production of milk increases BMR still further.

Individual Variation. Some people use more (or less) energy for basal metabolic activities than would be expected, taking into consideration the factors just listed. It is not uncommon to find variation by as much as 20% in either direction; and even greater differences have been observed.

Physical Activity and Three Factors That Influence It

The second largest use of energy, typically, is for physical activity. This is the only form of energy expenditure over which you have much control.

The amount of energy a person uses for physical activity can vary markedly from one day to the next. This contrasts with BMR, which usually isn't much different on two successive days. The proportion of energy most people use for physical activity is 20% to 40% of total kcalories, although the manual laborer or serious athlete could use 50% or more in this way.

Three factors influence the amount of energy you use for physical activity: the type of activity you engage in, the length of time you do it, and your body weight.

Type of Activity. Types of activity that require the most energy are those that involve intense use of the body's largest muscles (Figure 5.9). For example, walking expends more energy than sitting and typing, because more large muscles are involved in walking. Running, even though it involves many of the same muscle groups as walking, uses more energy per unit of time because the intensity of activity is greater.

Duration of Activity. Time is the second factor to be considered in calculating energy expenditure. Obviously, the longer an activity is continued, the more energy will be used.

It is sometimes difficult to estimate how much time is actually involved in an activity if it is performed only intermittently. For example, people who spend eight hours during the day at a downhill ski area do not spend eight hours doing downhill skiing: they spend much of the day standing in lift lines, sitting on lifts, stopping on the hill to plan the next part of the run, and taking breaks in the chalet. It is likely that only a couple of hours of skiing occur during the eight hours.

Body Weight. Body weight also influences energy expenditure. The heavier a person is, the more energy he or she expends in moving that mass. This means that if you and a larger friend exercise together, your friend will use more energy than you will while performing the same exercise for the same length of time.

Recording Activity and Estimating Its Energy Value. Table 5.3 takes into account all three of these factors: it gives the kcaloric cost of various activities per kilogram of body weight per minute of activity. This infor-

Figure 5.9 Energy cost of various activities. These activities use different amounts of energy. (a) The person lying still uses no energy for activity. (b) The chess players use about 30 kcalories per hour for their slight activity. (c) The musician probably uses double that amount, depending on how much he moves as he plays. (d) Square dancers may use 500 kcalories per hour. (e) The runners are the highest energy users; a 154-pound person running 7-minute miles uses almost 900 kcalories per hour for the activity alone.

mation will enable you to compare the relative amounts of energy that different activities require. You can also calculate your kcaloric expenditure for a specific activity of known duration, or even for a whole day's activities.

Figure 5.10 shows a log of part of a day's activity, and the form that was used to calculate how much energy was used. This procedure, called the factorial method, is done as follows:

1. Make a list of your activities for a 24-hour period, also recording the time at which you started each new activity to the closest five minutes. (If this is not done carefully, the results will be worthless.)

Table 5.3   Energy Cost of Some Activities

Activity	kcal/kg/minute	Activity	kcal/kg/minute
Bicycling (racing)	0.127	Painting outside	0.057
Bicycling (leisurely)	0.042	Playing ping-pong	0.073
Canoeing (leisurely)	0.024	Piano playing	0.018
Carpentry	0.045	Rowing in a race	0.267
Cleaning (light)	0.030	Running ($5\frac{1}{2}$ min/mile)	0.269
Cooking	0.015	Running (7 min/mile)	0.208
Dancing (fast)	0.148	Running (9 min/mile)	0.173
Dancing (slowly)	0.050	Sewing (hand or machine)	0.007
Dishwashing	0.017	Singing (loud)	0.013
Dressing, personal care	0.025	Sitting (writing)	0.007
Driving a car	0.015	Skating	0.058
Eating	0.007	Skiing (cross-country, level)	0.099
Field hockey	0.114	Skiing (cross-country, uphill)	0.254
Grocery shopping	0.040	Sleeping	0
Football	0.112	Squash	0.192
Garage work (repairs)	0.046	Standing (relaxed)	0.008
Golf	0.065	Stock clerking	0.034
Gymnastics	0.046	Swimming (2 mph)	0.132
Horseback riding (walk)	0.023	Tennis	0.089
Horseback riding (gallop)	0.112	Violin playing	0.010
Judo	0.175	Volleyball	0.030
Knitting	0.012	Walking (3 mph)	0.039
Laboratory work	0.018	Walking (3 mph, carrying 22 lb)	0.046
Laundry (light)	0.022	Walking (4 mph)	0.057
Lying still, awake	0	Walking downstairs	0.012 kcal/flight
Painting inside	0.014	Walking upstairs	0.036 kcal/flight

Compiled from data published by Taylor and McLeod, 1949; Durnin and Passmore, 1967; McArdle et al., 1981; and Passmore and Durnin, 1955. Values have been modified to eliminate energy expended for BMR and SDE (discussed later in the chapter). Since values for the same activity vary from one source to another, these values are unavoidably less precise than they appear.

2. At the end of the day, calculate the number of minutes spent doing each activity.

3. Find each activity on Table 5.3, and enter the kcal/kg/min values in the appropriate column.

4. Multiply each value by the number of minutes you did the activity.

5. Multiply each value by your current weight in kilograms.

6. Total all values. The sum is the *approximate* number of kcalories you used just for activity on that day.

Thermogenesis and Factors That (May) Influence It

thermogenesis—production of body heat in response to food intake and/or cold environmental temperatures

Thermogenesis is the production of heat by the body by means other than basal metabolic processes and physical activity. Thermogenesis pertains to heat that is produced in response to food intake and in response to cold environmental temperatures (Jequier, 1983).

specific dynamic effect (SDE)—production of heat resulting from the digestion, absorption, transport, and storage of food

Response to Food Intake. For decades, researchers have known that heat is produced when people digest, absorb, transport, and store food. This phenomenon is called the specific dynamic effect (SDE) of food. Approximately 6–10% of the energy a person consumes is used in this way.

Figure 5.11 gives a visual perspective to the proportions of total energy expenditure attributable to BMR, various levels of activity, and SDE.

Activity	Time started	Number of minutes	Kcal/kg/minute	Kcal used/kg	Weight in kg	Kcal
Sleeping	Midnight	450	0	0	81.8	0
Eating	7:30am	10	0.007	0.07	81.8	6
Dressing, washing	7:40	30	0.025	0.75	81.8	61
Cleaning up rooms	8:10	10	0.030	0.30	81.8	25
Walking (about 4 mph)	8:20	20	0.057	1.14	81.8	93
Sitting quietly	8:40	10	0.002	0.02	81.8	2
Sitting (writing)	8:50	50	0.007	0.35	81.8	29

(Continued chart for rest of the day)

					Total activity kcal	

Figure 5.10 Factorial method for calculating kcalories used for activity alone. (BMR and thermogenesis are not included in these calculations.)

Current research suggests that another thermogenic effect of diet may occur in some people when they take in much more energy than they expend for usual BMR, activity, and SDE functions. These people seem to have a mechanism for dissipating some of their surplus kcalories by producing more body heat, which is subsequently lost to the environment. This phenomenon has been termed adaptive thermogenesis; it may be the body's attempt to keep weight stable when there is a glut of energy.

Some researchers suggest that adaptive thermogenesis is a normal mechanism, but it may be defective in some people, who convert most of their surplus energy intake into body fat. Theoretically, such a defect could explain some cases of obesity (Danforth and Landsberg, 1983; Jequier, 1983). However, at present it is not known whether this defect is a *cause* or a *consequence* of obesity (Jequier, 1983).

Response to Environmental Cold. Thermogenesis also occurs in response to cold exposure. This phenomenon is seen especially clearly in hibernating animals, which maintain a steady body temperature despite varying environmental temperatures during the hibernating period. Such heat production is called nonshivering thermogenesis. The extent to which humans experience this response to cold is still under study.

Some scientists theorize that both adaptive thermogenesis and non-shivering thermogenesis may occur in people whose bodies contain (in addition to the usual white fat tissue) a second type of fat called brown fat (Jequier, 1983). It is brown because it contains a much larger number of mitochondria, the cellular structures in which much of the body's energy is produced.

brown fat—type of fat that contains more mitochondria (cellular energy-producing bodies) than white fat

Brown fat is known to exist in animals that hibernate and in newborn human infants. An infant uses it for maintaining body temperature after leaving the warmth of its mother's womb. Whether human adults retain this tissue—or how much they might have—are interesting areas of current research.

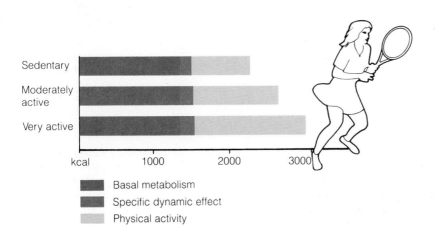

Sedentary

Moderately active

Very active

kcal   1000   2000   3000

■ Basal metabolism
■ Specific dynamic effect
▨ Physical activity

Figure 5.11 Components of the energy usage of a 55-kg (121-lb) adult. Although a person's basal metabolic rate does not vary greatly from day to day, energy expended for physical activity can. Specific dynamic effect is a very small component. Variation in total daily energy usage between seemingly like individuals can be substantial.

There Are Several Ways to Estimate Your Daily Energy Needs

A number of methods have been suggested for estimating how many kcalories a person is likely to use all together for BMR, activity, and SDE. Several are offered here: two are tables that give typical values, another is based on rough calculations, and the last is based on usual intake.

RDA Estimate

The RDA committee has collected data on typical daily kcaloric usage by people of different ages and sex; they appear in Table 5.4. The committee departed in this instance from its usual method of establishing an RDA, that is, including the needs of 97.5% of the population. Rather, it cited average values for energy intake recommendations, and showed ranges of usage that occurred. The ranges reflect how different a given individual's needs might be from the "typical" value.

Table 5.4   Recommended Energy Intake for People of Stated Mean Heights and Weights

Category	Age (years)	Weight (kg)	Weight (lb)	Height (cm)	Height (in.)	Energy needs (with range) (kcal)	
Infants	0.0–0.5	6	13	60	24	kg × 115	(95–145)
	0.5–1.0	9	20	71	28	kg × 105	(80–135)
Children	1–3	13	29	90	35	1300	(900–1800)
	4–6	20	44	112	44	1700	(1300–2300)
	7–10	28	62	132	52	2400	(1650–3300)
Males	11–14	45	99	157	62	2700	(2000–3700)
	15–18	66	145	176	69	2800	(2100–3900)
	19–22	70	154	177	70	2900	(2500–3300)
	23–50	70	154	178	70	2700	(2300–3100)
	51–75	70	154	178	70	2400	(2000–2800)
	76+	70	154	178	70	2050	(1650–2450)
Females	11–14	46	101	157	62	2200	(1500–3000)
	15–18	55	120	163	64	2100	(1200–3000)
	19–22	55	120	163	64	2100	(1700–2500)
	23–50	55	120	163	64	2000	(1600–2400)
	51–75	55	120	163	64	1800	(1400–2200)
	76+	55	120	163	64	1600	(1200–2000)
Pregnancy						+300	
Lactation						+500	

Adapted from "Recommended Dietary Allowances, 9th edition, 1980, with permission of the National Academy Press, Washington, D.C.

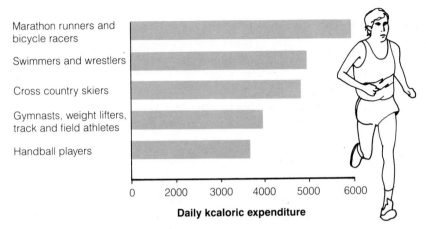

Figure 5.12 Typical daily kcaloric expenditure of male athletes training for various sports. (Data from Pařízková, J., and V.A. Rogozkin. 1978. *Nutrition, Physical Fitness, and Health*. pp. 84 and 121. Baltimore: University Park Press.)

Your energy usage is likely to fall within the range shown for your sex and age. However, if your body size is substantially different from the reference person's, or if you are extremely physically active, your energy usage may differ from that suggested on the table.

Estimate for the Dedicated Athlete

Because an athlete involved in a competitive program spends an extraordinary amount of time and effort performing in his or her chosen sport, the daily need for kcalories may be considerably higher than the upper end of the range suggested by the RDA table. Figure 5.12 gives approximate energy needs of male athletes involved in some sports. The daily energy needs of female athletes are approximately 10% less than those of men for a given sport.

The person who participates in these sports sporadically for exercise and enjoyment should not expect to expend the same number of kcalories as the more serious athletes, on whom Figure 5.12 is based.

Calculated Estimate of Energy Usage for One Day

Many formulas, some complex and others not so complex, have been developed for estimating kcalories expended in a day. Here we present less intricate formulas that can yield approximations of energy used for BMR, physical activity, and SDE. Even though these are estimates, the fact that the calculations involve data specific to you is likely to improve their accuracy over the tabular estimates.

Estimating BMR.

Method

1. Convert your ideal body weight to kilograms by dividing it by 2.2 lb/ kg. (Until it is more thoroughly explained in Chapter 10, consider your ideal weight to be the weight at which you are most comfortable. It is likely to be a better reflection of lean body mass than actual weight is.)

Example: Ann, a fully-grown and normal weight student, weighs 134 pounds.

$$\frac{134 \text{ lb}}{2.2 \text{ lb/kg}} = 60.9 \text{ kg}$$

60.9 kg
× 24 kcal/kg/day
1462 kcal/day

2. Multiply your ideal weight in kilograms by 24 kcal/kg/day (based on typical usage of 1 kcal/kg/hour). The product is your BMR. This method is not so precise as to reflect differences in BMR between men and women.

Estimating Energy Expenditure for Physical Activity. You can use either the factorial method shown in Figure 5.10, or the simpler method shown here.

Method

Example: On a typical weekday, Ann sits in class for several hours, walks between classes and her dormitory, and sits again while she eats, studies, and socializes. Her activity level is on the lower end of the light range on those days. On weekend days, she studies for a few hours and spends several hours in outdoor recreation; then her activity is in the moderately active range.

Example for Ann's weekday:

1462 kcal (BMR)
× 0.3

439 kcal

1. Decide which of the following activity levels is characteristic of you, or where you might fit between two levels:

Activity level	% of BMR
Not very active	30–40%
Moderately active	40–50%
Very active	50–100%

The majority of students use between 30% and 50% (of the number of kcalories used for BMR) for physical activity; far fewer students use 50–100%.

2. Multiply your BMR by the percentage that approximates your activity level. The product is an estimate of the energy you use just for activity in a day.

Estimating Energy Expenditure from Thermogenesis. This calculation reflects only estimated specific dynamic effect. Since scientists are not certain what contributions might be made by either adaptive or nonshivering thermogenesis, this calculation does not take them into account.

Method

Example

  1462 kcal (BMR)
+ 439 kcal (activity)
  1901 kcal
× 0.1
  190 kcal

1. Add together the number of kcalories used for BMR and activity.
2. Calculate 10% of that sum. This represents kcalories used for SDE.

Estimating Total Energy Expenditures.

Method

Example

1462 kcal
 439 kcal
 190 kcal
   0
   0
2091 kcal

Add together:
Kcal used for BMR
Kcal used for activity
Kcal used for SDE
300 kcal if pregnant
500 kcal if lactating
TOTAL

Figure 5.13 Variation in daily energy expenditure.
These people, although they may be involved in the same activities throughout a day, expend different amounts of energy.

Record of Typical Energy Intake

A final means of estimating your daily energy usage is to determine what your typical daily kcaloric intake is. Energy intake and expenditure are roughly equivalent values, provided you are neither gaining nor losing weight at the time, and provided your activity level is fairly constant from day to day.

By keeping diet records for several consecutive typical days, calculating their energy values, and then averaging them, you can get an idea of how much energy you use daily.

SUMMARY

■ Energy is obtained by eating food. Energy occurs in several forms in the body, and is needed not only for physical activity but also for many processes that keep us alive. Energy intake and output are both commonly measured in kilocalories (kcalories, kcal); one kilocalorie is the amount of heat needed to raise the temperature of 1 kilogram of water one degree Celsius (1°C).

■ A food's energy value depends on its content of protein, fat, and carbohydrate. Protein provides 4 kcal per gram, fat provides 9, and carbohydrate provides 4 (alcohol provides 7). Foods vary widely in composition, even within the same food group. Food composition tables, nutrition labels, and your own calculations can all be used to determine the energy nutrient content of your diet.

■ Food energy that is not needed right away is stored in the body, though not always in the same form in which it was consumed. Carbohydrates are broken down to produce glucose, which is either used fairly quickly for energy or stored as glycogen. Proteins are broken down and reassembled into body proteins or, in an emergency, converted to glucose and used for energy production. Fats are either used fairly quickly for energy or stored as body fat (the same is true of alcohol). Excess carbohydrate and protein components are also stored as body fat; once they are, for the most part they are not converted back to their original form.

■ Although the body can use carbohydrate, fat, and protein for energy production, protein is not generally used for energy unless availability of carbohydrate and fat is inadequate.

■ Although carbohydrate and fat are used simultaneously for energy production, the proportions of each used depend on several factors.

■ The metabolic processes that take place in body cells to produce energy are collectively called biological oxidation. Aerobic oxidation requires oxygen, and is fueled mainly (though not exclusively) by fat; anaerobic oxidation produces energy without oxygen by a process called glycolysis, and is fueled by carbohydrate.

■ The body uses energy for three basic types of functions.
(1) Basal metabolism refers to all the processes that must take place continuously to sustain life. The number of kcal required to maintain these processes for a specified amount of time is called the basal metabolic rate (BMR); it accounts for 50–70% of a typical North American's daily energy expenditure. It is influenced by such factors as body size, age, sex, and general health.
(2) Physical activity is the only form of energy

expenditure over which you have much control, and unlike BMR it can vary markedly from day to day. Factors influencing the amount of energy you use for physical activity are the type of activity you engage in, the length of time you engage in it, and your body weight.
(3) Thermogenesis refers to the production of body heat in response to normal food intake (specific dynamic effect or SDE); surplus kcalories (adaptive thermogenesis); and/or cool environmental temperatures (nonshivering thermogenesis). SDE accounts for about 6–10% of the energy a person consumes.

■ Thermogenesis is an active area of nutrition research, and is thought to be related to the presence of brown fat. In comparison with the usual white fat tissue, brown fat has many more mitochondria (cellular energy-producing bodies).

■ Energy usage tables, calculations of energy usage and expenditure, and records of energy intake can all provide estimates of your daily energy needs.

REFERENCES

Astrand, P. O., and K. Rodahl. 1977. *Textbook of work physiology*. New York: McGraw-Hill Book Company.

Briggs, G. M., and D. H. Calloway. 1984. *Nutrition and physical fitness*. New York: Holt, Rinehart & Winston.

Costill, D. L. 1979. *A scientific approach to distance running*. Los Altos, CA: Tafnews Press.

Costill, D. L., and J. M. Miller. 1980. Nutrition for endurance sport: Carbohydrate and fluid balance. *International Journal of Sports Medicine* 1:2–14.

Danforth, E., and L. Landsberg. 1983. Energy expenditure and its regulation. In *Obesity*, ed. M. R. C. Greenwood. New York: Churchill Livingstone.

Durnin, J. V. G. A., and R. Passmore. 1967. Energy, work, and leisure. In *Energy and protein requirements*, FAD/WHO technical report No. 522, 1973.

Ganong, W. F. 1981. *A review of medical physiology*. Los Altos, CA: LANGE Medical Publications.

Guyton, A. C. 1981. *Textbook of medical physiology*. Philadelphia: W. B. Saunders Company.

Horton, E. S. 1982. Effects of low energy diets on work performance. *American Journal of Clinical Nutrition* 35:1228–1233.

Jequier, E. 1983. Thermogenic responses induced by nutrients in man: Their importance in energy balance regulation. In *Nutritional adequacy, nutrient availability and needs*, ed. J. Mauron. Basel: Birkhauser Verlag.

Lemon, P. W. R., and F. J. Nagle. 1981. Effects on exercise on protein and amino acid metabolism. *Medicine and Science in Sports and Exercise* 13:141–149.

Margaria, R. 1971. The sources of muscular energy. *Scientific American* 226(no.3):84–91.

McArdle, W. D., F. I. Katch, and V. L. Katch. 1981. *Exercise physiology*. Philadelphia: Lea and Febiger.

National Research Council, National Academy of Sciences (NAS). 1980. *Recommended Dietary Allowances.* Washington, DC: NAS.

Passmore, R., and J. V. G. A. Durnin. 1955. Human energy expenditure. *Physiological Reviews* 35: 801–840.

Pike, R. L., and M. L. Brown, 1984. *Nutrition: An integrated approach.* New York: John Wiley and Sons, Inc.

Sherman, W. M., D. L. Costill, W. J. Fink, and J. M. Miller. 1981. Effect of exercise-diet manipulation on muscle glycogen and its subsequent utilization during performance. *International Journal of Sports Medicine* 2:114–118.

Taylor, C. M., and G. McLeod. 1949. *Rose's laboratory handbook for dietetics*, 5th edition, p. 18. New York: Macmillan Company.

Worthington-Roberts, B. S. 1981. Diet and athletic performance. In *Contemporary developments in nutrition*, ed. B. S. Worthington-Roberts. St. Louis: The C. V. Mosby Company.

6

Carbohydrates

IN THIS CHAPTER: Carbohydrates Have Four Major Functions in the Human Body ▪ Types and Amounts of Carbohydrates in Foods Vary ▪ The Body Deals with Different Carbohydrates in Different Ways ▪ Carbohydrates Affect Certain Health Conditions ▪ Assess Your Own Carbohydrate Intake Compared to Recommendations

In recent years, carbohydrates have earned a rather schizophrenic reputation. One commonly held belief is that they are fattening; many weight-reduction diets in the popular press include only very limited amounts of high-carbohydrate foods. However, athletes (who are also concerned about controlling body weight) are counseled about the *benefits* of a high-carbohydrate diet.

Confusion may come from the fact that there are several types of carbohydrates. Sugars, starches, and fiber are all forms of carbohydrate, and each has somewhat different characteristics and functions. Therefore, general statements about "carbohydrate" (as if it were a single substance) are often inaccurate because they may not be true of all forms.

Even particular kinds of carbohydrates seem to have split personalities. Sugar, maligned as a "poison" by British scientist John Yudkin, is touted by others as the best source of quick energy. Fiber, long ignored as a nonnutrient, now enjoys such heightened status that it is being deliberately added to foods. However, some articles now caution that unusually high fiber intakes may interfere with the body's access to other nutrients.

This chapter examines these claims about carbohydrates, while considering how the body uses carbohydrates, what foods contain them, and how they relate to various health problems. First, let's take a look at why we need them.

Carbohydrates Have Four Major Functions in the Human Body

1. Providing energy. Carbohydrates are the fundamental human fuel: they generally furnish more than half of our energy needs.

    Although carbohydrates are said to furnish four kcalories of energy per gram, that statement needs qualification, since not all forms of carbohydrate are energy providers. Sugars and starches are; they are called available carbohydrates. Dietary fiber, however, isn't; it is only minimally available for human energy production.

2. Sparing protein. Remember that protein can serve as an alternate energy source if available carbohydrate and fat do not meet immediate needs. If your body experiences an energy shortage in general or a carbohydrate shortage in particular, protein will be sacrificed.

    Because there are certain other important physiological functions that only protein can accomplish, it is desirable to save or "spare" it for those special uses. Therefore, when a person consumes at least the recommended level of available carbohydrate, it functions as a protein sparer.

available carbohydrates—sugars and starches that can be hydrolyzed by human digestive processes

3. Participating in fat metabolism. A small amount of available carbohydrate is needed to metabolize fat. Even when the body is deriving a high proportion of its energy from fat (as during prolonged, moderate exercise), some carbohydrate is essential to the biochemical process.

4. Providing bulk to the intestines. Fiber has a different, yet important, function: it provides solid material in the lower gastrointestinal tract, giving intestinal muscles the opportunity for healthy muscular work.

Types and Amounts of Carbohydrates in Food Vary

The vast majority of the carbohydrates we eat are produced by plants. Milk and some products made from milk are the only significant animal sources.

This section describes the forms of carbohydrate in foods, both as they occur in nature, and as they can be made available by processing. Table 6.1 gives a preview of the types of carbohydrate found in nature and their sources.

Sugars

Sugars are the smallest and least complicated of the carbohydrates; they are of varying sweetness, and are soluble in water. Their solubility allows them to move readily through the watery systems of plants and animals. Names of sugars are easy to recognize by their -*ose* endings; examples are glu*cose*, fruc*tose*, su*crose*.

Glucose is a good example of a simple sugar. You have already encountered glucose in Chapter 5 (on energy), where it was described as a small carbohydrate molecule found in the blood. It is important not only in the human system, but glucose is a key substance in all living systems, plant and animal.

Table 6.1   Major Carbohydrates Occurring in Foods, as Produced by Nature

Source	Major Sugars		Available polysaccharides	Fiber (minimally available polysaccharides)
	Monosaccharides	Disaccharides		
Plants	Glucose Fructose	Sucrose Maltose	Starches Dextrins	Cellulose Hemicellulose Pectins Gums
Animals	Lactose			

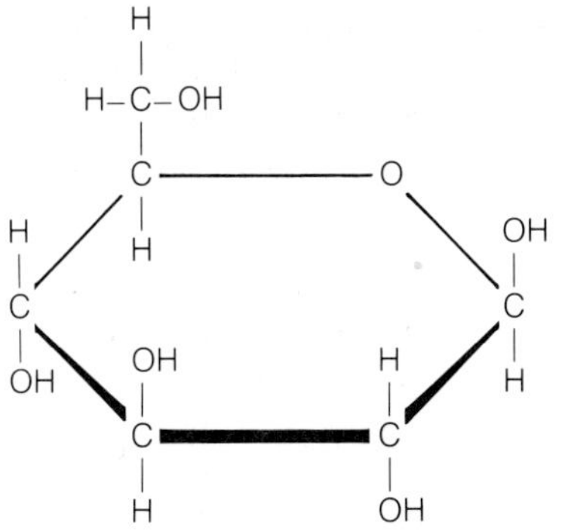

Figure 6.1 The structure of glucose. This structural model of a single molecule of glucose exemplifies the organization of carbohydrates: their units have a carbon skeleton, with oxygen, hydrogen, and hydroxyl groups attached to the carbon. *Key:* C = carbon, H = hydrogen, O = oxygen, and OH = hydroxyl group.

The chemist depicts glucose as shown in Figure 6.1. Although you will not see many chemical structures in this book, an occasional one gives you an idea of the composition and relative complexity of various substances. This one illustrates that six carbon atoms (or sometimes five) form the skeleton of the less complex sugar molecules. Hydrogen (H), oxygen (O), and —OH groups called hydroxyl groups are attached to the carbons in an arrangement that is specific for each type of sugar.

Sugars—in fact, all carbohydrates—contain the equivalent of about one water molecule for each carbon, as the term *carbohydrate* suggests.

Scientists refer to substances that contain carbon—such as carbohydrates, fats, proteins, and vitamins—as organic substances. All living organisms, both plant and animal, use and/or produce organic materials.

The public has given a somewhat different meaning to the term *organic*. Many people assume it to mean "grown without use of laboratory-produced chemicals." This popular definition is not scientifically accurate, and it is not a legal definition. Therefore the term "organic" on a food label guarantees nothing about the conditions under which the food was grown. [More about this in Chapter 14 (on processing).]

organic—carbon-containing; refers to many substances regardless of whether they originate in nature or in a laboratory

Sugars in Nature. The cells of green plants produce carbohydrate molecules by photosynthesis, a sunlight-requiring process in which carbon dioxide and water are combined to yield glucose and oxygen.

Some of the *glucose* that is synthesized by plants remains in that form, and some of it is converted into another sugar, *fructose,* by rearrangement of the hydrogen, oxygen, and hydroxyl groups. These sugars and a few other less common ones that consist of independent units with 5- or 6-carbon skeletons are called monosaccharides.

Some of the glucose and fructose combine into disaccharides, which consist of two monosaccharide units linked together. Two molecules of glucose can unite to form a molecule of *maltose*, or a molecule of glucose can join a molecule of fructose to form *sucrose*. Several forms of sugar usually exist simultaneously in a food.

In which plants are sugars found? Actually, all plants contain some sugar in their juices, although the amounts vary from one part of a plant

monosaccharides—the simplest sugars, having 5- or 6-carbon skeletons (examples: glucose, fructose)

disaccharides—simple sugars consisting of two monosaccharide units linked together (examples: maltose, sucrose)

Figure 6.2 Examples of sugars in two processed foods.
You can find out whether processed foods contain sugary components by checking their ingredient lists. However, it is not possible to tell exactly how much sugar is present. You can get only a rough idea from the ingredients' positions on the list: they are required to be ranked from the heaviest to lightest amount included in the product.

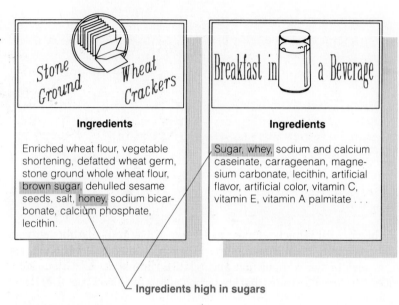

Stone Ground Wheat Crackers

Ingredients

Enriched wheat flour, vegetable shortening, defatted wheat germ, stone ground whole wheat flour, brown sugar, dehulled sesame seeds, salt, honey, sodium bicarbonate, calcium phosphate, lecithin.

Breakfast in a Beverage

Ingredients

Sugar, whey, sodium and calcium caseinate, carrageenan, magnesium carbonate, lecithin, artificial flavor, artificial color, vitamin C, vitamin E, vitamin A palmitate . . .

Ingredients high in sugars

to another. Fruits usually contain more liberal amounts of sugars; most roots, leaves, stems, and tubers contain less; and seeds have varying amounts. There are a few unexpectedly high sources, though, such as sugar cane and sugar beet.

A major sugar that occurs naturally in animal foods is the disaccharide *lactose*, which is found in animal milks. Lactose consists of a unit of glucose joined to a unit of *galactose*, another 6-carbon sugar molecule.

Sugars and Processing. The preceding discussion explains that *nature* produces sugars within foods. However, many foods also contain sugar that people—not nature—have put there. Ever since we learned how to concentrate the sugars from naturally sweet sources, sweeteners such as maple syrup, molasses, brown sugar, white sugar (pure sucrose), and honey have been added to food. (Of course, the honey bee gets the credit for production of the last one.)

Food science has also made it possible to create sweet syrups from the starches in grains such as corn, rice, and barley. It is also possible to make glucose, sometimes called *dextrose*, from starch; and there is a feasible way to produce pure fructose, sometimes called *levulose*. Lactose can be separated from whey, the watery by-product of cheesemaking.

sugar alcohols—compounds structurally related to sugars and used as sweeteners

Sugar alcohols (compounds structurally related to sugars) can also be produced for use as sweeteners. *Mannitol* and *sorbitol* are the forms most commonly used, particularly in "sugarless" chewing gum and candies. Other carbohydrate terms you may see are *turbinado sugar* (a steam-cleaned, partially refined sugar); and *total invert sugar* (a modified, liquefied form of sucrose that is used commercially).

Sugars that are produced technologically are chemically identical to their counterparts from nature and are metabolized in the same way. The body cannot distinguish between the two.

Read the ingredient lists on the labels of foods you eat, and see how many sugar sources you can identify. Figure 6.2 shows two examples.

You can get a rough idea of how much added sugar a food contains by noting the position of the sugars on the list, since ingredients must be ranked according to their weights in the product, from the greatest to the least. (Foods for which there is a federally standardized recipe recorded in the Code of Federal Regulation do not require an ingredient list. Hundreds of common foods such as mayonnaise and macaroni have standards of identity.)

Starches and Dextrins

Some of the glucose produced in plants is converted into *starches* and *dextrins*, which are the insoluble, nonsweet forms in which plants store energy. Because they are composed of from ten to hundreds of units of glucose linked together, they are also referred to as available polysaccharides or complex carbohydrates.

polysaccharides or **complex carbohydrates**—carbohydrates composed of many monosaccharide units linked together (examples: starches, dextrins)

Starches and Dextrins in Nature. Starches are both larger molecules and more prevalent in nature than dextrins. They usually concentrate in plant seeds, roots, and tubers. Grains, nuts, and legumes; root vegetables; and potatoes are particularly good sources of starch. Fruits have much less starch.

Starches, Dextrins, and Processing. Processing can alter the nature of starches in food. When starch is exposed to dry heat (as it is in the production of cold cereals or in the baking of bread), some of the large starch molecules are broken down into dextrins. Starches that have been further broken down into units of the disaccharide maltose are called *malted starches;* these are often found in cereals. *Modified starch*, which you find in some processed foods such as puddings, is pure starch that has been treated to enhance its ability to thicken or gel (Sanderson, 1981).

Fiber

Thus far, we have noted only that fiber is only minimally available for human energy use and that it provides bulk to the intestinal contents. You might think that we can dismiss it quickly as being relatively unimportant. However, recent studies have turned fiber into a prominent and controversial topic on the nutrition research frontier.

Fiber in Nature. Fiber is often defined as a plant food component that cannot be broken down by human digestive processes. Many forms of fiber are polysaccharides made of sugar units joined together in linkages that human enzymes cannot separate. This is why fiber is largely unavailable for energy production: it cannot be broken into units small enough for absorption.

fiber—a plant food component that humans cannot digest, although bacteria or other organisms may (example: cellulose)

People usually think of fiber as an insoluble, rigid substance, but it's more complex than that. There are several types of fiber. One is *cellulose*,

Frontier

Figure 6.3 Examples of fiber in two processed foods.
Fibers, both insoluble and soluble, are used as food additives

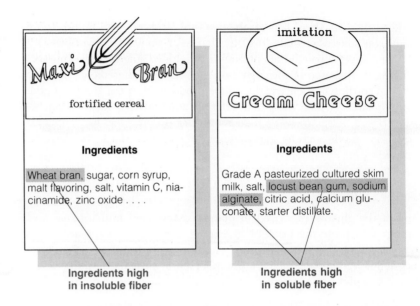

fortified cereal

Ingredients

Wheat bran, sugar, corn syrup, malt flavoring, salt, vitamin C, niacinamide, zinc oxide . . . .

Ingredients high
in insoluble fiber

imitation
Cream Cheese

Ingredients

Grade A pasteurized cultured skim milk, salt, locust bean gum, sodium alginate, citric acid, calcium gluconate, starter distillate.

Ingredients high
in soluble fiber

which is found in all plant cell walls. A cotton ball is an example of pure cellulose.

Another is hemicellulose, a fiber structurally related to cellulose, which is also present in plant cell walls. Fruits, vegetables, grains, nuts, and seeds contain both of these types of fiber. They are concentrated in the protective outer layers of whole grains (Southgate, 1976), which are called the *bran layers*, and in seeds and edible skins and peels.

Besides these generally insoluble, solid kinds of fiber, there are also some soluble forms such as *pectins* and *gums* (Sanderson, 1981). Apples are a notable edible source of pectin. Otherwise, the soluble fibers are generally found in only small amounts in common plant foods.

Fiber and Processing. Food processing can bring about some changes in the fiber content of foods. On the one hand, the most fibrous parts of a food are sometimes removed and discarded during processing; apple skins are peeled away while making applesauce, and the bran layers of wheat are removed in the production of white flour.

On the other hand, fiber is sometimes added to food by processors in response to the positive public image fiber currently enjoys. For example, bran is being added to an increasing number of breakfast cereals. Bran is also marketed by itself so that consumers can add it to other foods. Cellulose that has been refined from wood is added to some breads, both to raise the fiber content and to lower the kcalories by substituting for some of the available carbohydrates.

Sometimes pectins and gums are refined and used as additives to thicken, gel, or stabilize foods, or to emulsify them so that their different components do not separate. Commercially, pectin is usually refined from citrus peel and apples, and is added to jams, jellies, and candies. Gums are extracted from less familiar sources: certain African and Asian shrubs, trees, and seed pods are the natural origins of these materials. They are used in ice cream, fruit drinks, and canned meats, to name just a few; you have seen them listed on labels as *guar gum, locust bean gum, gum tragacanth, gum arabic,* and *xanthan gum. Agar, carrageenan,* and *alginates* are extracts of seaweed that also have wide use as stabilizers and thickeners (Sanderson, 1981).

Figure 6.3 shows examples of fiber in processed foods.

Amounts of Carbohydrates in Various Kinds of Foods

Table 6.2 shows how the total amounts of digestible carbohydrates compare among foods from the SANE guide groups. Table 6.3 gives more detail by showing how much of each type of carbohydrate is present per serving of food.

Table 6.2 Amounts of Digestible Carbohydrate in Standard Servings of Various Foods

Grams of digestible carbohydrate	Fruits and vegetables	Grain products	Milk and milk products	Meats and alternates	Combination foods	Limited extras
50			Ice cream (1½ c)		85g. Cherry pie (⅐ of double-crust pie); 12" Cheese pizza (¼ pie); Bean burrito (6 oz)	
			Sweetened fruit yogurt (1 c)			
40		Cake with icing (2 oz)		Legumes (1 c)		Cola beverage (12 oz)
30					Spaghetti and meatballs (1 c); Macaroni and cheese (1 c)	
		Dry cereals (1 oz); Pasta, rice (½ c)				
20	Many sugared fruits (½ c)	Oatmeal cookies (2)	Plain yogurt (1 c)		Cream of mushroom soup (1 c)	Gelatin dessert (½ c)
		Cooked cereals (½ c)	Milk (1 c)			Sugar, honey, jelly (1 T)
	Potatoes, corn, peas (½ c)	Bread (1 slice)		Nuts (½ c)		
10	Many un-sugared fruits (½ c)				Chicken Chow Mein (1 c); Beef noodle soup (1c)	
	Carrots, beets (½ c)			Meat, fish, poultry (3 oz)		
0	Leafy vegetables (½ c)		Hard cheese (1⅓ oz)			Butter, oils

Table 6.3 Typical Carbohydrate (CHO) Contents of Some Foods (Grams per Serving)

Food	Measure	Total CHO	Naturally occurring sugars	Added sugars	Starch and dextrins	Fiber[a]
Fruits						
Fruits (no added sugar)	$\frac{1}{2}$ cup	11	10	0	1	*
Fruits (in heavy syrup)	$\frac{1}{2}$ cup	21	10	10	1	*
Fruit juice (no added sugar)	$\frac{1}{2}$ cup	11	10	0	1	tr[b]
Vegetables						
High CHO (for example, potatoes, corn, peas)	$\frac{1}{2}$ cup	15	3	0	12	**
Moderate CHO (for example, carrots, beets)	$\frac{1}{2}$ cup	6	3	0	3	**
Low CHO (for example, leafy greens, green beans, broccoli)	1 cup	3	tr	0	3	*
Grain products						
White bread	1 slice	13	tr	1	12	tr
Whole grain bread	1 slice	13	tr	1	12	*
Cornflakes	1 ounce	24	tr	2	22	*
Bran cereal	1 ounce	13	tr	5	8	***
Pasta or rice	$\frac{1}{2}$ cup	20	tr	0	20	tr
Bagel	$\frac{1}{2}$	15	tr	1	14	tr
Plain oatmeal cookies	2 medium	15	tr	10	5	tr

continued

[a]Each asterisk represents 2–3 grams of dietary fiber. (Adapted from Southgate, D.A.T., B. Bailey, E. Collinson, and A.F. Walker. 1976. A guide to calculating intakes of dietary fiber. *Journal of Human Nutrition* 30:303–313.)
[b]tr = trace

You may be surprised at the total carbohydrate values in some foods compared to others. For example, did you know that a cup of milk contains slightly more carbohydrate than an average serving of fruit, or that a can of cola beverage has as much carbohydrate as almost three slices of bread?

Appendices E and F give (available) carbohydrate values for hundreds of foods. Nutrition labels also identify (available) carbohydrate content per serving.

Notice that meat is not shown to contain any fiber. Even though the term "meat fiber" is used to refer to hard-to-chew animal tissues such as

Table 6.3   continued

Food	Measure	Total CHO	Naturally occurring sugars	Added sugars	Starch and dextrins	Fiber[a]
Dairy products						
Milk (no milk solids added)	1 cup	12	12	0	0	0
Milk (milk solids added)	1 cup	14	14	0	0	0
Plain yogurt (with solids)	1 cup	16	16	0	0	0
Sweetened fruit yogurt (with milk solids)	1 cup	42	20	22	tr	tr
Ice cream	1½ cup	48	12	36	0	tr
Hard cheese	1⅓ ounces	tr	tr	0	0	0
Meats and alternates						
Meat, fish, poultry	2 ounces	0	0	0	0	0
Eggs	2	0	0	0	0	0
Nuts	½ cup	12	tr	0	12	***
Legumes	1 cup	35[c]	[c]	0	35	****[d]
Combinations and limited extras						
Sugar, honey, molasses, syrup	1 tablespoon	12	12	0	0	0
Jelly, jam	1 tablespoon	12	0	12	0	0
Gelatin dessert	½ cup	17	0	17	0	0
Cola beverage	12 ounces	37	0	37	0	0
Butter, oils	1 teaspoon	0	0	0	0	0
Cherry pie, homemade, with double crust	⅐ of 7-inch pie	85	16	38	31	*

[c]Contain some indigestible sugars
[d]Varies from one type to another

gristle, meats do not contain fiber in the sense that is being used here—an indigestible substance. Meat gristle, difficult as it is to break apart in the mouth, is usually completely digested if swallowed.

Also note that in the fiber column of Table 6.3, there are asterisks rather than numerical values. We have not used numbers because the amount of fiber in specific foods is not known precisely. This is because none of the laboratory methods used for measuring fiber levels duplicates human digestive processes faithfully. The other way of determining fiber, which is by measuring the amount of fiber left in human feces, gives

Table 6.4   Comparisons between Crude Fiber and Dietary Fiber Values

Fiber	Crude fiber (CF)[a] (%)	Dietary fiber (DF)[b] (%)	DF/CF
Whole wheat bread	1.6	8.5	5.3
40% bran flakes	4.4	26.7	6.1
Broccoli, fresh	1.5	4.1	2.7
Cabbage, fresh	0.8	2.8	3.5
Lettuce	0.5	1.5	3.0
Carrots, canned	1.0	3.7	3.7
Tomato, fresh	0.5	1.4	2.8
Apple, flesh only	0.6	1.4	2.3
Banana	0.5	1.8	3.6
Strawberries	1.3	2.1	1.6
Peanuts	2.4	9.3	3.9

The various processes used for determining the fiber content of foods yield very different results. Furthermore, no one mathematical factor can be used to convert one value to the other, as this chart demonstrates.
[a]Watt, B.K. and Merrill, A.L.: *Composition of Foods: Agriculture Handbook No. 8.* Washington, DC: United States Department of Agriculture, 1963.
[b]Paul, A.A., and Southgate, D.A.T.: *McCance and Widdowson's Composition of Foods.* London: Medical Research Council, 1978.
Reprinted with permission from Slavin JL: Dietary fiber. *Dietetic Currents* 10:27–32, 1983. Published by Ross Laboratories, Columbus, Ohio 43216

inexact results because microorganisms in the colon metabolize some fiber; fiber that is excreted in such experiments therefore underrepresents the actual fiber level.

In spite of these difficulties, you will see numerical values for fiber listed on some nutrition labels. If you want to compare levels of fiber from one food to another, it is important to use values that were determined by the same method. These are terms that you may see:

■ Crude fiber   values were determined by laboratory processes that are much harsher than human digestion; scientists now regard these values as much lower than actual for certain types of fiber, but they still are displayed on some food packages.

■ Dietary or edible fiber   values were determined either by milder laboratory processes or by human fecal waste studies; they are sometimes lower than actual. Appendix G gives dietary fiber values for a number of foods, as determined by one of the better laboratory methods.

Table 6.4 compares the two types of values in certain foods, thus illustrating how little correspondence there is between the two.

The Body Deals with Different Carbohydrates in Different Ways

What happens to carbohydrates when people eat them? You have some idea from Chapter 3, in which the general process of digestion was described. Here we will relate that information specifically to carbohydrates, and then go on to see what the body does with the end-products of digestion.

Digestion and Absorption of Carbohydrates

Carbohydrate digestion begins with chewing. Chewing makes food particles smaller, and mechanically breaks apart some cell walls that may have digestible carbohydrates trapped within them.

The biochemical processes that carbohydrates go through in the digestive tract vary, depending on how complex their molecular structures are.

Monosaccharides. Monosaccharides, since they are already the smallest possible carbohydrate units, do not need to be changed in preparation for absorption. When they arrive in the small intestine, they are ready to be absorbed.

Disaccharides. Disaccharides need to be separated into their monosaccharide components before they can be absorbed. The small intestine is the main location along the tract that produces enzymes for this purpose.

Whenever a disaccharide is split, a molecule of water is required to accomplish the separation and complete the structures of the two resulting monosaccharide units. When water is used for separation reactions, the process is called hydrolysis. For example, one molecule of water is necessary for the hydrolysis of one molecule of sucrose into one molecule of glucose and one molecule of fructose. Once hydrolysis has taken place, the resulting monosaccharides are quickly absorbed.

hydrolysis—type of chemical breakdown reaction requiring water

Starches and Dextrins. Starches and dextrins are more complex and are acted on primarily in two regions of the alimentary canal. In the mouth, starch-splitting enzymes called amylases, which are present in saliva, begin the process of hydrolyzing the many bonds that hold starches and dextrins together. As a result of this initial action, shorter length dextrins and some maltose are formed. Since food does not remain in the mouth for long, however, there is not much time for hydrolysis to occur: much work remains to be done to carbohydrates after food is swallowed.

amylases—starch-splitting enzymes present in saliva

Little progress is made in the stomach, since the hydrochloric acid there destroys most of the amylases. Digestion actively resumes in the small intestine, where pancreatic amylases and intestinal disaccharidases complete the job on most of the carbohydrates present. After digestion to monosaccharides has occurred, absorption takes place.

Table 6.5 Summary of Phases of Carbohydrate Digestion				
	Mono-saccharides	Disaccharides	Starches and dextrins	Fiber
Mouth	—	—	Enzymatic hydrolysis to maltose and dextrins	—
Stomach	—	—	(Amylase inactivated by stomach acid)	—
Small intestine	Absorption	Enzymatic hydrolysis to monosaccharides by pancreatic and intestinal enzymes; absorption	Completion of digestion by pancreatic and intestinal enzymes absorption	— —
Large intestine	—	—		Bacterial digestion of some fiber; limited absorption

Digestion and absorption of carbohydrates usually occur quickly. If sucrose is consumed alone, it begins to show up as blood glucose in 1 to 5 minutes. Even from a mixed meal, blood glucose rises in 30 to 60 minutes. Glucose absorption is speeded up if sodium is present in the gut at the same time. The presence of fiber, however, may somewhat decrease the absorption of nutrients in general. Over 90% of the available carbohydrate in the diet is usually digested and absorbed by the healthy gut.

Fiber. These carbohydrates cannot be digested by human digestive processes; in the main they simply progress from one part of the tract to the next. In the large intestine, however, bacteria are able to digest a portion of the fiber. Recent research indicates that some of these bacterial end products can be absorbed and used for energy (McNeil, 1984).

Table 6.5 summarizes the what and where of carbohydrate digestion.

Failure to Digest and/or Absorb Carbohydrates

There is an important sequel to this chronicle of events: what happens to the carbohydrates that aren't digested and absorbed.

Carbohydrates that get to the colon face two possible ends. One is that the bacteria there will use some of them to meet their own energy needs. Colonic bacteria are able to digest a wide variety of carbohydrates, even some that are indigestible to humans, producing gas in the process. This is why people are likely to feel "gassy" after eating beans or members of the onion family: those foods contain some carbohydrates that people cannot digest but that bacteria can use readily.

The other possibility is that these carbohydrates will hold water in the colon, or even draw water from surrounding tissues into the lumen. The greater the amounts of carbohydrate and water involved, the faster the transit of the intestinal contents will be.

Usually, the amounts of fiber and available carbohydrates consumed result in normal transit times and in such small gas production that it goes unnoticed. However, there are are several circumstances in which more exaggerated reactions may occur.

Lactose Intolerance. Lactose intolerance or lactase insufficiency is a condition in which a person is unable to digest much lactose because his or her body produces only a low level of lactase, the enzyme that splits lactose molecules. If the person eats foods that contain a large amount of lactose, most of it will not be digested, but will move along to the colon.

lactose intolerance—reduced ability to digest lactose, resulting from unusually low lactase production

In cases of lactose intolerance, both of the possible consequences may occur: bacteria may metabolize some of the lactose, and the rest may draw water into the lumen. The person who has overconsumed lactose may experience intestinal cramping, followed by an explosive, watery diarrhea.

This condition is common among adults, especially those of African, Asian, or Mediterranean heritage. Approximately 70% of the world's population has it; those who are not affected are mainly people of Northern European ancestry (Kretchmer, 1972).

Lactose intolerance is a condition that usually develops gradually. These people's systems produced ample amounts of lactase when they were infants and very young children, but starting as early as two years of age or as late as the teens, their bodies began to produce less and less of it. Nevertheless, even though a person may produce very *little* lactase, he or she usually produces *some.* Therefore, the amount of lactose a person can tolerate is a very individual matter; each person with lactose intolerance has to find that out independently. The levels of lactose in various foods are shown in Table 6.6.

Table 6.6	Lactose Content of of Some Dairy Products	
Measure	Food	Grams lactose per serving
1 cup	Human milk	17
1 cup	Cow's milk (milk solids added)	14
$1\frac{1}{2}$ cups	Ice cream	13
1 cup	Cow's milk (no solids added)	12
1 cup	Buttermilk	12
2 cups	Cottage cheese	12
1 cup	Yogurt	9
$1\frac{1}{3}$ ounces	Cheddar cheese	tr

The lactose content of the diet is not the only determinant of the body's response, however. The body's reaction may be heightened if other stresses such as infection exist at the same time. Sometimes the presence of other food constituents such as dairy fats decrease the body's reaction.

Many people with lactase insufficiency tolerate yogurt, even though this food has a relatively high lactose content (Kolars, 1984). This tolerance may be possible because the bacteria used in the production of yogurt from milk—a process that results in the metabolism of some of the milk's lactose—become more active again when they are warmed by body temperature. The bacteria's enzymes then digest an additional amount of lactose before the substance arrives at the small intestine.

Scientists have developed a way of helping lactose-intolerant people to live with the condition. A preparation of powdered lactase has been developed that can be added to milk before it is consumed; the lactase hydrolyzes most of the lactose in a matter of minutes, without much changing the taste of the milk.

A brief, temporary form of lactose intolerance is experienced by some people after they have had a gastrointestinal infection.

Ingestion of Sugar Alcohols. Sugar alcohols, which do not require digestion, are absorbed relatively slowly due to the nature of the mechanism by which they are transported from the small intestine into the body. Therefore, a portion of ingested sugar alcohols usually fails to be absorbed, and moves on to the colon. If large amounts of them have been consumed, some people may experience symptoms similar to those of lactose intolerance. The amounts that are present in chewing gum are not usually large enough to cause this effect, but eating liberal amounts of sugar alcohol–sweetened candies could cause symptoms.

Athletic Activity. Sometimes athletes consume sugary foods or drinks before or during athletic activity, thinking that the sugars will provide the advantage of extra energy. They sometimes get an unwanted reaction instead—diarrhea.

This can happen if the intestines react to the activity (or the nervousness that may accompany competition) by moving their contents along more rapidly than usual. The undigested disaccharides or unabsorbed monosaccharides arriving in the colon result in the now familiar consequences. Even the specially formulated sugar-containing sport drinks designed for athletes are too high in sugars for some people's systems to absorb them well; most of these beverages should be diluted to reduce the likelihood of diarrhea.

BOGUS! "Starch Blockers" BOGUS! In the early 1980s, a weight-loss product was marketed that was supposed to prevent the digestion of starch by chemically inactivating the enzymes that would normally be involved. If digestion could be interfered with, the theory went, a person would be able to eat starches without getting kcalories from them.

Although the chemical had been tested in animals with some success, the "starch blocker" capsules as marketed proved to be largely ineffective in humans (Carlson et al., 1983). It is probably a good thing that they didn't work well. If large amounts of starch had gotten to the colon, the consumer would probably have experienced symptoms similar to those of lactose intolerance. As it was, the FDA prohibited further sale of the product because it had not been adequately tested.

Influences on Transport and Regulation of Carbohydrates

Almost immediately after monosaccharide units are absorbed into intestinal wall cells, much of the galactose and fructose is converted into glucose. The remaining sugars then travel via the bloodstream to the liver, where more of them are converted to glucose.

What happens to the glucose after this? Ultimately, of course, its purpose is to be used by the body's cells for energy production, but it is not all needed at once. As you learned in Chapter 5 (on energy), only a small amount of glucose is metabolized for energy right away. Another small amount stays conveniently close by in the bloodstream. The largest amounts are converted to glycogen (animal starch) for storage in liver and muscle, and into fats.

Several factors are involved in determining what route the glucose takes. They are the activity of the liver, several hormones, and muscles.

The Liver. When there is a surplus of glucose in the body, as is likely after every meal, the liver converts most of the glucose into glycogen and forms materials that will later be united into fat molecules.

However, when blood glucose falls to the lower end of the normal range (a general condition called hypoglycemia), the liver breaks glycogen apart into glucose and releases it into the blood, raising the glucose level back up. You can often sense when these functions are happening. When your blood glucose drops to low–normal, you initially feel hungry and possibly tired; but after a while, even if you don't eat anything, as glycogen is converted into blood glucose the hunger and tiredness seem less pronounced. This type of hypoglycemia and the body's reaction to it are totally normal. This differs from an abnormal type of hypoglycemia, which will be discussed shortly.

hypoglycemia—general condition in which blood glucose concentration falls to the lower end of the normal range

Hormones. Several hormones help regulate the blood sugar level. Insulin, a hormone produced by the pancreas, is one that has a major influence. Part of its function is to help glucose get into body cells.

When the blood glucose level rises, the pancreas produces more than the maintenance level of insulin and releases it into the bloodstream. The insulin acts on body cells, causing them to remove the excess glucose from the blood. It promotes the production of glycogen in both liver and skeletal muscle cells, and it promotes the formation of fat in both liver and fat cells. At the same time, it discourages the breakdown of fat for energy, which causes the body to rely more heavily on the recently acquired carbohydrate load for energy production.

When the blood sugar level falls, the pancreas increases its production of a different hormone, glucagon, which has the opposite effect of insulin.

insulin—hormone produced by the pancreas; helps to regulate the blood sugar level by promoting the removal of excess glucose from the blood and its storage as glycogen or fat

glucagon—hormone produced by the pancreas; has the opposite effect of insulin, helping to regulate the blood sugar level by promoting the breakdown of glycogen and fat

Figure 6.4 Relative blood levels of glucose, insulin, and glucagon. When the blood glucose level rises (b), as it does after a meal, the pancreas produces more insulin, which helps to lower the blood glucose level. When blood glucose falls too low (a), (e), the pancreas produces more glucagon, which causes blood glucose to rise. (Reference: Barrington, E.J.W. 1975. *An introduction to general and comparative endocrinology.* Oxford: Clarendon Press.)

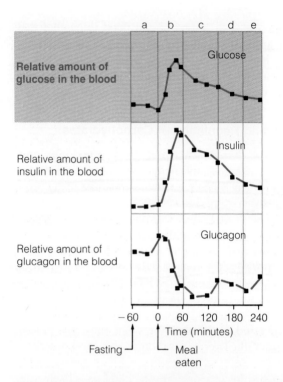

Glucagon encourages the liver to break glycogen back down into glucose. Glucagon also promotes the utilization of fat. Some other hormones have this same effect, particularly epinephrine, which is produced by the adrenal glands when the body has a sudden, high demand for energy.

Figure 6.4 shows the effects of various levels of blood glucose on the production of insulin and glucagon.

Muscles. Exercise prompts skeletal muscle cells to take in glucose from the bloodstream at a higher rate than they would have without the exercise. This glucose provides energy the muscles need for continued work.

These factors are automatically at work for us. We may be able to use these mechanisms to improve our performance in endurance activities such as distance bicycling, swimming, running, or skiing.

Applications for Athletes The popular wisdom is that sugar gives a person "quick energy." Since it gets into the bloodstream quickly after it is consumed, the idea sounds logical. But sugar can actually *interfere with endurance performance*, depending on the timing and amount of sugar intake.

Exercise physiologists found in various studies that consuming 300 kcalories of glucose an hour or a half hour before starting to exercise caused exhaustion to occur more rapidly during exercise than if water alone had been consumed (Costill, 1982). They believe that the insulin produced in response to the increased blood sugar interfered with the utilization of both glucose and fat for energy after the exercise began. To have optimal blood sugar and insulin levels, athletes should avoid carbohydrate during the final $1\frac{1}{2}$ to 2 hours before an event (Costill and Miller, 1980). It would be more advantageous to take in only water during this time.

If the event is one that will last for more than an hour and a half, athletes could use a *dilute* sugar solution *during the event* in place of plain water for hydration. This would supply a low level of sugar that would raise the blood glucose slightly without stimulating extra insulin production. The amount of sugar should not exceed 2 tablespoons per quart of water. If other beverages such as sport drinks or fruit juices are chosen, dilute them with *at least* an equal volume of water, depending on their sugar content. It is apparent that timing and the amount of sugar taken in make a great deal of difference.

Another application of carbohydrate utilization principles involves a much more extensive routine that may be useful for the *well-trained athlete* who is preparing for an endurance activity of *at least 90 minutes* (Costill, 1982). It is called carbohydrate loading, glycogen loading, or glycogen supercompensation. Rather than focusing on just the hour before exercise begins, this process begins about a week before the event.

The routine involves controlling both exercise and food consumption. The version described is a recent modification of earlier regimens developed for glycogen loading, and is discussed here because it is just as effective (Sherman et al., 1981), involves less discomfort, and is easier to accomplish than the older techniques.

These are the two aspects of the routine:

- **Exercise** On the sixth day before the event, exercise to exhaustion, using the type of activity in which you will be competing. This uses up stored muscle glycogen, and prompts greater production of enzymes that can synthesize glycogen. In succeeding days, progressively taper down your daily workouts so that you are not training at all on the day before the event.

- **Food consumption** On the sixth, fifth, and fourth days before the event, eat your normal diet of a variety of foods (probably about 50% of kcalories will come from carbohydrate). During the three days before the event, consume a high carbohydrate diet (70–80% of the kcalories from carbohydrate), with emphasis on starches. This furnishes a generous amount of glucose that allows glycogen stores to be repleted and to possibly double or triple normal levels in the muscles from which it was depleted in the earlier phase of the routine.

Studies show that when muscle glycogen is higher than usual, subjects can perform longer in laboratory tests before becoming exhausted (McArdle et al., 1981). Figure 6.5 illustrates this point.

People vary markedly in their reaction to glycogen loading in competitive situations. Those who like it say that it allows them to continue farther and/or faster at the end of a long endurance activity (such as the last 6 miles of a marathon) than they could otherwise have done. Others have not felt this benefit, but may have noticed the extra weight they

carbohydrate loading—controlling both exercise and food consumption in the days before competitive activity in such a way as to maximize muscle stores of glycogen

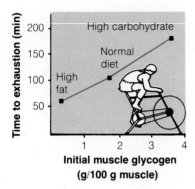

Figure 6.5 The relationship between diet, muscle glycogen, and endurance. When subjects were fed high fat/high protein diets for several days, leg muscle glycogen was low, and endurance for pedaling an exercise bicycle was lower than normal. When fed a high carbohydrate diet (approximately 80% of kcalories) for several days, both muscle glycogen and work increased dramatically. [From McArdle, W.D., Katch, F.I. and Katch, V.L: *Exercise Physiology: Energy, Nutrition and Human Performance.* Lea & Febiger, Philadelphia, 1981. (Adapted from Bergstrom, J. et al.: Diet, muscle glycogen and physical performance. *Acta Physiol. Scand.,* 71:140, 1967.)]

carried while they were glycogen loaded: for every gram of glycogen stored, 2.7 grams of water are also retained. Since glycogen loading can increase muscle glycogen to double or more the normal amount (normal is about 350 grams in a 150-pound man), the person may be carrying several pounds of extra water /weight in the major muscles used, which may cause feelings of heaviness and muscle stiffness.

Some unanswered questions remain about the effects of glycogen loading on heart and other body functions and on long-term health (Buskirk, 1981). For these reasons, it is recommended that use of glycogen loading be restricted to high school–level and older athletes, and then for no more than two or three times per year (American Dietetic Association, 1980). It may be wise to get expert advice from a health care professional who is familiar with both the effects of glycogen loading and your individual health status (Worthington-Roberts, 1981).

Abnormalities in Insulin Production and Function. Some people's bodies do not handle carbohydrate in the ways just described, due to an abnormality in the amount of insulin the pancreas produces. For example, it is possible that a person's pancreas may not produce enough insulin to accomplish its usual tasks. In such instances, sugar builds up in the blood because it cannot be taken into body cells for energy production or converted to glycogen or fat without insulin. This condition is called insulin-dependent diabetes: the person needs to inject insulin to make up for his or her own lack of it.

Do not assume that consumption of sugar or other carbohydrates causes diabetes; epidemiological evidence indicates that it does not. Rather, researchers theorize that diabetes may result from a hereditary tendency of a person's body to destroy insulin-producing cells, a process that may be hastened by such stress as a viral infection (Guyton, 1981).

Another possible abnormality occurs when a person (usually an adult) produces plenty of insulin, but for some reason the insulin cannot perform its role of carrying glucose into body cells. This circumstance, which is quite different from the condition just mentioned, is called non–insulin-dependent diabetes. Since people who get it are often overweight, it is primarily treated with a weight-reduction program, which may in itself

insulin-dependent diabetes—condition in which the pancreas does not produce enough insulin to regulate blood sugar adequately; thought to be hereditary in origin

non–insulin-dependent diabetes—condition in which adequate amounts of insulin are produced but not used normally; thought in many cases to be weight related

R.R.

bring the condition under control; sometimes an oral drug that helps lower blood glucose is also part of the treatment.

Yet another unusual metabolic situation occurs when insulin is *overproduced* in response to carbohydrate ingestion. In this case, a small rise in blood glucose from a normal diet causes a large outpouring of insulin from the pancreas, and blood sugar drops sharply below the normal range two to four hours after a meal. At the same time, sweating, palpitations, hunger, weakness, and anxiety occur. The condition is called reactive hypoglycemia (low blood sugar as a response to the diet). Reactive hypoglycemia differs from the normal hypoglycemia described earlier in that insulin is *over*produced in the reactive condition, driving the blood glucose level *below* the normal range; insulin is appropriately produced in normal hypoglycemia, usually lowering blood glucose to a low–normal level.

reactive hypoglycemia—condition in which low blood sugar results from overproduction of insulin

Although reactive hypoglycemia has received substantial popular press coverage, very few people have it. Among all the patients seen annually at the Mayo Clinic, fewer than 100 have this type of hypoglycemia (Service, 1977). A person who has it can avoid the symptoms by carefully controlling carbohydrate intake.

Carbohydrates Affect Certain Health Conditions

Carbohydrates have been accused, sometimes unjustly, of damaging health. Here we take a look at various salvos that have been fired at carbohydrates and examine their merits.

Overweight

Do carbohydrates make people fat? No, carbohydrates are not inherently fattening. Neither sugars nor starches are fattening per se. What makes people overly fat are excess kcalories from *any* source. Kcalories from carbohydrates are no more fattening than kcalories from proteins, fats, or alcohol . . . and they are probably not any less so.

Dental Caries (Tooth Cavities)

Dental caries occur when susceptible teeth are exposed over time to acids. Acids are commonly produced as a by-product of the bacterial metabolism of certain carbohydrates. Figure 6.6 shows the interactions of these factors, which are discussed next.

Susceptible Teeth. Some people's teeth are more prone to decay than others. An inherited trait can be responsible, but diet can also be involved. If a child has had access in utero (before birth) and throughout the tooth-forming years to a sufficient amount of the mineral fluoride, tooth surface structure will be harder and less susceptible to decay throughout life.

dental caries (cavities)—tooth enamel destruction caused by acid by-products of bacterial metabolism of certain carbohydrates

Acids. It is acids, not sugar itself, that actually cause decay by dissolving the minerals out of teeth. The most common source of these acids is

Figure 6.6 Overview of factors influencing production of dental caries (tooth cavities). For tooth decay to occur, all four of the factors must be present at the same time. None of these factors is directly responsible for caries production: cavities result when acids from bacterial metabolism of carbohydrates, especially sugars, demineralize tooth enamel.

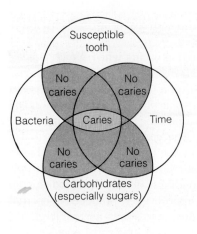

bacterial metabolism of carbohydrates, but there are other causes of decay as well. For example, people who frequently induce vomiting [as occurs in the binging/purging eating disorder (Schleimer, 1981)] are likely to have their tooth enamel damaged by its repeated contact with hydrochloric acid from the stomach.

Bacteria. Although a few other bacteria have been implicated in tooth decay, *Streptococcus mutans* is responsible for most of the acid production that leads to dental caries. It is a common resident of the normal mouth, but does not cause tooth decay unless the other factors conducive to decay are also present.

Carbohydrate. Mouth bacteria thrive on carbohydrate. The amount of acid they produce from it will vary, depending on the type of carbohydrate involved.

Sucrose and glucose are the carbohydrates that bring about the greatest acid production, and therefore are the most cariogenic (likely to lead to cavities). Pure fructose results in the production of between 80% and 100% as much acid as sucrose and glucose do (FAO, 1980). Therefore, it is not surprising that honey, which is a combination of glucose and fructose, has been found to be as cariogenic as pure sucrose (Randolph, 1981).

cariogenic—likely to cause cavity production

Other sugars are not as completely utilized by mouth bacteria for acid production. Approximately 50% of lactose, for example, may be converted to acid. The sugar alcohol sorbitol is only 10–30% utilized, and mannitol is not used at all (FAO, 1980). This explains why these two substances are commonly used in "sugarless" chewing gums.

Any foods that contain sucrose may lead to decay, even if they contain as little as 2% sucrose (Randolph and Dennison, 1981). Many studies show that the amount of sucrose in a food is not necessarily proportional to the number of caries produced by the food. For example, a study that involved rats showed a cereal containing 14% sucrose was more cariogenic than one containing 60% sucrose (Schactele, 1982).

Figure 6.7 A dietary deterrent to tooth decay. The chewing of high-fiber foods stimulates the production of saliva, which helps cleanse carbohydrates from the mouth.

Time. Decay results from the cumulative exposure of a tooth surface to acid. Therefore, the longer carbohydrate stays in the mouth, the more time there is for acid to be produced and to demineralize tooth enamel.

Sticky foods, such as caramels and raisins, that cling to tooth surfaces are more cariogenic than less sticky items. Frequency of eating is important as well, since acid production continues for at least 20 minutes after the last mouthful is swallowed (Schachtele, 1982). Therefore, it is less damaging to consume 18 grams of sucrose in a popsicle that is eaten at once than to get 18 grams of sucrose in several pieces of hard candy that are slowly dissolved in the mouth over a longer period of time.

Deterrents to Decay. Besides the implied suggestions in the preceding sections for discouraging tooth decay, there are several others. The chewing of fibrous foods, for example (Figure 6.7), stimulates the production of generous amounts of saliva, which has a cleansing effect (Randolph and Dennison, 1981). And high-protein/high-phosphate/high-fat foods such as cheese and nuts are also thought to discourage decay. Whether sugars are eaten alone makes a difference, too: sugars eaten within a meal have far less cariogenic activity than those eaten by themselves between meals (Gustafson et al., 1954).

Of course, good dental hygiene immediately after eating reduces the amount of time sugars are in the mouth, and is therefore also helpful. The American Dental Association incorporates many of these suggestions into its decay prevention program. It recommends a nutritious diet, limited snacking (especially of sweets), careful hygiene, and regular dental checkups (Council on Dental Health and Health Planning, 1983).

Deficiency Diseases

Some popular nutrition writers have suggested that refined carbohydrates, such as white sugar, white flour that has not been enriched, and pure starch, have nothing much to offer nutritionally except kcalories. They are right.

Then some go on to say that eating those substances (which are highly processed items) will cause people to develop deficiency diseases, but that eating foods that have not been heavily processed (such as honey and whole grain flour) will protect against deficiencies.

We have several concerns about the last statement. First of all, it goes too far by insinuating that *any* intake of low-nutrient-density foods will wreak nutritional havoc; it won't. Nutrition expert Alfred Harper states that consumption of foods "with a low content of essential nutrients should probably not exceed 20% of the diet for people who are not highly active" (Harper, 1977). Consuming up to that level is not likely to result in people being seriously shortchanged nutritionally.

Second, although it is generally true that lightly processed foods are nutritionally superior to their more heavily processed counterparts, minimal processing is no guarantee that a food will be of high nutrient density. For example, honey is not significantly more nutritious than white sugar. [More on this topic in Chapter 14 (on processing).]

Finally, there is one type of dietary carbohydrate that may relate directly to deficiency diseases, and that is fiber. Fiber and/or substances often found along with it in plants are able to prevent the absorption of some essential minerals by forming insoluble compounds that are subsequently excreted.

Some groups of people in Egypt and Iran, whose typical diets are extremely high in fiber and related compounds but marginal in minerals, have developed mineral deficiency syndromes on the typically limited diets of their regions. Much remains to be learned about the bioavailability (usability) of minerals when they are consumed with various kinds of fiber, and about how much fiber is too much. Therefore, despite the positive attributes we know fiber to have, like any other ingested substance it should not be overused.

Constipation

Adequate fiber in the diet relieves constipation. Fiber and the water it absorbs make the feces bulkier. Carrot fiber, for example, can hold 20 to 30 times its weight in water, whereas wheat bran can hold only about 5 times its weight (Cummings et al., 1976).

The bulky feces cause the colonic muscles to exercise more, which makes them stronger and able to function better. In addition, the fecal mass moves through the tract more easily because it is softer. When a diet contains the recommended amount of fiber, transit time is typically between 24 and 72 hours; if fiber intake is very low, transit time is likely to be longer.

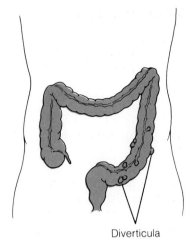

Figure 6.8 Diverticular disease. In diverticular disease, a common condition in the elderly, outpouchings form in the wall of the colon.

Diverticula

Vegetarians who rely largely on plant foods and therefore have high fiber intakes rarely experience constipation.

Diverticular Disease

Diverticular disease is a condition in which pressure in the lumen of the colon causes outpouchings (diverticula) to occur in its wall (Figure 6.8). A large portion of the elderly American population—as high as half—is thought to have this condition without necessarily being aware of it (Bureau of Foods, 1980). In fact, diverticula will not cause any pain unless waste collects in them and causes irritation, resulting in **diverticulitis**. (The suffix *-itis* means *inflammation*.)

diverticular disease—condition in which pressure in the lumen of the colon causes outpouchings called diverticula to occur in its walls

A diet generous in fiber has been found to help relieve the symptoms of uncomplicated diverticular disease (Almy and Howell, 1980). Some epidemiologists further believe that a high-fiber diet may help prevent the condition (Bureau of Foods, 1980), since another effect of increased fecal bulk and decreased transit time is decreased colonic pressure (Painter, 1975).

Colon Cancer

Cancer is a disease in which body cells multiply out of control. Research over the past several decades suggests that there may be over 100 different clinical conditions resulting from this process, all of which are therefore called cancer.

Certain components in the diet have been linked to cancer, and thus this topic is on the nutrition research frontier.

Dietary fiber has been suggested to provide protection against colon cancer. This suggestion comes of observations that populations that consume a high-fiber diet tend to have less colon cancer than populations that eat low-fiber diets (Burkitt and Trowell, 1975). (This epidemiological evidence

Frontier

was mentioned in Chapter 1.) However, high-fiber diets often have the coexisting characteristic of being low in fat. Therefore, it may be just as valid to suggest that the low fat feature of the diet is the protective factor—or possibly that neither low-fat nor high-fiber is protective (Hegsted, 1977).

At the same time, however, populations that eat diets low in fiber while high in animal fat and protein are known to have higher rates of cancer of the bowel, breast, and prostate. Such observations led to the hypothesis that fiber protects against cancer, which in turn has led to animal testing.

Several animal studies have shown that certain individual components of food fiber protect against chemically induced cancers (Vahouny, (1982b); however, all studies are not consistent in this finding. It is not appropriate to assume that dietary fiber would have the same effect in humans, since it differs from the separated fiber components used in the animal experiments (Committee on Diet, Nutrition, and Cancer, 1982). David Kritchevsky, a noted researcher in this area, sums up the state of the art: "Currently available data do not permit clear-cut conclusions regarding diet and colon cancer in man" (1981).

Cardiovascular Disease

The effect of diet on cardiovascular (heart and blood vessel) disease is a topic that has been on the nutrition frontier for decades. Dietary fats are believed to be more influential in the development of cardiovascular (CV) disease than carbohydrates are, so we will devote a major section in Chapter 7 (on fat) to this health concern, including the definition of many important terms.

Suffice it to say here that different forms of carbohydrates seem to have different effects on CV diseases because of their influence on blood cholesterol, a fatty substance in blood. The higher your total blood cholesterol is, the greater statistical likelihood you have of developing CV disease.

Some forms of fiber lower blood cholesterol: pectin and gums have been shown to do this in studies of both animals and humans. The amount of fiber that was necessary to accomplish this in one experiment, however, was more than people would be likely to consume in a normal diet: it took six apples per day to provide the test amount of pectin (Truswell, 1978). Refined pectin and gums are often used for such studies. This is an example of a food constituent being used in a nonfood way: as a drug.

Another researcher (Vahouny, 1982a) suggests that dramatic levels of fiber may not be necessary to achieve some benefit; increasing the intake of fibrous foods may lead to small, persistent decreases in blood cholesterol levels that may significantly lessen risk over a long period of time. Others doubt this, and the debate continues.

Many studies have been done to determine whether wheat bran has a cholesterol-lowering effect; it does not (Kritchevsky, 1982).

The effect of other carbohydrates on CV disease is less clear-cut (Story, 1982). Studies that have attempted to determine whether sugars or starches increase blood cholesterol have yielded mixed results; future work may provide more definitive answers.

It is interesting to note that epidemiological studies of groups of Seventh Day Adventist vegetarians—whose diets are likely to be high in fiber and starch—show 40% less heart disease than the general population (Glueck and Connor, 1978). However, such studies have not ascertained which dietary constituent (if any) is responsible for the decreased risk. It is also possible that the effect may be due to differences in other lifestyle factors such as less smoking and little alcohol consumption.

Assess Your Own Carbohydrate Intake Compared to Recommendations

Now we will deal with the matter of how much is the right amount of carbohydrate to consume, and whether you get it.

Recommended Minimal Intake for Total Available Carbohydrate

Even though it is a biochemically important substance, there is no RDA for carbohydrate, since it can be produced from protein. However, if body proteins were used heavily for carbohydrate production, physiological damage would eventually result. Therefore, estimates have been made of how much carbohydrate is needed to provide for important functions and to preserve body protein.

Experts in this country recommend that *at the very least*, a person should take in daily 100 grams of carbohydrate, which is needed for the functioning of the central nervous system, and for meeting the needs of red blood cells and aiding in the digestion of fat. The United Nations Food and Agriculture Organization and World Health Organization suggest a more generous *minimum* of 180 grams daily.

If you add up the carbohydrate in the minimal amount of foods recommended by the SANE guide, you will find that it ranges anywhere from about 110 to 200 grams, depending on which foods are selected, especially on whether legumes are used as meat alternates.

Using a 24-hour period, keep a food record for yourself, identifying how much carbohydrate was in each item eaten (Table 6.3 is a quick reference for many items), and totaling the carbohydrate values. Did you get at least the minimal recommended amount? Individuals who use starchy foods as the mainstay of their diets get considerably more. The long-standing practices of Asians, who use rice as a staple food; the Irish, who use potatoes; and Eastern Europeans, who use bread, illustrate that many groups of people can usually meet these recommended intakes for carbohydrate with no difficulty.

Another way carbohydrate recommendations are expressed is as a percentage of kcalories. The energy chapter noted that for most people 50% to 60% of kcalories should come from carbohydrate. This holds true for athletes as well: those who take in less than 40% of their kcalories from carbohydrate are likely to become progressively glycogen depleted and tire faster (Buskirk, 1981).

A 24-hour food record can also be used to find out what percentage of your energy intake is from carbohydrate. After you have recorded all

Figure 6.9 Assessment of carbohydrate intake for one day.

Food	Amount eaten	Energy (kcal)	(Available) carbohydrate (g)
Orange juice (frozen)	1 cup	120	29
Peanut butter sandwich:			
Whole wheat bread	2 slices	120	24
Peanut butter	4 T.	380	12
Strawberry jam	2 T.	110	28
Apple	1 medium	80	20
Ice cream	¾ cup	203	24
Broiled chicken	4 ounces	160	0
Boiled rice	1 cup	225	50
Lettuce salad:			
Iceberg lettuce	⅙ head	11	3
French dressing	1 oz.	130	6
2% milk	2 cups	240	24
Saltine crackers	12	150	24
Cola beverage	12 oz.	145	37
		2074	281

Totals

                                                     × 4

Kcalories from carbohydrate   1124

% of kcalories from carbohydrate   54%

foods eaten, write down the macronutrient values of each item (Appendices E and F). Calculate (as shown in the energy chapter, Chapter 5) what percentage of your kcalories came from carbohydrate that day. Figure 6.9 gives an example.

Did your intake fall within the recommended range, or was it closer to the 46% average for Americans in 1979, according to USDA data? In the developing countries, in contrast, 75% of the total kcalories consumed come from available carbohydrates (FAO, 1980).

Suggested Intake for Fiber

It is difficult to recommend a specific fiber intake. The consequences of taking in different kinds and amounts of fiber are not entirely understood. Nonetheless, it is reasonable to make these recommendations based on servings of foods in the SANE guide:

- Consume several servings of fruits and vegetables per day in whole form and with edible peels, rather than as juice.

- Consume two or three servings of grains per day in whole grain rather than refined form.

■ *If* you include refined bran or a bran product in your diet, limit it to one serving per day. It is not necessary to use bran or bran products, particularly if you follow the first two recommendations.

SUMMARY

■ Sugars, starches, and fiber are all forms of carbohydrate that differ somewhat in their characteristics and functions. As a group, they have four major functions in the body: (1) they provide energy, (2) they allow protein to be spared for its own unique functions, (3) they participate in fat metabolism, and (4) they provide bulk in the intestines.

■ The types and amounts of carbohydrates in foods vary. All are organic substances regardless of their origin. Sugars are the smallest and simplest carbohydrates; glucose is a typical and important example. Mono- and disaccharides are found in all plant foods; the disaccharide lactose occurs in animal milks. Sugar can also be added to foods during processing; you can get a general idea of how much added sugar a food contains from the food label. Starches and dextrins (polysaccharides) are also commonly found in plant foods, and can be altered in or added to processed foods. Sugars and starches are available for human energy production and are thus considered available carbohydrates.

■ Fiber cannot be digested by human processes, but it is nevertheless important to the healthy functioning of the digestive tract. Fiber is a plant food component that exists in many forms, and can be removed from or added to foods during processing. The fiber content of specific foods is difficult to quantify; different types of analyses produce crude fiber and edible fiber values, neither of which is highly accurate.

■ A healthy person digests and absorbs carbohydrates quickly and efficiently. Disaccharides are hydrolyzed in the small intestine, where all monosaccharides are then absorbed. Starch digestion begins in the mouth with the activity of amylases, and then resumes in the small intestine. Fiber progresses along the upper tract without modification. Carbohydrates that are not digested (including fiber) and move along to the colon are used by bacteria and draw water from surrounding tissues into the lumen; normally neither event causes problems. However, under conditions of lactose intolerance, unusually high ingestion of sugar alcohols, or the stress of athletic activity, carbohydrates are sometimes not digested or absorbed properly and cause discomfort.

■ Several factors determine what happens to glucose, the ultimate product of carbohydrate digestion. Some is used right away for energy production and some remains in the bloodstream, but most is converted to glycogen or fat for storage. The hormones insulin and glucagon, both produced by the pancreas, help to regulate the blood glucose level.

■ Athletes in some cases can maximize their muscle glycogen using a diet and exercise regimen called glycogen loading.

■ Various abnormalities in carbohydrate metabolism can be traced to problems in insulin production or function. These include insulin-dependent diabetes, non–insulin-dependent diabetes, and reactive hypoglycemia.

■ Carbohydrates affect certain aspects of health in various ways. In combination with bacteria and over a period of time, they can figure in the production of dental caries; glucose and sucrose lead to the greatest degree of bacterial acid production and are therefore the most cariogenic carbohydrates. Fiber can relieve constipation and help prevent diverticular disease, but if ingested in large amounts it can interfere with the bioavailability of certain minerals. Fiber may or may not provide some protection against certain types of cancer and cardiovascular disease; this is an active area of research and debate.

■ Recommendations exist for minimal carbohydrate intake in both gram amounts (100–180 g minimum) and as a percentage of total kcalorie intake (50–60%). You can assess your own intake using a 24-hour food record and the food composition tables at the back of this book.

REFERENCES

Almy, T.P., and D.A. Howell. 1980. Diverticular disease of the colon. *New England Journal of Medicine* 302:324–331.

The American Dietetic Association. 1980. Nutrition and physical fitness: A statement. *Journal of the American Dietetic Association* 76:437–443.

Barrington, E.J.W. 1975. *An introduction to general and comparative endocrinology.* Oxford: Clarendon Press.

Bureau of Foods, Food and Drug Administration, Department of Health and Human Services. 1980. *The role of dietary fiber in diverticular disease and colon cancer.* Bethesda, MD: Life Sciences Research Office, Federation of American Societies for Experimental Biology.

Burkitt, D.P., and H.C. Trowell, eds. 1975. *Refined carbohydrate foods and disease: Some implications of dietary fiber.* London: Academic Press.

Buskirk, E.R. 1981. Some nutritional considerations in the conditioning of athletes. *Annual Reviews of Nutrition* 1:319–350.

Carlson, G.L., B.U.K. Li, P. Bass, and W.A. Olsen. 1983. A bean alpha amylase inhibitor formulation (starch blockers) is ineffective in man. *Science* 219:393–395.

Committee on Diet, Nutrition, and Cancer. 1982. *Diet, nutrition, and cancer.* Washington, DC: National Academy Press.

Costill, D.L., and J. M. Miller. 1980. Nutrition for endurance sport: Carbohydrate and fluid balance. *International Journal of Sports Medicine* 1:2–14.

Costill, D.L. 1982. Fats and carbohydrates as determinants of athletic performance. In *Nutrition and athletic performance: Proceedings of the conference on nutritional determinants in athletic performance,* ed. W. Haskell, J. Scala, and J. Whittam. Palo Alto, CA: Bull Publishing Company.

Council on Dental Health and Health Planning, Council on Dental Research, and Council on Dental Therapeutics. 1983. Statement on diet and dental caries. *Journal of the American Dental Association* 107:78.

Cummings, J.H., M.J. Hill, D.J.A. Jenkins, J.R. Pearson, and H.S. Wiggins. 1976. Changes in fecal composition and colonic fiber due to cereal fiber. *American Journal of Clinical Nutrition* 29:1468.

Food and Agriculture Organization (FAO) of the United Nations. 1980. *Carbohydrates in human nutrition: A joint FAO/WHO report.* Rome: FAO.

Glueck, C.J., and W.E. Connor. 1978. Diet–coronary heart disease relationships reconnoitered. *American Journal of Clinical Nutrition* 31:727–737.

Gustafson, B.E., C.E. Quensel, L.S. Lanke, et al. 1954. The Vipeholm dental caries study. *Acta Odontologica Scandinavica* 11:232.

Guyton, A.C. 1981. *Textbook of medical physiology.* Philadelphia: W.B. Saunders Company.

Hardinge, M.G., J.B. Swarner, and H. Crooks. 1965. Carbohydrates in foods. *Journal of the American Dietetic Association* 46:197–204.

Harper, A.E. 1977. Twenty commentaries. *Nutrition Today* 12(no.6):20.

Hegsted, D.M. 1977. Food and fibre: Evidence from experimental animals. *Nutrition Reviews* 35(no.3):45–50.

Kolars, J.C., M.D. Levitt, M. Aouji, and D.A. Savaiano. 1984. Yogurt—an autodigesting source of lactose. *New England Journal of Medicine* 310:1–3.

Kretchmer, N. 1972. Lactose and lactase. *Scientific American* 227(no.4):70–78.

Kritchevsky, D. 1981. Dietary fiber and disease. In *Controversies in nutrition,* ed. L. Ellenbogen. New York: Churchill Livingstone.

Kritchevsky, D. 1982. Fiber revisited. *The Professional Nutritionist*: Summer 1982.

McArdle, W.D., F.I. Katch, and V.I. Katch. 1981. *Exercise physiology*. Philadelphia: Lea and Febiger.

McNeil, N.I. 1984. The contribution of the large intestine to energy supplies in man. *American Journal of Clinical Nutrition* 39:338–342.

Painter, N.S. 1975. *Diverticular disease of the colon—A deficiency disease of Western civilization*. London: William Heinemann Medical Books Ltd.

Randolph, P.M., and C.I. Dennison. 1981. *Diet, nutrition, and dentistry*. St. Louis: The C.V. Mosby Company.

Sanderson, G.R. 1981. Polysaccharides in foods. *Food Technology* 35:50–57, 83.

Schachtele, C.F. 1982. Changing perspectives on the role of diet in dental caries formation. *Nutrition News* 45(no. 4):13–14.

Schleimer, K. 1981. Anorexia nervosa. *Nutrition Reviews* 39:99–103.

Service, F.J. 1977. Hypoglycemia. *Contemporary Nutrition* 2(no. 7): July 1977.

Shallenberger, R.S. 1974. Occurrence of various sugars in foods. In *Sugars in nutrition*, ed. H.L. Sipple and K.W. McNutt. New York: Academic Press.

Sherman, W.M., D.L. Costill, W.J. Fink, and J.M. Miller. 1981. Effect of exercise–diet manipulation on muscle glycogen and its subsequent utilization during performance. *International Journal of Sports Medicine* 2:114–118.

Slavin, J. L. 1983. Dietary fiber. *Dietetic Currents* 10(no. 6).

Southgate, D.A.T. 1976. The definition and analysis of dietary fibre. *Nutrition Reviews* 35:31–37.

Southgate, D.A.T., B. Bailey, E. Collinson, and A.F. Walker. 1976. A guide to calculating intakes of dietary fibre. *Journal of Human Nutrition* 30:303–313.

Story, J.A. 1982. Dietary carbohydrate and atherosclerosis. *Federation Proceedings* 41(no. 11):2797–2800.

Truswell, A.S. 1978. Diet and plasma lipids—A reappraisal. *The American Journal of Clinical Nutrition* 31:977–989.

Vahouny, G.V. 1982a. Dietary fiber, lipid metabolism, and atherosclerosis. *Federation Proceedings* 41(no. 11):2801–2806.

Vahouny, G.V. 1982. Conclusions and recommendations of the symposium on "Dietary fibers in health and disease," Washington, DC, 1981. *American Journal of Clinical Nutrition* 35 :152–156.

Worthington-Roberts, B.S. 1981. Diet and athletic performance. In *Contemporary developments in nutrition*, ed. B.S. Worthington-Roberts. St. Louis: The C.V. Mosby Company.

7

Lipids

IN THIS CHAPTER: Lipids Have Six Important Functions · Different Types of Lipids Are Found in Foods · The Amounts of Lipids in Different Foods Vary Considerably · Lipids Take Many Forms during Digestion, Absorption, and Transport · Lipids Concentrate in Specific Kinds of Body Substances · Lipids Are Involved in Major Health Problems · Assess Your Own Lipid Intake Compared with Recommendations

Have you ever noticed on the ingredient list of a food product label the terms *monoglycerides* and *diglycerides?* Or *lecithin?* Or have you ever had a laboratory test done to determine the level of your *blood cholesterol?* These are examples of the various compounds that are called lipids.

Lipids are fatty substances that usually do not dissolve in water but that do dissolve in ether; fats (solid lipids) and oils (liquid lipids) are general terms that apply to many members of this group.

lipids—fatty substances that usually do not dissolve in water due to their chemical structure

Fats, oils, and their chemical relatives have earned a bad reputation among the general public in recent years. One reason is cosmetic; our society has come to think that body fat is ugly. Other reasons are health related. We have learned over the years to be concerned about our levels of blood cholesterol, knowing that this form of fat has been implicated in the development of atherosclerosis, a type of cardiovascular disease.

Yet, although we think negatively about lipids, we nonetheless enjoy eating them, and find ourselves perenially tempted by them. Lipids often contribute to the tantalizing aromas of foods; lipids also largely account for the sense of satiety (hunger satisfaction) that is experienced from eating rich foods. Magazines that place an article about new, buttery desserts alongside a feature on how to slim down exemplify these conflicting attitudes about fat.

This chapter will help give a balanced perspective on the topic. It starts by emphasizing the positive values of lipids: they have important functions besides those you have already read about in previous chapters. We will discuss the many forms of lipids found in foods, both as nature produces them and as food technology modifies them; how the body handles lipids; how much fat a person needs; and how health can be affected by consuming various amounts of lipids for long periods of time.

Lipids Have Six Important Functions

Fats serve important purposes, both as they occur in the diet and as they are found in the body.

1. *Provide essential nutrients.* An essential nutrient in lipids is a compound called linoleic acid. If a child does not get enough of this essential fatty acid, his or her growth is impaired. If your diet is deficient in linoleic acid for many months, your skin will become scaly and rough. Fortunately, linoleic acid is widespread enough in the food supply that most people who eat a varied diet are likely to fulfill their own needs.

   linoleic acid—essential fatty acid present in lipids

   Current research indicates that linolenic acid, another widely available fatty acid, may also be essential (Holman, Johnson, and Hatch, 1982).

function of Lipids

2. *Carry fat-soluble vitamins into the body.* Some vitamins—A, D, E, and K—are absorbed into the body much more easily if they are dissolved in fat. (This is a good example of how nutrients influence each other in the body.)

3. *Provide energy.* Lipids are the most potent providers of energy, at the level of 9 kcalories per gram. This is more than twice as much energy as carbohydrates and proteins have to offer per unit of weight. (Remember that each of these provides 4 kcalories per gram.)

   Body fat, which is called adipose tissue, is energy stored in compact form. We would be very much larger and heavier than we are now if the kcalories we carry as fat were stored as glycogen instead. For example, if the energy contained in 25 pounds of fat were stored in your body as glycogen, the glycogen would weigh about 55 pounds, and the water associated with it would weigh over 150 pounds, making you more than 180 pounds heavier than the 25 pounds of fat would.

adipose tissue—body fat

4. *Provide components for body structures.* You know that lipids are present in adipose tissue; but you may be surprised to learn that lipids are necessary components of cell membranes, some hormones, nerve coverings, vitamins, and some digestive secretions.

   Cholesterol is one lipid that performs a variety of these functions. It is important to keep in mind that cholesterol, which has had so much bad press, is a necessary substance. It is so important that people's bodies actually produce it, usually in a larger amounts than they consume in their diets.

5. *Insulate the body thermally.* If you are of average weight, roughly half of the adipose tissue in your body is just under the skin and is called subcutaneous fat. Located there, it constitutes an internal blanket that helps hold in your body heat. Whether you consider this an advantage or a disadvantage depends on how much subcutaneous fat you have and what the usual temperature of your environment is.

subcutaneous fat—adipose tissue located just under the skin

6. *Protect vital organs.* The rest of your adipose tissue surrounds your internal organs, where it cushions them from shocks and bruises.

Different Types of Lipids Are Found in Foods

Lipids are categorized according to their structural similarities. We will deal here with glycerides, phospholipids, and sterols. They are of major importance because of their prevalence in the diet and body, and their implications for health.

Glycerides in Nature

glycerides—the most common lipids, consisting of one, two, or three fatty acids attached to a molecule of glycerol; triglycerides have three fatty acids

Glycerides are the most common forms of lipids. By definition, glycerides consist of a molecule of the 3-carbon compound glycerol to which one, two, or three fatty acids are attached *(mono-, di-, or triglycerides)*. Figure 7.1 shows the general form of a triglyceride.

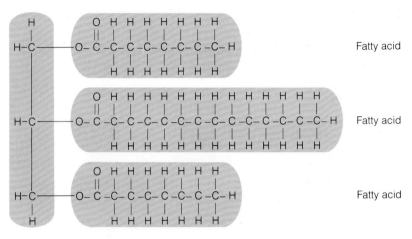

Glycerol

Fatty acid

Fatty acid

Fatty acid

Figure 7.1 The structure of a triglyceride. Triglycerides, which consist of a molecule of glycerol with three fatty acids attached, are the most common forms of lipids found in foods and in the body. Smaller amounts of diglycerides (with two fatty acids) and monogly-cerides (one fatty acid) are also found.

Triglycerides account for about 90% of the weight of lipids in foods (Friedman and Nylund, 1980); fats and oils are both largely triglycerides. Mono- and diglycerides also occur in nature, as do some unattached or "free" fatty acids.

Even though the name of these compounds draws attention to the glycerol portion of the lipid molecule, the attached fatty acids are the components responsible for giving different glycerides their characteristics. Fatty acids differ from each other most significantly in their chain length and in their degree of saturation.

Chain length refers to the number of linked carbon atoms in the fatty acid skeleton. Chain length is significant because the shorter the fatty acid chains, the more likely a glyceride is to be liquid at room temperature. (Milk fat has many short chain fatty acids.) Triglycerides with long fatty acids, such as those found in red meats, are solid at room temperature. Fatty acids may have anywhere from 4 to 22 carbons; oleic acid, the most common fatty acid in nature, has 18 carbons in its chain (Institute of Shortening and Edible Oils, Inc., 1982).

A characteristic with even more far-reaching significance than chain length is the *degree of saturation.* Saturation refers to the number of hydrogen atoms attached to the carbons in the fatty acid skeletons. If the fatty acid chain can accommodate more hydrogen than it currently does, the fatty acid is said to be unsaturated, and the unsaturated carbons will be connected by double bonds. Figure 7.2 illustrates that a fatty acid with no double bonds between carbons is a *saturated fatty acid* (SFA); a fatty acid with one double bond is a *monounsaturated fatty acid (MUFA);* and a fatty acid with two or more double bonds is a *polyunsaturated fatty acid (PUFA).*

saturation—the degree to which hydrogen atoms fill all available positions along the fatty acid skeleton; a saturated fatty acid is holding as many hydrogens as it has room for, whereas an unsaturated fatty acid is not

Triglycerides containing mostly SFAs are usually solid at room temperature, and are generally found in animal products, such as beef fat and butter. Triglycerides containing mostly PUFAs are usually liquid at room temperature, and are generally found in plant products, such as cottonseed oil and corn oil. Notable exceptions to this generalization are that coconut

Figure 7.2 Fatty acids of varying degrees of saturation. (a) A saturated fatty acid (SFA), in which the structure is filled with as much hydrogen as it can hold. (b) A monounsaturated fatty acid (MUFA), in which there is one double bond between carbons that could accommodate more hydrogen. (c) A polyunsaturated fatty acid (PUFA), which is characterized by two or more double bonds between carbons that could accommodate hydrogen. This particular PUFA is the essential fatty acid linoleic acid, which has two double bonds between carbons.

(a)

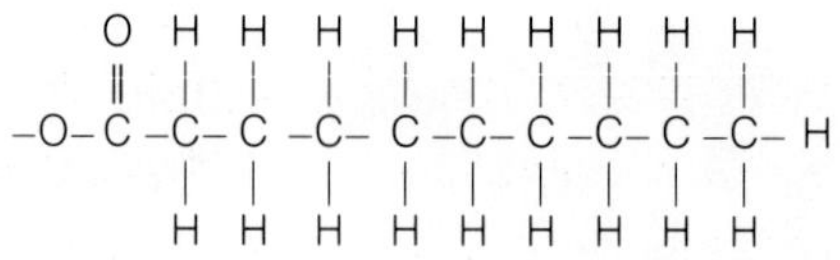

(b) Double bond

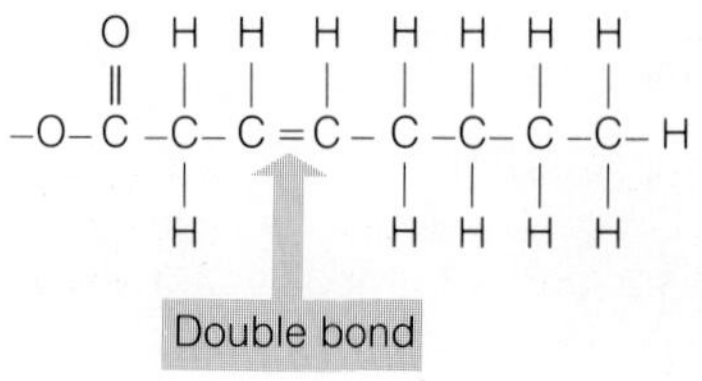

(c) Double bonds

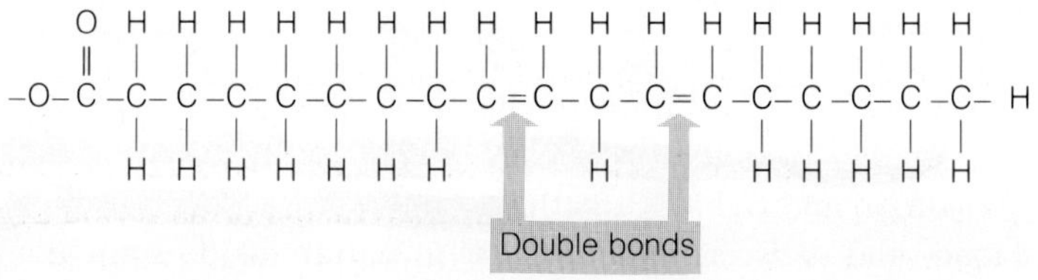

and palm oils, which are plant oils commonly used in processed foods, contain a high proportion of SFAs. Another exception is fish oils, which might be expected to contain primarily SFAs, but, in fact, contain many PUFAs. Table 7.1 summarizes the differences between plant and animal triglycerides.

Phospholipids in Nature

phospholipids—compounds similar to triglycerides, but having a phosphorus-containing unit in place of one of the fatty acids

lecithins—type of phospholipid that mixes well with both watery and oily substances

Phospholipids are compounds that resemble triglycerides except that a phosphorus-containing unit is substituted for one of the fatty acids. Lecithins, a common and important group of phospholipids found in cell membranes, have the biologically useful characteristic that they mix well with both watery and oily substances, which is an unusual trait that a few types of lipids have. This property classifies them as emulsifiers.

Sterols in Nature

sterols—class of lipids often found in hormones and vitamin precursors

cholesterol—important sterol that is both produced by the body and ingested in certain foods of animal origin

Sterols are unlike other lipids in the organization of their carbon, hydrogen, and oxygen components. Nonetheless, they qualify as lipids because of their physical insolubility in water and solubility in ether.

Undoubtedly the most well known sterol is cholesterol, a compound produced by animals, including humans. Cholesterol is found particularly in eggs and organ meats such as liver. Although cholesterol and saturated fats are both lipids typically found in animal products, they are distinctly different from each other. Other sterols in foods and in human skin are forerunners of vitamin D; they will be discussed in Chapter 12 (on vitamins).

Table 7.1   General Differences between the Triglycerides in Plants and Animals

	Degree of saturation	Physical state	Food examples
Plant triglycerides	Monounsaturated fatty acids or polyunsaturated fatty acids (Exception: coconut and palm oils have saturated fatty acids)	Liquid (oil) at room temperature	Oils of corn, peanut, olive, soybean, safflower, and so on Avocado
Animal triglycerides	Saturated fatty acids (Exception: many fish oils have unsaturated fatty acids)	Solid (fat) at room temperature (Exception: fish oils, milk fat)	Butter, cheese Meat fat

Lipids and Processing

Food science has developed ways to modify food fats, just as it has carbohydrates. For example, it is possible to separate fats and oils from their natural sources (such as butter and lard, and soybean, peanut, and safflower oils) so they can be used as ingredients or as frying agents. Food technology can also ensure the shelf life and appeal of fats and oils through techniques such as refining, bleaching, and deodorization.

Food science makes use of the properties of some of the naturally occurring lipids: mono- and diglycerides are good emulsifiers, for example, and are therefore used as additives to prevent the separation of watery and fatty fractions of products such as salad dressings, margarines, and baking batters. Lecithin can also serve that purpose.

Another application of food science to lipid modification is the hydrogenation of oils. This process forces hydrogen into oils with a high PUFA content, thereby increasing their degree of saturation and making them firmer. Hydrogenation can be controlled to be partial or complete. A whole range of margarines and shortenings on the market have been hydrogenated to varying degrees; you can judge the extent by how firm or soft they are. Figure 7.3 shows examples of lipids listed on food labels.

In addition to the lipids that technology has already made available, another product may become available in the future if current tests result in FDA approval. This is sucrose polyester, an indigestible compound of fat components and sucrose units. It looks, smells, and tastes like common dietary fats, but since it cannot be digested, it provides no kcalories (Research Sources Information Center, 1982).

hydrogenation—the forcing of hydrogen into unsaturated oils to make them firmer

The Amounts of Lipids in Different Foods Vary Considerably

Although you can sometimes see how much lipid is in a food by simply looking at it (such as the fat on meat, or butter on bread), fats are often hidden in food (such as shortening in pie crust or fat in avocado). Table

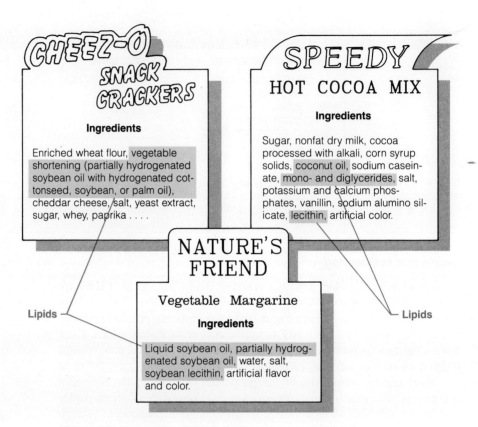

Figure 7.3 Examples of lipids in three processed foods.

7.2 compares the approximate amounts of lipids that are actually present in various foods and food groups—whether you can see them or not.

Glycerides

As found in nature, fruits, vegetables, and grains have little fat. However, fats are often added during the processing or home cooking of these items, and this can substantially raise the lipid level of a product. Look at what happens when potatoes are processed into potato chips, and notice the difference in lipid levels between bread and cake (Table 7.2).

The foods that are naturally higher in fat include some dairy products, many meats, and nuts. In the case of dairy products, food technology has developed ways of removing fat to provide some lower fat options: skimmed milk is almost devoid of fat, for example, as are products made from it, such as yogurt cultured from skim milk. Cheeses made partly from skimmed milk, such as mozarella, Parmesan, and low-fat cottage cheese, have less fat than their full-fat counterparts. You can discover the lipid levels of many other specific foods by checking Appendices E and F.

Table 7.2   Amounts of Lipids in Standard Servings of Various Foods

Grams of lipid

Grams of lipid	Fruits and vegetables	Grain products	Milk and milk products	Meats and alternates	Combination foods	Limited extras
35				Walnuts (2 oz)		
30				Peanuts roasted in oil (2 oz) / Dry roasted peanuts (2 oz)	Pecan pie ($\frac{1}{7}$ of pie)	
25						
20	Avocado ($\frac{1}{2}$)		Ice cream ($1\frac{1}{2}$ c) / Processed cheese (2 oz)		Chicken and noodles (1 c) / Chop suey with meat (1 c) / Fruit pie ($\frac{1}{7}$ of double crust pie)	Italian salad dressing (1 oz)
15	Potato chips (1 oz)	Fried snack foods (1 oz) / Frosted chocolate cake (2 oz) / Oatmeal cookies (3 small)	Cheddar Cheese ($1\frac{1}{3}$ oz) / Whole milk (1 c)	Bologna (2 oz) / Fried fish, chicken (2 oz) / Ham, ground beef (2 oz) / Eggs (2)		Cream cheese ($1\frac{1}{3}$ oz) / French salad dressing (1 oz) / Bacon (2 slices)
10						
5	Most plain fresh, frozen, canned fruits and vegetables ($\frac{1}{2}$ c)	Quick breads (1 slice) / Plain bread (1 slice) / Plain rice, pasta, most cereal ($\frac{1}{2}$ c)	2% milk (1 c) / Skim milk (1 c)	Broiled chicken, no skin (2 oz) / Cooked legumes (1 c)	Pizza ($\frac{1}{4}$ of 12″ cheese pie) / Vegetable beef soup (1 c)	Oil, butter, margarine, mayonnaise (1 t) / Sour cream (2 T)
0						

Cholesterol

Compared to glycerides, cholesterol occurs in only minute amounts in foods. An average serving of food may contain many *grams* of triglycerides, but it will contain only *milligrams* of cholesterol.

As we mentioned earlier, cholesterol is found only in products of animal origin. Table 7.3 compares the amounts of cholesterol in standard serving sizes of certain foods. Notice that there are not many concentrated sources of cholesterol: eggs and liver are the only commonly eaten foods that stand out.

Lipids Take Many Forms during Digestion, Absorption, and Transport

There are many different forms of lipids in the body. This is quite different from the situation with carbohydrates, in which dietary forms are mostly converted into glucose or glycogen. The various dietary forms of lipids are broken apart during digestion, but many are reformed into other lipid compounds before they leave the intestinal cells. All these lipid compounds can be converted into other lipids in the liver or as they circulate in the bloodstream.

In this section we narrow the focus to discuss how the body handles just two important types of dietary lipids: triglycerides (since they represent the overwhelming majority of lipids we consume) and cholesterol (because it is an important structural material and associated with heart disease).

Digestion of Triglycerides and Cholesterol Compounds

Dietary lipids must be broken into particles small enough to be absorbed by the cells of the small intestine. When triglycerides are consumed, the first digestive enzymes they encounter are in the stomach. The vast majority of lipid digestion, though, takes place in the small intestine. Two types of substances found there—bile and lipases—play vital roles in preparing lipids for absorption.

bile—substance produced by the liver that emulsifies glycerides in the small intestine

Bile is a liquid synthesized in the liver. It contains cholesterol, lecithin, and *bile salts* (various sterols). The bile salts divide large drops of triglycerides into smaller droplets, making them more available to digestive enzymes.

lipases—enzymes that digest lipids

Lipases, the enzymes that digest lipids, are produced primarily in the pancreas but also in the small intestine (Guyton, 1981). They break down triglycerides into monoglycerides, glycerol, and fatty acids. These substances are then incorporated along with bile salts into conglomerations called micelles. Micelles ferry the lipid fragments into direct contact with the intestinal cell membrane. There, they release the lipid fragments for absorption into the intestinal wall cells, after which most of the remaining components are recycled to continue the process.

micelles—aggregates of glyceride components and bile salts, designed to transport lipid fragments into direct contact with intestinal wall cells

Table 7.3   Cholesterol in Some Foods

Food	Household measure	Cholesterol (mg) 0 100 200 300 400 500
Fruits and vegetables		
All types	$\frac{1}{2}$ c	
Grain Products		
Bread, plain	1 slice	
Cake	1 piece	X
Cereal, pasta, grains	$\frac{1}{2}$ c	
Egg noodles	$\frac{1}{2}$ c	XX
Milk and milk products		
Milk, whole	1 c	X
Milk, 2%	1 c	X
Milk, skimmed	1 c	
Cheese, Cheddar	$1\frac{1}{3}$ oz	XX
Ice cream	$1\frac{1}{2}$ c	XXXXX
Meats and alternates		
Beef, lean cuts	3 oz	XX
Beef, fatty cuts	3 oz	XXX
Chicken, not fried	3 oz	XX
Fish, not fried	3 oz	XX
Eggs	2 medium	XXXXXXXXXXXXXXXXXXXXXXXX
Legumes, nuts	$\frac{1}{2}$ c	
Liver, calves'	3 oz	XXXXXXXXXXXXXXX
Limited extras		
Alcoholic beverages	1 serving	
Butter	1 T	X
Cream cheese	$1\frac{1}{3}$ oz	XX
Mayonnaise	1 T	
Vegetable oils	1 T	

The Xs on the right of this chart show how much cholesterol is found in standard servings of some foods. Each X represents 25 mg of cholesterol.

Data sources: (1) Pennington, J.A.T., and H.N. Church. 1980 *Food values of portions commonly used*. Philadelphia: J.B. Lippincott Company. (2) Weihrauch, J. L. 1984. *Provisional table on the fatty acid and cholesterol content of selected foods*. Washington, DC: Data Research Branch, Consumer Nutrition Division, United States Department of Agriculture.

Table 7.4	Summary of Phases of Digestion of Two Types of Lipids	
	Triglycerides	Cholesterol compounds
Mouth	—	—
Stomach	Very small amount of enzymatic hydrolysis	—
Small intestine	Enzymatic hydrolysis to glycerol, fatty acids, and monoglycerides by pancreatic and intestinal enzymes; ferrying by micelles to intestinal wall cells; absorption aided by bile salts	Enzymatic hydrolysis to pure cholesterol and associated compounds; ferrying by micelles to intestinal wall cells; absorption aided by bile salts
Large intestine	—	—

Normally, this system works very effectively; if there is an abundance of bile salts present, 97% of all fats are usually absorbed by a healthy small intestine (Guyton, 1981).

Cholesterol in food is often found with a fatty acid attached to it. The fatty acid must be removed for cholesterol to be absorbed; this is accomplished by enzymes in the small intestine. Cholesterol is best absorbed when micelles are available to ferry it to the intestinal wall cells. On the average, only about 50% of dietary cholesterol is absorbed (National Dairy Council, 1979b).

Table 7.4 summarizes the phases of digestion of these two lipids.

Preparation for Transport

It is not enough that lipids *get into* the body; they must also be able to *move around* in the watery media of the bloodstream and the lymphatic system. Short- and medium-chain fatty acids and glycerol are water-soluble as they are; they are absorbed from the intestinal wall cells into the bloodstream, and move to the liver via the portal vein. But long-chain fatty acids, cholesterol, and phospholipids are insoluble in water; they must be put into a water-soluble form, or they would clump together and possibly clog up the vessels. The body accomplishes this by forming conglomerations of fatty acids, phospholipids, and cholesterol, and encasing them in a surface coat that includes protein. The resulting soluble compounds are called lipoproteins (Figure 7.4).

The principal type of lipoprotein formed in the intestinal wall cell is the chylomicron. Chylomicrons move from the intestinal wall cells into the lacteals of the lymphatic system, which eventually joins the bloodstream (see Figure 3.8).

lipoproteins—water-soluble aggregates of fatty acids, phospholipids, cholesterol, and protein, that are able to be transported in the bloodstream

chylomicron—principal type of lipoprotein formed in the intestinal wall cells

Formation of Lipoproteins in the Liver and Bloodstream

The liver serves as the metabolic clearinghouse for many lipids. After the various end-products of fat digestion and chylomicrons from the intestinal cells pass through the liver or interact in the bloodstream, they are subject to reorganization once again. At this time they are converted into still other lipoproteins.

A blood test reveals the entire variety of lipoproteins produced at various locations in your body. For example, even those produced in the intestine from recently eaten fats will be found in the blood because lipoproteins circulate for a time before they are reprocessed.

The various lipoproteins in the bloodstream are differentiated by the varying amounts of triglyceride, phospholipid, cholesterol, and protein that make up their molecules. On an equal volume basis, lipids weigh less than water and proteins because they are less dense. The relative amounts of these substances in a lipoprotein determine its overall density, which is the factor that led to the naming scheme for lipoproteins. The major lipoproteins in the blood, and their major components (Kritchevsky and Czarnecki, 1980; and Nishida, 1982), are:

chylomicrons—approximately 85% triglyceride by weight

very low density lipoprotein (VLDL)—approximately 50% triglyceride

low density lipoprotein (LDL)—more cholesterol than any other lipoprotein

high density lipoprotein (HDL)—some cholesterol, very little triglyceride, and more protein than any other lipoprotein

The level of chylomicrons (and therefore of triglycerides) in the blood varies considerably from one time of day to another, since their production closely follows the intestinal absorption of lipids. On the other hand, LDL and HDL (and therefore blood cholesterol) remain much more constant throughout the day and even from one day to the next.

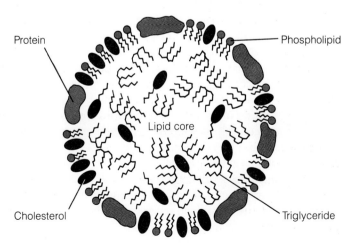

Protein

Phospholipid

Lipid core

Cholesterol

Triglyceride

Figure 7.4 General structure of lipoproteins.

The amount of cholesterol in the blood remains quite stable because the body makes up for variations in the diet by producing cholesterol in the liver, and in the small intestine to a lesser extent. In general, if much cholesterol has been absorbed from food sources, the body produces less; if the diet contains only low levels, the body produces more (Nishida, 1982). On the average, a person's body produces about 700 mg of cholesterol per day, compared to the approximately 225 mg it absorbs from the diet (McNamara, 1982).

The body can produce cholesterol from fragments of any of the energy nutrients, thereby ensuring that your system will never be in short supply. The liver incorporates this cholesterol into lipoproteins also, so cholesterol from both sources is able to circulate in the blood. (Since the body has a mechanism for regulating the blood cholesterol level, it may seem surprising that some people find themselves with an excess of it. We will return to this topic later.)

The liver also plays a central role in converting excess carbohydrate, protein, and alcohol into triglycerides. These are then processed into lipoproteins in the same way that the products of fat digestion are.

Lipids Concentrate in Specific Kinds of Body Substances

Fat droplet — Nucleus

Cell membrane

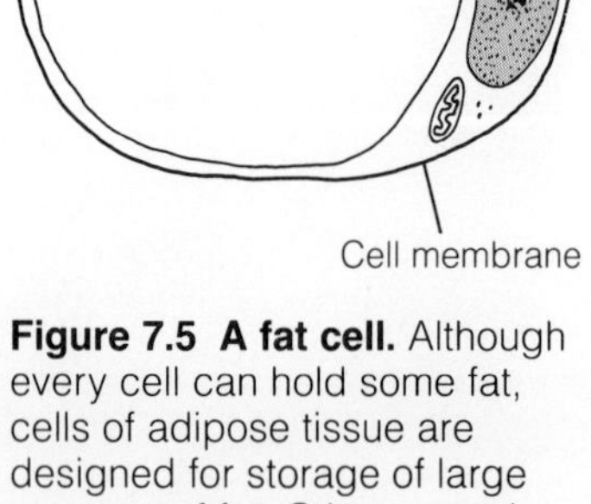

Figure 7.5 A fat cell. Although every cell can hold some fat, cells of adipose tissue are designed for storage of large amounts of fat. Other normal cell components—the nucleus and other bodies—are compressed into a small portion of the fat cell.

Thus far we have dealt with how lipids get into the body or are produced by it, and how they then become equipped to move through the bloodstream. At any one time, the amount of lipid present in the blood is quite small compared to the total amount you have elsewhere in your body. For example, several hours after a meal you probably have fewer than 10 grams of triglyceride in the lipoproteins circulating in your blood, but may have over 10,000 grams of triglyceride in your adipose tissue.

In this section we focus on where lipids go when they leave the bloodstream, which cells they move into, and what they do once they get there.

In order for lipids to be taken into body cells, they need to be freed from their protein wrappings and broken into smaller units; an enzyme produced in blood vessel capillaries does this. Different types of lipids tend to concentrate in particular structures. We will start by discussing where triglycerides go, since they represent approximately 95% of the lipids in the human body.

Triglycerides

Some triglycerides, after they are freed from chylomicrons or VLDL, make their way into actively metabolizing cells for energy production. Triglycerides that are used for energy are used up, of course, in the process. The remaining triglycerides enter cells for storage. Although all cells can store some, the specialized cells of adipose tissue take in most of them. Figure 7.5 shows an adipose tissue cell bulging with its stored triglyceride; compare it with Figure 3.4, which represents cells not specifically designed for fat storage.

Stored fat constitutes approximately 15% of an average adult male's body weight, and 20% to 25% of a female's, but these percentages vary considerably from person to person depending on kcalorie intakes and outputs.

Where the adipose tissue forms on the body is also subject to individual variation. It relates partly to what sex you are: males tend to collect more abdominal fat, whereas females usually collect more on hips, buttocks, and thighs. Further, every individual has an inherited predisposition to accumulate adipose tissue in particular body regions.

If conditions change and the body needs to mobilize some of this stored fat for energy use, it can easily do so; the fat cells give up some of their triglyceride, shrinking themselves in the process, but never completely disappearing.

Phospholipids

Phospholipids are principally found in cell membranes. There they serve the extremely important function, along with the proteins and cholesterol in the membranes, of controlling what comes into and goes out of the cells.

Choline, a component of the phospholipid lecithin, has come into the limelight in recent years. Choline is a precursor (early form) of a neurotransmitter—a chemical substance that is released from a nerve cell when it fires, conveying the nerve impulse to another cell (Wurtman, 1982). Acetylcholine, the neurotransmitter of which choline is a part, plays a role in memory performance. Further, it has been found that increasing the intake of lecithin increases the formation of acetylcholine. This has led to the hypothesis that increasing lecithin intake might improve memory. Logical as this seems, in a double-blind study of normal adults who took lecithin or a placebo, subjects did not perform better on memory tests even when the lecithin raised their acetylcholine levels to almost double normal levels (Harris et al., 1983).

However, research is currently being conducted to see whether people with disease conditions that include memory loss might benefit from increased lecithin intake.

choline—component of the phospholipid lecithin

neurotransmitter—chemical substance that conveys a nerve impulse from one cell to another

acetylcholine—neurotransmitter that plays a role in memory; choline is a precursor of this substance

Cholesterol

Cholesterol metabolism has been a subject of intensive research for several decades. Even so, there is still much to learn, and there are areas of disagreement to be settled.

At any given time, less than 20% of the cholesterol in the body is located in the bloodstream; there it is carried primarily in the lipoproteins LDL and HDL, with LDL accounting for 65% of the total amount found in the blood (National Dairy Council, 1979b). How cholesterol is handled by the body may depend largely on which of the two lipoproteins it is part of.

HDL cholesterol, it is hypothesized, is predestined for removal from

Frontier

Frontier

the blood. HDL circulates in the body for a time, picking up additional cholesterol as it travels. Eventually, HDL arrives at the liver, where its cholesterol is incorporated into bile and thus removed from the bloodstream (Nishida, 1982). (Bile, you remember, is excreted into the small intestine to aid in fat digestion. After digestion has occurred, some of the bile is excreted with the feces, but most of it is reabsorbed. The cholesterol in the reabsorbed bile does not tend to return to the blood: it remains in the bile, alternately being secreted and reabsorbed.) By far the most abundant use of cholesterol in the body is to become part of bile (Guyton, 1981).

LDL cholesterol, however, is thought to be more likely to remain in the blood and/or body tissues. LDL circulates throughout the body, making its cholesterol available as a building material for cell membranes, hormones, or nerve coverings. Some LDL may also go to the liver to become part of bile (National Dairy Council, 1979b).

It is thought that another stopping place for LDL cholesterol may be the linings of blood vessels, where it can cause harm. This brings us to a discussion of the relationship between lipids and health problems.

Lipids Are Involved in Major Health Problems

So far we have been concerned with how food lipids are digested and rebuilt into body lipids, and why they are important to the body's healthy functioning. By its nature this discussion has emphasized the positive aspects of lipids. Now, though, it is time to take a look at the other side of lipids—at the health problems they may cause.

Overweight

Here we must reiterate what was said in the carbohydrate chapter about overweight: it results from surplus kcalories from *any* source. Admittedly, however, it is relatively easy to overconsume kcalories on a diet that is high in lipids because lipids are so concentrated in energy. From this perspective, it is reasonable to say that a high intake of lipids may result in overweight.

Atherosclerosis and Coronary Heart Disease (CHD)

atherosclerosis—disease in which certain materials gradually accumulate in the lining of blood vessels, interfering with their function

Atherosclerosis is the major disease affecting the blood vessels. Blood vessel diseases account for more deaths in the United States and other developed countries than any other cause. Although the number of such deaths has been declining steadily in the United States, these diseases still account for approximately half the deaths in this country each year (Harper, 1983).

Atherosclerosis develops slowly, probably over a period of several decades. A variety of evidence suggests that dietary lipids may play a role in the development of atherosclerosis. Before these factors are discussed, however, it will be useful for you to be familiar with the following background and definitions of terms.

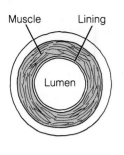
Muscle   Lining
Lumen

Normal

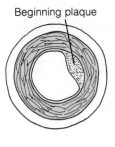
Beginning plaque

Early injury

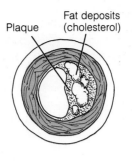
Plaque   Fat deposits (cholesterol)

Atherosclerosis

Figure 7.6 The likely sequence of events in the development of athero-sclerosis. This figure shows a cross-section of an artery.

A Theory about the Origin of Atherosclerosis. Although atherosclerosis has been the subject of thousands of studies of various kinds, *there is currently no absolute proof as to what causes it.* A widely accepted theory proposes that a minor injury to a blood vessel lining (such as could be caused by high blood pressure) prompts certain blood cells, cholesterol, and other substances in the blood to attach to the injured site, which in turn causes the blood vessel to produce more cells to cover over the area. As the process continues, the newly formed material, which is called *plaque,* progressively narrows the opening (lumen) of the blood vessel and causes it to lose its flexibility in that area (Figure 7.6).

Two possible consequences of plaque buildup in blood vessels are that a narrowed vessel could become completely closed, or that a rise in blood pressure could become severe enough to cause a vessel to rupture. Either occurrence interrupts the delivery of oxygen and nutrients to the body cells that had been served by the injured vessels, and those cells die. If the group of cells that die is very important and/or very extensive, the person dies. With less damage, varying degrees of recovery are possible.

Two areas of the body in which the effects of atherosclerosis are most obvious are the brain and the heart. After the blood vessels to these regions have been narrowed considerably, they may not be able deliver enough blood to those areas and pain may result. A greater danger is that a clot or muscular spasm will completely close the narrowed lumen, denying nourishment to the cells beyond it; if circulation is not restored within a couple of hours those cells will die.

If atherosclerosis interrupts blood flow in the brain, a stroke or cerebrovascular accident **(CVA)** occurs. If atherosclerosis causes interference with blood flow to the heart muscle, the result is called a heart attack, myocardial infarction (MI), or coronary occlusion.

Although both heart attacks and strokes can result in death, they are not always fatal; determining factors are how extensive the damage is, how promptly the person receives care, and what the quality of the care is.

The process of the development of this disease in all of the body's blood vessels, including those of the heart, is called cardiovascular (CV) disease; when it occurs in the heart, it is usually called coronary heart disease (CHD). Here we will look mainly at what is known about CHD,

stroke, cerebrovascular accident—result of interruption of blood flow to the brain

heart attack, myocardial infarction, coronary occlusion—result of interruption of blood flow to the heart

cardiovascular disease—gradual impairment of the body's blood vessel function; coronary heart disease (CHD) refers specifically to impairment of the heart's blood vessels

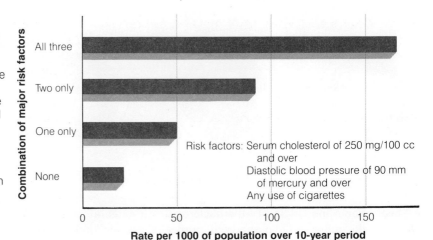

Figure 7.7 The effect of three major risk factors on the incidence of heart attacks in white American males. When the data from many studies were assembled in the National Cooperative Pooling Project, the impact of having one, two, or all three of the risk factors was evaluated. Each additional risk factor almost doubled the risk. (Adapted from Farrand, M.E., and L. Mojonnier. 1980. Nutrition in the multiple risk factor intervention trial (MRFIT). *Journal of the American Dietetic Association* 76:347–351.) Diastolic blood pressure is the lower number in a blood pressure value, such as 125/72. The 72 indicates the pressure in the arteries when the heart is relaxing. The upper number is the systolic pressure, the pressure in arteries when the heart is contracting.

risk factors—characteristics associated with an increased chance of developing a given health problem

since it is a common type of atherosclerosis, and much research has been done on it.

Risk Factors for CHD. Although we are not certain of the cause(s) of CHD, epidemiological and animal studies have shown that it occurs with greater frequency in association with certain characteristics called risk factors. Almost 40 risk factors have been identified (Ernst and Levy, 1980).

Data from many large studies have shown some risk factors have higher correlations with CHD than others (Kannel, 1978). Some of the high risk factors cannot be changed: being male, growing older, and having a family history of atherosclerosis are *uncontrollable factors*. Certain *clinical measurements* also indicate risk; these include high blood pressure, high blood cholesterol, abnormal electrocardiogram (test of electrical activity of the heart), and the presence of diabetes. In addition, particular *living habits* correlate with risk, such as smoking, consuming too many kcalories and/or fats, being physically inactive, and taking oral contraceptives. Of all of these, blood cholesterol in excess of 250 mg per 100 ml of blood, high blood pressure, and smoking emerge as the major risk factors (Farrand and Mojonnier, 1980).

Figure 7.7 shows how these three factors affected the occurrence of first heart attacks during a ten-year period in middle-aged white American males, a population segment prone to CHD.

Several important points are made by this figure: (1) the more of these risk factors the men had, the more likely they were to have a heart attack; (2) even if they had none of these three risk factors, 20 out of 1000 had heart attacks anyway; and (3) even if they had *all* three of these risk factors, 830 out of 1000 did *not* have heart attacks. It is obvious that although these factors are influential, they do not explain all occurrences of heart disease.

Studies of some groups of vegetarians in our population also suggest that these three factors are not the only ones involved. Although many groups of vegetarians have lower-than-average blood cholesterol levels, lower blood pressure (Dwyer, 1979), and do not smoke, nonetheless *some* vegetarians still develop CHD. For example, heart disease causes death among some Seventh Day Adventist vegetarians—but their incidence of death from CHD is only one-quarter to one-half that of age-matched groups in the general population (American Dietetic Association, 1980a).

Blood Cholesterol As a Risk Factor for CHD. Blood cholesterol is a more complicated risk factor than just indicated. Remember that cholesterol is carried in the blood in lipoproteins of various densities. Since LDL cholesterol tends to accumulate in the body and may become part of atherosclerotic plaque, and HDL cholesterol is taken out of circulation for use in bile, the relative amounts of these different lipoproteins in the blood influence risk. A person is at greater risk if LDL is high and HDL is low. If you are having a blood test done to determine your risk of CHD, you will get more useful information from an HDL/LDL test than from a test for total cholesterol.

However, most large studies that have correlated blood cholesterol levels with incidence of CHD, or blood cholesterol with diet, have measured total cholesterol values instead (Figure 7.8). (Such studies are faster and less expensive to do.) For now, we do not have more detailed data to work with; more studies will be done in the future that evaluate for HDL and LDL.

Lowering Blood Cholesterol through Dietary Change. Much research has been done to determine how diet influences blood cholesterol. In 1979, a panel of experts was assembled by the American Society for Clinical Nutrition to evaluate data from epidemiological, human, and animal CHD research. Their charge was to see what could legitimately be said about how various aspects of diet influence risk factors and incidence of CHD. After extensive review of the literature, they made these statements about ways to lower blood cholesterol by controlling lipids in the diet:

- ■ Reduce total fat in the diet   (Known to lower blood cholesterol. Believed to be safe.) The expert panel saw this approach as reasonable, based largely on extensive epidemiological data that showed less CHD in populations that eat lower levels of fat (Glueck, 1979).

- ■ Reduce saturated fat in the diet   (Known to lower blood cholesterol. Believed to be safe.) Since human studies have shown saturated fat to have a cholesterol-raising effect, limiting the consumption of saturated fat should help prevent a blood cholesterol rise. Similar conclusions can be drawn from epidemiological data, so the expert panel approved of this approach.

- ■ Reduce cholesterol in the diet   (Thought to have slight, if any, effect in lowering blood cholesterol. Believed to be safe.) Only some of the studies done with people consuming low cholesterol diets show a blood cholesterol-lowering effect; however, populations that normally consume low cholesterol diets in conjunction with low fat diets have lower blood cholesterol levels (McGill, 1979).

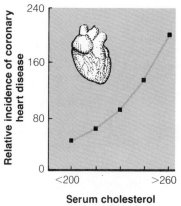

Figure 7.8 The relationship between blood cholesterol level and risk of coronary heart disease. High levels of serum cholesterol correlate with a higher incidence of CHD. These data were compiled by researcher Ancel Keys from three major studies on white American males. (Adapted from Glueck, C.J., and W.E. Connor. 1978. Diet–coronary heart disease relationships reconnoitered. ©*American Journal of Clinical Nutrition* 31:727–737. American Society for clinical Nutrition.)

- Increase polyunsaturated fatty acids in the diet (Known to lower blood cholesterol. Not known to be safe.) Although research with human subjects has demonstrated the cholesterol-depressant effect of PUFAs (Hegsted et al., 1965), there are no data to demonstrate that this diet is healthy over time. An experiment of several years' duration showed a lowering of blood cholesterol and a decrease in new heart disease, but little change in overall mortality (Turpeinen, 1979). Questions have been raised as to whether a high PUFA intake may correlate with a higher incidence of cancer (Glueck, 1979).

The extent to which these techniques have been found to lower blood cholesterol is extremely variable. One investigator points out that of the studies he reviewed, the greatest decrease in blood cholesterol that was achieved was 16% (Olson, 1979). Most often, the decrease is less than that, and may even be nothing at all in some people. The response seems to depend on genetic limitations, age, weight fluctuation, and the nature and aggressiveness of the measures used. In some people, losing surplus body fat may be the most effective means of all for reducing an elevated blood cholesterol. In summary, a modified diet should not be expected to deliver more than it can, but its possible helpfulness shouldn't be ignored, either.

Does Lowering Risk Factors Reduce the Incidence of CHD?

Intervention studies have been conducted to try to determine whether lowering CHD risk factors actually lowers the incidence of CHD. A number of large human studies have shown intervention to be helpful; others have shown that it is not.

Most of these studies used several interventions simultaneously. A serious limitation of such studies is that it is difficult to tell which lowered risk factor was most closely associated with the reduction of CHD. For example, a five year study done in Oslo, Norway, demonstrated a 47% lower incidence of heart attacks among men who changed their diet to reduce blood cholesterol, and also decreased or quit smoking (Hjermann et al., 1981). Which change was associated with how much benefit?

Another study, the Multiple Risk Factor Intervention Trial (MRFIT), collected data in many regions of the country on thousands of middle-aged men who were at high risk for heart disease. One group of patients was treated by their regular community physicians using standard treatment. The other category received more intensive interventions from specialists who counseled them on smoking less and making dietary changes to lower serum cholesterol, and prescribed medication for their high blood pressure. Over an average follow-up period of seven years, risk factors declined in both groups, but more markedly in the specially treated group. Oddly enough, the difference between the death rates of the two groups was not statistically significant (MRFIT, 1982). (It has been suggested, though not proved, that the blood pressure medication taken by the special group may have had some adverse effects.)

Finally, the Lipid Research Clinics of the National Institutes of Health conducted a seven-year study involving middle-aged men with high blood cholesterol. One group followed a cholesterol-lowering diet. The other group used the diet plus a cholesterol-lowering drug. Patients who had been using the drug experienced a substantial lowering of blood cholesterol, heart attacks, and disease deaths, but those who used the diet alone experienced little change (Lipid Research Clinics Program, 1984). Although this was heralded as proof that lowering blood cholesterol lowers risk, some scientists point out that it demonstrates effectiveness of the drug rather than the diet.

Recommending Diet Changes. Nutrition and health experts are divided about who should be encouraged to make dietary changes in an attempt to avoid or delay CHD. The experts are likely to fall into one of two groups.

One group believes that the entire population should make dietary changes without delay. Health agencies and professional societies in many countries have already made risk-lowering recommendations to their populations. In the United States, the American Heart Association and some other organizations suggest limiting fat intake to 30–35% of kcalories, reducing saturated fat intake, and limiting dietary cholesterol to 300 mg/day.

The second group believes we should wait for conclusive evidence that specific dietary changes do cause reductions in CHD before recommending such changes to the general population. Scientists who hold this point of view are generally skeptical about the relationship between diet and CHD; they feel the intense focus on dietary causes may distract scientists from studying other factors that might prove even more important (Harper, 1983). Nonetheless, most believe we should identify and treat high-risk individuals. (Approximately one-fourth of American adults have blood cholesterol above the high-risk level of 250 mg per 100 ml of blood.) The American Medical Association has adopted this point of view, although its Council on Scientific Affairs subsequently suggested that "consideration should be given to extending the dietary recommendations to the patient's entire family," since one person at risk in a family means there are likely to be others (1983).

Therefore, if you want to follow the advice of world experts on this matter, you are in a tough spot, since even the experts can't agree. However, you now have an overview of the factors apparently associated with CHD; if you need help in determining what your own risk factors are, a physician can assist. You also have information about the dietary factors that help lower the risk factors—and their limitations.

Cancer

Cancer accounts for the second largest number of deaths per year in the United States. Statistical projections suggest that one person out of four will develop cancer during his or her lifetime, and one in eight or ten will die of the disease. As with atherosclerosis, a great deal of evidence links cancer with dietary lipids.

Many experts believe that cancer is over 100 separate diseases that afflict different body organs by different mechanisms. The most common sites affected are the lungs, colon, breast, pancreas, prostate, stomach, and blood (Visek and Milner, 1982).

Cancer occurs when normal body cells, whose growth and division

cancer—general term for what are probably many diseases, all characterized by uncontrolled cell growth

are carefully regulated in healthy individuals, undergo changes that allow them to ignore the usual control signals. If the body's processes for recognizing and destroying such cells are not functioning normally, the abnormal cells can compete with healthy ones for oxygen and nutrients, and eventually spread throughout the body if conditions present encourage their growth. This process, like atherosclerosis, often takes place over a period of several decades (although there are exceptions).

carcinogens—environmental factors thought to influence the development of cancer

Lack of Proof Regarding Causes. Although there seems to be a genetic aspect to cancer development, epidemiological data suggest that most human cancers are influenced by one or more environmental factors called carcinogens (Alfin-Slater and Aftergood, 1981). Figure 7.9 indicates the percentage of male and female cancers that have been attributed to specific environmental factors including diet. Note that diet is suspected to be involved in about 60% of cancers in females, and about 40% of cancers in males (Wynder and Gori, 1977). Lipids are thought to be among the dietary substances that may encourage the growth of cancers.

Total Dietary Lipids As a Risk Factor for Cancer. According to the comprehensive report of the National Academy of Sciences' Committee on Diet, Nutrition, and Cancer, lipids seem to be more closely associated with the development of cancer than any other dietary constituent (1982); however, opinion is divided on this point (Pariza, 1984; Willett and MacMahon, 1984).

Several kinds of data support the hypothesis that lipids are associated with cancer. Epidemiological data from many countries show a strong positive correlation between the average daily dietary fat intake of a population, and the incidence of cancer of the breast, colon, and prostate (National Academy of Science. Committee on Diet, Nutrition, and Cancer, 1982). Figure 7.10 shows the relationship between daily fat intake and

Figure 7.9 The proportion of cancers in males and females in the United States attributable to specific environmental factors. (Adapted from Wynder, E.L., and G.B. Gori. 1977. Contribution of the environment to cancer incidence: An epidemiologic exercise. *Journal of the National Cancer Institute* 58:825–832.)

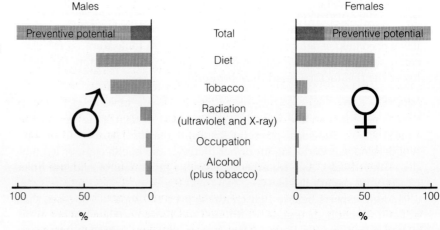

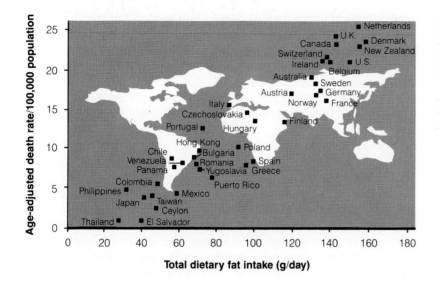

Figure 7.10 Dietary fat per capita consumption correlated with deaths due to breast cancer in different countries. (Adapted from Carroll, K.K. 1975. Experimental evidence of dietary factors and hormone-dependent cancers. *Cancer Research* 3:3374–3383.)

incidence of death due to breast cancer when data from various countries are compared.

The data become more convincing when you note what happens to people who leave their homeland and its diet, and adopt a new country and its diet; in a generation or two, the incidence of cancer among those people resembles that of the adopted country rather than that of the homeland (Willett and MacMahon, 1984).

Certain vegetarian groups have been found to have considerably lower rates of cancer than the general population. Although it may be tempting to attribute this finding to the fact that vegetarian diets are often lower in fat, other aspects of diet and lifestyle could influence the incidence of cancer in these population groups. For example, Seventh Day Adventists, approximately 50% of whom avoid meat, experience lower rates of cancer. However, they generally do not smoke or consume alcohol either, which could also be expected to lessen their incidence of certain types of cancer. Nonetheless, mortality rates among Seventh Day Adventists are only 50–70% of the general population rates for sites *other* than those related to smoking and drinking. They are also lower for sites *unrelated to fat consumption* (American Dietetic Association, 1980a; National Dairy Council, 1979a). More research is obviously needed to explain the reasons —which are likely to be multifactorial—for the impressively lower rates of cancer among Seventh Day Adventists.

Animal tests strengthen the relationship between dietary fat and cancer (National Academy of Science, Committee on Diet, Nutrition, and Cancer, 1982). Animals fed a high-fat diet develop more tumors than those fed very low-fat diets. This effect may be partially due to the fact that a low-fat diet is usually a low-kcalorie diet, which is known to discourage cancer growth in animals.

Specific Kinds of Lipids As Risk Factors for Cancer. Attempts have been made to see whether one type of fat is more closely associated with cancer than another. In general, the association between total fat and cancer is stronger than the association between any specific type of lipid and cancer (Cheney and Worthington-Roberts, 1981).

Epidemiological data suggest that of the various types of lipids, saturated fats have the strongest association with cancer. Polyunsaturated fat seems only weakly associated (Cheney and Worthington-Roberts, 1981). However, animal studies tend to show the opposite: that PUFAs are more closely associated with cancer than SFAs are. Much more needs to be learned about this topic.

A suggestion has also been made that hydrogenated fatty acids may be related to cancer, especially of the breast (Willett and MacMahon, 1984). The structures of fatty acids produced during hydrogenation are slightly different from those usually found in nature. It has been suggested that when these different structures are incorporated into cell membranes, the body's defenses against cancer may be lowered, and may eventually give way to cancer. Future research will be directed at answering this question.

Finally, there seems to be a general lack of correlation between intake of dietary cholesterol and incidence of cancer (Cheney and Worthington-Roberts, 1981). That seems straightforward enough. However, the matter of blood cholesterol and cancer incidence may be a different matter: some studies have suggested that if blood cholesterol is low (less than 190 mg/100 ml), the statistical risk of cancer is increased. Thorough evaluation of several epidemiological studies now suggests, however, that blood cholesterol may have been low as a *result of* a growing cancer, rather than the low blood cholesterol being a *cause of* cancer (Levy, 1982).

Guidelines for Reducing the Risk of Cancer through Diet. The Committee on Diet, Nutrition, and Cancer issued interim guidelines for reducing cancer risks through diet in June, 1982. Their first recommendations concerned lipids: eat less fat, both saturated and unsaturated, so that it accounts for only about 30% of kcalories. (Other recommendations were to include fruits, vegetables, and whole grains; to minimize the consumption of foods that are salt-cured, salt-pickled, or smoked; and to consume alcohol in moderation, if at all.)

As though in response to critics who say that not enough is known to make such recommendations, the committee stated: "It is not now possible, and may never be possible, to specify a diet that would protect everyone against all forms of cancer. Nevertheless, the committee believes that it is possible on the basis of current evidence to formulate interim dietary guidelines that are both consistent with good nutritional practices and likely to reduce the risk of cancer. These guidelines are meant to be applied in their entirety to obtain maximal benefit." The American Cancer Society and the American Institute for Cancer Research have also endorsed these guidelines.

With cancer, as with heart disease, consumers must decide which scientific arguments make the most sense to them, and whether their own diets put them at risk.

**Consumption of food energy,
protein, fat, and carbohydrate**

% of 1909-13 average

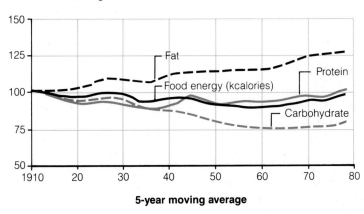

5-year moving average

Per capita civilian consumption

Figure 7.11 Trends in consumption of kcalories and the energy-yielding nutrients. This graph illustrates how intakes of kcalories, carbohydrates, fats, and proteins over the past seven decades compare with 1910 levels. Note that fat intakes have risen substantially, while overall carbohydrate consumption has decreasd markedly. (Reference: U.S. Department of Agriculture. 1981. *Food consumption, prices, and expenditures.* Statistical bulletin No. 656. Washington, DC: USDA Economics and Statistics Service.)

Assess Your Own Lipid Intake Compared with Recommendations

With the effects of lipids on health left unsettled, you may think it would be difficult to make any recommendations regarding fat intake. However, scientific organizations that are familiar with the literature on both lipid needs and risks have made recommendations in these two areas—needs for essential fatty acid, and recommended limit for total fat.

For linoleic acid, the essential fatty acid, the recommended intake is 1–2% of kcalories (National Research Council, 1980). Since the USDA estimates that Americans get approximately 6% of their kcalories as linoleic acid, there is little risk of your developing essential fatty acid deficiency.

You are more likely to be concerned about the total amount of fat in your diet. In the United States, the typical consumption of fat accounts for approximately 40% of total kcalories (Science and Education Administration, 1980). However, the RDA committee recommends limiting fat to 35% of energy, especially if energy intake is below 2000 kcalories. (This allows for obtaining the other needed nutrients.) This intake is also appropriate for the athlete (American Dietetic Association, 1980b). A joint committee of the U.N. Food and Agriculture Organization (FAO) and the World Health Organization (WHO) suggests a 30–35% upper limit of kcalories from fat for people in developed countries. Such recommendations indicate the need for a reversal of the upward trend in fat consumption seen in the United States since the turn of the century (Figure 7.11). (In contrast, the FAO/WHO committee expresses concern about fat intake in the developing countries—that people in these countries should try to *increase* their intake to 15–20%!)

You can figure out what percentage of kcalories you consume as fat by following these steps given on the next page, using a form similar to the one shown in Figure 7.12.

Figure 7.12 Assessment of fat intake for one day.

Food	Amount	Energy (kcal)	Fat (grams)
Eggs, boiled	2	160	12
Bagel, enriched	1	165	1
Butter	1 tablespoon	100	12
2% milk, solids added	1 cup	125	5
Sandwich:			
Whole wheat bread	2 slices	120	2
Butter	1 tablespoon	100	12
Corned beef	3 ounces	185	10
Broccoli, cooked frozen	1 cup	50	1
Yogurt, plain lowfat with solids	1 cup	145	4
Apple	1	80	1
Swiss steak, from round	5 oz. lean	250	8
Green beans, cooked frozen	½ cup	18	tr
Orange	1	65	tr
Ice cream	1 cup	270	14
Cola	12 ounces	145	0
Totals		1978	82
Kcalories from fat (82×9)		738 kcalories	
% of kcalories from fat $(738 \div 1978)$		37%	

1. Record your food and beverage intake for a typical 24-hour period.

2. Using Appendices E and F, find values for energy and grams of fat for each item you listed, and record them in the appropriate columns.

3. Total both columns.

4. To find out how many kcalories of fat you consumed, multiply the grams of fat by 9 kcalories/gram.

5. Calculate the percentage of kcalories from fat by dividing fat kcalories by total kcalories, and multiply by 100.

How did you come out? Is your fat intake within the recommended 30–35%? Whatever it was, don't forget that a one-day record is not necessarily representative of your overall intake; keep records for several days if you want a better indication of your typical lipid intake.

Although it seems that the problems we have in relation to fat come from our overindulgence, we should not plan to cut fat out totally—perhaps just cut down on it. In fact, we should *not* try to totally eliminate fat from our diets: it performs many vital functions for us.

SUMMARY

■ Because of their chemical structure, **lipids** generally do not dissolve in water but do dissolve in such substances as ether. People think negatively about lipids but enjoy eating them, and evidence of these conflicting attitudes is everywhere.

■ Lipids have six important functions: (1) they provide the essential nutrient linoleic acid; (2) they carry fat-soluble vitamins into the body; (3) they provide energy, stored in compact form as adipose tissue; (4) they form body components such as cell membranes and some hormones; (5) they insulate the body in the form of subcutaneous fat; and (6) they are deposited in places where they can protect internal organs.

■ Glycerides are the most common forms of lipids, and consist of one, two, or three fatty acids attached to the 3-carbon compound glycerol. Triglycerides (having three fatty acids) account for about 90% of the weight of lipids in foods. Fatty acids vary in chain length and in their degree of saturation with hydrogen atoms: at room temperature, triglycerides containing long, saturated fatty acids are usually solid (fats), whereas those containing short or unsaturated fatty acids are usually liquid (oils).

■ Other lipids common in nature are phospholipids, such as the lecithins present in cell membranes, and sterols, such as cholesterol and the precursors of certain vitamins.

■ Food science has developed many ways of modifying food fats, such as separating fats and oils from their natural sources, and hydrogenating unsaturated fatty acids to make them firmer.

■ The amounts of lipids in different foods vary considerably, and are not always obvious on inspection. Food naturally higher in triglycerides are many dairy products, many meats, and nuts. Cholesterol occurs in variable amounts in food of animal origin, and is present in amounts much smaller than triglycerides. Cholesterol is also synthesized in your body.

■ Lipids take many forms during digestion, absorption, and transport. Triglycerides are broken down into their components by lipases and then, along with bile salts, incorporated into micelles and transported to the intestinal wall cells. Cholesterol also reaches intestinal cells by this route. Once in the cells, these non–water-soluble substances are packaged along with proteins into water-soluble lipoproteins, which can be carried readily in the bloodstream. Lipoproteins are also synthesized in the liver. There are four types of lipoproteins; chylomicrons, very low density lipoprotein (VLDL), low density lipoprotein (LDL), and high density lipoprotein (HDL).

■ Lipids concentrate in specific kinds of body substances. Triglycerides are either used immediately for energy or stored as body fat. Phospholipids are found mainly in cell membranes. The fate of cholesterol in the body is currently being studied intensively. Some cholesterol, especially that transported by HDL, is secreted in the bile; other cholesterol remains in the blood; and some remains in body cells, including the linings of blood vessels.

■ Lipids are involved or suspected of involvement in the development of several major health problems. Atherosclerosis is the major disease affecting the blood vessels and is one of the most common causes of death in North America. Although no clear proof of cause and effect is currently available, a variety of evidence suggests that dietary lipids play a role in its long-term development. Strokes and heart attacks, caused by interruptions of blood flow to the brain and heart, respectively, are serious consequences of atherosclerosis. Many risk factors have been studied intensively in an attempt to learn more about the cause and prevention of this disease. Cancer, a general term for many diseases characterized by uncontrolled cell growth, also may be influenced by dietary lipid consumption.

■ You can assess your own lipid intake using techniques you have already learned. You may wish to limit your fat intake to 30–35% of the kcalories you consume, if you are concerned about your weight or health.

REFERENCES

Alfin-Slater, R.B., and L. Aftergood. 1981. Nutrition and cancer. In *Controversies in nutrition*, ed. L. Ellenbogen. New York: Churchill Livingstone.

American Dietetic Association. 1980a. Position paper on the vegetarian approach to eating. *Journal of the American Dietetic Association* 77:61–69.

American Dietetic Association. 1980b. Nutrition and physical fitness. *Journal of the American Dietetic Association* 76:437–443.

American Medical Association Council on Scientific Affairs. 1983. Dietary and pharmacologic therapy for the lipid risk factors. *Journal of the American Medical Association* 250:1873–1879.

Carroll, K.K. 1975. Experimental evidence of dietary factors and hormone-dependent cancers. *Cancer Research* 35:3374–3383.

Cheney, C. and B.S. Worthington-Roberts. 1981. Diet and cancer. In *Contemporary developments in nutrition*, ed. B.S. Worthington-Roberts. St. Louis: C.V. Mosby.

Dwyer, J. 1979. Vegetarianism. *Contemporary Nutrition* 4(no.6). Minneapolis: General Mills Inc.

Ernst, N., and R.I. Levy. 1980. Diet, hyperlipidemia and atherosclerosis. In *Modern nutrition in health and disease*, eds. R.S. Goodhart and M. E. Shils. Philadelphia: Lea and Febiger.

Farrand, M.E., and L. Mojonnier. 1980. Nutrition in the multiple risk factor intervention trial (MRFIT). *Journal of the American Dietetic Association* 76: 347–351.

Food and Agriculture Organization of the United Nations (FAO) and World Health Organization. 1980. *Dietary fats and oils in human nutrition.* Rome: FAO.

Friedman, H.I., and B. Nylund. 1980. Intestinal fat digestion, absorption, and transport. *American Journal of Clinical Nutrition* 33:1108–1139.

Glueck, C J. and W.E. Connor. 1978. Diet-coronary heart disease relationships reconnoitered. *American Journal of Clinical Nutrition* 31:727–737.

Glueck, C.J. 1979. Appraisal of dietary fat as a causative factor in atherogenesis. *American Journal of Clinical Nutrition* 32:2637–2643.

Guyton, A.C. 1981. *Textbook of medical physiology.* Philadelphia: W.B. Saunders Company.

Harper, A.E. 1983. Coronary heart disease—an epidemic related to diet? *American Journal of Clinical Nutrition* 37:669–681.

Harris, C.M., M.W. Dysken, P. Fovall, and J.M. Davis. 1983. Effect of lecithin on memory in normal adults. *American Journal of Psychiatry* 140 (no. 8):1010–1013.

Hegsted, D.M., R.B. McGandy, M.L. Myers, and F.J. Stare. 1965. Quantitative effects of dietary fat on serum cholesterol in man. *American Journal of Clinical Nutrition* 17:281–295.

Hjermann, I., I. Holme, K. VelveByre, and P. Leren. 1981. Effect of diet and smoking intervention on the incidence of coronary heart disease. *Lancet* 2:1303–1313.

Holman, R.T., J.B. Johnson, and T.F. Hatch. 1982. Linolenic acid deficiency in man. *Nutrition Reviews* 40:144–147.

Institute of Shortening and Edible Oils, Inc. 1982. *Food fats and oils.* Washington, DC: Institute of Shortening and Edible Oils, Inc.

Kannel, W.B. 1978. Status of coronary heart disease risk factors. *Journal of Nutrition Education* 10:10–14.

Kritchevsky, D., and S.K. Czarnecki. 1980. Lipoproteins. *Contemporary Nutrition* 5(no.5). Minneapolis: General Mills, Inc.

Levy, R.I. 1982. Cholesterol and disease—what are the facts? *Journal of the American Medical Association* 248:2888–2889.

Lipid Research Clinics Program. 1984. The lipid research clinics coronary primary prevention trial results. *Journal of the American Medical Association* 251:351–374.

McGill, H.C. 1979. Appraisal of cholesterol as a causative factor in atherogenesis. *American Journal of Clinical Nutrition* 32: 2632–2636.

McNamara, D.J. 1982. The diet–heart question: current status. *Nutrition News* 45:9 –10. Rosemont, IL: National Dairy Council.

Multiple Risk Factor Intervention Trial Research Group. 1982. Multiple risk factor intervention trial: Risk factor changes and mortality results. *Journal of the American Medical Association* 248:1465–1477.

National Academy of Science. Committee on Diet, Nutrition, and Cancer. 1982. *Diet, nutrition, and cancer*. Washington, DC: National Academy Press.

National Dairy Council. 1979a. Nutrition and vegetarianism. *Dairy Council Digest* 50(no. 1):1–6. Rosemont, IL: National Dairy Council.

National Dairy Council. 1979b. Cholesterol metabolism. *Dairy Council Digest* 50(no.6):31–36.

National Dairy Council. 1983. Diet, nutrition, and cancer. *Dairy Council Digest* 54(no.6):31–36.

National Research Council, National Academy of Sciences (NAS). 1980. *Recommended dietary allowances*, 9th edition. Washington, DC: NAS.

Nishida, T. 1982. Diet, lipoproteins, and atherosclerosis. *Illinois Research* 24(no.1):13–15.

Olson, R.E. 1979. Are professionals jumping the gun in the fight against chronic diseases? *Journal of the American Dietetic Association* 74:543–550.

Pariza, M.W. 1984. A perspective on diet, nutrition and cancer. *Journal of the American Medical Association* 251:1455–1458.

Pennington, J.A.T., and H.N. Church. 1980. *Food values of portions commonly used*. Philadelphia: J.B. Lippincott Company.

Research Resources Information Center. 1982. Weight loss with fat substitute. *Research Resources Reporter*, September 1982. Washington, DC: Division of Research Resources, National Institutes of Health.

Science and Education Administration. 1980. *Food and nutrient intakes of individuals in 1 day in the United States, Spring, 1977*. National food consumption survey preliminary report No. 2. Washington, DC: United States Department of Agriculture.

Turpeinen, O. 1979. Effect of cholestero-lowering diet on mortality from coronary heart disease and other causes. *Circulation* 59:1–7.

United States Department of Agriculture. 1981. *Food consumption, prices, and expenditures*. Statistical Bulletin No. 656. Washington, DC: USDA Economics and Statistics Service.

Visek, W.J., and J.A. Milner. 1982. Diet and cancer. *Illinois Research* 24:16–18.

Weihrauch, J.L. 1984. *Provisional table on the fatty acid and cholesterol content of selected foods*. Washington, DC: Data Research Branch, Consumer Nutrition Division, United States Department of Agriculture.

Willett, W.C., and B. MacMahon. 1984. Diet and cancer—an overview. *New England Journal of Medicine* 310:633–638 and 697–701.

Wurtman, R.J. 1982. Nutrients that modify brain function. *Scientific American* 246(no.4):50–59.

Wynder, E.L., and G.B. Gori. 1977. Contribution of the environment to cancer incidence: An epidemiologic exercise. *Journal of the National Cancer Institute* 58:825–832.

8

Proteins

IN THIS CHAPTER: Proteins Have a More Complex Structure Than the Other Macronutrients ▪ Dietary Protein Needs Are Actually Needs for Nitrogen and Essential Amino Acids ▪ Protein and Its Derivatives Have Three Major Types of Functions ▪ Food Technology Can Make or Modify Proteins and Their Derivatives ▪ The Body Handles Protein Very Efficiently ▪ Too Little or Too Much Dietary Protein Carries Some Risk ▪ Assess Your Own Protein Intake Compared with Recommendations

Play the word association game for a few seconds. *Protein*. What words do you think of? Meat? Lean? Lively? Strong? Lithe . . . fit . . . energetic . . .? Many people associate protein with muscle, vitality, and fitness. And they're certainly right to associate protein with life and vitality, because protein is a component of every cell that lives: the cells of your body, a bacterium, an apple, a pine tree, a rhinoceros—every living thing.

A very inadequate intake of protein for a long period of time will result in loss of muscle tissue, poorer physical and mental performance, and a gradual breakdown of vital organ tissues, impairing their functioning. If the diet is grossly deficient in kcalories at the same time—which is the usual situation when protein intake is low—death may result. People in the developing countries face this double deficit all the time. Such lessons cannot fail to impress us with the importance of getting enough protein and kcalories.

Perhaps our knowledge of this vital need has influenced Americans to value protein above other classes of nutrients. Just page through a household magazine to see how protein and its most popular sources are treated: most meals are planned around the primary protein source; people spend hundreds of dollars and devote backyard and kitchen space to grills that are designed primarily to cook meats; and most people spend the largest portion of their food dollars on meats, fish, and poultry, the most popularly selected sources of protein (although less expensive options are available). There is no question about the status protein enjoys in our society. The name itself reinforces it: the Greek word *protos*, from which the word protein is derived, means "first."

This supervaluing of protein has led to another predictable phenomenon: *we tend to give it credit for more than it can deliver.* Look at the ads in various sports magazines for protein supplements that claim to improve performance, or at articles about diets that imply that protein will melt fat off your body. In light of scientific evidence, however, it is clear that these claims have *over*rated protein.

To get a more thorough understanding of what protein is and what it does, we should look first at its structure.

Proteins Have a More Complex Structure Than the Other Macronutrients

Protein is an umbrella term that includes thousands of related substances. In the body, some of them are solids, and others are found dissolved within fluids in living systems. The major unifying feature shared by the thousands of different proteins is that they are all composed of building blocks called amino acids.

proteins—thousands of related nitrogen-containing, organic substances that have structural, regulatory, and energy-providing functions.

The Structure of an Amino Acid

An amino acid, being an organic substance, contains carbon, hydrogen, and oxygen. Unlike other organic nutrients, amino acids also contain nitrogen as a necessary part of their structure, and sometimes sulfur as well.

Every amino acid consists of an *amino group*, which contains the nitrogen; an *acid group*; and a *side group* of one or several connected atoms, which gives the amino acid its identity. Figure 8.1 shows the general structure of an amino acid and a specific example.

Approximately 20 amino acids are commonly found in nature. Every living cell can produce some but not all of the 20, as long as it has the elemental ingredients to work with—the carbon, hydrogen, oxygen, and nitrogen (Munro and Crim, 1980). Since carbon, hydrogen, and oxygen are liberally available from other dietary sources, the cell has no trouble coming up with those elements, but it has a critical need to obtain nitrogen in order to synthesize amino acids.

Once amino acids have been produced, they can then be linked together by peptide bonds. If two amino acids have been joined, the resulting substance is a *dipeptide*; three amino acids create a *tripeptide*. A larger number of connected amino acids constitute a polypeptide. A protein may be made up of one or more polypeptides.

The Structure of a Protein

The structure of a protein is infinitely more complicated—there are sometimes hundreds of amino acids in a single protein molecule. Furthermore, a molecule of a particular protein is bent, folded, or coiled into a very specific three-dimensional shape that is hard to depict in a drawing. However, structures of the smaller and simpler proteins can be "flattened out" for artistic convenience; Figure 8.2 shows one. Each three-letter abbreviation represents an amino acid.

Notice that the same kind of amino acid appears many times in a single molecule of a protein. Also notice that the amino acids are in a specific order: if one is in the wrong place, or if one amino acid substitutes for another, a different protein may result.

An analogy using letters and words demonstrates the point. Let's say that the letters A, E, M, S, and T each represent a different amino acid. If

amino acids—the approximately 20 "building block" molecules the body uses to construct proteins

peptide bonds—the linkages that hold amino acids together in a protein molecule

polypeptide—a chain of four or more linked amino acids

Figure 8.1 The structure of an amino acid. Amino acids, the building blocks of proteins, contain an amino group; an acid group; and a side group of one or more atoms, which is different for each amino acid. (*Note the presence of nitrogen, the distinctive element in all amino acids.)

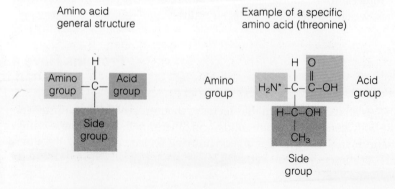

Amino acid
general structure

Example of a specific
amino acid (threonine)

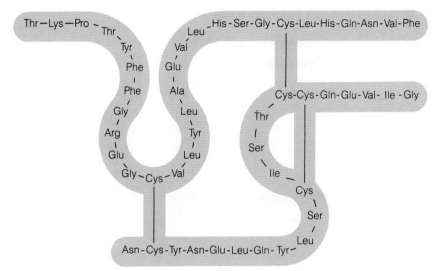

Figure 8.2 The structure of a protein: one example. This figure depicts a relatively small protein, the hormone insulin. Each three-letter abbreviation represents an amino acid; one amino acid appears many times in a single molecule. The amino acid cysteine can form cross-links between parts of the amino acid chain, giving shape to the molecule.

you combine these "amino acids" in different ways, you can make different "proteins," such as *steam*, *mates*, *teams*, and *meats*. If you add other letters—like an R and another S—you can then make *masters* and *streams*. Omitting some of the letters, you can make *stem*, *same*, *mesas*, *rate*, and so on. All are distinctly different "proteins," although they were all derived from the same six "amino acids." This analogy breaks down when we consider molecule size: our "proteins" should have hundreds of letters.

The cells of every living organism have the capability of synthesizing their own proteins, provided they have the right amino acids available. All species of plants and animals construct the unique proteins they need for supporting their own life and growth. Using the letter analogy once again, wheat might produce the proteins *steam* and *rate*, among the many it makes for itself; mosquitoes might make *same* and *masters* proteins; and humans might synthesize *teams* and *stem* proteins, besides others.

How does the body know how to assemble its different proteins? The answer is found in the nucleus of every body cell, where materials called *deoxyribonucleic acid (DNA)* and *ribonucleic acid (RNA)* contain the information that governs the synthesis of each protein. To extend the letter analogy, DNA and RNA direct the "spelling" of proteins.

When a cell needs to make a particular protein, it draws from the assortment of amino acids available to it at that time. If a cell needs to continue making *masters*, but all it has to work with are *A*, *E*, *M*, *S*, and *T*, it cannot synthesize any more of that protein.

The foods we take in contain proteins, but not the same ones as our own bodies are made from. The fact that food proteins are not identical to human proteins is not a problem: digestion dismantles food proteins so we can use the components for reassembling our own body proteins (more on this topic later).

Now let's take a more specific look at exactly what it is that humans need from dietary protein.

Dietary Protein Needs Are Actually Needs for Nitrogen and Essential Amino Acids

essential amino acids—those the body needs for protein synthesis but cannot produce for itself, and so must obtain from foods

It is something of a misnomer for us to speak of "protein needs": more accurately, we first and foremost need sufficient *nitrogen* from food proteins. Second, need enough of certain amino acids that are necessary for human protein synthesis but that cannot be produced within the body; these are called essential amino acids.

These two concerns are often referred to as issues of protein *quantity* and *quality*.

Quantity of Protein—Adequate Nitrogen

Recall our earlier statement that living cells can synthesize some amino acids if they have a nitrogen source; and then, once they have the amino acids, they can synthesize their own unique proteins. In a practical sense, then, the most important protein intake issue is quantity: getting enough protein in the diet to provide the necessary nitrogen for amino acid production.

Table 8.1 Amounts of Protein in Standard Servings of Various Foods.

Grams of Protein	Fruits and vegetables	Grain products	Milk and milk products	Meats and alternates	Combination foods	Limited extras
20					12" Cheese pizza ($\frac{1}{4}$ pie)	
				Lean chicken (2 oz)	Chicken chow mein (1c)	
				Peanuts ($\frac{1}{2}$ c)		
15			Processed cheese (2 oz)	Lean beef (2 oz)	Bean burrito (6 oz)	
			Hard cheese ($1\frac{1}{3}$ oz)	Peanut butter ($\frac{1}{4}$ c)		
				Fish (2 oz)		
			Milk— with solids (1c)	Tofu (6 oz) Eggs (2)	Spaghetti & meatballs (1c)	
10			Milk— no solids (1c)		Macaroni and cheese (1c)	
	Peas ($\frac{1}{2}$ c) Corn, potatoes ($\frac{1}{2}$ c)	Popcorn (3c) Bread, roll (1)	Pudding (1c)		Cream of mushroom soup (1 c)	Gelatin dessert ($\frac{1}{2}$ c) Cream cheese ($1\frac{1}{3}$ oz)
5	Fruit—all kinds ($\frac{1}{2}$ c) Lettuce, green beans ($\frac{1}{2}$ c)	Pasta, ckd. ceral ($\frac{1}{2}$ c) Tortilla, waffle (1) Cookies (3 small)	Ice cream ($1\frac{1}{2}$ c)		Beef-noodle soup (1)	Butter, salad dressing, carbonated beverages
0						

Table 8.2   Essential and Nonessential Amino Acids

Amino acids essential in the diet	Amino acids not essential in the diet
Histidine	Alanine
Isoleucine	Arginine
Leucine	Asparagine
Lysine	Aspartic acid
Methionine	[a]Cysteine
Phenylalanine	Glutamic acid
Threonine	Glutamine
Tryptophan	Glycine
Valine	Proline
	Serine
	[a]Tyrosine

[a]The amino acids cysteine and tyrosine are not essential, but can substitute in part for methionine and phenylalanine, respectively.

Table 8.1 shows the protein contents of various foods, grouped according to the SANE guide. You can see that, in general, dairy products, meats and alternates, and foods made from these offer the greatest amount of protein per serving. But notice that most foods (except some of the limited extras) offer at least *some* protein.

When you see that protein is in almost all of the foods in the four basic groups of the SANE guide, you can see why protein intake and kcalorie intake are so closely related. If your diet is very low in kcalories, it is also likely to be low in protein and therefore nitrogen. On the other hand, if you eat enough of the basic foods to satisfy your energy needs, you will usually get enough protein at the same time. If, however, a large proportion of your kcalories comes from the foods in the very-low-protein limited extras group, your protein intake may be inadequate.

Quality of Protein—Adequate Amounts of Essential Amino Acids

The second protein intake issue is one of quality. To be judged of good quality, a food protein must contain adequate amounts of essential amino acids the body needs for protein synthesis but cannot produce by itself.

Nine amino acids are essential in the diet (National Academy of Sciences, 1980). Table 8.2 lists them, as well as the 11 nonessential amino acids (the ones the body can produce).

Not only have scientists learned that these amino acids are indispensable, but they have also estimated what amounts of most of them are needed by the human body. Figure 8.3 illustrates our relative needs for specific essential amino acids. To be judged of good quality, a food protein should contain them in those approximate proportions.

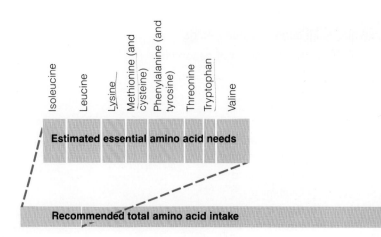

Represents 0.8 gram protein per kilogram of body weight

Figure 8.3 Relative amounts of essential amino acids and total protein needed by adults. This figure makes two points: the first is that the essential amino acids are not all needed in the same amounts. (Histidine is not shown because the level needed by adults has not yet been established.) The other point is that all together, the essential amino acids represent only a small fraction of the recommended total amino acid (protein) intake.

In general, higher quality food proteins come from animal sources, whereas lower quality proteins generally come from plant sources. More specifically, the food proteins that match human needs *best* are found in eggs, milk, and fish. The proteins in eggs and milk are of such high quality that scientists sometimes refer to them as "reference proteins," and compare the quality of others to them. *Good* quality proteins are also found in meats, poultry, cheese, and soybeans (a notable plant source).

The proteins in other legumes, nuts and seeds, grains, and vegetables get a *fair* rating; that is, some may have relatively low levels of one or two essential amino acids and very high levels of others, whereas different proteins may be low (or high) in different amino acids. At any rate, the proportion of amino acids in a fair quality protein does not—by itself—match our essential amino acid needs particularly well. A protein of blatantly *poor* quality is gelatin. (Note that this animal protein is an exception to the general rule.)

What are the practical implications of this discussion of protein quality of individual foods? It may have little significance for many of you, but for others it may have practical application.

Protein quality is not a widespread concern because the assortment of amino acids present in one individual food is not as important as the whole assortment available from everything that is eaten at the same time. People eat different foods together, with some food having greater or lesser amounts of particular amino acids in them than others. Several foods eaten

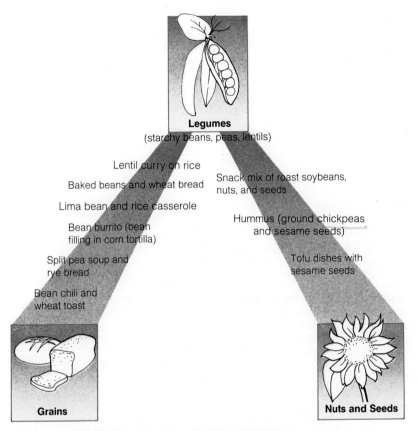

Lentil curry on rice

Baked beans and wheat bread

Snack mix of roast soybeans, nuts, and seeds

Lima bean and rice casserole

Hummus (ground chickpeas and sesame seeds)

Bean burrito (bean filling in corn tortilla)

Split pea soup and rye bread

Tofu dishes with sesame seeds

Bean chili and wheat toast

Figure 8.4 Complementary protein relationships important to some vegans. Low quality protein in a plant food can be made more biologically valuable by combining it with another food that makes up for its amino acid shortfalls. Generally, legumes have complementary relationships with grains and with nuts and seeds.

together often contain *in combination* about the right proportions of amino acids.

This phenomenon of one food supplementing low levels of amino acids in another is called complementing or mutual supplementation. Examples of foods whose amino acids complement each other are shown in Figure 8.4. Note that many of these combinations have been commonly used in various world cultures—from the famous American peanut butter sandwich to the more exotic hummus of the Middle East.

Now look at Figure 8.3, and notice what a small proportion of the total recommended intake for amino acids needs to come from essential amino acids. If you consume your RDA for proteins, you'll probably get as much as you need of the essential amino acids. Many North Americans take in almost double the protein they need, which gives them a glut of both essential and nonessential amino acids.

Some groups of people in North America could profit from deliberately complementing proteins, though. *Vegetarians who abstain from all*

complementing, mutual supplementation—situation in which foods are eaten together, whose amino acids are *collectively* in proportion with human needs

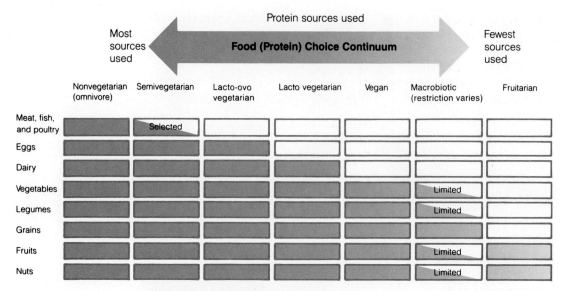

Figure 8.5 **Some types of vegetarianism.** The term *vegetarian* means different things to different people. This figure identifies some types of vegetarians, according to how great a variety of protein sources they allow themselves.

animal products—which contain both the highest quantity and quality of protein—could probably achieve better overall dietary protein quality by using protein complementation than by leaving their food combinations to chance. This is particularly true for growing children and pregnant and lactating women, whose protein needs are higher (Dwyer, 1979).

Note that there are many different kinds of vegetarians; they do not all need to be concerned about complementing. To make the distinction, we need first to describe the better known types of vegetarians (National Dairy Council, 1979; American Dietetic Association, 1980a):

semivegetarian—avoids only selected kinds of meat, fish, or poultry (flesh)

lacto–ovo vegetarian—avoids eating flesh, but uses dairy products and eggs

lacto–vegetarian—avoids eating flesh and eggs, but uses dairy products

vegan—avoids all foods of animal origin

macrobiotic vegetarian—progresses through ten dietary stages, starting with widely inclusive, then becoming increasingly restricted

fruitarian—includes fruit, nuts, honey, and/or olive oil

Figure 8.5 supplies this information in graphic form.

The types of vegetarians who can easily meet their protein quantity and quality needs by following basic dietary guidelines such as the SANE guide are semi-, lacto–ovo, and lacto–vegetarians. Vegans, especially those who are growing, may profit from complementing protein sources as just described. Macrobiotic vegetarians and fruitarians are likely to have inadequate intakes of protein as well as of many other nutrients.

Before we leave the topics of protein quantity and quality, we should discuss how protein is shown on a nutrition label, since it relates to both matters.

Nutritional Labeling of Proteins

Recall that the top of a nutrition label gives the number of grams of protein and other macronutrients in a serving of food. The bottom part of the label goes on to indicate what percentages of the U.S. RDA for protein and some other nutrients are present in a serving of the food.

To account for the differences in protein quality between foods, two standards exist in the U.S. RDA for protein: one that is used for foods that have higher quality protein, and one for those of lower quality (Deutsch, 1975). Since theoretically the body can make better use of the higher quality protein, its U.S. RDA is set at 45 grams. For the lower quality protein, the U.S. RDA is 65 grams.

Therefore, when the protein content of a food is expressed as a percentage of the appropriate standard, the consumer does not need to have any knowledge of what quality of protein is present, since it is already adjusted for in the standard. Figure 8.6 compares two examples.

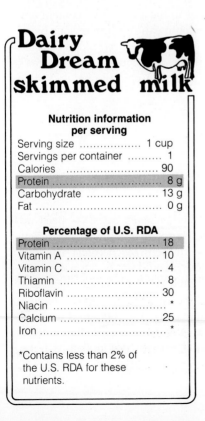

Dairy Dream skimmed milk

Nutrition information per serving

Serving size .... 1 cup
Servings per container 1
Calories 90
Protein .... 8 g
Carbohydrate .... 13 g
Fat .... 0 g

Percentage of U.S. RDA

Protein 18
Vitamin A 10
Vitamin C 4
Thiamin 8
Riboflavin 30
Niacin .... *
Calcium 25
Iron .... *

*Contains less than 2% of the U.S. RDA for these nutrients.

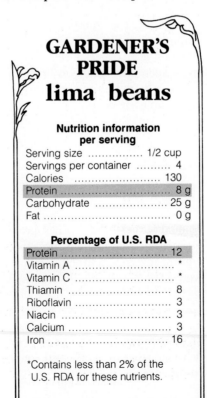

GARDENER'S PRIDE lima beans

Nutrition information per serving

Serving size .... 1/2 cup
Servings per container 4
Calories 130
Protein .... 8 g
Carbohydrate .... 25 g
Fat .... 0 g

Percentage of U.S. RDA

Protein 12
Vitamin A .... *
Vitamin C .... *
Thiamin 8
Riboflavin 3
Niacin 3
Calcium 3
Iron 16

*Contains less than 2% of the U.S. RDA for these nutrients.

Figure 8.6 Protein quantity and quality as expressed on nutrition labels. The top parts of these two nutrition labels indicate that a serving of each food contains 8 grams of protein. However, the quality of the milk protein is better than that of the lima beans. To reflect this difference, different protein standards exist in the U.S. RDA for higher quality protein (45 g) and for lower quality protein (65 g). Therefore the percentage of the U.S. RDA standards that each food satisfies is different.

Protein and Its Derivatives Have Three Major Types of Functions

One way of underscoring protein's crucial role in the body is to note its involvement in all three general types of functions nutrients can have. Proteins provide body structure, regulate various body processes, and are an energy source. In this section we look at examples of how protein performs each of these functions.

Providing Structure

Protein is a part of every living cell: it is part of the cell membrane (along with phospholipids and cholesterol), the cytoplasm, and the small bodies floating in the cytoplasm, including the nucleus. Therefore, it is a key component in the structure of the body.

Proteins that give structure and definition to the body are found in such tissues as skin, muscles of internal organs, skeletal muscle, connective tissue, and the matrix (framework) of bones and teeth. Many different kinds of proteins make up these tissues.

To a certain extent, the composition of body proteins is also variable from one person to another, depending on the DNA recipe inherited. For example, a slight difference in normal proteins results in individuals having A, B, AB, and O blood types. Occasionally, an organism is genetically programmed to make a consistent error in protein synthesis. This can produce serious physical problems, even though the change might appear to be minor. For example, small variations in the amino acid content and arrangement of the blood protein hemoglobin can result in serious blood diseases, such as sickle cell anemia. In this condition, red blood cells are misshapen and unable to function normally. The course of this disease, which is found almost exclusively in Blacks, is a painful one, and often results in early death.

Regulating Processes

Proteins influence a variety of body functions.

Metabolic Reactions. Special proteins called *enzymes* serve to speed up most of the body's biochemical reactions. There are thousands of different types of enzymes in the human body. Without them, biochemical reactions would occur so slowly that life as we know it could not be supported.

Other proteins influence metabolic reactions. For example, *hemoglobin* is a blood protein that carries oxygen to be used for energy production in body cells. *Myoglobin* is a related protein present in muscle. If the level of these proteins in the body is low, the amount of oxygen that can be delivered to cells will also be low, and energy production will be compromised.

Hormonal Activity. Hormones, some of which are proteins or dipeptides, are chemical messengers produced in one part of the body to affect a process in another region. Among the many processes that hormones affect are basal metabolism, the emptying of the stomach, and reproduction. Insulin is an example of a protein hormone.

Body Defenses. Because proteins are present in skin, they are part of the body's first line of defense against infection. However, the skin cannot protect against all invaders.

If disease-causing organisms, which contain protein themselves, get past the skin and gain entry into the body, body proteins called antibodies identify the foreign invaders and destroy them. This is the same mechanism that is at work when the body undergoes an allergic reaction (to be discussed later in this chapter).

Mineral Balance. The proteins in cell membranes function as gatekeepers that control the access of certain electrolytes to the cell. For example, sodium ions are actively pumped out of the cell by these proteins, whereas potassium ions are pumped in. The appropriate location of these electrolytes is critical to the function of nerves and muscles. Without the right balance of these minerals in intracellular and extracellular fluids, such vital functions as the beating of the heart cannot take place.

Fluid Balance. Protein is involved in fluid balance in two ways. It is indirectly involved through its role in mineral balance, as discussed above.

Its second influence is more direct. In Chapter 4 you learned that water tends to move from an area with a greater concentration of water to an area of lesser concentration of water (greater concentration of particles). Soluble proteins, along with electrolytes, are among the dissolved particles that influence fluid shifts. For example, the soluble proteins in blood help maintain the fluid volume within blood vessels. If protein intake is severely inadequate for several weeks, blood protein levels will fall, and some fluid will move from the blood into interstitial spaces.

Acid–Base Balance. Body systems require their fluid environments to have a specific pH. An excess of acid or base could interfere with the chemistry of a system and its functioning. A protein-digesting enzyme called pepsin functions best in the highly acidic environment of the stomach. For another example, if the blood's normally slightly basic status were slightly altered, its enzyme systems would not be able to function. In the most severe cases of acid–base imbalance, death can result.

Fortunately, the body has several mechanisms that take effect before such dire consequences occur. One of these is the *protein buffering system.* If either excess acid or base is produced in the body, soluble proteins, along with other substances, are usually capable of counteracting the excess so that the system can continue to function normally. This is possible because amino acids have chemical characteristics that are both acidic (the acid group) and basic (the amino group). If there is excess acid in a system, the soluble proteins can diminish the circulating acidity. If there is excess alkali, they can decrease the pH.

Nerve Impulse Transmission. Two amino acids, *tryptophan* and *tyrosine*, have been identified as precursors of neurotransmitters. [We discussed another neurotransmitter precursor, choline, in Chapter 7 (on lipids).] As with choline, researchers are working to learn how diet may affect the production of these neurotransmitters, and how they in turn may affect behavior and nervous system function within the space of a few hours.

The fact that diet can influence these important biochemicals leads people to fantasize about the possible effects of controlling behavior or mental function by eating certain types of foods. (Wouldn't it be great to be able to guarantee that your memory and thought processes would be in top form if you ate certain foods before an exam?) However, this area is still highly experimental; it is too early to suggest applications of most of these theories to real-life situations.

Neurotransmitter researcher Richard Wurtman suggests a way that diet might affect behavior. It involves the neurotransmitter serotonin, which is made within the brain from the essential amino acid tryptophan. Among the many physiological functions of serotonin is its ability to promote sleepiness. If the level of tryptophan in the brain is increased, the production of serotonin is increased, and sleepiness ensues.

serotonin—a neurotransmitter having several functions, including the ability to promote sleepiness

Since tryptophan is an amino acid, and proteins are rich in amino acids, you might think that high-protein foods would therefore cause sleepiness. Wurtman suggests that this is not the case. He hypothesizes that after a high-protein meal, many amino acids compete with tryptophan to get into the brain, so the amount of tryptophan that gains entry is not particularly high. However, after a high-carbohydrate meal, insulin lowers the blood levels of these competing amino acids, just as it lowers blood glucose. This enables tryptophan to get into the brain more easily, where it produces serotonin and promotes sleepiness. So, according to Wurtman, if you want to be alert after a meal, you might eat less carbohydrate (1982).

The nonessential amino acid tyrosine is a precursor for the neurotransmitters *dopamine* and *norepinephrine*. These substances are known to have an effect on blood pressure and depression. Studies are in progress to determine what the practical applications of such relationships might be.

Along with the excitement generated by this frontier area of research, scientists also sound a warning: *do not experiment on yourself by taking single purified amino acids*. Some people have experienced nausea and vomiting from doing so. Of more concern are the as-yet-unknown effects there may be on the human brain or on the metabolism of other organs. Animal studies show such serious effects as growth retardation, nervous system changes, and loss of appetite when purified amino acids are consumed (Harper et al., 1970), so it is possible that humans may experience serious effects as well. At the very least, large doses of one amino acid are likely to interfere with the utilization of others.

Providing Energy

Like carbohydrates and lipids, proteins can be metabolized for energy; they yield 4 kcalories per gram. However, as you learned in Chapter 5 (on energy), the body will primarily use available carbohydrates and fats, saving proteins for their unique uses if possible.

There are several circumstances in which the body *does* use substantial protein for energy. If carbohydrate and fat are insufficient to meet the body's energy needs, protein will be used for this purpose. Or if the central nervous system needs glucose but no carbohydrate is available, certain protein components can be dismantled to yield it. (This reemphasizes the protein-sparing function that carbohydrates have.) Or, if there is a glut of protein, the surplus will be used for energy. (Many Americans find themselves in this situation.)

Food Technology Can Make or Modify Proteins and Their Derivatives

Just as food science has the technology to refine the other macronutrients, it can also modify proteins in foods.

Proteins in Processed Foods

Soybeans are a high-protein food that is processed in many different ways (Clydesdale and Francis, 1977). For example, recent technology enables soy protein to be separated from most of the other soybean components into *soy protein isolates*. These can be spun into strands of texturized vegetable protein and then shaped and flavored into *meat analogues* that resemble foods such as hot dogs, veal cutlets, or meatballs. Sometimes the manufacturer improves on the protein quality of these products by adding needed amino acids.

Soy protein concentrates, another derivative, are also produced by removing some of the nonprotein components of soybeans, but not as many as are removed to make isolates. Soy protein concentrates are used to provide texture, and to aid in emulsification, fat absorption, and water absorption.

The practice of modifying soybeans to produce new forms of food is far from new; Oriental cultures have done so since antiquity. *Tofu* is a curd product made from water in which soybeans have been soaked; the soy proteins in the water are separated and pressed into a cake, resulting in a product with a texture resembling soft cheese. People who use it should realize that a large serving—6 ounces—is needed to provide as much protein as a 2-ounce serving of meat. *Miso*, an Oriental soybean paste that is used as a flavoring ingredient or condiment, also is a soy-protein-containing food. However, it does not usually contribute much protein to the day's diet, since only small amounts of it are likely to be used at once.

Another protein that is commercially isolated is *casein*, a cow's milk protein. Casein or its derivative, *sodium caseinate*, is used as an ingredient

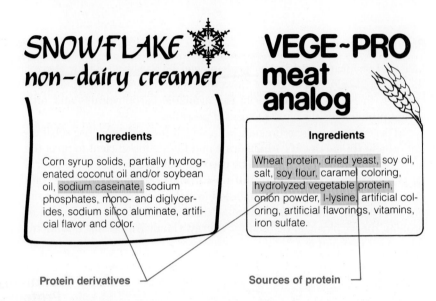

Figure 8.7 Examples of protein or protein derivatives in two processed foods.

in foods such as frozen dessert toppings and coffee whiteners. Refined proteins also find a brisk market as nutritional supplements, even though most Americans have no need for them. Figure 8.7 shows some examples of proteins or their derivatives as found in processed foods.

Amino Acids in Processed Foods

Products such as powdered amino acids and/or dipeptides used as protein supplements represent technology that has been carried a step further. These products are variously marketed as weight-reduction aids, protein supplements for athletes, or special-purpose hospital feedings. The only one of these uses that is appropriate is for hospital feedings for patients whose alimentary tracts are not able to handle the digestion of whole food proteins. Later in this chapter, we will explain why protein supplements are unnecessary for athletes, and Chapter 10 (on body fatness) will deal with the inadvisability of using such products as the basis of weight reduction regimens.

Another application of food science involving proteins and their derivatives has been the identification and testing of a sweet dipeptide that is being used increasingly in the North American food supply as a sugar substitute; it is called *aspartame*. It is not an important amino acid contributor since very little aspartame is likely to be used at one time, and since it contains only the two amino acids phenylalanine and aspartic acid. We mention it here just because it is a relatively new protein-related product of food technology. More discussion about aspartame is found in Chapters 10 and 15.

The Body Handles Protein Very Efficiently

Knowing how complex the structure of protein is, you might expect the body to have difficulty dismantling it. In fact, the body treats proteins pretty harshly, beginning in the stomach; but obviously the treatment is effective since approximately 98% of dietary proteins are eventually reduced to units small enough to be absorbed (Guyton, 1981).

Digestion, Absorption, and Transport of Dietary Proteins

After being chewed and swallowed, the proteins in food meet their first chemical challenge in the stomach.

The Role of the Stomach. Hydrochloric acid produced in the stomach begins the process of taking apart the large protein molecules. The first step in unfolding protein structure is called denaturation. (Proteins can be denatured outside the body, too, by heat, alcohol, and certain other chemicals.)

denaturation—unfolding of the three-dimensional structure of a protein

In addition, a stomach enzyme called pepsin breaks some of the long protein strands into polypeptide units containing many amino acids. We mentioned earlier that pepsin is specially designed to work in the harsh acid climate of the stomach. Most of the body's other enzymes would themselves be digested by stomach acid, but this one finds the acid environment ideal. In fact, if the stomach juices are not acid enough, pepsin cannot function (Guyton, 1981).

Pepsin has its limits, though; it usually just begins breaking down proteins so they are more vulnerable to the battery of enzymes they will face in the small intestine.

The Role of the Small Intestine. In the small intestine, many other proteases from the pancreas take up the task of dividing the long, unraveled protein and polypeptide strands into units small enough for absorption. The pancreatic enzymes succeed in reducing most proteins to tripeptides, dipeptides, and single amino acids.

proteases—protein-digesting enzymes

The remaining small groups of amino acids are digested further by enzymes released from the intestinal wall cells themselves. The products of hydrolysis are then absorbed, travel via the portal vein to the liver, and pour into the general circulation. Table 8.3 summarizes these steps.

Irregularities in Digestion, Absorption, and Transport of Proteins

Sometimes the body does not perform in the expected way when proteins or their derivatives are ingested. Food allergies and the so-called Chinese restaurant syndrome are examples of such abnormalities.

Food Allergy: A Fluke in Absorption. Even though the proportion of dietary proteins that fail to be completely digested is quite small, dietary proteins or their subunits can have a dramatic effect if they slip through the intended barrier of the intestinal wall cells. Examples of people in

Frontier

Table 8.3 Summary of Phases of Protein Digestion

	Proteins
Mouth	—
Stomach	Unraveling of protein strands by acid; hydrolysis by enzyme pepsin to polypeptides
Small intestine	Hydrolysis by pancreatic enzymes to amino acids, dipeptides, and tripeptides; hydrolysis by enzymes from intestinal wall cells to amino acids; absorption
Large intestine	—

antigens—foreign substances, such as proteins, that can provoke an immune response in persons

antibodies—proteins that protect the body against antigens by binding to and inactivating them

whom this might happen are infants, whose gastrointestinal tracts are immature (Fontana and Moreno-Pagan, 1980) and people who have a gastrointestinal illness (Allison, 1982).

Proteins and polypeptides from food are foreign to the body. If these fragments are absorbed, they have the potential to cause food allergy in a person who is genetically predisposed to such sensitivity. If sensitization occurs, absorption of the same foreign protein or fragments (called antigens) at a later date will cause proteins already present in the immune system (called antibodies) to seek out and bind to the invading protein units. This reaction may result in allergic symptoms.

Allergies can manifest themselves in surprising ways. An allergy to an absorbed food protein or protein component may cause symptoms far removed from the gastrointestinal tract. A person with a food allergy might experience respiratory symptoms (such as asthma or sneezing); skin symptoms (rash, hives); nervous system symptoms (headache, dizziness); cardiovascular symptoms (rapid heartbeat); urinary symptoms (blood in the urine); or gastrointestinal symptoms (vomiting, diarrhea).

Food allergies may be difficult to diagnose, not only because they can take so many forms, but also because the symptoms may take up to 72 hours to occur. On the other hand, some people react to offending foods almost immediately.

Opinions vary somewhat as to which foods most commonly lead to allergic reactions. A pediatrician and a pediatric allergist include on their list cow's milk, eggs, seafood, wheat, soybeans, nuts, seeds, chocolate, oranges, and tomatoes (Fontana and Moreno-Pagan, 1980). A thorough review article by the National Dairy Council implicates nuts and peanuts, eggs, cow's milk, soybeans, wheat, fish, and shellfish (National Dairy Council, 1983).

Because food allergies are more likely to occur in infants whose immature intestines are not yet very effective at preventing the entry of large groups of amino acids, the best practice is to delay introducing the common allergens to an infant's diet until the gut is ready to handle them. This is an especially wise tactic for an infant with a family history of allergies.

If an infant does develop food allergies, is he or she saddled with them forever? No, usually food allergies subside by about the age of 5. In an allergic child, however, the possibility always exists that other types of substances, such as inhaled pollens or dust, may result in sensitivities when the child is older (Fontana and Moreno-Pagan, 1980).

We have a few final cautions about food allergies. Because they manifest themselves with such a wide variety of symptoms, some people are tempted to ascribe any puzzling adverse physiological or behavioral symptoms—such as arthritis or mental or emotional illness—to food allergy, without having an adequate scientific basis for such a connection.

People who severely restrict their diets for a long period of time in an attempt to avoid presumed allergens may develop nutritional problems if their "allergy diet" ignores basic nutritional needs. Dietary self-treatment can also become a serious problem if it prevents such people from getting an accurate diagnosis of their condition, which should be the basis for treatment.

Therefore, people who suspect food allergies are advised to seek out a physician with specialized training in allergy diagnosis and treatment.

Chinese Restaurant Syndrome: A Continuing Puzzle. Chinese restaurant syndrome comprises a group of adverse reactions experienced by a few people when they ingest Chinese food, which usually contains large amounts of the flavor-enhancer *monosodium glutamate (MSG)*. MSG is a derivative of glutamic acid, a nonessential amino acid. Although the presence of small amounts of these compounds in the body is normal and causes no unpleasant reactions, the amounts that are absorbed when MSG is used as an additive have been linked to the group of symptoms known as Chinese restaurant syndrome.

People who have an attack of Chinese restaurant syndrome complain of some or all of these symptoms for several hours after eating the offending food(s): severe tightness in the chest, asthma, sensations of warmth and tingling, stiffness and/or weakness of the limbs, headache, lightheadedness, heartburn, and gastric discomfort (Nutrition and the M.D., 1982). Although the symptoms of Chinese restaurant syndrome are not life-threatening, they can be unpleasant and frightening if mistaken for more serious problems.

A considerable amount of circumstantial evidence has been accumulated against MSG in regard to this syndrome, but scientists cannot yet explain why this amino acid derivative (not a polypeptide or whole protein, the usual source of food allergy) causes this reaction in some people.

Digestion, Absorption, and Transport of Body Protein

Besides getting amino acids from food proteins, our bodies have another source: they reuse amino acids from worn out body proteins. It is estimated that approximately 3% of adult body proteins are replaced daily

(Worthington-Roberts, 1981). The amount of amino acids made available to the body in this way may be as much as four to five times that which is needed from the diet (Pellett, 1978).

It's hard to imagine how the body can supply so much protein until you recognize how often some cells are replaced. For example, the innermost cells of the gastrointestinal tract are replaced every two to three days. After they slough off the alimentary canal, they are digested and absorbed in exactly the same way as dietary proteins.

Some dismantled internal proteins are not reused. A small portion of them are broken down and excreted. External proteins, such as those found in skin, hair, and nails, cannot be reclaimed.

Too Little or Too Much Dietary Protein Carries Some Risk

One of the themes of this book is that it is important to get enough of the essential nutrients—but not too much. For every class of nutrients, problems can occur with either underconsumption or overconsumption. Proteins are no exception.

Shortage of Protein

Although we have made the point that in our society it is usually quite easy to get enough protein, there are places in the world where the common foods are very low in protein, or where there is simply an inadequate quantity of food of any kind. In either of these circumstances, concern about inadequate protein is legitimate.

"Pure" Protein Deficiency. Protein deficiency by itself is a rare phenomenon. In just a few places in the world, where the food choice is extremely limited and the staple food is extremely low in protein, is protein deficiency seen in its pure form.

Cassava (a starchy root) and yams are foods that have only about a third of the protein provided by grains on a weight basis. A study done in Nigeria, where these foods are staples, found that only 5% to 8% of the kcalories in people's diets came from protein (Worthington-Roberts, 1981). Protein deficiency manifested itself in low weight gains during pregnancy; low maternal milk production; high infant mortality (40% in the first five years); extremely low weights and heights in children; poor intelligence scores for children; and increased susceptibility to infections. When protein was supplemented, all of these abnormalities were reversed.

Protein–Energy Malnutrition (PEM). It is much more common to find long-term protein deficiency associated with severe energy deficiency: this condition is called protein–energy malnutrition (PEM), a fairly widespread situation in the developing countries. Usually the problem is that people simply do not have enough food. PEM would be relieved if these people had access to more of what their diet already contained.

PEM affects young children more than others, because their need for protein and other nutrients is greater per unit of body weight. PEM man-

protein–energy malnutrition (PEM)—long-term protein deficiency associated with severe energy deficiency; fairly widespread in the less developed countries

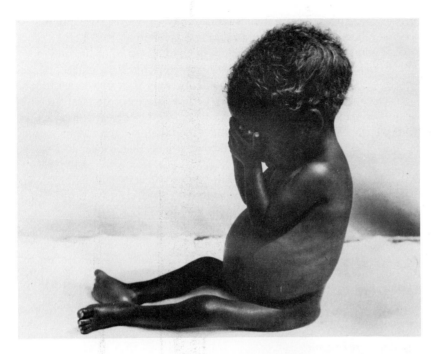

Figure 8.8 A child with kwashiorkor. Although this child may not appear malnourished to the casual observer, she is: the swelling caused by fluid in her tissues camouflages her protein-energy malnutrition. The other signs are more obvious—her dark hair has turned reddish, she has a skin condition, and she is feeling great misery.

ifests itself in a variety of ways; two severe conditions are marasmus and kwashiorkor. Although kwashiorkor originally was thought to result from protein deficiency alone, more recent thinking is that it also involves inadequate energy intake (Hegsted, 1978).

Marasmus is a condition in which a person becomes thinner and thinner from a progressive loss of fat and muscle tissue. People with marasmus are extremely weak and listless, and have decreased resistance to infection.

Kwashiorkor produces quite different physical symptoms; the body becomes swollen with fluid because there is less protein than is normal in the blood, and fluid from the bloodstream is thus allowed to migrate into the tissues. Sometimes the swelling makes the person look healthfully chubby, but other signs quickly disprove this image: dark hair has become red, a dermatitis (skin condition) has developed, and the person obviously feels miserable. Once again, resistance to infection is reduced. Liver damage is characteristic. A child with kwashiorkor is pictured in Figure 8.8.

It is not known what determines which form of PEM an individual living under these circumstances will develop (Hegsted, 1978); often, marasmus and kwashiorkor occur together in the same group of children.

Susceptibility to Infection. As stated previously, in its most severe forms, inadequate dietary protein results in poorer resistance to infection. However, even in milder dietary inadequacies of energy and/or protein, the body's defenses for dealing with invading microorganisms are weaker and/or slower to respond (Chandra, 1983).

Because infection raises the body's need for both kcalories and protein, it creates an even wider gap between what the body needs and what the diet supplies. For this reason, PEM and infection create a downward spiral in the health of many people in the developing countries. Diseases such as

marasmus—a serious form of PEM characterized by progressive fat and muscle loss

kwashiorkor—a serious form of PEM in which liver damage results in fluid shifts that create a swollen appearance

measles, which would run a short course in well-nourished populations, become killers among poorly nourished people (Vitale, 1979).

Of course, people in the developing countries are not the only ones who ever experience this decrease in disease resistance: it can also happen to people in developed countries who deliberately, seriously shortchange themselves on kcalories and protein, as people who are on overly aggressive weight-reducing diets do. The effect can be the same—a disease that would have been easily resisted under nondieting circumstances may establish itself and be difficult for the overzealous dieter to shake.

Fatty Liver. If the liver has inadequate access to protein due to long-term dietary deficiency, fats can accumulate in the liver. [Recall from Chapter 7 (on lipids) that the body uses protein to create lipoproteins, the form in which lipids are transported in the body.]

Protein deficiency can also occur among alcoholics in the developed countries if their intake of alcohol replaces a large part of their food intake. However, in alcoholics, the development of fatty liver is also influenced by the fact that the liver preferentially metabolizes the alcohol for its energy source, allowing fat to accumulate that would normally have been used for energy (Lieber, 1976).

Excess of Protein

Many of you may not feel that information about dietary protein shortages concerns you; often, college students find that their dietary protein status is adequate or higher than their recommended intake. However, for those of you who have found that your protein intake is twice or more what the recommendations suggest you need, this section may have more personal meaning.

Increase in Body Fat. As with any of the macronutrients, an excess of protein can result in the creation of additional body fat, if total kcalories consumed are beyond the kcalories needed.

Possible Accompanying High Fat Intake. Many commonly consumed high-protein foods are also high in fat. If you have a high intake of high-protein/high-fat foods, the total fat content of your diet will be high, making you a candidate for the problems associated with high fat intake. On the other hand, you can obviously be deliberate about choosing the lower-fat/high-protein foods. Table 8.4 gives you examples of options within dairy, flesh (meat, poultry, fish) protein, and plant protein foods.

For a more comprehensive picture of which high-protein foods are high or low in fat, refer back to the fat rulers at the bottom of Figures 2.7 and 2.8, the milk products and meats and alternates food groups.

Dehydration. When very high levels of protein are consumed, the body dismantles the amino acid surplus. The separated amino groups are metabolized into urea, which is excreted in the urine.

A sizeable volume of water is needed to excrete urea in the urine. To metabolize 100 kcalories of protein, the body uses 350 grams of water,

Table 8.4 Fat Levels That Accompany 7–8 Grams of Protein in Various Kinds of Foods

Food	Protein (grams)	Fat (grams)
Milk and milk products		
Skim milk	8	0
Cheddar cheese	7	9
Animal protein sources		
Haddock, broiled	7	2
Beef ribeye	7	13
Plant protein sources		
Lentils	8	0
Peanuts	8	15

whereas 100 kcalories of carbohydrate or fat use only 50 grams (Worthington-Roberts, 1981). Therefore if a person who consumes a great deal of protein does not also consume a lot of water, dehydration is a possibility. This is the reason that high protein weight-reduction diets often recommend consuming large volumes of water. It also explains why athletes consuming high-protein diets are in double jeopardy of dehydration—due to both urinary losses and perspiration.

Calcium Loss. Some studies show that people who consume protein at levels at least twice as high as the amount recommended by the RDA are likely to experience a net loss of calcium from the body if they are consuming less than the RDA for calcium.

In terms of food, this means that the person who eats a lot of meat but avoids the recommended two servings of dairy products per day *may* be slowly but steadily losing bone calcium. (Many other factors, such as level of dietary phosphorus, sex, age, and activity level can also affect this situation.) This situation does not pose a short-term risk, but may contribute to the long-term development of osteoporosis, a condition in which bone mass gradually decreases with aging in the adult (Nutrition Reviews, 1981).

osteoporosis—condition in which bone mass gradually decreases with age

Assess Your Own Protein Intake Compared with Recommendations

Since protein has so many important functions, you would surely not want to shortchange yourself of it. However, you will probably be surprised at how easy it is for a healthy adult to get the amount of protein he or she needs.

How Protein Needs Are Determined

How do scientists know how much protein is enough for a healthy adult? You might think that they could simply measure the amount of protein that is lost from the body in a day's time to find out how much should be replaced. In general, that is what they do. The major losses occur via the urine, in which the breakdown products of some internal proteins are excreted; nitrogen is measured to determine how much protein has been discarded. Much smaller amounts of protein are lost in the feces, sweat, skin, hair, and nails; collection and analysis of these amounts present their own challenges.

But it is not enough to measure the body's losses: intake of dietary protein is another important part of the equation. Some of the urinary nitrogen may come from excess protein that was in the diet. If a person has eaten more protein than his or her body needs for replacement of worn tissues, the unneeded amino acids are either metabolized for energy or are converted to fat and stored. In either case, the nitrogen from the surplus is excreted in the urine along with the *un*recycled nitrogen from worn internal tissues.

Protein needs, then, are determined in metabolic studies that measure both intake and output of nitrogen. If output and intake are equal, the person is said to be "in balance." If output is greater than intake, the person is losing protein, or is in "negative balance"; this occurs with injury, surgery, illness, and starvation. If intake is greater than output, the body is creating new protein and is in "positive balance"; this occurs during growth, pregnancy, lactation, healing, and muscle-building.

There have been thousands of studies about protein metabolism. They have shown that people's protein needs vary slightly from one individual to another; this is consistent with the generalization we made earlier about people's somewhat unique needs for levels of nutrients. The studies also show that there is a strong relationship between the need for protein and the need for kcalories: a person who is losing weight needs more protein to stay in balance than a person who is maintaining body weight (Munro and Crim, 1980). This is because some of the protein is used for energy.

When the RDA committee members consider recommendations for

Figure 8.9 Different protein needs for various people (per unit of body weight).

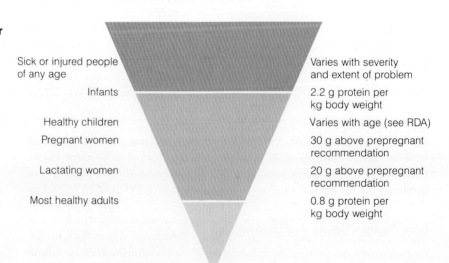

Sick or injured people of any age — Varies with severity and extent of problem

Infants — 2.2 g protein per kg body weight

Healthy children — Varies with age (see RDA)

Pregnant women — 30 g above prepregnant recommendation

Lactating women — 20 g above prepregnant recommendation

Most healthy adults — 0.8 g protein per kg body weight

protein intake, they take into account as many of these factors as they can. To allow for individual variation, they include a generous margin in the recommendation. They also add a margin to cover for the fact that people's diets are made up of proteins of varying quality; the recommendations do assume, though, that those diets contain both animal and plant proteins.

However, be aware that the protein RDAs are not adequate for a person who is losing weight rapidly or who is ill. During illness and after surgery or serious accidental injury, the appropriate recommendation for protein could be double or more the amount recommended for the healthy person, depending on the nature of the illness and/or the extent of the surgery or injury (Munro and Crim, 1980).

Recommended Protein Intakes for the Healthy Adult

Guidelines for protein intake are most often given in two ways.

Based on Ideal Body Weight. The RDA committee advocates that you calculate your recommended daily protein intake based on body weight. (If you are substantially overweight or underweight at the moment, use your ideal body weight in the calculation; your protein needs are based primarily on lean body tissue, and do not change much when your body contains different amounts of fat.) First convert your weight to kilograms; then simply multiply it by 0.8 gram per kilogram to get the recommended daily intake. This is how the figures on the RDA table were derived: 56 grams of protein per day for the 70-kilogram man, and 44 grams for the 55-kilogram woman.

People who are developing new tissue need more dietary protein. According to the 1980 RDA, women who are pregnant should consume 30 grams more each day than they should if not pregnant; when they are lactating, they should add 20 grams to what was recommended before pregnancy. (Some experts think that these values are higher than they need to be.)

Children's needs vary according to their ages; in the first six months after birth, they should take in 2.2 grams of protein per kilogram of body weight. As they get older, the recommendation per unit of body weight gradually drops until it gets to the adult level of 0.8 gram per kilogram. Figure 8.9 summarizes these recommendations.

Based on Kcaloric Intake. Another common guideline for protein intake is a suggested percentage of kcalories that should come from protein. For most adults, 10% to 12% of kcalories is adequate, but the elderly might need 12% to 14% to be sure to stay in balance (National Academy of Sciences, 1980). Do not evaluate the protein content of weight-reduction diets based on this percentage standard.

Most people easily meet this percentage recommendation; a recent food consumption survey of almost 10,000 Americans found that, on the average, they got 16% of their kcalories from protein (Science and Education Administration, 1980).

Promises that can't be kept.
Protein or amino acid powders
are often marketed for muscle
building. They are neither necessary nor effective; only a regular, graduated body-building
program can add muscle mass
within genetic limits.

These two methods will not always yield the same results; for example, the latter method is likely to give a higher figure for the physically
active person. The first method—the one based on body weight—is more
accurate.

For the athlete. Do athletes need more protein? For many centuries, it was
believed that a high-protein diet would help a person excel at physical
activity, because protein was thought to be the fuel required by muscle.
For this reason, some of the original Olympic contenders ate meals primarily of high-protein foods: meat, milk, and eggs.

However, in 1866 two German scientists published the results of
experiments proving that protein was *not* the preferred energy substrate
for the working muscle. Many studies have reinforced those early findings
(Mayer and Bullen, 1974). From these studies, researchers concluded that
the amount of protein typically needed by the athlete was within the amount

recommended by the RDA—0.8 gram per kilogram of body weight, even for the person who was doing deliberate muscle-building with a regular, graduated program of weight-lifting (Durnin, 1978). Some recent work suggests that protein use by individuals who exercise daily may be *somewhat* higher than previously thought—but fat and carbohydrate are still undeniably the major energy sources (Hoerr et al., 1982).

Other studies have been done to compare the performance of people consuming very high-protein diets to those consuming lower but still adequate levels. Such research has been *unable to detect better performance at higher levels of protein intake* (Rasch et al., 1969; Consolazio et al., 1975). So, if you know of people who testify that a very high-protein intake has helped their athletic performance, it has probably been the placebo effect at work; in other words, a high protein intake was part of the person's "psych-up."

On the other hand, we do not recommend that athletes should necessarily cut down all the way to RDA levels, if they customarily consume somewhat more than that. Some experts in sports physiology and nutrition advocate that adult athletes take in 1 gram of protein per kilogram of body weight (Astrand and Rodahl, 1977; Durnin, 1978); or 10% to 15% of kcalories from protein (American Dietetic Association, 1980b). Even researchers who believe the athlete's protein use is somewhat higher than RDA levels state that "the standard American diet, which provides protein in excess of 1 gram/kilogram body weight per day, should be adequate for their protein needs" (Hoerr et al., 1982). These recommendations will provide more protein than is likely to be needed for usual protein maintenance, and also will provide a surplus for repairing an occasional injury (especially from contact sports) or providing energy during an unexpectedly heavy demand (from more than two hours of continuous, strenuous exercise) (Buskirk, 1981).

Of course, athletes who are still growing need to take in amounts in keeping with the higher RDAs for protein for their ages.

How to Calculate Your Protein Intake

Figure 8.10 gives an example of a one-day protein intake assessment.

Use the following steps to find out how your own actual intake compares to your recommended intake:

1. Record your food and beverage intake for a typical 24-hour period.

2. Using Appendices E and F, find values for energy and protein for each item you listed, and record them in the appropriate columns.

3. Total the energy and protein columns.

4. Compare your total protein intake to your recommended level of protein intake.

5. If you are a vegan (especially if growing, pregnant, or lactating), check to see whether you have consumed complementary protein sources together.

Figure 8.10 One-day protein assessment. A 170-pound adult male student recorded this intake, and analyzed it for protein quantity. It more than satisfied his recommended intake of 62 grams. Note that all three eating occasions center around a high-protein item; this student's first meal of the day was a large noon meal, followed by two smaller meals.

Food	Amount	Energy (kcalories)	Protein (grams)
Chili con carne	1 cup	340	19
Crackers	4 squares	50	1
Sandwich			
White enriched bread	2 slices	140	4
Turkey	2 ounces	117	18
Mayonnaise	2 T	130	tr
Hamburger			
Beef patty	2 ounces	124	16
Bun	1	120	4
Green beans	½ cup	15	1
Sloppy Joe sandwich			
Meat	2 ounces	124	16
Bun	1	120	4
Tomato sauce	2 T	11	tr
Ice cream	2 cups	540	10
Totals		1831	93

From the information you produce by doing this assessment, you can also calculate what percentage of your kcalories for the day came from protein. You have done this previously for other nutrients.

The goal of this chapter has been to give a perspective on protein's legitimate uses: its role in structure, in regulation, and as reserve energy. We hope that you will now be able to sort out which of the claims about protein in the popular press represent wishful thinking, and which are based on fact.

SUMMARY

■ We tend to value protein far above the other classes of nutrients, to the point of giving it credit for more than it can deliver.

■ There are thousands of different proteins that differ widely in complexity and function. However, all consist of amino acids joined together by peptide bonds to form linear chains called polypeptides. Every amino acid consists of an amino group, an acid group, and a characteristic side group. Approximately 20 amino acids are commonly found in nature, and every living cell can produce some of them if it has the necessary raw materials.

■ Dietary protein needs are actually needs for nitrogen (to make those amino acids the body can produce itself) and for essential amino acids (those the body cannot produce, but must obtain in foods). Protein is widespread in our food supply, but not all protein is of the same quality; in general, animal sources are better than plant sources in terms of matching human needs for essential amino acids. However, several foods eaten together often contain—*in combination*—acceptable proportions of amino acids, a phenomenon known as complementation.

■ Protein's crucial role in the body is evident from its many functions: (1) providing cell and tissue structure; (2) regulating a wide variety of body processes including metabolic reactions, hormonal activity, body defenses, mineral and fluid balance, acid–base balance, and nerve impulse transmission; and (3) providing energy (in emergencies, or if present in surplus).

■ Proteins can be modified by food technology just as the other macronutrients can. Soy protein isolates and concentrates commonly turn up as meat analogues and texturizers, respectively. Protein supplements of various kinds are marketed for several purposes, few of which are really legitimate. The dipeptide aspartame is an increasingly common sugar substitute.

■ The body handles dietary protein very efficiently. Denaturation (unfolding) and digestion begin in the stomach with the action of pepsin, and proteases take over the breakdown process in the small intestine. Occasionally a foreign protein is absorbed in fragments large enough to provoke an immune response, in which case the susceptible individual is said to have a food allergy (the symptoms of which can be far removed from the digestive tract). The body is also very efficient at recycling many of its own proteins.

■ As for the other nutrients, there is an optimal range of protein intake. Pure protein deficiency is rare, but in the less developed countries protein-energy malnutrition, a result of general food shortage, is fairly widespread. Two severe forms of this disorder are marasmus and kwashiorkor. In addition to its other consequences, inadequate protein intake can lead to increased susceptibility to infection and to fatty liver. Excess protein in the diet can lead to an increase in body fat and in some cases to dehydration or calcium loss.

■ A healthy adult can easily meet his or her protein needs by eating a balanced diet. Protein intake guidelines are usually based either on body weight or on the total number of kcalories consumed. Needs vary among individuals; athletes have been shown not to benefit from consuming protein far in excess of the RDAs, though people who are recovering from illness or injury may need considerably more than the recommended amounts.

REFERENCES

Allison, R.G., ed. 1982. *An evaluation of the potential for dietary proteins to contribute to systemic diseases*. Bethesda, MD: Federation of American Societies for Experimental Biology.

American Dietetic Association. 1980a. Position paper on vegetarian approach to eating. *Journal of the American Dietetic Association* 77:61–69.

American Dietetic Association. 1980b. Nutrition and physical fitness: A statement. *Journal of the American Dietetic Association* 76:437–443.

Astrand, P.O., and K. Rodahl. 1977. *Textbook of work physiology*. New York: McGraw-Hill Book Company.

Buskirk, E. R. 1981. Some nutritional considerations in the conditioning of athletes. *Annual Reviews of Nutrition* 1:319–350.

Chandra, R.K. 1983. Nutrition, immunity, and infection: Present knowledge and future directions. *Lancet* (March 26)1:688–691.

Clydesdale, F.M., and F.J. Francis. 1977. *Food, nutrition, and you*. Englewood Cliffs, NJ: Prentice-Hall, Inc.

Consolazio, C.F., H.L. Johnson, R.A. Nelson, J.G. Dramise, and J.H. Skala. 1975. Protein metabolism during intensive physical training in the young adult. *American Journal of Clinical Nutrition* 28:29–35.

Deutsch, R.M. 1975. *Nutrition labeling: How it can work for you*. Bethesda, MD: The National Nutrition Consortium.

Durnin, J.V.G.A. 1978. Protein requirements and physical activity. In *Nutrition, physical fitness, and health*, eds. J. Parizkova and V.A. Rogotzkin. Baltimore, MD: University Park Press.

Dwyer, J. 1979. Vegetarianism. *Contemporary Nutrition* 4(no.6). Minneapolis: General Mills, Inc.

Fontana, V.J., and F. Moreno-Pagan. 1980. Allergy and diet. In *Modern nutrition in health and disease*, eds. R.S. Goodhart and M.E. Shils. Philadelphia: Lea and Febiger.

Guyton, A.C. 1981. *Textbook of medical physiology.* Philadelphia: W.B. Saunders Company.

Harper, A.E., N.J. Benevenga, and R.M. Wohlhueter. 1970. Effects of ingestion of disproportionate amounts of amino acids. *Physiological Reviews* 50:429–558.

Hegsted, D.M. 1978. Protein-calorie malnutrition. *American Scientist* 66:61–65.

Hoerr, R.A., V.R. Young, and W.J. Evans. 1982. Protein metabolism and exercise. In *Diet and exercise: Synergism in health maintenance*, eds. P.L. White and R. Mondeika. Chicago: American Medical Association.

Lappe, F.M. 1982. *Diet for a small planet.* New York: Ballantine Books.

Lieber, C.S. 1976. Alcohol and nutrition. *Nutrition News* 39(no.3):9–10. Rosemont, IL: National Dairy Council.

Mayer, J., and B.A. Bullen. 1974. Nutrition, weight control, and exercise. In *Science and medicine in exercise and sport*, eds. W.R. Johnson and E.R. Buskirk. New York: Harper and Row Publishers.

Munro, H.N., and M.C. Crim. 1980. The proteins and amino acids. In *Modern nutrition in health and disease*, eds. R.S. Goodhart and M.E. Shils. Philadelphia: Lea and Febiger.

National Academy of Sciences (NAS). 1980. *Recommended dietary allowances.* Washington, DC: NAS.

National Dairy Council. 1979. Nutrition and vegetarianism. *Dairy Council Digest* 50(no.1):1–6. Rosemont, IL: National Dairy Council.

National Dairy Council. 1983. Food sensitivity. *Dairy Council Digest* 54(no.2):7–11.

Nutrition and the M.D. 1982. Chinese restaurant syndrome. *Nutrition and the M.D.* 8(no.12):1.

Nutrition Reviews. 1981. High protein diets and bone homeostasis. *Nutrition Reviews* 39:11–13.

Pellett, P.L. 1978. Protein quality evaluation revisited. *Food Technology* 32:60–76.

Rasch, P.J., J.W. Hamby, and H.J. Berns, Jr. 1969. Protein dietary supplementation and physical performance. *Medicine and Science in Sports* 1:195–199.

Science and Education Administration. 1980. *Nationwide food consumption survey 1977-78. Preliminary report 2. Food and nutrient intakes of individuals in one day in the United States, Spring, 1977.* Washington, DC: United States Department of Agriculture.

Vitale, J.J. 1979. *Impact of nutrition on immune function.* Columbus, OH: Ross Laboratories.

Worthington-Roberts, B.S. 1981. Proteins and amino acids. In *Contemporary developments in nutrition*, ed. B.S. Worthington-Roberts. St. Louis: The C.V. Mosby Company.

Wurtman, R.J. 1982. Nutrients that modify brain function. *Scientific American* 246(no.4):50–59.

PART THREE

Entrées

Pasta

TAKE OUT

RESTAURANT

北京広東東四川

EATING IN THE 1980s

9

Why You Eat What You Do

IN THIS CHAPTER: Many Factors Influence Food Availability ▪ Innate, Cultural, and Individual Factors Influence Food Preferences ▪ Influences on Food Consumption Interact with Each Other ▪ Food Habits Can Be Changed by Using Behavior Modification Techniques

Why do you eat what you do? "That's simple," you may be thinking, "I eat what I eat because I *like* it." That's okay for openers—personal preference is a strong factor in food choice—but there's probably much more to your selection than a simple matter of sensory appeal.

If you stepped up to a cafeteria line at lunchtime today and were presented with a choice of a chef's salad with meat and egg, or a hot dish of macaroni and cheese, which would you take? You might opt for the salad because you would expect to feel refreshed by its crispness. But perhaps you avoid meat for philosophical reasons, so you lean toward the macaroni and cheese instead. It's possible that neither one appeals to you; where is the roast beef, anyway? That's something you could really sink your teeth into, you might be thinking.

Or if you were in the grocery store cereal aisle deciding whether to try some cooked cereal instead of the dry types you've favored for the last several years, what could cause you to switch? Perhaps you've seen one of your roommates eating hot cereal, obviously enjoying it. Maybe it reminded you for a fleeting moment of an especially chilly morning in fall way back when you were in elementary school, when your mother spooned some steaming oatmeal into a dish for you with the comment, "Try this—it will keep you nice and warm 'til you get to school." You might have seen an ad on TV just last night mentioning that there's "nothing artificial" in a particular brand of hot cereal . . . and now you find yourself noticing that it is much cheaper than any of the cold cereals that you normally eat.

Will you do it? Will you make the break from a firmly entrenched habit to try something different?

As you can see from even these limited examples, a multitude of factors besides your liking particular foods can influence food selection. We will identify and discuss these factors in this chapter, and show how interrelated they are.

In general, what you *choose* to eat is contingent on what is *available* to you and what you *favor*. For most of us, current eating practices were shaped primarily by the foods we were given as children and by how we reacted to those items.

The chapter concludes with a section on making *changes* in food habits. We are not suggesting that every reader needs to modify his or her food habits: many of you are discovering as you evaluate your current food practices that they are very healthful ones and are well worth continuing. But others of you will find some way(s) in which your eating could be improved, and you will want to do something about it. We offer some general guidelines on how to go about making changes in your diet—suggestions that will help you succeed at the challenging business of changing long-term habits.

You can't eat what you don't have. Many factors influence what foods are available to you. Some of these you will recognize as influences on you individually. Others have more direct effects on people who deal with food at the commercial level, such as farmers and distributors, but they shape your food supply just as surely.

We include examples of influences on food availability at the national and international level; these will give you a chance to see just how favorable North America's situation is, and why food choices are more limited in many other areas of the world.

Basic Agricultural Production Resources

Four conditions must be present for producing food.

Land. Land with topsoil is basic to most food production, since it supplies the chemical substances that plants need to grow. Animals, in turn, eat plants and other animals to get the chemicals that originated in the soil.

If there is a need to increase food production, the key question is, "How much farmable acreage is not yet being cultivated?" Recent estimates are that even in densely populated southeast Asia, only about three-fourths of the cultivable land is now in use; in South America proportionally even more land is available (Scrimshaw and Taylor, 1980). However, much of this land needs improvement before it can be farmed, and this requires capital investment. If people can't raise the money needed for land reclamation, they are no better off (for the time being) than if they didn't have the land at all.

Although it is encouraging that more cultivable land exists, some negative factors are at work as well. Some land that is currently used for agriculture is being lost due to erosion by wind and/or water, excess buildup of minerals, and urban and highway sprawl.

North America does not feel the pinch regarding land availability as acutely as the more densely populated regions of the world do. In fact, we have such a large quantity of land for meeting our own food needs that periodically we take acreage *out* of cultivation in order to limit production, if there are financial incentives to do so.

Water. Some agricultural experts believe that fresh water will be the most limiting of the basic food production resources in the last quarter of this century. Although *rainfall* has been relied on for aeons to furnish water for crops, the increasing practice of irrigation (which has made more land

Figure 9.1 Energy in agriculture. Energy from a variety of sources can be used to increase food production. Human labor was the original form used, and it is still the major source in many areas of the world today. Although machine-assisted production makes it possible for a small number of farmers to produce food for large numbers of people, agriculture that relies heavily on petroleum contributes to the depletion of a finite energy source.

available for cultivation) now draws heavily on *underground* supplies of fresh water, and these are being depleted in some areas.

The need for underground water for agricultural purposes and the growth of certain major urban centers now puts farmers and city-dwellers in competition with each other for fresh water in some areas. As with land, North Americans have enjoyed such plentiful sources in the past that we have been casually extravagant in our use of this resource. Undoubtedly, the conservation measures that so far have touched us directly—such as shutting off fountains that used to run continuously, limiting or discontinuing the practice of watering lawns, and serving water in restaurants only on request—are only the beginning. There are many other ways in which this resource can be spared.

Water is also important as the natural habitat of certain animal foods: fish and shellfish from oceans, lakes, and rivers make important contributions to the diets of many people. However, we have come to learn that food from these sources also has a limit. Therefore a new technology—fish farming—is being developed to provide ideal conditions for fish reproduction and growth. In this way, maturing fish are protected from natural predators so that the number of young that grow to a size suitable for food use is hundreds of times what nature would have allowed. The current expense of this technology limits its use at present.

Climate. Besides suitable land and sufficient water, several other factors influence whether specific plants will grow. Sufficient sunlight is a requisite for plant growth, as is an appropriate temperature range that lasts for a season long enough to allow a crop to mature. Some plants thrive in the heat of year-round tropical climates; others do well in a cool environment with a short growing season.

Many experts suggest that the climate of an area is not fixed for all time. Some theorize that the earth is in a cooling-off period now, and that we are gradually entering another ice age. In contrast, other experts hypothesize that the increasing number of minute pollutant and dust particles in the atmosphere is forming a "greenhouse" over the industrial parts of the world that will hold in the sun's warmth and make the temperature higher than it would otherwise have been. Either of these possibilities would affect what crops can be grown and where.

Energy. For a crop to produce a yield that is greater than wild growth would provide, energy must be invested by people, with or without the help of animals and/or machinery. The production of some types of crops requires a great deal of energy input, whereas others are much less energy-intensive. Farmer's decisions about what crops to plant are partly influenced by the readily available energy sources, whether human labor, water buffaloes, or tractors and gasoline.

In the United States, the agricultural system (from food production up to consumption) relies heavily on fossil fuel use. This highly mechanized system allows a relatively small proportion of the population to produce food for the entire population (Figure 9.1). However, to grow 1 kcalorie of food, process it, and bring it to the table, we use about 9 kcalories of fossil fuel (Steinhart and Steinhart, 1978). On the other hand, in China, where human labor provides most of the energy, only 1 kcalorie of fossil fuel is used to produce about 20 kcalories of food, an almost 200-fold difference in need for a finite energy source per kcalorie produced. It has been estimated that if the whole world used as energy-intensive agricultural methods as the United States does, the world's supply of petroleum would be exhausted in a few decades (Pimintel et al., 1978).

Energy has another important implication for agriculture. The production of chemical fertilizer depends on energy being available, and appropriate application of fertilizer to an intensively farmed soil can increase crop production to as much as four times what the unfertilized yield would have been (Brown, 1970). Unfortunately, many farmers in developing countries simply don't have the money to buy chemical fertilizers.

Figure 9.2 World population: Past and present. Although early population growth was very gradual, the growth in recent history shows a dramatic increase. If this trend continues, proportional increases in food production will be necessary to provide proper nutrition. [Reference: Westing, A.H. 1981. A note on how many humans that have ever lived. *Bioscience* 31(no.7):523–524.]

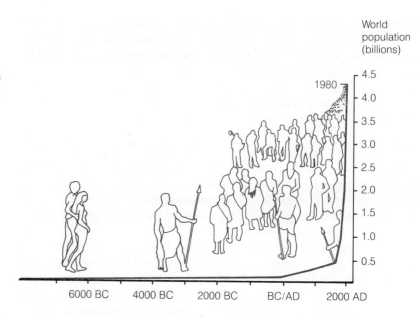

Demand for Food

The amount of arable land and the quantity of food that can be produced are concerns for everyone because the demand for food is increasing. Some of the demand comes from people who are now hungry and who want more and better food.

The other aspect of demand is population: how many bodies need to be nourished? The timeline in Figure 9.2 shows how population has been changing. The production of food will have to increase dramatically to keep up with the likely additions to the world's population, unless there is a drastic reduction in the rate of population growth.

Technology

Transportation methods, from oxcart to airplane, allow for food choices beyond what the immediate area has to offer. Papayas from the Philippines can be purchased in the United States, and watermelons from Mexico can be found in the northern part of Canada.

However, the flow of food in the other direction does not always proceed so smoothly: in many areas of the world where people are starving, food cannot reach them because there is no way to get it to them. Washed-out roads and the absence of landing fields have led to the failure of many relief efforts.

Food preservation techniques also help overcome the limitations of geography and season. When foods are dried, dehydrated, irradiated, canned, cooled, frozen, or sterilized in a retort pouch, they can be available far beyond the time of production and harvest. Apples, picked in autumn, can be used year-round, thanks to the many ways in which they can be preserved.

These combined technologies have enabled us to have everyday access to foods that would have been regarded as exotic just a century ago. When your great-grandmother was a girl, would she have been able to have pineapple whenever she wanted it?

Politics

Groups of people with power can influence both how much and what kinds of food are available to an area. Historically, conquering soldiers from other countries brought food customs with them that eventually influenced the food habits of the subjugated people. The influence was not all one way, though, since the native foodways also affected the soldiers' habits in time, bringing about a blend of cuisines.

Governments vary in the extent to which they influence the production and distribution of food. In some countries, influence is so direct and far-reaching that the government monitors the entire production process, and later collects and distributes most of the crop. When the disposition of food is determined by the government, the intent of the rulers determines whether the people's needs will be taken seriously. In some Communist countries, it is reported, people receive food based partly on their needs for energy, depending on the type of work they do. But if governments or business concerns are more interested in international trade than in meeting their populations' needs, they may sell a food product to another country instead of making it available to their own people.

Other governments may be less direct about their involvement, but nonetheless they exert influence through certain incentives or disincentives. For example, in the United States, a farmer may feel it is too risky to raise a particular crop if there is no government price support or protective tariff for the product that will guarantee a certain minimal income from it. He or she may decide to grow an economically safer crop instead.

Governments can also play the very helpful role of protecting its citizens from dangerous items that may appear in the food supply. Particularly in the developed countries, it is a governmental function to ban or remove foods from the marketplace. In the United States, such tasks are shared primarily by the Food and Drug Administration (FDA), the Department of Agriculture, and the Department of Commerce.

Political decisions are often economic decisions at the same time. For example, the government makes political/economic decisions about who is eligible for financial food assistance through programs such as food stamps and school lunches. Whether or not people receive these grants can make a substantial difference in what foods are available to them.

Economics

At the national and international level, economics has a far-reaching effect on the food supply. If the people of a country are hungry and poor, they cannot afford the agricultural supplies and technology that could improve food production: as mentioned earlier, such farmers often cannot buy fertilizer, which could dramatically increase crop yield. A poor economy

Figure 9.3 The effect of income on the composition of the diet. The percentages of kcalories that come from various nutrients and food sources change with the economics of a country. Populations with higher per capita incomes consume more animal products, fats, and sugar while they eat fewer starchy foods than low-income people do. (Adapted from Périssé, J., F. Sizaret, and P. Francois. 1969. The effect of income on the structure of the diet. *FAO Nutrition Newsletter* 7:1.)

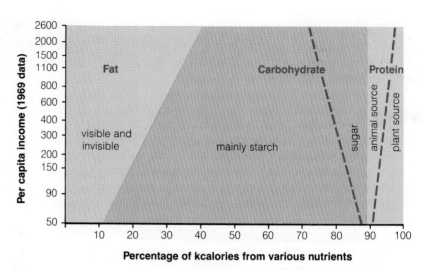

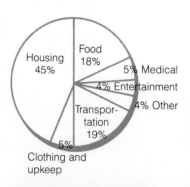

Figure 9.4 How the United States consumer dollar is spent. (Data source; U.S. Department of Agriculture. 1981. *Food composition, prices, and expenditures.* USDA Statistical Bulletin No. 656. Washington, DC: USDA Economics and Statistics Service.)

usually cannot afford food processing plants and effective storage systems, either. In some developing countries, loss of food due to infestation and rotting is as high as 40% of the crop. In the United States, with the benefit of such technologies, these losses are held to about 10%.

If a country cannot produce and preserve adequate food for its needs due to economic reasons, it is also in no position to buy food from other countries. It is even more expensive to buy from outside your borders than it is to produce your own food. Thus, few countries import even 10% of their food.

The status of the economy influences both the amounts and types of foods that are available to people. Périssé et al. (1969) have documented how the types of food consumed in 85 countries differed according to average per capita incomes. Figure 9.3 shows graphically that people with more money consume more animal products, fats, and sugars. People in leaner economic circumstances rely much more heavily on starchy plant foods. Do not assume that all of these economically related changes are nutritionally desirable: they simply state *what has been done* by populations in different financial situations.

You can probably understand how economics influences food availability in a personal way if you have ever had "too much month left at the end of the money," and had to forego some kinds of foods you would have liked to buy in favor of less expensive items.

According to the U.S. Bureau of Labor Statistics, in 1979 food represented an average of about 18% of families' total expenditures (Figure 9.4). The percentage of income spent for food varies with the level of income, though: USDA statistics show that in 1979 a family that had a gross income of approximately $6500 spent close to $1500 for food (23%), whereas a family earning $17,500 spent $2500 (14%) (USDA, 1981). As income rises, total dollars spent for food increase, but the percentage spent for food goes down. The situation in the United States stands in stark contrast to that of the developing countries, where food purchases consume as much as 70% of some families' incomes.

Economics influence food selection in other ways than simply financial ability to buy a certain food item. For example, if you are on a tight budget, you are not likely to have a freezer, which would limit your purchase of frozen foods. And what about cooking facilities? If you are living in a room with a hot plate rather than in an apartment with an oven, you're not likely to buy a turkey to fix for dinner. If you can afford to rent a small refrigerator for your dormitory room, the foods available to you for snacks will be different than if you stash your food in the closet. And on and on.

Although availability sets the outer limits on our food choices, this is not a real problem in the developed countries. For example, in the United States, large supermarkets have an estimated 12,000 different items for sale. In the country as a whole, there are thought to be between 35,000 and 60,000 different processed foods (Molitor, 1980).

How do we go about making choices from among such an overwhelming array of options?

Innate, Cultural, and Individual Factors Influence Food Preferences

The vastness of the food marketplace appears to be a mixed blessing. A student who grew up in Mexico but now lives in the United States expressed it one way when she said, "It's a lot harder to eat a good diet here than it was in Mexico; here, there is so much more to choose from."

In an article entitled "Pickin' and Choosin' in the Supermarket," Daniel I. Padberg agrees that "having more consumer choices is not unambiguously advantageous." He points out that choosing is confusing because choices depend not only on the issues of cost and quality, but on time as well. (We believe that there are even more factors involved.) The consumer is sometimes in a dilemma when forced to choose between a product that may offer time-saving convenience at one cost, and nutritional and/or aesthetic quality at another. What if the consumer wants all of them: moderate cost, convenience, sensory appeal, and nutritional quality? It becomes increasingly difficult to make decisions based on several variables as the market gets larger and larger.

But we do find ways of coping with the enormous number of food options with which we're confronted: we settle down to a core group of foods on which to rely. The experts estimate that in the United States, only 100 generic items account for 75% of the total amount of food consumed (Molitor, 1980).

Let's look now at the variety of factors that influence food choices.

An Inborn Factor

It is hypothesized that people's universal liking for sweet foods, in contrast to sour, bitter, or salty tasting items, is innate. It has been suggested that this is an important survival trait, since sweet foods are usually good sources of energy, which is basic to existence.

Babies who are tested in their first few days of life uniformly respond happily when they are given sweetened water. On the other hand, water with a fishy taste will bring scowls or crying. This liking of the sweet taste continues through the early years: in general, children's attitude about this taste is, "the sweeter, the better." But by the time people reach adulthood, there is a limit to how much sweetness they like. Adults can identify a "bliss point" at which the level of sweetness is most pleasing to them; they do not rate a higher or a lower concentration of sugar as favorably (Moskowitz, 1980).

The instinctive preference for sweet foods in the early years can be modified substantially by later experience and conditioning. For example, a group of laborers in Bangalore, India, consume a diet consisting of a wide variety of sour-tasting foods. These people, although they also respond favorably to sweetness, have developed a strong liking for the sour taste through conditioning that began in their formative years.

Cultural Factors

Wherever we are, the people around us influence our food choices. Sharing food has a significance that goes beyond nutrition: anthropologists point out that "in all societies, both simple and complex, eating is the primary way of initiating and maintaining human relationships" (Farb and Armelagos, 1980). Therefore, eating and socializing experiences become inextricably intertwined with each other.

Family and Caretakers. Starting with the first days of life, food and affection are usually given to a baby together during feeding by its caretakers. Therefore infants experience both physiological and emotional satisfaction and security when eating. Because they want to repeat these feelings of security as well as satisfy their hunger, their interest in eating is reinforced from the start.

As we grow older, foods that we associate with positive childhood experiences probably continue to generate feelings of being cared about and secure. Foods that are a traditional part of family celebrations, for example, may have favorable emotional associations for us. Or the foods that used to be served at a typical Sunday night supper, when the family gathered together to relax at the end of a busy weekend, may continue to warm us when we enjoy them in later years. The pleasant feelings associated with certain foods can influence us to choose them over other options.

On the other hand, it is also possible that certain foods associated with childhood may have an unhappy connotation, making it less likely that a person will favor those foods later. The untouched mound of zucchini on your plate during childhood may have been the cause of repeated power struggles that left you feeling ineffective in controlling your own life, and subconsciously turns you away from that vegetable even today.

Unfortunately, the emotional security that foods can engender can also be misapplied: some adults, for example, consume excessive amounts of favored foods to make themselves feel better emotionally. Used in this way, eating can become a substitute for adult ways of achieving security,

Figure 9.5 Influence of national origin on food choice. The ethnic groups from which a person originates can exert a strong influence on food choice.

such as building solid interpersonal relationships and being involved in activities that give a sense of individual worth.

National Origin.   The ethnic group from which a person originates can exert a strong influence on food choice. Even after people move from their homeland, they often maintain their prior food customs as an important part of their identity and security. Your family may have lived in North America for several generations, but your Italian grandmother gets tremendous satisfaction from preparing, eating, and watching you enjoy her homemade ravioli. Eating the foods of your forebears gives you a link to your relatives in this country as well as to those still in their ethnic homeland (Figure 9.5).

Cultures often have a very basic "superfood" that has been the key to their survival over the ages, and around which the rest of their cuisine has developed. The rice of the Orient and the wheat bread of Europe are examples of cultural superfoods. Cultures may assign mystical properties to these foods that further increase their status among the people.

Foods other than superfoods have also been construed to have supernatural powers. For example, the British in past centuries believed that spices and milk were foods that could make people sad; and that plain, robust beef produced plain, robust men. In some cultures even today, people believe that it is important to balance the hot, cold, wet, and dry "humors" thought to be inherent in particular foods.

The assigning of extraordinary powers to consumables is also found

Figure 9.6 Influence of religion on food choice. Religious traditions may pervade an individual's daily eating habits or have their major effect on special holidays, such as the Jewish Passover.

today in a pseudo-scientific folklore that suggests that supplements of zinc or vitamin E beyond RDA levels can increase sexual potency, or that pangamic acid can increase athletic performance.

Much can be learned about a culture from its foods: the climate, economy, political situation, and religions of a country are reflected in its diet. In the United States, a melting pot of cultures, the increasing popularity of folk fairs, international foods groups, and ethnic restaurants give people the opportunity not only to reaffirm their own roots but to learn about other backgrounds as well.

Religious and Philosophical Groups. Certain groups make decisions about what foods are acceptable based on their moral perspectives and consequent systems of ethics. Seventh Day Adventists avoid eating animal flesh because they do not want to sustain themselves at the expense of another animal's life. (Or, as a leader of the former Shaker community at Pleasant Hill, Kentucky, so graphically phrased it, "Why make a graveyard of your stomach, when there are so many other good, wholesome things to eat?") The Latter Day Saints (Mormons) prefer not to consume caffeine, a stimulant, because it has a drug effect.

Hunger-consciousness groups concerned about feeding the world's population within the limitations of current agricultural resources suggest that a diet should emphasize plant foods and deemphasize foods of animal origin. They point out that such an emphasis would allow a greater volume of food production, thus providing nourishment for more people.

Philosophical or religious groups that share dietary practices have a more visible bond of identity with their group than the philosophy alone would provide. Some Jews, for example, adhere to demanding dietary laws. Jewish scholars suggest that the primary reason for retaining these practices is the sense of oneness with other Jews—both now and through the ages—that these group behaviors maintain, and the sense of uniqueness they create for the group (Figure 9.6).

Acceptability Continuum. Each culture holds attitudes about the acceptability of available items as foods. At one end of the continuum, you find the foods that are unanimously enjoyed by the population, including the cultural superfoods; the broad middle ground is occupied by an assortment of foods that have variable acceptance; and at the other end you find items that, although potentially nourishing, are rejected by a population for some reason. A group may even identify some of these latter items as taboo, or forbidden, foods.

In the United States, it is hard to think of foods that everybody accepts or that everybody rejects, since our population has been influenced by such diverse cultures. Therefore most foods in the United States occupy the wide middle range on the acceptance continuum. But for given subgroups, favored and rejected foods can be identified. For example, Americans of northern European ancestry tend to like dairy products but dislike insects. Of course, items that are repulsive to one group of people may be perfectly acceptable to another: in some regions of Africa, insects make important contributions to the diet.

The following Slice of Life notes other examples.

SLICE OF LIFE:
Differences in Food
Acceptance among Cultures

R.M. Deutsch, in his book *The New Nuts among the Berries,* points out that early cultures based their food choices on a tangled folklore inspired by observation, superstition, and taboo. He goes on to say:

We in the age of science are not so different. Americans wince at the idea of sitting down to a nice, juicy horse steak. Yet in France, horsemeat is widely sold as a delicacy, while the Indian is repelled by the meat of the cow.

We cannot understand tribes which find eggs and chicken disgusting food, but who love a good mouse or dog. To touch upon the ultimate in civilized repugnance, we are certainly loath to dine on one another. Yet before 1250 A.D., certain Tibetans ate the dead bodies of their parents . . . . Curiously, while most of us think of cannibalism as directed toward enemies, there are records of many cultures in which only the eating of loved ones was acceptable.

Reprinted with permission.
"The New Nuts Among the Berries," Ronald
M. Deutsch. Palo Alto, CA: Bull Publishing Co.
1977

Advertising. Since so many foods are in the middle range of acceptance in North America, food producers are intensely competitive in trying to persuade people to switch from the product they currently use to the producer's item. Interestingly, research has shown that when one brand of product was heavily advertised—for example, breakfast cereals—the sales of that brand of cereal went up, but so did the purchase of other brands (Gallo and Connor, 1982).

The fact that people are drawn to a product class through advertising

Table 9.1   Amount of Advertising Given to Various Types of Foods

MORE ADVERTISING

Foods for which the A/S[a] ratio is more than double the average	Foods for which the A/S ratio is above average
Alcoholic beverages	Confectionery products
Baked goods, frozen	Cookies and ice cream cones
Cake and other dessert mixes	Crackers and pretzels
Catsup; other meat sauces	Drinks, bottled and canned
Cereals, breakfast	Milks (flavored) and yogurt
Dinners, frozen	Potato chips
Macaroni, spaghetti, noodles	Vegetables, frozen
Margarine	Vegetable juices, canned
Mayonnaise	
Soups; canned specialties	
Sweeteners and syrups	
Tea; instant coffee	

AVERAGE AMOUNT OF ADVERTISING

LESS ADVERTISING

Foods for which the A/S ratio is below average	Foods for which the A/S ratio is the lowest
Bread, white; rolls	Beef; veal
Coffee, roasted	Cheese, natural and processed
Cottage cheese	Chicken; turkey
Dry beans, canned	Fish, frozen and processed
Fruits and vegetables, dried	Ice cream and ices
Fruit juices, canned	Lamb
Meats, canned	Milk, fluid
Oils	Nuts, canned
Rice, milled	Pork
Sausages	Vegetables, canned
Seafood, canned	Wheat flour
Sweet yeast goods	

[a]These lists are based on the advertising/sales (A/S) ratio, which is a measure of promotional aggressiveness. Note that many of the more heavily advertised products are high in energy value and low in other nutrients.
Reference: Gallo, A.E., and J.M. Connor. 1982. Advertising and American food consumption patterns. *National Food Review* 19:2–6.

is significant in discussions of nutrition since some of the most aggressively promoted products are for foods of relatively poor nutritional quality. Table 9.1 lists foods for which the advertising investment is high compared to the return in sales, and those for which little advertising is done in proportion to sales. If advertising attracts people to a product class, it is interesting to speculate on the impact there might be on people's nutritional intake if milk were advertised with as much aggressiveness as carbonated beverages are.

A study that looked specifically at the effect of television commercials on nursery-school children (Galst and White, 1976), found that children pressured their mothers at the supermarket to buy cereals and candy, the product classes most frequently advertised on TV during the course of the study. The children who were most caught up in watching the commercials tried to influence their mothers' purchases most often.

Television Programs. TV portrayal of food use may influence the food consumption patterns of the viewers, independently of advertising: on-camera food choices and frequency of consumption by actors and actresses may have a subtle influence on viewers' habits. Two studies showed that major network prime-time TV shows depict 9 (Gerbner et al., 1981) and 7.67 (Way, 1983) eating and other food-related activities per hour. Despite such frequency, few of the actors are overweight or have other associated health problems.

Regarding the quality of the food consumed, less nutritious items are shown being eaten more often than foods that are of higher nutritional quality by ratios of approximately 3:1 (Kaufman, 1980) and 2:1 (Way, 1983). More research is needed to show whether and/or to what extent such messages affect the viewers' "nutrition socialization" process. The effect of food references in other media could be similarly explored.

Status. Foods that are scarce and expensive enjoy higher status than other foods: using them demonstrates to others that you are affluent enough to afford them. You might choose to order lobster tails rather than a toasted cheese sandwich—even if you liked them equally—to impress your companions or even the waiter. And it is possible that somebody entertaining an important guest might choose a wine of rare vintage and high cost, not because his palate demanded it, but rather because he could gain status in his guest's eyes by being knowledgeable and able to afford a fine wine.

Peer Groups. Peer groups, or subgroups distinguished by age, sex, occupation, or other interests, also influence their members' food choices. This accounts for certain foods and/or restaurants falling in and out of favor with particular groups of people: foods that become "in" with teenagers and eating places that become teenage hangouts are common results of peer influence (Figure 9.7).

Members of a group may change their choices to align themselves more closely with a group member of higher status. When the most financially successful member of a group of business executives shows a strong preference for a particular brand of Scotch whiskey, some associates are likely to recognize its "superiority" as well. Sexism also has an influence:

Figure 9.7 Influence of peer groups on food choice. Teens are particularly vulnerable to the influence of their peers' food preferences.

certain men may feel disinclined to choose a salad as an entree because it has a feminine connotation to some members of society.

Unique Personal Factors

As we noted at the beginning of the chapter, you also eat what you eat because you *like* it. There is no doubt that the final determinant of what you eat is your own individual characteristics and preferences.

Sensory Preferences.   Sensory characteristics that distinguish foods from each other are tastes (sweet, sour, bitter, salty); smells; flavors (blends of taste and smell); textures (crisp/limp, tender/tough, firm/soft, dry/soggy, smooth/lumpy); temperatures; colors; and shapes and sizes. You undoubtedly have preferences in each of these categories, and like them combined in certain ways with other characteristics.

Degree of Familiarity.   Another way in which you are unique is the degree to which you rely on familiarity in choosing food. Some people are very adventuresome and are eager to try new foods. Others much prefer to eat the foods they have had many times before.

Psychological Importance of Food.   Do you eat to live, or live to eat? Some people who are very food-centered begin to think about their next eating opportunity as soon as they have finished the last; they derive much comfort from eating. Other people tend to forget about food until hunger reminds them; different aspects of their living fill their time and provide their major satisfactions. Most of us find ourselves between these two extremes.

Beliefs about Health Effects of Food.   Beliefs can, but not necessarily will, affect your choice of food. You are influenced by your own perceptions of the effects various foods have on you: if you feel stomach pain after eating spicy foods, or gassiness after eating certain vegetables, you will probably eat them less often or in smaller amounts.

Some of your beliefs arise from what you have learned about nutrition from other sources such as radio, TV, magazines, newspapers, and books. Unfortunately, popular nutrition information is not always reliable, as Table 9.2 shows. Nonetheless, you have integrated some of that informa-

Table 9.2	How Popular Magazines Rate on Nutrition	
Rating	**Magazine**	**Accuracy (%)**
Excellent	Better Homes and Gardens	100
	Changing Times	100
	Fifty Plus	100
	Parents	100
	Reader's Digest	100
	Redbook	100
	Science '82, Science '83	100
	Scientific American	100
	Seventeen	100
	Good Housekeeping	95
	Self	94
	Essence	93
	Health	93
	Consumer Reports	90
	Glamour	90
Generally reliable	Vogue	89
	American Health	88
	Consumers' Digest	86
	Mademoiselle	84
	Consumers' Research	82
Inconsistent	National Enquirer	77
	Ladies' Home Journal	75
	McCall's	75
	Runner's World	70
	Family Circle	64
Unreliable	Cosmopolitan	47
	Saturday Evening Post	36
	Prevention	31
	Let's Live	20
	Harper's Bazaar	18

The American Council on Science and Health (ACSH) reviewed nutrition articles in 30 widely circulated magazines, and rated them for scientific accuracy, as shown in this table.
Adapted from Hatfield, D. 1984. New ACSH Survey Rates Magazine Nutrition Accuracy. *ACSH News & Views* 5(no.3):1–10.

Figure 9.8 Spending of the United States food dollar. This graph shows into what channels food money went in 1980: more than a third went for food eaten away from home. The affluence and lifestyle of many Americans cause us to eat more expensive away-from-home food than people in most other cultures. (Adapted from Padberg, D.I. 1981. Pickin' and choosin' in the supermarket. In *1981 yearbook of agriculture.* Washington, DC: Government Printing Office.)

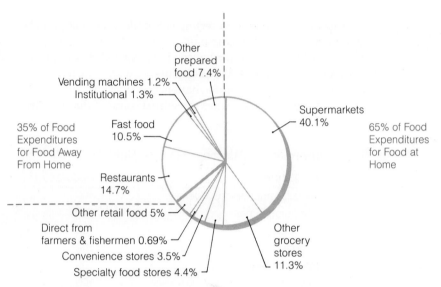

tion into the knowledge base from which you make day-to-day eating decisions.

What you believe to be true about the effects of nutrition on health may or may not be accurate, but it can nonetheless influence your choices. The effect of such beliefs is substantial: USDA reported in a 1979 survey done by their agency that two-thirds of the families they interviewed had made recent dietary changes for health reasons.

Lifestyle. Your chosen lifestyle influences your eating. Are you always in a rush? That will probably direct you toward convenience grocery items or restaurant meals. This is apparently the case with many Americans: more than a third of the food dollar is spent for food away from home (Figure 9.8). On the other hand, if you are often at home for several leisurely hours at a stretch, you may take the time to prepare more meals "from scratch."

What are your cooking skills, and how willing are you to learn to make new things? Do you thrive on routine and enjoy the same regularity in your meal schedule, or do you skip some meals and eat whenever it's convenient? Are you a health buff who is deliberate about getting the right exercise and food to enhance your well-being? Many lifestyles link with different food-related behaviors.

Influences on Food Consumption Interact with Each Other

Although our discussion of food availability and preference dealt with each factor separately, in real life they act in combination, influencing each other.

Consider how multifactorial the matter of food consumption is. You probably can see now why particular groups of people who have lived together in an area and have been influenced by the same factors for a long period of time have developed distinctive ethnic food patterns. You can even recognize which groups are being referred to from descriptions of their typical cuisines. For example, who uses corn and beans as a mainstay of their diet? Or whose diet emphasizes fish, rice, and vegetables?

The fact that your eating is strongly influenced by factors other than your own preference does not mean that you are enmeshed for life in your current eating pattern. For one thing, *the external factors that influence your eating are constantly undergoing change;* so will your eating habits. Food habits are dynamic even though changes occur rather slowly.

For another thing, you can influence some of the factors that influence availability: the consumer definitely has power in the marketplace, especially when people of similar intent take the same action. In the 1970s, pressure from parents of young children influenced the major baby food manufacturers to stop putting sugar and salt into their basic products. Manufacturers pay attention to consumers, particularly if their influence significantly depresses the sales of their products.

Further, *you can change your eating habits if you are determined to do so.* But it takes effort to override the many long-term influences that have brought your eating habits to what they are today. In the next section, we will discuss some tools that can be useful in changing eating practices, if a person chooses to do so.

Food Habits Can Be Changed by Using Behavior Modification Techniques

Changing eating habits is more likely to be successful if the person involved uses techniques that psychologists recognize as generally helpful for modifying behaviors (Hilgard et al., 1979). The following suggestions are particularly applicable to eating behaviors.

Influence of personal factors on food choice. Each individual favors certain foods because of sensory characteristics, psychological factors, beliefs about the healthfulness of the food, and lifestyle considerations.

Let's say that you have decided to increase your consumption of fruits and vegetables, after a long period of semi-neglecting these foods.

Self-Monitoring

Technique. First find out what you are eating. The most direct way to do this is to keep a record of your daily intake. Keep pencil and paper close at hand so that you can record what you consume, instead of trying to remember it hours later. Make note of time, items, amounts of food and beverages ingested, where you were at the time, whom you were with, what mood you were in, and whether you were hungry before you ate. This record not only documents your current behavior, which can help

Time	Food	Amount consumed	Location of eating	Others present	Mood
8:30 am	Wheat cereal	2 cups	kitchen	—	?
	2 % milk	1 cup			
	Coffee	1 cup			
11:00 am	Sweet roll	1 medium	outside classroom	class members	tense (exam)
12:30 pm	Beef, macaroni, tomato casserole	1 cup	union cafeteria	friends	relaxed
	Bread	2 slices			
	Butter	3 pats			
	Cola	12 oz			
	Chocolate pie	1 piece			
6:15 pm	Fried fish	5 oz	kitchen	roommate	happy, relaxed
	Hash browned potatoes	1 cup			
	Lettuce salad	1 cup			
	2 % milk	1½ c			
	Frosted white cake	1 piece			
9:30 pm	Corn snacks	3 oz	living room	—	pressured
	Root beer	12 oz can			

Figure 9.9 A record of food intake for possible behavior modification

you understand your eating pattern, but it also establishes a baseline against which you can compare your behavior as it changes (Figure 9.9).

Example. Presumably, your initial diet records will be devoid of fruits and vegetables. On the other hand, you might be surprised to see a glass of fruit juice or a mixed item containing vegetables show up here and there. You need to know what you are really eating to assess whether the change you intend to make is needed and realistic.

Being Realistic in Your Goals

Technique. Once you know how you are eating, you can design some realistic new behaviors for yourself. Set goals you honestly believe you can attain, but don't expect to get there in one step.

It is axiomatic that small changes in habits have a greater chance of success than sweeping changes have. Approach the changes gradually, incorporating the one easiest new behavior at a time until it becomes a comfortable part of your eating pattern; then move on to the next easiest habit to change.

Example. Maybe you discovered that despite your lack of attention to fruit and vegetable consumption, you inadvertently took in a couple of servings each day anyway. You might decide that since you already get two servings without even trying, you ought to be able to increase that by another two servings to reach the recommended minimum of four. To begin with, you decide to just add one serving at lunch, since it is a change you think will be an easy one for you.

Controlling Conditions

Technique. When you review your diet records, you may be able to identify certain situations in which you are more likely than in others to eat the way you want to. Once you know what those circumstances are, you may be able to help control your behavior by setting up the appropriate conditions.

Example. You notice from your food records that you eat more fruits and vegetables when you and your apartment mate fix dinner together than when you make your own, since your combined thoughts and efforts go into the joint meals. Maybe you could plan a few more shared dinners per week than currently happen.

Modifying Eating Behaviors

Technique. Observe the way you typically conduct yourself at a meal. At what pace do you eat? Do you eat things in a particular order, or alternately? What effect do these patterns have on the amount of each item you eat? Which behaviors can you change to help you achieve your goal?

Example. You might discover that you are more likely to finish your dinner salad if you eat it before the entree instead of with the meal or at the end when you are no longer feeling hungry.

Self-Reinforcement of the New, Desired Behaviors

Technique. Recently learned behaviors are reinforced if people quickly reward themselves for a job well done. Many different kinds of rewards work for people—it all depends on the individual.

Some people may feel sufficiently rewarded by seeing their progress in their food records. Other people may prefer to reward themselves by watching TV or phoning a friend. It is preferable to give rewards for good behaviors than to punish undesired behaviors, since rewards have longer lasting effects on behavior than punishments do.

Example. It may be enough of a reward for you to underline the increasing number of fruits and vegetables on your diet record as you review it at the end of each day. Comparing your recent records to the baseline versions may be sufficiently rewarding to prompt you to continue your new food behaviors until they become habitual.

These techniques of behavior modification can be useful in making dietary changes of many different kinds. So far, their most popular application has been for weight control, which will be mentioned again later.

From the material in this chapter, you can see that each person's unique food habits derive from the interaction of an extensive network of factors that influence food availability and personal preference. We are continually making subtle, unconscious changes in our diets as these factors change around us. But deliberate changes are more challenging to accomplish; fortunately, there are tools we can use to enhance our chances of success if there is a compelling reason to modify the way we eat.

SUMMARY

■ The foods you choose to eat reflect a whole spectrum of influences, ranging from what is *available* to you to what you *favor*.

■ Many factors influence food availability: basic agricultural production resources (land, water, climate, energy); demand for food; technology (transportation methods, food preservation techniques); politics; and economics. North Americans are in an especially privileged position, having a wide variety of nutritious foods reliably available all year round.

■ Innate, cultural, and individual factors also influence food preferences. An inborn liking for sweet foods, our family lives and cultural/religious heritage, the impressions made by advertising, the influence of peers, and unique personal factors all contribute in important ways to our eating choices.

■ Although these influences on food consumption exert a strong effect on your individual eating habits, you can make changes in your habits if you are determined to do so. The most effective techniques for changing food habits involve behavior modification. Self-monitoring is the best way to see whether you habits are in fact what you think they are; if you do decide to make changes, it is important to be realistic in your goals, to control conditions to the extent possible, to modify your behavior one step at a time in ways that are acceptable to you, and to give yourself positive reinforcement for desired changes.

REFERENCES

Brown, L.R. 1970. Human food production as a process in the biosphere. *Scientific American* 223(no.3):160–173.

Deutsch, R.M. 1977. *The new nuts among the berries.* Palo Alto, CA: Bull Publishing Co.

Farb, P., and G. Armelagos. 1980. *Consuming Passions.* Boston: Houghton Mifflin Company.

Gallo, A.E., and J.M. Connor. 1982. Advertising and American food consumption patterns. *National Food Review* 19:2–6.

Galst, J.P., and M.A. White. 1976. The unhealthy persuader: the reinforcing value of television and children's purchase-influencing attempts at the supermarket. *Child Development* 47:1089–1096.

Gerbner, G., L. Gross, M. Morgan, and N. Signorielli. 1981. Health and medicine on television. *New England Journal of Medicine* 305:901–904.

Hatfield, D. 1984. New ACSH survey rates magazine nutrition accuracy. *ACSH News & Views* 5(no.3): 1–10.

Hilgard, E.R., R.L. Atkinson, and R.C. Atkinson. 1979. *Introduction to psychology.* New York: Harcourt Brace Jovanovich, Inc.

Kaufman, L. 1980. Prime time nutrition. *Journal of Communication* 30:37–46.

Molitor, G.T.T. 1980. The food system in the 1980s. *Journal of Nutrition Education* 12(no.2) supplement:103–111.

Moskowitz, H.R. 1980. Searching for good taste in food. *The Professional Nutritionist* 12(no.4):7–10.

Padberg, D.I. 1981. Pickin' and Choosin' in the Supermarket. In *1981 yearbook of agriculture.* Washington, DC: Government Printing Office.

Périssé, J., F. Sizaret, and P. Francois. 1969. The effect of income on the structure of the diet. (FAO) *Nutrition Newsletter* 7:1.

Pimintel, D., L.E. Hurd, A.C. Bellotti, M.J. Forster, I.N. Oka, O.D. Sholes, and R.J. Whitman. 1978. Food production and the energy crisis. In *The feeding web*, ed. J.D. Gussow. Palo Alto, CA: Bull Publishing Co.

Scrimshaw, N.S., and L. Taylor. 1980. Food. *Scientific American* 243(no.3):78–88.

Steinhart, J.S., and C.E. Steinhart. 1978. Energy use in the U.S. food system. In *The feeding web*, ed. J.D. Gussow. Palo Alto, CA: Bull Publishing Co.

U.S. Department of Agriculture. 1981. *Food composition, prices, and expenditures.* USDA Statistical Bulletin No. 656. Washington, DC:USDA Economics and Statistics Service.

Way, W.L. 1983. Food-related behaviors in prime-time television. *Journal of Nutrition Education* 15: 105–109.

Westing, A.H. 1981. A note on how many humans that have ever lived. *Bioscience* 31(no.7):523–524.

10

Energy Imbalance and the Weight Debate

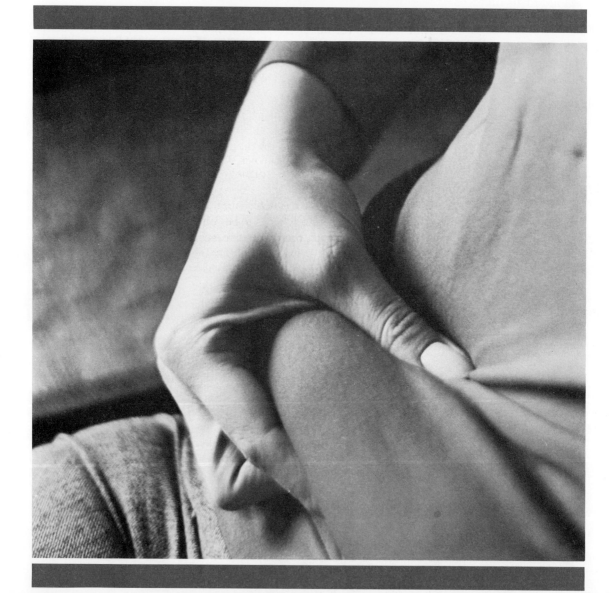

IN THIS CHAPTER: Too Much or Too Little Fat Interferes with Health and Living ▪ How Do People Arrive at Their Individual Body Weights? ▪ You Can Estimate Your Ideal Body Weight from a Combination of Guidelines ▪ Energy Imbalance Has Both Physical and Psychological Effects ▪ People Have Tried Thousands of Techniques for Losing Body Fat ▪ Opposite Techniques Can Be Used to Add Body Weight

Thin is in. Who could believe otherwise? Look at the number of articles about how to lose weight that appear in popular magazines and tabloids. Look at the support services that abound to aid people in North America in their quest for thinness—diet businesses, restaurants that specialize in low kcalorie fare, exercise spas, even hypnosis and acupuncture treatments are offered to help people shed body fat.

Because not many people can afford to use the expensive services of elegant residential "fat farms," the business community has recognized a lucrative potential in less elaborate services and special products. We now have access to low-kcalorie convenience foods, so-called "weight loss drugs," exercise equipment, and computerized diet scales that give digital read-outs of kcalories in foods, among many other products.

Although the attention our culture devotes to the cosmetic aspect of body weight may seem excessive, it is not inappropriate for us to be concerned about body weight from a health perspective. Some experts regard overweight as our number one nutrition problem. It has been linked to the development of chronic conditions—such as heart disease and diabetes—that complicate life and make it less pleasant; and, especially at higher levels, it is associated with early death. We will have more to say about the health hazards of overweight in this chapter.

Why do so many people have trouble controlling body weight, when much of the animal kingdom regulates body weight automatically? There are several scientific theories about why people become overweight, which we will look at shortly. We will also open a Pandora's box by asking the question of *what ideal weight is*. (To paraphrase that familiar adage about the weather: everybody talks about ideal body weight, but nobody knows exactly what it is.) And of course we'll discuss techniques—both healthy and unhealthy—that have been used for weight reduction.

All this emphasis on overweight seems to ignore those people with the opposite problem: extreme thinness. People who would like to be heavier but consistently lose the weight gains they have made feel just as frustrated as overweight people who cannot achieve their desired body weights. It is hard for either group to appreciate the other's problem.

What can we say to you who are unhappily underweight? The truth is that there has been very little research directed at moderately underweight individuals in the developed countries. There is some information that can be gleaned from epidemiological studies, though. We will use such materials to address your concerns, but we admit openly that we do not have as much data to work with regarding this problem. We can only hope that the implications of low body weight will become a more thoroughly studied topic in the future.

The only manifestations of underweight that have received intensive scientific scrutiny in the developed countries are eating disorders such as anorexia nervosa. These conditions are complex, and we will discuss them in a separate chapter following this one.

Although this entire chapter deals with overweight and underweight in some detail, keep in mind that *the majority of college students do not have either problem.* If you are in that fortunate situation, this chapter has a message for you anyway: why it is important to stay at your ideal weight. It may also improve your understanding of how difficult it is to make a deliberate change in body weight—a fact that the rest of you already know.

Let's begin by discussing what's unhealthy about extremes in body fat.

Too Much or Too Little Fat Interferes With Health and Living

People who are overly fat or excessively thin encounter problems in almost every aspect of living.

Effects of Too Much Body Fat

In the United States, an estimated one-third of the adults weigh 10% or more above their desirable weights (Office of Health Research, Statistics, and Technology, 1979). Depending on the criteria used, 3–20% of American children are thought to be obese (Alford and Bogle, 1982; Knittle, 1972).

Before going any further, we should define some common terms as they are used in the technical literature: overweight is often used to mean 10–20% above ideal body weight; obese means more than 20% above ideal body weight. In this book we will often use the term overfat to include both. We favor this term because it indicates that the concern is about people who have surplus *fat*, not about those who are heavier than average because they have a large frame or an unusually large amount of muscle.

overweight—10–20% above ideal body weight

obese—more than 20% above ideal body weight

overfat—term used in this book to refer to surplus fat in any amount

Health Risks. People who are overfat have a statistically greater likelihood than people in the general population of developing these problems:

- high blood pressure
- atherosclerosis
- enlarged heart
- cancer of the endometrium (lining of the uterus) and breast in women
- diabetes of the adult-onset type
- gall bladder disease
- arthritis and gout
- kidney problems
- skin disorders

- menstrual irregularities, ovarian abnormalities, and complications of pregnancy

- upper respiratory problems

- increased accident-proneness

- greater surgical risk
  (Van Itallie, 1979; Rimm and White, 1980).

[Remember that statistical association is not proof of causation (Van Itallie and Hirsch, 1979). For example, overfatness per se does not cause heart disease directly, but the high blood pressure that is often associated with excess body weight can (Keys, 1980).] The risk of developing these problems is influenced by many factors including the amount of the excess fat (Van Itallie, 1979); the individual's age (Rimm and White, 1980); and the age at which the excess fat storage began (Van Itallie, 1979).

Even more serious than the aggravation of chronic problems is the fact that people who are considerably overfat die younger—of coronary heart disease, diabetes, strokes, and various digestive diseases (Van Itallie, 1979).

Psychosocial Problems. People who are severely overfat testify that this condition carries both psychological and social penalties; research confirms this (Brownell and Wadden, 1983). Obese people have experienced discrimination in all settings, including at school and in the job market. Such treatment often results in a negative self-image, feelings of loneliness, and a sense of not being able to fulfill oneself. At lesser degrees of overfatness, it is reasonable to presume that there is less stigma.

Practical Problems. Besides leading to health and psychosocial problems, being very overfat brings with it many inconveniences in living, because so much of our environment is scaled for people of average size. Furniture may not be big enough or strong enough for the very fat person; he or she may find it difficult to get behind the wheel of a car; and attractive clothes that fit may be hard to find and expensive. Even people who carry just 20 pounds of surplus fat can sometimes identify with these problems, although they experience them to a much lesser degree.

Effects of Too Little Body Fat

Although there is less information available on the consequences of underweight in the developed countries, we have learned about a number of ill effects.

Health Risks. Epidemiological studies done in the more developed countries show that the relationship between mortality and body weight is U-shaped: that is, both underweight and overweight people are at greater risk of death, particularly the 5–10% at each end of the scale (Brunzell, 1983).

Normal functioning of the immune system can also be influenced by underweight. Although people who are normally lean do not have a hampered immune response, in prolonged, severe protein-energy malnutrition the body is less able to defend itself against infection (Sherman and Johnston, 1982).

Low body fatness in females is associated with delay or loss of menstrual function, which may lead to reproductive problems and general deterioration of health. This phenomenon occurs in an estimated 5–20% of female athletes (including dancers) who train vigorously (Mann, 1981). However, there may not be a direct cause-and-effect relationship, since menstruation does not cease at the same percentage of body fat in all individuals (Scott and Johnston, 1982).

Menstruation also stops in those who lose a great deal of body fat for other reasons, such as in the eating disorder anorexia nervosa. Here, the *rate* of fat loss seems to have an influence: menstruation may cease even before body fat stores drop to low levels. This fact suggests that hormonal activity may be involved as well (Nutrition and the M.D., 1982).

Impact on Fitness and Feeling of Well-Being. The Minnesota Starvation Studies, done during World War II using conscientious objectors or military volunteers as subjects, point out other effects of lower-than-normal body weight (Brozek, 1982). For six months, men were fed diets containing approximately half the number of kcalories needed for maintenance of their weight; the result was that they dropped to about 76% of their prestarvation weights.

From 10% weight loss and downward, they had less strength than formerly. The effect on endurance was even more marked: their capacity for aerobic work, indicated by oxygen consumption, also began to deteriorate rapidly after 10% weight loss (Taylor et al., 1957). Both effects are shown in Figure 10.1.

Roughly two-thirds of these subjects reported losses in their feeling of well-being. They had a hard time concentrating, frequently felt "downhearted" and listless, and lost interest in interacting with other people. These effects eventually reversed as the men regained their original weights.

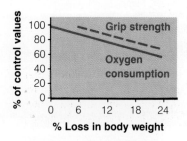

Figure 10.1 Effect of below-normal body weight on strength and work capacity. When men lost more than 10% of their normal body weights, their grip strength decreased. Their capacity for aerobic work also fell, as indicated by oxygen consumption.

How Do People Arrive at Their Individual Body Weights?

How do people come to weigh what they do, and why do people gain or lose body fat? These questions can be answered on two different levels. On one level, the answer is simple. People gain fat because they consume more energy than they expend—3,500 calories more to gain one pound of fat; they lose fat if they expend more energy than they consume. Their long-term experiences with fat gains and losses (plus normal growth) bring people to their current body weights.

However, the matter of *why*, at times, there may be imbalances between energy intake and output becomes considerably more complicated. We need to look at both sides of the energy equation to explore this matter.

Frontier

Factors That Influence Energy Intake

A number of factors seem to influence people's energy consumption.

Hunger. Humans, along with much of the rest of the animal kingdom, have an inborn mechanism called hunger that prompts energy intake that approximates recent energy output. There are two predominant theories about how hunger occurs. One is that two centers in the brain largely control hunger and satiety (satisfaction) by responding to levels of circulating nutrients, hormones, and neurotransmitters. The other theory is that the liver may have a primary role in intake regulation, sensing levels of circulating macronutrients and metabolites, and initiating nerve messages to start or stop eating (Friedman, 1982).

hunger—physiological drive to consume energy in roughly the amounts expended

There are other influences as well: stomach distention depresses intake, even if the material in the stomach does not have nutritive value. Timing of eating is significant, too: a snack eaten before a meal will cause the largest reduction in intake at the meal if the interval between the snack and the meal was 5 to 30 minutes (Kissileff, 1983).

Many women experience the effects of hormones on hunger beginning a few days before their menstrual periods. At that time of heightened hormonal activity, women may have high-carbohydrate food cravings that peak at the first or second day of the period and decrease thereafter, sometimes leaving a small residual weight gain (Simonson, 1982).

A currently popular theory about hunger and body weight regulation is called the set-point theory (Keesey and Corbett, 1984). This theory states that each person has a particular weight, or set-point, that he or she tends to maintain, and at which the body handles energy intake in a metabolically normal way. Although it may be possible to temporarily gain or lose weight by deliberate changes in food intake, body weight will return to the set-point after the person resumes eating in response to hunger. Eating in response to hunger is called *internal regulation.*

set-point theory—theory that each person tends to maintain the body weight arrived at by eating in response to hunger

Does this mean that you are shackled with your current set-point once and for all? Not necessarily, according to the scientists who support this theory: they hypothesize that the set-point can be lowered by regular, moderate exercise (Bennett and Gurin, 1982).

Classical studies on the relationship between activity, food intake, and body weight were done in the mid-1950s in a mill in India, where different jobs called for very different amounts of physical effort (Mayer et al., 1956). Some employees were engaged in sedentary work, others in light and medium activity, and the remainder in heavy and very heavy manual labor. Records were kept of the different groups' energy intakes and body weights.

The results are shown in Figure 10.2. Although most of the groups balanced their intakes with their needs, at the very lowest activity level, people consumed as many kcalories as some of the manual laborers. This energy imbalance of the sedentary workers resulted in their being the heaviest group. It appears that at least light activity is necessary for appetite regulation to work as it should. This research has its critics. Although animal studies and some later human studies support these findings, there is still debate about the role of exercise in energy intake regulation (Bjorntorp, 1982).

Figure 10.2 The relationship of physical activity to energy intake and body weight. Does level of physical activity determine how much a person eats? This research suggests that it may. Most workers ate a suitable number of kcalories to provide for the work they did (lower graph); the exception was that the least active workers ate as much as some of the hardest workers did. The consequences are shown in the upper graph: the least active workers were also the heaviest. (Source: Mayer, J., P. Roy, and K.P. Mitra. 1956. Relation between caloric intake, body weight, and physical work: Studies in an industrial male population in West Bengal. *American Journal of Clinical Nutrition* 4:169–175.)

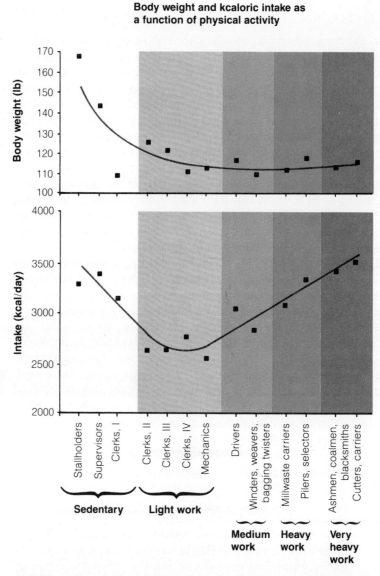

Body weight and kcaloric intake as a function of physical activity

appetite—drive to eat that arises from nonphysiological factors

Appetite. Whereas the term hunger is used to refer to physiological factors that prompt a person to eat (internal regulation), the term appetite is often used to refer to nonphysiological factors that encourage eating (*external regulation*). Some experts believe that such factors are even more influential than physiological ones in prompting people to start and stop eating (Drewnowski, 1983).

Appetite can be sparked by such cues as time of day, seeing or smelling food, or needing a reward. Mood is another factor that has some influence on most people's eating. It is common for people to embellish a happy occasion with food; many also eat when they are tired, under stress, bored, or in transition between activities. Some also eat when they are lonely, insecure, frustrated, or even hostile (Simonson, 1982). On the other hand, these same emotions can disinterest others in eating.

The literature on obesity contains many contradictions regarding the extent to which overfat people respond to external cues. Some articles state that overfat people respond more readily to external cues and consequently take in excess kcalories (Mahan, 1981); others say that external cue responsiveness is not necessarily different in overfat people than in those of average fatness. Some researchers claim that overfat people eat the same number of kcalories or even less than their normal weight peers; others say that they eat more (Forbes, 1981). The truth may be that any of the above is possible, depending on the individuals involved.

It has also been suggested that some obese people attempt to satisfy deeper psychological needs through food. For example, some people achieve a sense of power from having a large body size, which encourages them to overeat consistently. Others, not wanting to have to deal with sexual or other adult activities, may deliberately maintain either obesity or extreme thinness to make themselves unappealing or immature-looking (Simonson, 1982). A feminist psychologist suggests that eating, especially for some women, may be a way of "swallowing rage" that is prompted by the limitations society has put on women (Orbach, 1979).

Kcaloric Density of Foods. Foods high in fat and sugar appeal to many people, and have become increasingly represented in the processed, convenience, and fast foods available to us. For example, fried fast-food chicken may provide as many as double the number of kcalories as broiled chicken due mainly to the added fat. A cake-mix cake to which you add a box of pudding mix, extra oil, fruit, and eggs will provide substantially more kcalories per piece than the basic cake alone would furnish. If a person substitutes many energy-dense foods for their lower-kcalorie counterparts without compensating elsewhere in the diet, his or her body fat will increase.

Causes of overfatness. Although it is true that repeated intentional overeating can result in storage of an excessive amount of body fat, there are many other reasons why overfatness may occur. (See text.)

Figure 10.3 Various cultural ideals of body fatness. Attitudes about ideal body weight vary from time to time and from culture to culture.

Prevailing Cultural Attitudes. The series of pictures in Figure 10.3 illustrate that attitudes about ideal body weight vary from time to time and from culture to culture. What prompts these attitudes in a society is a complex matter, involving not only aesthetics, but economic and (more recently) health considerations as well. For example, in some very poor societies it is considered desirable to be fat, because it demonstrates the relative wealth of the person who can afford enough food to become overfat. In other cultures, a fat woman is regarded as content.

These beliefs are distinctly different from the current North American attitude that prizes extreme leanness. This influence is so strong that weight reduction products and services are a $20 billion dollar industry in the United States annually. *Psychology Today*, in a special issue on food, suggested that "food seems to have replaced sex as a source of guilt" (Keen, 1978). In their book *Breaking the Diet Habit*, authors Polivy and Herman agree: "As indulgence waxes in some spheres of life (e.g., sexuality, consumerism), it is unconsciously countered by self-discipline in other spheres of life—and dieting is self-discipline par excellence" (1983).

Note that popular concepts of what is ideal are not necessarily in our best interest as far as health is concerned. More will be said about this in Chapter 11 (on eating disorders).

Genetic Characteristics. There are a few physical disorders that tend to have high food intake associated with them. People with such rare conditions as Prader-Willi syndrome or related genetic disorders usually have a higher proportion of body fat than their unaffected peers.

Factors That Influence Energy Output

Let's go back to the basic ways people use energy—for basal metabolism, physical activity, and thermogenesis—to identify some possible variations in energy expenditure.

Basal Metabolic Rate. In Chapter 5 (on energy) we described a few different methods for estimating your basal metabolic rate (BMR). However, a few people may have BMRs that differ by as much as 20% in either direction from those of most people of the same surface area, age, and sex (Bray, 1983). Therefore, BMR can account for either a smaller or larger energy use than the estimates suggest.

One variable may be the amount of thyroid hormone people produce, which affects the rate at which their metabolism functions. *Hyper*thyroid individuals use more energy than those with normal thyroid activity, and *hypo*thyroid people use less.

Another hypothesis some researchers are testing is that obese people may use less energy than normal in the process of transporting sodium out of cells and back into the interstitial fluid. This abnormality, when added up for all the cells of the body, would account for significant energy output differences. Some studies of obese animals have shown that sodium transport in their liver and skeletal muscle cells uses less energy than in normal-weight animals. It is not yet known whether a similar condition may cause energy conservation with consequent overfatness in some humans (Bray, 1983).

Physical Activity Level. An obvious suspicion as to why some people "get fat" is that they exercise less than other people. Indeed, studies on some groups of overfat people have shown that they are less physically active than their peers of normal fatness.

On the other hand, recent research on a group of overfat people demonstrated that although they moved less, they expended just as much energy in the process as their normal-fat peers because they were *moving a greater weight when they did move* (Bray, 1983). (Remember that energy usage is the product of activity, time, and body weight.) The reduced activity of overfat people may be more a consequence of their condition than a reason for it.

Before we leave this topic, recall that because activity also plays a role in intake regulation, it has a double function in balancing energy intake and output.

Thermogenesis. In Chapter 5 (on energy), we described thermogenesis as including specific dynamic effect (heat produced during digestion, absorption, transport, and storage of food); adaptive thermogenesis or thermic response to food (additional heat produced when surplus kcalories have been consumed); and nonshivering thermogenesis (heat produced in response to environmental cold). Various researchers hypothesize that the amount of energy used for each of these purposes may be related to the amount of body fat a person has.

Although specific dynamic effect is thought to represent a fairly constant percentage of kcalories consumed, some studies show that less energy is used for this purpose by obese people than by their lean counterparts (Danforth and Landsberg, 1983).

Other studies have shown that obese people have only a very small thermic response to overfeeding (Danforth and Landsberg, 1983). Presumably they convert more of the extra kcalories to fat than their normal-weight peers do. Studies done with prison volunteers in the 1960s showed that when people of average body fatness deliberately ate much more food than they normally would, they did gain weight, but not nearly as much as they "should have" according to the standard of one pound for every 3500 surplus kcalories (Sims, 1973).

Finally, even the body's ability to use energy for nonshivering thermogenesis may differ between fat and lean people, if animal experiments are an accurate model. Some obese strains of laboratory animals do not produce sufficient heat to stay alive when their environment becomes cold (Himms-Hagen, 1983). Although human experiments have not yet been done, it is possible that some people may be similarly unable to produce extra heat in the cold.

So, after all this, why are some people fat, others thin, and others "just right"? We've seen that no single explanation applies to all cases: there are likely to be different reasons—genetic and/or environmental—why different people store more (or less) body fat than the average person. Furthermore, it is possible that more than one of these factors is at work in an individual at any given time. At least we have learned that it is not appropriate to indict all overfat people as being self-indulgent or out of control.

Now that you have been exposed to the uncertainties of what influences fatness, you may be prepared to step onto additional shifting sand—the matter of ideal body weight.

You Can Estimate Your Ideal Body Weight From A Combination of Guidelines

It's easy to recognize extremes in body weight such as those pictured in Figure 10.4, which are far from ideal. However, it's not as easy to identify what *is* ideal. Do you know how much you should weigh? To find the answer to that question, chances are you would look for a height/weight table.

Height/Weight Tables

Height/weight tables are based on sex, height, and sometimes frame size; the recommended weights are given in a range. Although this is not very specific information—the ranges on some tables are 30 pounds or more— it at least offers a guideline or "ballpark" suggestion for desirable weights. If you looked long enough, you could find many versions of height/weight tables, each of which gives somewhat different recommendations (Weigley, 1984).

For decades, the guidelines most familiar to Americans have been the tables published by the Metropolitan Insurance Company. These tables are based on the weights at which people have lived the longest, according to data collected by the insurance industry.

In 1983, Metropolitan published new tables, based on more recent data, to replace those that had been in use since 1959. The new tables recommend weights that are higher by 5–6% for men and women of medium height (Table 10.1).

Although the Metropolitan tables have been widely accepted as authoritative by the general public, health statisticians have criticized the insurance company tables on several grounds. For example, death at various weights may be associated with other factors than the weight itself, such as smoking, but the data do not take this into consideration. Another criticism is that the population sample on which the study was based (that is, people who have purchased life insurance) is not representative of the

Figure 10.4 Body weight extremes. It is obvious that the sideshow attractions in this picture are underfat and overfat. It is not so easy to determine what weights would be ideal for them, although there are several ways to estimate (see text).

Table 10.1 1983 Metropolitan Height and Weight Tables

Men

Height Feet	Inches	Small frame	Medium frame	Large frame
5	1	123–129	126–136	133–145
5	2	125–131	128–138	135–148
5	3	127–133	130–140	137–151
5	4	129–135	132–143	139–155
5	5	131–137	134–146	141–159
5	6	133–140	137–149	144–163
5	7	135–143	140–152	147–167
5	8	137–146	143–155	150–171
5	9	139–149	146–158	153–175
5	10	141–152	149–161	156–179
5	11	144–155	152–165	159–183
6	0	147–159	155–169	163–187
6	1	150–163	159–173	167–192
6	2	153–167	162–177	171–197
6	3	157–171	166–182	176–202

Women

Height Feet	Inches	Small frame	Medium frame	Large frame
4	9	98–108	106–118	115–128
4	10	100–110	108–120	117–131
4	11	101–112	110–123	119–134
5	0	103–115	112–126	122–137
5	1	105–118	115–129	125–140
5	2	108–121	118–132	128–144
5	3	111–124	121–135	131–148
5	4	114–127	124–138	134–152
5	5	117–130	127–141	137–156
5	6	120–133	130–144	140–160
5	7	123–136	133–147	143–164
5	8	126–139	136–150	146–167
5	9	129–142	139–153	149–170
5	10	132–145	142–156	152–173
5	11	133–148	145–159	155–176

These weight ranges show weights in pounds at ages 25–29 based on lowest mortality. Tables have been adjusted to represent weights without clothes and heights without shoes.

continued on next page

general population, so the tables are not suitable to apply to everybody (Keys, 1979). Third, a legitimate question has been raised as to whether body *weight* per se is actually the right factor to look at: the real culprit

Table 10.1 continued

How to Determine Your Body Frame Size by Elbow Breadth

To make a simple approximation of your frame size, extend your arm and bend the forearm upwards at a 90 degree angle. Keep the fingers straight and turn the inside of your wrist away from your body. Place the thumb and index finger of your other hand on the two prominent bones on *either side* of your elbow. Measure the space between your fingers against a ruler or a tape measure.[a] Compare the measurements on the following tables.

These tables list the elbow measurements for medium-framed men and women of various heights. Measurements lower than those listed indicate that you have a small frame, and higher measurements indicate a large frame.

Height	Men	Elbow breadth
5'1"–5'2"		$2\frac{1}{2}"-2\frac{7}{8}"$
5'3"–5'6"		$2\frac{5}{8}"-2\frac{7}{8}"$
5'7"–5'10"		$2\frac{3}{4}"-3"$
5'11"–6'2"		$2\frac{3}{4}"-3\frac{1}{8}"$
6'3"		$2\frac{7}{8}"-3\frac{1}{4}"$

Height	Women	Elbow breadth
4'9"–4'10"		$2\frac{1}{4}"-2\frac{1}{2}"$
4'11"–5'2"		$2\frac{1}{4}"-2\frac{1}{2}$
5'3"–5'6"		$2\frac{3}{8}"-2\frac{5}{8}"$
5'7"–5'10"		$2\frac{3}{8}"-2\frac{5}{8}"$
5'11"		$2\frac{1}{2}"-2\frac{3}{4}$

[a]For the most accurate measurement, have your physician measure your elbow breadth with a caliper.
Adapted from 1983 Metropolitan Height and Weight Tables. Reprinted courtesy of the Metropolitan Life Insurance Company.

that causes health problems and early death is probably body *fat*. Although the two often correspond, that is not always the case (Keys, 1979). For example, a person who has an unusually large amount of muscle may be overweight according to the tables but not necessarily overfat. (The last criticism is true of any height/weight tables, not just Metropolitan's.)

Despite such criticisms, some insurance companies are so confident of the validity of these data for their purposes that they charge lower life insurance premiums for people who are at the lower-mortality weights. The Metropolitan Insurance Company is sensitive to these concerns and others, though, and has named this most recent version of their tables simply "Metropolitan Height and Weight Tables" without labeling them as "ideal" or even "desirable."

A key message here is that ideal weight based on sex, height, and frame size is difficult for the experts to identify explicitly. However, there is fairly general agreement among various recent tables. Since the recommendations are expressed in rather broad ranges, they are useful only as a rough guideline for any individual; nonetheless, they are better than nothing. Anybody who is markedly outside the weight range for his or her height should check with a physician for further individualized evaluation.

Body Mass Index

body mass index—body weight (in kilograms) divided by height (in meters) squared; a standard some experts have proposed for ideal weight determination

Another standard suggested by some scientists for ideal weight determination is body mass index (BMI), which is body weight (in kilograms) divided by height (in meters) squared. Many experts in obesity research believe that this number provides a more reliable basis on which to judge overfatness than the height/weight table ranges.

BMI can be determined without doing any calculation. You can use the special chart (called a *nomogram*) in Figure 10.5 to convert your height and weight to BMI, and to see whether it is within the acceptable, underweight, or obese range (DHEW, 1980).

Percentage of Body Fat

Since it is thought that body fatness is even more important to health than weight per se, several means of measuring body fat have been developed. The most accurate is underwater weighing, a method that requires specialized equipment and is used for research.

A much easier but less accurate method is to use skinfold calipers to measure the thickness of the fat layer beneath the skin at various body sites, and then to use tables to convert the measurements into body fat percentages. Because this procedure can be done quickly and with less expensive equipment (good calipers can be purchased for approximately $200), measuring of skinfolds has become increasingly popular among dietitians, doctors, athletic coaches, and trainers. Appropriately used in expert hands, skinfold measurements can show comparisons in fatness between people, or in the same person from one time to another. However, the accuracy of estimating the absolute percentage of body fat from skinfolds is questioned.

Due to slight differences in technique and/or equipment, different practitioners can get different measurements on the same person. The locations (and the number of locations) that are measured also make a difference: generally, the more sites that are measured, the more reliable the results will be. Then, depending on which of several available tables are used for converting the skinfold measurements into body fat percentages, the values can differ. Finally, there are no research data that document what percentages of body fat correlate with the greatest longevity or disease prevention, so the method cannot determine what a person's ideal percentage of body fat or weight should be after all.

Even so, people are interested in this method, especially since they have heard legitimate criticisms of the height/weight tables. Because skinfold measurement involves a newer technology with its own mystique of equipment, charts, and tables, people may put more faith in this method than it deserves.

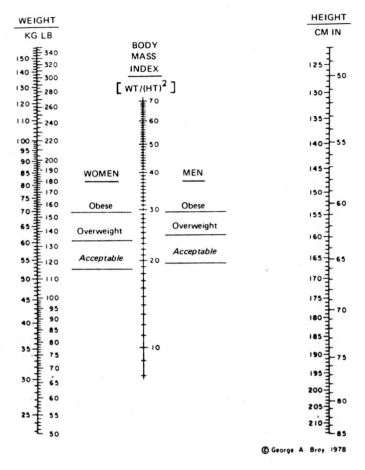

Figure 10.5 Nomogram for body mass index (BMI). To determine your BMI, use a straightedge between your weight in Column A and your height in Column B. The point where the line crosses Column C is your BMI. Note the obese, overweight, and acceptable ranges. [Adapted from Department of Health, Education, and Welfare (DHEW). 1980. Obesity in America: An overview. In *Obesity in America*, ed. G. A. Bray. Washington, DC: DHEW.]

However, as we mentioned earlier, skinfold measurements do have value: done at intervals by a person who is highly skilled in using the method, it can be determined whether fat deposits are increasing or decreasing. This can be particularly valuable to a person who is both dieting and exercising: the person's body weight may not be changing at all, but fat may be decreasing while muscle is being added. Without skinfold testing, the person who sees no change in the weight shown on the scale might be inclined to say, "This program's not working," and abandon what might actually be a very successful fat loss program.

The "Mirror" Test

Some popular publications suggest that a reliable and very easy way to evaluate for body fat is to spend a few moments of naked truth in front of a full-length mirror to see whether there is anything that jiggles that shouldn't. There is no doubt that our intake excesses or shortfalls are evident at such a moment, but we doubt that most people have the ability to be objective in that situation.

Society's concept of "ideal" appearance—that is, to be fashion-model or distance-runner slim—influences many people (especially women) to judge themselves too harshly in comparison with how they would be judged from a health perspective. Furthermore, if people have accumulated a greater amount of surplus fat in one body area, they often focus on it and regard themselves as generally more overfat than they are.

In a survey that compared college students' *self-concept* of their weights to their *actual* weights, it was found that 63% of the female subjects perceived themselves to be one category of weight heavier than they actually were (for example, slightly overweight instead of normal weight). Furthermore, 46% of the women wanted to be slightly underweight rather than of normal body weight. In contrast, over 75% of the men wanted to be in the normal weight category; also, they were more accurate at estimating their current weights (Miller et al., 1980).

Best Functional Weight

It may be possible to use another subjective standard, which is to ask yourself at what weight you function best both physically and mentally. If you give similar answers to all of the following questions, this method may help you to zero in on your own best body weight.

At what weight do you:

- Have enough stamina to live through each day with reasonable vitality?

- Have the ability to concentrate well on the task at hand?

- Keep from feeling hungry or being obsessed with food until shortly before the next mealtime?

These questions are admittedly very subjective; besides, your answers could be influenced by other factors. But under normal circumstances, these questions can help you come to an individually determined ideal weight in a way that the other external standards cannot.

Your Status

You have just read your way through several criteria that are used for determining ideal body weight: height/weight tables, body mass index, skinfold measurements, the mirror test, and best functional weight. You have probably applied some of these standards to yourself already. The different methods may have yielded slightly different recommendations for your ideal weight, but that should not be surprising, since all of these methods are imperfect. Most of you have probably found that your body weight is appropriate for you.

On the other hand, some of you will find that your current weight does not fall within the ranges recommended by the objective tests. Yet you may say, "This is the weight at which I function best. Besides, whenever I intentionally lose or gain, I always return to this weight afterwards." In that case, if your food intake meets your nutritional needs and you get at least a moderate amount of exercise, it may be wisest for you to accept your current body weight and get on with other important aspects of living.

However, if you are above the weight ranges and seldom exercise, or are below the ranges and eat erratically, some changes may be in order. You should ask your doctor's advice about whether to attempt to gain or lose fat.

Methods for fat gain and loss are described in an upcoming section. But first, to provide background for understanding what happens when using those methods, we will discuss what is thought to happen physiologically and psychologically in response to energy surplus and deficit.

Energy Imbalance Has Both Physical and Psychological Effects

In recent years, considerable research has been carried out to learn what happens in the body when excessive or deficient amounts of energy-producing food is consumed.

Physiological Responses

You might be wondering, "What more is there to say? When you consume more energy than you expend, you gain body fat. When you eat less, you lose fat." In fact, there is more to say.

Fat Cell Responses to Energy Surplus or Deficit.   Obesity researchers Jules Hirsch and Jerome Knittle have developed the following theory about body fat development: as a body gains fat, it does so either by adding more fat cells (a condition called hyperplastic obesity), or by enlarging those it already has (hypertrophic obesity), or both. Hyperplastic and hyperplastic-hypertrophic obesity usually start in childhood, whereas hypertrophic obesity usually begins during adulthood, according to studies done on both laboratory animals and humans (Hirsch and Knittle, 1970). More recent findings suggest that although the above generalizations usually hold true, new fat cells can be created at any age, if existing fat cells reach a certain critical size and there is still more fat to deposit (Bjorntorp, 1983).

According to these researchers, when weight is lost, fat cells shrink but never disappear entirely. Furthermore, the fat cells endeavor to maintain a certain minimal size: if they become smaller than that size, body mechanisms work to restore their lost mass.

Consider the person with normal-sized cells but an above-normal number of them. According to this theory, when that person loses weight, the fat cells shrink to less-than-normal size, and forever after hunger to be refilled. This person, say some researchers, is likely to regain weight quickly when dieting is stopped. On the other hand, the person with large-sized fat cells but a normal number of them theoretically has an easier time of it: when he or she diets, the large cells are reduced to normal size, and are more likely to stay that way. (Table 10.2 summarizes this information.)

Metabolic disorders such as diabetes, hypertension, and high blood cholesterol occur more often in people who have large fat cells. Fortunately,

hyperplasia—increase in number of cells

hypertrophy—enlargement of cells already present

hyperplastic-hypertrophic obesity—obesity caused by both addition and enlargement of fat cells

Frontier

Table 10.2   Types of Obesity as Proposed by Hirsch and Knittle

Type	Description	Consequences
Hyperplastic obesity	Person has a large number of fat cells that are normal in size; the condition is usually established during childhood	If weight is lost, regain is likely
Hypertrophic obesity	Person has a normal number of fat cells that are large in size; the condition is usually established during adulthood	If weight is lost, it is less likely to be regained; diabetes and/or high blood lipids may occur with overweight; reversal is likely with weight loss
Hyperplastic-hypertrophic obesity	Person has a large number of fat cells that are large in size; the condition is usually established during childhood, but may occur at any age	Combination of the above consequences

such people often have better success at weight loss, and the accompanying health problems are often reversed simultaneously (Bjorntorp, 1983).

Hirsch and Knittle's theories are quite controversial, but have sparked much interesting research.

Composition of Lost Weight. What happens to the fat cells, however, is not the whole story.

When there is a shortage of energy, the body draws from its own stores of all available macronutrients, not just from fat, to make up for the shortfall between intake and output. In the most extreme case—that is, a complete fast during which only water is consumed—the body initially derives over half of its energy from fat, and about one quarter each from carbohydrate and protein. As the fast progresses, the amount of energy derived from fat increases slightly; the amount from protein decreases progressively; and carbohydrate, after it is depleted in the first couple of days, contributes no more (Worthington-Roberts, 1981).

Since there is a substantial amount of water associated with both body carbohydrate and protein, this water is lost when body carbohydrate and protein are used for energy. Each gram of glycogen and protein has approximately three grams of water associated with it (although protein may have more), whereas each gram of fat is likely to be associated with less than a gram of water.

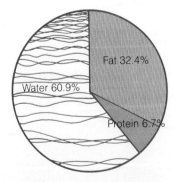

Figure 10.6 Composition of weight lost during short-term fasting. Obese subjects on a starvation regimen averaged the losses shown above during a ten-day period. (Reference: M.-U. Yang and T. B. Van Itallie. 1976. Composition of weight lost during short-term weight reduction. *Journal of Clinical Investigation* 58:722–730. The Rockefeller University Press.)

Figure 10.6 shows what percentages of weight lost were due to water, fat, and protein losses during a 10-day starvation study. Water represented more than three-fifths of the weight lost, whereas fat represented only one-third; the remainder was protein. This explains why the decrease in weight during a fast is so drastic initially, and also why the weight can be regained so rapidly with refeeding and rehydration. Substantial amounts of protein are lost for several weeks on such a regimen.

Studies of a somewhat less extreme weight reduction program showed a similar pattern, especially in the first three days. Figure 10.7 shows the proportions of weight loss attributable to protein, fat, and water losses at the beginning and end of a 26-day low-kcalorie diet. The study involved

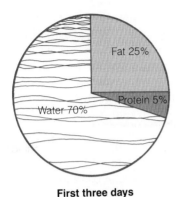

First three days
of restriction
(days 1–3)

Last three days
of restriction
(days 21–24)

Figure 10.7 Composition of weight lost during very low-kcalorie dieting. When you go on a very low kcalorie diet, what body substances account for the weight you lose? Initially, most of what you lose is water; gradually your loses become just fat and protein, as the results from the illustrated study show. (Adapted from F. Grande. 1961. Nutrition and energy balance in body composition studies. In "Techniques for Measuring Body Composition" 1961, with the permission of The National Academy Press Washington, D.C.)

physically fit soldiers in their early twenties who consumed a 1000 kcalorie diet instead of their usual 3200 kcalorie intake. Note that after three weeks of dieting, all the lost weight could be attributed to fat and protein.

From this information, you can see how damaging it is for a person to begin fasts or very low kcalorie diets repeatedly. Each restart prompts protein loss and dehydration which, in turn, cause loss of strength and vigor. Wrestlers who subject themselves to such crash programs to wrestle in a lower weight classification may be sacrificing some of their muscle and strength in the process. Dieters who fast to compensate for previous overindulgences are likely to feel quite listless as a result. A less severe, more consistent restriction of energy intake results in less protein loss while promoting fat loss.

Ketosis. When a person's energy deficit is severe, and/or if the diet is very low in carbohydrate, the body breaks down a greater amount of fat than it normally would. If the minimal amount of carbohydrate needed for fat metabolism is not available, as is often the case in severe restriction, the body cannot completely oxidize the fat into energy, carbon dioxide, and water. Rather, it leaves some fat fragments called ketone bodies or ketoacids lingering in the blood.

Ketone bodies, if produced in small amounts, are uneventfully eliminated in the urine. However, when faced with a drastic energy deficit, the body produces more ketoacids than can be cleared by the kidneys, and a condition called ketosis results. Diets that lead to this condition are called ketogenic diets.

Some people think that ketosis provides an advantage to the dieter, believing that the lost ketone bodies will lead to more rapid fat loss. However, it is unlikely that more than 60 kcalories per day are lost in this way, so the effect on fat loss is minimal (Yang and Van Itallie, 1976). Others claim that ketosis suppresses appetite; testing has not confirmed this.

A major concern nutritionists have about ketogenic diets is that they promote dehydration, because extra water is removed from the body in the process of excreting the ketones. Ketogenic diets have been found to

ketone bodies or ketoacids— fat fragments that remain in the blood if fat is not completely metabolized

ketosis—condition in which the body produces more ketoacids than can be cleared readily by the kidneys; often results in dehydration and stress on the body's buffering systems

ketogenic diets—diets that lead to ketosis

cause three times as much water loss as more balanced diets of the same number of kcalories (Yang and Van Itallie, 1976). Furthermore, a high level of ketones stresses the body's buffering systems, since ketone bodies are acidic. Although it would be very unusual for the buffering systems to fail in an otherwise healthy person, a rare instance could theoretically result in death. Moderate, gradual fat losses at the rate of two to three pounds per week will not produce severe ketosis.

Rate of Fat Loss. As weight loss progresses, the dieter is pleased. However, the dieter's body attempts to defend itself against further losses by gradually reducing the amount of energy expended for basal metabolic processes. Basal energy expenditure goes down by as much as 20-25% as dieting progresses, resulting in slower fat loss.

Psychological Responses

Early in this chapter we mentioned personality changes observed in studies of dietary restriction. Feeling "downhearted," social isolationism, and poor concentration were noted in these studies, and continue to be recognized as typical responses to large kcalorie deficits. Dieters may also be hyper-

---

SLICE OF LIFE:
Self-Concept during Dieting

In their book *Breaking the Diet Habit*, authors Polivy and Herman share this observation:

Whether or not one's sense of self is weak before dieting begins, it certainly seems to be affected by the dieter mentality once in force. Thus, ordinarily intelligent, effective people begin to question their self-worth if the number on the bathroom scale is higher than it was last week. A presumably normal, nonpathologic friend and professional colleague confided, "I can hardly bear to face the world when the scale reads over 120 pounds. I feel fat, ugly, and worthless. Even one pound above my limit (120 pounds) makes me feel depressed. As long as I weigh 118, I feel fine. At 119 I'm already starting to worry, 120 is worse, and anything over that is panic time. On the other hand, 115 makes me euphoric—at least for the one day it lasts! I feel attractive, lively, and sociable, able to take on anything."

The obsession with slenderness can thus become overwhelming, to the point where one's entire self-image and self-esteem are based on weight. . . .Actual appearance no longer seems to be the primary issue; instead, the goal is to hit the "winning number" on the scale. Intelligence, talent, accomplishments, all pale to insignificance in determining the person's self-esteem next to a digit on a ten-dollar, generally inaccurate, weight-measuring device.

---

emotional, and may experience tension, irritability, and preoccupation with food.

Recent research provides additional insights. It describes the typical dieter as a restrained, externally regulated eater (Polivy and Herman, 1983). Restrained eaters are more likely to eat greater amounts of food when anxious or depressed, when more food is available, and after they believe they have "blown" their diets. The consequence, according to these researchers, is that *restrained eaters are likely to eat **more** (eventually and overall) than if they were eating in response to genuine hunger.* In this way, they contend, *dieting often causes people to gain weight rather than lose it.* Dieting also tends to elevate the whole issue of body weight to one of primary importance in the person's self-image, as the Slice of Life indicates.

Surprisingly, there even can be negative psychological reactions to *successful* weight loss attempts. As mentioned earlier in this chapter, some overfat people use their condition as a means of avoiding activities with which they are not comfortable, such as sports or personal interactions. If they lose their surplus body fat, others may try to involve them in the activities they would rather avoid; this can be threatening. Some people may actually gain back their lost weight to regain their protection against these involvements (Russ et al., 1984).

People Have Tried Thousands of Techniques For Losing Body Fat

It is amazing how many claims, theories, and treatments for losing weight have been developed: information about *29,000* of them has been collected at Johns Hopkins University (Simonson, 1982). Some focus on regulating food intake, others emphasize increasing energy output, and a few include both. There are even some that accomplish neither of these, relying on measures such as temporary water loss to fool a person into thinking that some fat has been lost. Such programs are not only deceptive, but may be dangerous as well.

As for success rates, all weight loss methods are successful for some people but unsuccessful for others. When the long-term results of weight loss methods employing dietary, behavioral, and/or pharmacological means were evaluated, only 5–25% of the people studied managed to keep the unwanted weight off in the years that followed. In other words, 75–95% regained some or all of the lost weight (DHEW, 1980).

It would save many people a lot of effort if we knew how to predict accurately by physical criteria which overfat people were likely to succeed at significant long-term weight loss, and by which method(s). This is one of the anticipated thrusts of obesity research in the coming decade (Greenwood, 1983). To date, there have been more conclusions drawn regarding which behavioral, psychological, and environmental factors help predict success. For example, people who are most likely to be successful at weight loss are those whose friends and family support their efforts, and who have a good attitude about dieting and losing weight (Brownell, 1984).

Table 10.3 Types of Restricted Diets Used for Weight Reduction[a] (*Note that most of the diets are not safe or effective.*)

Diet type	Description	Possible health effects
Balanced diets of 1200 kcalories or more	Usually consist of ordinary, readily available, high-nutrient-density foods in limited amounts; often moderate in protein and carbohydrate, and most restricted in fat	Can meet the RDA if carefully chosen; weight loss is usually 1–2 pounds per week; can be liberalized to stabilize weight for safe lifetime use
Diets of fewer than 1200 kcalories	Usually composed of ordinary, readily available, high-nutrient-density foods in very limited amounts; often moderate in protein and very restricted in fat and carbohydrate	Diet often fails to meet the RDA for many nutrients; ketosis may occur; weight loss is often 3 or more pounds per week, much due to water loss; regain is more likely than with slower weight loss
High-carbohydrate, high-fiber diets	Emphasize whole grain breads, cereals, raw fruits and vegetables, moderate amounts of animal proteins, dairy products, avoidance of highly processed foods; supplemental fiber is sometimes recommended	Calculated nutrient intake is nearly adequate, but fiber (especially if supplemented) may reduce availability of minerals
Formula low-kcalorie diets	Powders, liquids, or wafers constitute diet of 1000 kcalories with supplemented vitamins and minerals; provide 20% protein, 30% fat, and 50% carbohydrate	Adequate in vitamins and minerals; may be constipating; ketosis may occur; requires no food choice decisions or contact with food; often discontinued due to monotony or unpalatability; weight regain is likely because old eating habits remain; more acceptable as one meal per day within a low-kcalorie diet plan
Low-carbohydrate, high-protein, high- or moderate-fat diets	Emphasize high-protein foods, severely limit carbohydrate to 50g; usually low in kcalories because allowed foods become unappealing	Diet may meet RDA if chosen carefully; ketosis occurs, causing fluid loss; can cause increase in blood fat and cholesterol levels; may cause menstrual dysfunction, dehydration, osteoporosis, aggravation of gout, kidney failure or stones; much of lost weight due to water loss

Continued on next page

Considering the plethora of treatments available, we will be able to discuss only the major types of techniques. They can be grouped into restricted diets, modification of eating behaviors, psychological approaches, drugs and surgical interventions, increased physical activity, and combinations of these.

Restricted Diets

An incredible array of weight reduction diets have enjoyed temporary popularity. Many, after they have run their course, emerge later with new names and various modifications. One review paper identified 22 separate diets of the low carbohydrate type that were in fashion between 1953 and 1979 (Blonz and Stern, 1981).

Table 10.3   continued

Diet type	Description	Possible health effects
One-food diets	Emphasize one food or food type, such as fruit, rice, or ice cream, as mainstay of the diet	Inevitably deficient in some nutrients, excessive in others; discarded quickly because of monotony; lost weight regained
Fasting	Water and no-kcalorie beverages allowed; vitamin and mineral supplements given; person usually hospitalized for monitoring	May result in nutrient deficiencies, low blood pressure, ketosis, emotional disturbances; death may result if prolonged; causes weight loss of 3–5 pounds per week; regain begins when person begins eating again but has not learned new eating behaviors; former weight usually regained in time
Protein-supplemented fasting[b]	Like fast, but with protein supplement of up to 1.5 g/kg of ideal body weight; protein in form of lean animal products, liquid protein isolates, or amino acids	May result in ketosis, nausea and vomiting, diarrhea or constipation, weakness, muscle cramps, mineral imbalance, irritability; former weight usually regained in time; over 50 deaths attributed to use of over-the-counter liquid protein products

[a]Reference: L. K. Mahan. 1979. A sensible approach to the obese patient. *Nursing Clinics of North America* 14(no.2):229–245.
[b]Reference: T. B. Van Itallie. 1980. Conservative approaches to treatment. In *Obesity in America,* ed. G. Bray. Washington, DC: Department of Health, Education, and Welfare.

Because there are so many different diets and because they change so quickly, here we will identify general types of diets, their characteristics, and their health effects; you can make the association with diets in fashion at present.

The quality of the weight reduction diets in the public eye at any given time is likely to vary substantially, ranging from those that are safe and could be successful to those that are very hazardous. For example, 58 sudden cardiac deaths occurred among obese dieting women, most of whom were using a form of purified protein diet that was extremely low in kcalories (Friedman et al., 1982).

Table 10.3 describes various types of diets and their possible effects. Notice that many of the diets restrict fat consumption the most, which is logical because of its high kcaloric density. One effective way to limit fat is to limit certain animal products while allowing more liberal use of many plant foods. Some diets therefore resemble semi-vegetarian, lacto-ovo vegetarian, or vegan eating styles. The idea that such diets lead to weight loss is not a new one. Early studies of vegetarians showed that vegans who were not deliberately restricting their energy intakes tended to be approximately 20 pounds lighter than nonvegetarian control subjects (Hardinge and Stare, 1954).

Also note that of all the types of diets, the balanced weight reduction diets of 1200 kcalories or more are the only ones that earn the enthusiastic support of most professional nutritionists and physicians; the experts have reservations about all of the others.

Characteristics of Safe and Potentially Effective Fat Loss Programs. Anyone who wonders about the safety and potential usefulness of a particular diet for personal use can check it out by answering these questions:

1. Is it nutritionally sound or "balanced"? Does it fit the guidelines for a nutritious diet, such as the SANE guide and/or analysis using food composition tables? It should contain at least 1200 kcalories per day, since it is very difficult to meet the RDA for many nutrients at lower energy levels.

2. Does it promote fat loss at the rate of one to two pounds per week? In other words, is the recommended intake of kcalories 500–1000 kcalories less per day than your usual energy expenditure would be?

3. Is it composed of ordinary foods that you can afford and obtain easily?

4. Would you be willing to adopt it as your eating plan not just while you lose weight, but in a slightly modified form afterward—perhaps for the rest of your life?

If you can give positive answers to these questions, the diet is probably safe and has a chance of working for you.

How to Design Your Own Personalized Weight Loss Diet. One reason that diets fail is that people try to follow programs that depart drastically from their habitual way of eating, and eventually abandon them altogether. The more extreme a diet is, the more exaggerated the physiological and psychological reactions to it will be. People who need to lose fat would probably do better to design their own individualized diets, geared to the amount of change they know they can tolerate at one time—and, of course, geared to the principles of good nutrition.

Here is a suggested way of planning an individualized diet for fat loss:

1. Keep a food record for several days, recording the way you typically eat while maintaining a steady weight.

2. Analyze the nutritional quality of your intake using the SANE guide to be sure your basic needs are being met. If there are food group shortages, plan how to make up for them in a way acceptable to you.

3. Evaluate your intake for types of foods that are providing excess kcalories:
   a. Check the limited extras column for low-nutrient-density foods.
   b. Check food group foods for their relative fat and sugar contents, using the rulers at the bottom of the food group lists in the SANE guide in Chapter 2.
   c. Check food group columns for types of foods you consumed at levels considerably above the minimal recommendations, for example 150% or more of the minimums.

4. Using kcalorie values from Appendices E and F, decide which of the items you identified in step 3 you would be willing and able to modify or forego. The energy value of the foods you attempt to cut out should add up to 500–1000 kcalories per day. Remember: the objective is *to reduce energy intake moderately and consistently while retaining nutritional quality*; don't cut your kcalorie intake back more severely than by 1000 kcalories per day. (Exception: if you added foods in step 2, you will need to reduce your energy intake to compensate for the kcalorie value of those foods.)

5. Based on the typical features of your food record, design a general eating pattern for yourself (or more than one, if your daily schedules and eating patterns are of two or three different types), omitting those 500–1000 kcalories that you believe you can give up successfully.

6. Follow your individualized pattern during your weight loss period. Allow enough time! (Don't start a diet two weeks before an important event.) After you have reached your weight goal, you can liberalize your eating pattern slightly, but be careful to monitor your weight to find out what level of intake is needed to maintain it.

Use of Low Kcalorie Sweeteners and Fat. If people reduce their sugar intake in an attempt to lose weight, they may crave something sweet. Substitutes for sugar that taste sweet but have few or no kcalories can add pleasure to their eating.

Low-kcalorie sweeteners vary in their characteristics. One of the two primary ones in use at present is *saccharin*, which is 300–500 times as sweet as sugar and has no kcalories, but leaves a bitter aftertaste. The other sweetener, *aspartame*, is a dipeptide that is 120–280 times as sweet as sugar, has very few kcalories, and leaves no aftertaste. These sweeteners are available in North America both in food products and separately (Randolph and Dennison, 1981). Other substitute sweeteners are being tested. Concerns about the safety of saccharin and aspartame are discussed in Chapter 15 (on additives).

Low-kcalorie sweeteners are widely consumed in "diet" soft drinks, low-kcalorie candies, and other special products. To test whether the consumption of such products actually reduces people's overall energy intake, a study was conducted in which the sweetener aspartame was substituted for sugar. This reduced the kcaloric density of the diet by about 15% without materially changing food volume or taste. The subjects, who were able to eat as much as they wanted, voluntarily decreased their overall energy intake by 15% when consuming the aspartame-sweetened foods (Van Itallie, 1984).

Three substances sometimes mistakenly thought to be low calorie sweeteners are mannitol, sorbitol, and xylitol. These are carbohydrate derivatives commonly used in "sugarless" gum and some "diet" candies. They have kcalorie values equivalent to that of sugar (see Chapter 6).

An artificial fat, *sucrose polyester*, is currently being tested. It looks, tastes, and smells like fat, but cannot be digested or absorbed by humans.

Although early tests look promising, it remains to be seen whether this substance will actually aid in weight loss if it becomes generally available.

Behavior Modification

The general features of behavior modification were described in Chapter 9: self-monitoring, being realistic in goal-setting, controlling conditions, modifying eating behaviors, and self-reinforcement. It is possible to use behavior modification for weight control by applying these principles.

In its original and purest form, behavior modification for weight control pays very little attention to the nutritional value—except perhaps the energy content—of foods, and a great deal of attention to the where, when, how long, why, and with whom of eating. The process consists of analyzing food intake records to identify cues that trigger inappropriate eating, and then slowly, carefully reshaping eating behaviors and the living environment. The emphasis is on making changes gradually so that the new

SLICE OF LIFE:
Behavior Modification for
Weight Control

Diane threw the apple core into the waste basket, and then remembered, "Better put that on my food diary for today." She took out the form on which she had been recording her intake. It read:

Time	Minutes spent eating	M or S*	H**	Activity while eating	Place of eating	Food and quantity	Others present	Feeling while eating
8:10a.m.	17	M	1	standing, fixing lunch	kitchen	1 c O.J. / 1 c corn flakes / ½ c whole milk / 2 t. sugar / black coffee	———	sleepy
10:30a.m.	10	S	1	sitting, taking notes	classroom	12 oz cola	class	busy
11:45a.m.	2	M	2	sitting, talking	union	1 sandwich / 1 apple / 2 cookies / black coffee	friends	good
2:30p.m.	15	S	1	sitting, studying	library	12 oz cola	friend	bored
5:30p.m.	15	M	3	sitting, talking	kitchen	1 chicken leg / 1 baked potato / 2 T. butter / lettuce / 1 oz dressing / 1 c whole milk / 4 cookies	roommate	good
8:15p.m.	10	S	0	sitting, studying	living room	12 oz cola	———	tired

continued on next page

* M or S: Meal or snack
** H: Degree of hunger (0 = none; 3 = maximum)

behaviors become habitual and comfortable before further changes are undertaken (Simonson, 1982). The program further tries to assure success by having the person make the easiest change first. Some behavior modification programs also incorporate information about nutrition and/or include modification of exercise habits as well as eating behaviors.

The Slice of Life on these pages gives an example of part of the process.

Common helpful ways to change the environment might be to remove high kcalorie snack foods from the house, to keep foods out of direct sight, and to buy only small amounts of food at one time (Atkinson et al., 1984). A typical behavior to work on is slowing the pace of eating so that a given amount of food is enjoyed for a longer period of time, providing more satiety than if it were gulped down quickly. (It is said to take approximately 20 minutes from the time you begin to eat until food starts to relieve your hunger.) A tactic that helps eliminate impulse eating or overeating is to preplan the day's meals (Atkinson et al., 1984).

A recent innovation in behavior modification programs is the teaching

She added the information about the apple and glanced over the other entries on the sheet. This had been her fourth day of keeping a food diary. She felt optimistic that this behavior modification method would help her lose the 12 pounds she had gained last semester. She hoped so. The two diets she had read about in magazines and tried on her own hadn't worked; in fact, she now weighed three pounds more than when she had started them.

Later that week, before her behavior modification group meeting, she discussed the week's food diaries she had kept with the dietitian leading the sessions. She could quickly see some habits that had added unneeded kcalories to her intake, such as her liberal intake of cola and cookies. Other habits were less obvious, such as her use of whole milk instead of a lower-fat version. With the leader's help, she listed them all, and then put them in order from the easiest to the hardest for her to change.

Her goal for the following week was to make just the easiest change on the list. She chose to limit herself to two colas per day, although the leader suggested that another alternative would be to switch to an artificially sweetened beverage instead. She decided to substitute a short walk for the third cola, making stops at the water fountain to replace the fluids it would have provided.

Diane left the session feeling confident that she could manage this much change—after all, she wasn't giving up colas entirely, and she thought she'd really enjoy the walks.

of methods for coping with interpersonal situations that often trigger eating (Friedman et al., 1982). For example, a person who usually heads for the snack vending machine after his daily encounter with a disagreeable coworker might learn some better techniques for handling the situation. Another useful element in some programs is to work on changing certain aspects of self-concept that could be self-defeating (Stunkard, 1984).

Several self-help manuals are available to lead the user step by step through the record keeping and decision making that are part of the behavior modification process (Ferguson, 1975, 1976; Stuart and Davis, 1975; Ikeda, 1978). In some regions, group sessions offered by qualified professionals can provide helpful support until a person feels confident about being in charge of his or her own eating behaviors.

Studies show that the average weight loss when using such programs is one pound per week (Brownell and Wadden, 1983). Behavior modification therefore offers more consistent results than methods that focus on diets. However, followup studies beyond one year of completing the program are needed. It should be noted that in contrast to most other weight reduction therapies, there are almost no reports of adverse reactions to weight loss from this form of treatment (DHEW, 1980).

The newest form of behavior therapy involves helping people learn to eat in response to real hunger. Championed by Polivy and Herman and others, this method arises out of the conviction that humans will achieve the natural weight range that is physiologically predetermined and appropriate for them if they respond to their bodies' expressions of hunger and satiety. These investigators believe that many people have learned to ignore the messages about hunger by continuously trying to restrict themselves in order to lose body weight or maintain an unnaturally low weight. Their program therefore involves getting such individuals back in tune with the body's signals.

The major distinction between the earlier type of behavior modification and the newer version is that the newer one relies more on internal regulation, whereas the earlier type entails more external regulation.

Increased Physical Activity

It is possible to lose weight by only increasing physical activity while keeping energy intake the same.

A study involving women who were 10–60% overweight showed that they lost from 10 to 38 pounds by walking for at least half an hour per day for a year, with no changes in their energy intake (Gwinup, 1975). It is obvious that the exercise chosen for weight loss must be an activity that is pleasurable and possible to do regularly, or it will not be done consistently enough to cause weight loss.

Exercise is also an excellent adjunct to a kcalorie-restricted diet, because it can help maintain the basal or resting metabolic rate at a normal level instead of dropping, as usually occurs during dieting (Donahoe et al., in press). A related benefit is that lean body mass is likely to be maintained or even increased instead of decreasing, as often occurs with dieting alone (Zuti and Golding, 1976; Stern, 1983).

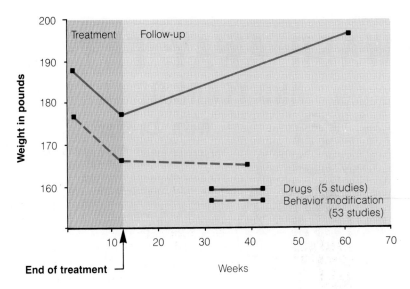

Figure 10.8 Long-term success for weight loss using drug therapy or behavior modification. This illustration shows that both drug therapy and behavior modification were successful in helping people lose weight during the active treatment phase. However, after treatment was discontinued for those individuals using drugs, their weight rose to higher than pretreatment levels. After the conclusion of a behavior modification series, however, people maintained their losses. (Source: R. B. Stuart, C. Mitchell, and J. A. Jensen. 1981. Therapeutic options in the management of obesity. In *Medical Psychology: Contributions to Behavioral Medicine.* New York: Academic Press.)

Psychological Methods

Although psychoanalysis, group psychology, and hypnosis have all been used for weight control, adequate studies have not been done to determine their effectiveness.

Self-help groups such as Weight Watchers, TOPS, Overeaters Anonymous, and related groups employ different weight reduction procedures but share the feature of group support. In a limited number of studies done on such programs, success rates have been comparable to those of medically supervised programs (Friedman et al., 1982).

Drugs and Surgical Interventions

Several different pharmacological methods have been used to promote weight loss. They are designed to decrease intake and/or to increase energy output. Amphetamines and related compounds, hormones such as thyroid hormone or human chorionic gonadotropin, diuretics, and other drugs have enjoyed popularity for weight reduction at various times (Friedman et al., 1982). Each drug has one or more negative effects.

Long-term success using drug therapy for weight loss is usually poor; Figure 10.8 shows how it compares with behavior modification programs after the formal treatment period has ended. For this reason, and because of the accompanying dangers of drug treatment programs, their use should generally be discouraged. However, this does not rule out the possibility of beneficial drugs being available in the future.

Several types of surgery have been developed to bring about weight loss. The most drastic of these is major surgery that modifies the gastrointestinal tract. Since the surgical procedures involve some risk, the possibility of serious complications, and substantial expense, these methods are

Ineffective products for reducing body fatness. People want to believe that fat can be diminished without dieting or exercising. This phenomenon is not new: half a century ago, the ad shown here undoubtedly sparked wishful thinking in many people—but produced dubious results. Today's media contain hundreds of current examples.

primarily used on people who are morbidly obese (100 pounds over or double their ideal weight). Such individuals are likely to be at greater risk from not having the surgery than from having it. Therefore, surgery may be the preferred treatment for these people (Stunkard, 1984). Weight loss is usually about one third of their original weight, and they usually stabilize above their ideal weights (Kral, 1983).

Jaw wiring (to prevent intake of solid foods) and acupuncture (thought by some to modify appetite), though less drastic, are of dubious long-range benefit. Fat suctioning and lipectomy (surgical removal of fat) are performed in some areas of the country, but are expensive and unlikely to be successful in the long term.

BOGUS! Ineffective Products BOGUS!

The marketplace is glutted with products that promise weight loss but either can't deliver it or accomplish it by causing dehydration but no significant fat loss. Nonetheless, unwary and wishful consumers spend millions of dollars on these products annually. Starch blockers were described in Chapter 6 (on carbohydrates) as a case in point. Other products include the algae spirulina, plastic wraps, latex exercise or sweat suits, skin creams, and electrical muscle stimulators (Willis, 1982; Miller, 1983).

Another misleading approach has been to give ordinary fat a new name and suggest that it can be reduced by means other than decreasing energy intake and/or increasing output. For example, the fat that causes the puckered look on thighs and buttocks has been named "cellulite" by some opportunists; special pills, lotions, and other products and methods have been marketed to deal with it. However, under the microscope, it proves to be nothing more or less than ordinary fat, and yields only to diet and/or exercise (Fenner, 1980).

Surprisingly, some weight loss products appear on the market without having FDA approval, since manufacturers of such items often claim that their product does not require premarket screening (Willis, 1982). A product might not come to the FDA's attention until somebody has been seriously harmed by it.

A consumer should be particularly wary of products that promise to "melt away" fat or "magically change your metabolism"; the former effect is impossible, and the latter is either a hoax or a substantial danger.

Opposite Techniques Can Be Used to Add Body Weight

A person who is considerably underweight, or has lost weight without trying to, would be best advised to have a thorough physical exam just to be sure that there is no physical problem responsible for the low weight.

Then, to attempt to tip the energy balance in favor of weight gain, consider these suggestions, many of which are simply the opposite of techniques suggested for fat loss:

- *Consume more energy.* Starting with a nutritionally adequate diet, eat larger meals, eat more often, and/or increase the energy density of the foods chosen. You may have noticed that there are some special supplements available for weight gain, but be wary of those that are mainly fat, because they can increase your fat intake above the recommended levels. You can be more liberal in your intake of limited extras; for you, they are really "not-so-limited" extras. However, your emphasis should still be on high-nutrient-density foods.

- *Undertake modification of eating behaviors.* Set some reasonable goals for slow, gradual weight gain. Make a step-by-step plan for how to accomplish the goals, and implement the easiest change first.

- *Decrease aerobic physical activity if you do much of it.* Sustained aerobic activity is a substantial energy-burner, so hold such exercise to a moderate level that will achieve fitness, but not more. For general maintenance of fitness, the American College of Sports Medicine recommends three to five exercise sessions per week of 15–60 minutes each, depending on the intensity of the exercise (1978).

- *Consider body-building.* If your muscles need further development, a moderate, progressive program of weight lifting can help you add more "muscle pounds" along with the new "fat pounds" your extra energy intake will produce. (But be wary of the dietary recommendations of body builders; many practice poor eating habits.)

■ *Accept your genetically determined limits.*   If you find that even when you implement these suggestions you do not achieve your goal weight (or you initially achieve it but then lose it quickly), you may need to accept the fact that your body is regulated at a lower level of fatness. Maintaining a larger amount of fat may require more time, effort, and expense than you consider worthwhile, and you may decide that your resources could be applied more productively to other kinds of goals.

SUMMARY

■ Although the attention our culture devotes to the cosmetic aspect of body weight seems excessive, it is appropriate to be concerned about weight from a health standpoint. However, the issue of what ideal weight means or should be is not at all obvious, and many people are more concerned about their weight than they need to be.

■ Certain hazards are associated with being either too fat or too thin. Overfat people have statistically higher risk of developing many types of health problems, and have to deal with numerous psychosocial and practical problems as well. People who have too little body fat have less endurance, and in some extreme cases are more susceptible to infectious diseases.

■ Many factors influence how people arrive at their individual body weights. Energy intake is regulated both internally (by hunger) and externally (by appetite). The set-point theory suggests that each person tends to maintain the body weight arrived at by eating in response to hunger alone. Other factors that can influence body weight are the kcaloric density of foods consumed, prevailing cultural attitudes, genetic characteristics, basal metabolic rate, physical activity level, and thermogenesis.

■ You can estimate your ideal body weight from a combination of guidelines, all of which *approximate* what healthy individuals of a given sex, height, and build should weigh. These guidelines include height/weight tables, body mass index, and percentage of body fat, as well as the more subjective "mirror test" and your own assessment of your best functional weight.

■ An interesting theory has been proposed about what happens at the cellular level during energy imbalance. It is theorized that the body responds to the presence of excess energy by either adding more fat cells (hyperplasia), enlarging those it already has (hypertrophy), or both. Energy deficits are thought to result in decreased fat cell size but not number.

■ During an energy shortage, the body derives different percentages of its energy from fat, carbohydrate, and protein, depending on the length and severity of the shortage. Abrupt and severe kcalorie deprivation leads to protein loss and dehydration; if carbohydrate intake is also very limited, fat cannot be metabolized properly and ketosis can result. A more moderate weight loss plan will be less likely to produce these effects.

■ Characteristic psychological responses to energy imbalance have also been observed: feelings of listlessness, tension, irritability, and preoccupation with food and body weight are common responses to large kcalorie deficits. There can even be negative psychological reactions to *successful* weight loss attempts.

■ People have tried thousands of techniques for losing body fat, ranging from very sensible to very dangerous. All weight loss methods are successful for some people but unsuccessful for others. The major types include restricted diets, modification of eating behaviors, psychological approaches, drugs and surgical interventions, increased physical activity, and combinations of the above. Those plans that are based on a well-balanced, nutritious diet and involve the least drastic departure from habits a person can live with permanently seem to have the greatest chances of long-term success. This is also true of techniques used for adding body weight, for those who have this concern.

REFERENCES

Alford, B.B., and M.L. Bogle. 1982. *Nutrition during the life cycle*. Englewood Cliffs, NJ: Prentice-Hall, Inc.

American College of Sports Medicine. 1978. Position statement on the recommended quantity and quality of exercise for developing and maintaining fitness in healthy adults. *Medicine and Science in Sports and Exercise* 10(no.3):vii–x.

Atkinson, R.L., C.S. Russ, P.A. Ciavarella, E.S. Owsley, and M.L. Bibbs. 1984. A comprehensive approach to outpatient obesity management. *Journal of the American Dietetic Association* 84(no.4):439–444.

Bennett, W., and J. Gurin. 1982. Do diets really work? *Science 82* (no.2):42–50.

Bjorntorp, P. 1982. Interrelation of physical activity and nutrition on obesity. In *Diet and exercise: Synergism in health maintenance*, eds. P.L. White and T. Mondeika. Chicago: American Medical Association.

Bjorntorp, P. 1983. The role of adipose tissue in human obesity. In *Obesity*, Vol. 4, *Contemporary Issues in Clinical Nutrition*, ed. M.R.C. Greenwood. New York: Churchill Livingstone.

Blonz, E.R., and J.S. Stern. 1981. Obesity and fad diets. In *Controversies in nutrition*, ed. L. Ellenbogen. New York: Churchill Livingstone.

Bray, G.A. 1983. The energetics of obesity. *Medicine and Science in Sports and Exercise* 15:32–40.

Brownell, K.D., and T.A. Wadden. 1983. Behavioral and self-help treatments. In *Obesity*, Vol. 4, *Contemporary Issues in Clinical Nutrition*, ed. M.R.C. Greenwood. New York: Churchill Livingstone.

Brownell, K.D. 1984. The psychology and physiology of obesity: Implications for screening and treatment. *Journal of the American Dietetic Association* 84(no.4):406–414.

Brozek, J.M. 1982. *The effects of malnutrition on human behavior*. American Dietetic Association (ADA) audio cassette tape 9, 1982. Chicago, IL: ADA.

Brunzell, J.D. 1983. Obesity and risk for cardiovascular disease. In *Obesity*, Vol. 4, *Contemporary Issues in Clinical Nutrition*, ed. M.R.C. Greenwood. New York: Churchill Livingstone.

Danforth, E., Jr., and L. Landsberg. 1983. Energy expenditure and its regulation. In *Obesity*, Vol. 4, *Contemporary Issues in Clinical Nutrition*, ed, M.R.C. Greenwood. New York: Churchill Livingstone.

Department of Health, Education, and Welfare (DHEW). 1980. *Obesity in America*, ed. G.A. Bray. Washington, DC: DHEW.

Donahoe, C.P., D.H. Lin, D.S. Kirschenbaum, and R.E. Keesey. In Press. Metabolic consequences of dieting and exercise in the behavioral treatment of obesity. *Journal of Consulting and Clinical Psychology.*

Drewnowski, A. 1983. Cognitive structure in obesity and dieting. In *Obesity*, Vol. 4, *Contemporary Issues in Clinical Nutrition*, ed. M.R.C. Greenwood. New York: Churchill Livingstone.

Fenner, L. 1980. Cellulite: Hard to budge pudge. *FDA Consumer* 14(no.4):4-7. Washington, D.C.: Department of Health and Human Services.

Ferguson, J.M. 1975. *Learning to eat*. Palo Alto, CA: Bull Publishing Company.

Ferguson, J.M. 1976. *Habits, not diets*. Palo Alto, CA: Bull Publishing Company.

Forbes, G.B. 1981. Is obesity a genetic disease? *Contemporary Nutrition* 6(no.8). Minneapolis: General Mills, Inc.

Friedman, M.I. 1982. New perspectives on the metabolic basis of hunger and satiety. *Contemporary Nutrition* 7(no.5). Minneapolis: General Mills, Inc.

Friedman, R.B., P. Kindy, Jr., and J.A. Reinke. 1982. What to tell patients about weight loss methods. *Postgraduate Medicine* 72:72–80(Part 1); 85–90(Part 2); 91–96(Part 3).

Grande, F. 1961. Nutrition and energy balance in body composition studies. In *Techniques for measuring body composition*. Washington, DC: National Academy of Sciences.

Greenwood, M.R.C. 1983. Genetic and metabolic aspects. In *Obesity*, Vol. 4, *Contemporary Issues in Clinical Nutrition*, ed. M.R.C. Greenwood. New York: Churchill Livingstone.

Gwinup, G. 1975. Effect of exercise alone on the weight of obese women. *Archives of Internal Medicine* 135:676–680.

Hardinge, M.G., and F.J. Stare. 1954. Nutritional studies of vegetarians. *Journal of Clinical Nutrition* 2:73–82.

Himms-Hagen, J. 1983. Brown adipose tissue thermogenesis in obese animals. *Nutrition Reviews* 41:261–267.

Hirsch, J., and J.L. Knittle. 1970. Cellularity of obese and nonobese human adipose tissue. *Federation Proceedings* 29:1516–1521.

Ikeda, J.P. 1978. *For teenagers only: Change your habits to change your shape.* Palo Alto, CA: Bull Publishing Company.

Keen, S. 1978. Eating our way to enlightenment. *Psychology Today* 12(no.5):62–87.

Keesey, R.E., and S.W. Corbett. 1984. Metabolic defense of the body weight set-point. In *Eating and its disorders*, eds. A.J. Stunkard and E. Stellar. New York: Raven Press.

Keys, A. 1979. Is overweight a risk factor for coronary heart disease? *Cardiovascular Medicine* 4:1233–1243.

Keys, A. 1980. Overweight, obesity, coronary heart disease and mortality. *Nutrition Reviews* 38:297–307.

Kissileff, H.R. 1983. Satiety. *Contemporary Nutrition* 8(no.1). Minneapolis: General Mills, Inc.

Knittle, J.L. 1972. Obesity in childhood: A problem in adipose tissue cellular development. *Journal of Pediatrics* 81:1048–1059.

Kral, J.G. 1983. Surgical treatment. In *Obesity*, Vol. 4, *Contemporary Issues in Clinical Nutrition*, ed. M.R.C. Greenwood. New York: Churchill Livingstone.

Mahan, L.K. 1979. A sensible approach to the obese patient. *Nursing Clinics of North America* 14(no.2):229–245.

Mahan, L.K. 1981. Obesity: New knowledge and current treatments. In *Contemporary developments in nutrition*, ed. B.S. Worthington-Roberts. St. Louis: The C.V. Mosby Company.

Mann, G.V. 1981. Menstrual effects of athletic training. In *Medicine and sport*, eds. J. Borms, M. Hebbelinck, and A. Venerando. New York: Karger.

Mayer, J., P. Roy, and K.P. Mitra. 1956. Relation between caloric intake, body weight, and physical work: Studies in an industrial male population in West Bengal. *American Journal of Clinical Nutrition* 4:169–175.

Miller, R.W. 1983. EMS: Fraudulent flab remover. *FDA Consumer* Reprint Number 1983-381-174/36. Washington, DC: U.S. Government Printing Office.

Miller, T.M., J.G. Coffman, and R.A. Linke. 1980. Survey on body image, weight, and diet of college students. *Journal of the American Dietetic Association* 77:561–566.

Nutrition and the M.D. 1982. Hormonal responses to semi-starvation states. *Nutrition and the M.D.* 8(no.9):1–2.

Office of Health Research, Statistics, and Technology; Public Health Service. 1979. Overweight adults in the United States. *Advancedata* 51:1–10. DHEW Publication No. (PHS)79-1250. Hyattsville, MD: U.S. Department of Health and Human Services.

Orbach, S. 1979. *Fat is a feminist issue.* New York: Berkley Books.

Polivy, J., and C.P. Herman. 1983. *Breaking the diet habit.* New York: Basic Books, Inc., Publishers.

Randolph, P.M., and C. Dennison. 1981. *Diet, nutrition, and dentistry.* St. Louis: The C.V. Mosby Company.

Rimm, A.A., and P.L. White. 1980. Obesity: Its risks and hazards. In *Obesity in America*. Washington, DC: Department of Health, Education, and Welfare.

Russ, C.S., P.A. Ciavarella, and R.L. Atkinson. 1984. A comprehensive outpatient weight reduction program: Dietary patterns, psychological considerations, and treatment principles. *Journal of the American Dietetic Association* 84(no.4): 444–446.

Scott, E.C., and F.E. Johnston. 1982. Critical fat, menarche, and the maintenance of menstrual cycles: A critical review. *Journal of Adolescent Health Care* 2(no.4):249–260.

Sherman, A.R., and P.V. Johnston. 1982. Nutrition and immunity. *Illinois Research* 24(no.1):4–7.

Simonson, M. 1982. An overview: Advances in research and treatment of obesity. *Food and Nutrition News* 53(no.4).

Sims, E.A., E.S. Horton, and L.B. Salans. 1971. Inducible metabolic abnormalities during development of obesity. *Annual Reviews of Medicine* 22:235–250.

Society of Actuaries and Association of Life Insurance Medical Directors of America (ALIMDA). 1980. *1979 build and blood pressure study*. New York: The Metropolitan Life Insurance Companies.

Stern, J. 1983. Diet and exercise. In *Obesity*, Vol. 4, *Contemporary Issues in Clinical Nutrition*, ed. M.R.C. Greenwood. New York: Churchill Livingstone.

Stuart, R.B., and B. Davis. 1975. *Slim chance in a fat world*. Champaign, IL: Research Press.

Stuart, R.B., C. Mitchell, and J.A. Jensen. 1981.Therapeutic options in the management of obesity. In *Medical psychology: Contributions to behavioral medicine*, eds. C.K. Prokop and L.A. Bradley. Orlando, FL: Academic Press.

Stunkard, A.J. 1984. The current status of treatment for obesity in adults. In *Eating and its disorders*, eds. A.J. Stunkard and E. Stellar. New York: Raven Press.

Taylor, J.L., E.R. Buskirk, J. Brozek, J.T. Anderson, and F. Grande. 1957. Performance capacity and effects of caloric restriction with hard physical work on young men. *Journal of Applied Physiology* 10(no.3):421–429.

Tipton, C.M. 1982. Consequences of rapid weight loss. In *Nutrition and athletic performance*, eds. W. Haskell, J. Scala, and J. Whittam. Palo Alto, CA: Bull Publishing Company.

Van Itallie, T.B. 1979. Obesity: Adverse effects on health and longevity. *American Journal of Clinical Nutrition* 32:2723–2733.

Van Itallie, T.B. 1980. Conservative approaches to treatment. In *Obesity in America*, ed. G. Bray. Washington, DC: Department of Health, Education, and Welfare.

Van Itallie, T.B. 1984. The enduring storage capacity for fat: Implications for treatment of obesity. In *Eating and its disorders*, eds. A.J. Stunkard and E. Stellar. New York: Raven Press.

Van Itallie, T.B., and J. Hirsch. 1979. Appraisal of excess calories as factor in the causation of disease. *American Journal of Clinical Nutrition* 32:2648–2653.

Weigley, E.S. 1984. Average? Ideal? Desirable? A brief overview of height-weight tables in the United States. *Journal of the American Dietetic Association* 84(no.4):417–423.

Willis, J. 1982. About body wraps, pills, and other magic wands for losing weight. *FDA Consumer* 16(no.9):18–20. Washington, DC: Department of Health and Human Services.

Worthington-Roberts, B.S. 1981. Proteins and amino acids. In *Contemporary developments in nutrition*, ed. B.S. Worthington-Roberts. St. Louis: The C.V. Mosby Company.

Yang, M.-U., and T.B. Van Itallie. 1976. Composition of weight loss during short-term weight reduction. *Journal of Clinical Investigation* 58:722–730.

Zuti, B., and A. Golding. 1976. Comparing diet and exercise as weight reduction tools. *Physician and Sports Medicine* 4:49–53.

11

Eating Disorders

IN THIS CHAPTER: Classification and Terminology Are Still Being Established   ▪   People with Eating Disorders Have Typical Characteristics   ▪   Biological, Personal/familial, and Societal Factors Have Been Blamed for the Eating Disorders   ▪   Specialized Treatment Is Available   ▪   Most People Who Are Treated for Eating Disorders Improve

Many of you have already heard of anorexia nervosa and bulimia. These are abnormal food intake patterns called *eating disorders* that involve starving, binging, and/or purging.

It is not customary to devote much space to these conditions in an introductory nutrition text, because they are *not primarily nutritional problems*. They are mainly *psychological problems* that manifest themselves when people eat inappropriately to avoid dealing with their problems of living. However, they often result in nutritional difficulties. Furthermore, eating disorders are now well recognized and widespread, affecting some people in virtually all of the developed countries; therefore we believe that they warrant attention here.

Some people who develop eating disorders were originally following reasonable weight loss programs that they were controlling; but then, somehow, the program began to control them instead, and they adopted unreasonable dietary behaviors that were involuntary and dangerous. This chapter will offer some guidelines for recognizing the dangerous behaviors.

Note that we probably all, from time to time, misuse eating to some degree. For example, if we occasionally eat excessive amounts of food (on Thanksgiving or some other occasion) or eat very little on other days (for instance, on the day after a splurge) this is not indicative of an eating disorder. Eating disorders involve *frequent, extreme, involuntary* eating disturbances—not occasional, voluntary feasting or fasting. We want to help people understand the difference.

Finally, it is important to realize that eating disorders are serious conditions. They require treatment: some people die of them. Many others find their lives extremely limited by their obsession with food. However, if treated by qualified professionals (who often work as a team), people with eating disorders usually improve. Since the likelihood of recovery is better when the condition is treated early, if you suspect an eating disorder in yourself or somebody else, you should share your concerns with a qualified professional without delay. That person can help decide whether treatment is indicated, and can direct you, your friend, or family member to appropriate help.

Classification and Terminology Are Still Being Established

Although the condition now called *anorexia nervosa* was recognized in a few people in the late 1800s, intense concern about it and related conditions has developed mainly in the last two decades. Since this is a relatively new area of scientific scrutiny, the eating disorders have not yet been fully classified or named to the experts' satisfaction (Halmi, 1983a).

Among the terms that have been coined to identify eating disorders are anorexia nervosa, bulimia, bulimia nervosa, bulimarexia, compulsive eating jags, dietary chaos syndrome, stuffing syndrome, and counter-regulation (Wardle and Beinart, 1981). Not only is there great variety in the terms used, but there are also differences in the meanings given to various terms. For example, "anorexia nervosa" is sometimes used to refer only to the condition in which people starve themselves; in other cases the same term is applied to those who alternately binge and starve. To compound the confusion, the term in either case is a misnomer, because it literally means "loss of hunger from mental causes," but many people who have the disorder *do* experience hunger. *Bulimia*, or derivations of that term, are applied to eating behaviors that include binging. To try to reduce confusion here, we will avoid using these terms, and instead will talk about starving, binging, or purging behaviors, or combinations thereof.

* Name wrongly Applied

Although the combination of behaviors that might be seen in any one individual varies widely, here we will limit the discussion to the more common types: binging/purging; starving; and starving/binging/purging in combination.

People with Eating Disorders Have Typical Characteristics

Since this area of inquiry is so new, our knowledge about various eating disorders is quite uneven. A considerable amount of data have been collected on starving and the combination of starving, binging, and purging. People who show these behaviors are more often hospitalized due to their obvious symptom of severe weight loss, so information about them is more accessible for research purposes, and has enabled experts to characterize these disorders quite thoroughly. (Identification of patients is never revealed in the literature.)

The data about binging/purging are much more limited. Nonetheless, we will discuss what is known about this disorder, since it involves a much larger number of people, and has its own dangers. We encourage you to be alert to new information on this condition as it becomes available.

In general, there are two traits seen in people with any eating disorder:

- They misuse the eating function, relying almost totally on it (by either eating or not eating) to provide the satisfactions that other life experiences should generate, such as security, feelings of effectiveness, and a sense of self-determination.

- They view a particular body weight as being essential to their getting what they want out of life, whether this means having friends, getting married, launching a career, or reaching other goals.

In this section we will look at characteristics that seem to be associated with the three most common types of abnormal eating behaviors, but keep in mind that there is much individual variation from these generalizations.

Table 11.1   Characteristics Associated with Binging and Binging/Purging (No Routine Starving)

Living habits	Physical signs and symptoms	Psychological traits
Recurrent episodes of binge eating with intent of purging later	May be thin, normal weight, or overfat	Pursuit of thinness
Binging done secretly	Frequent weight fluctuations of ten pounds or more	Awareness that eating pattern is abnormal
Use of vomiting, enemas, laxatives, or diuretics for weight loss	Tooth decay	Fear of not being able to stop eating voluntarily
Occasional brief fasts	Swollen glands	Feeling that life is dominated by food
Intermittent alcohol and other drug abuse	Dehydration	Depressed mood and self-deprecating thoughts following eating binges
	Electrolyte disturbances	Distorted belief of weighing more than actual weight
	Menstrual disturbances	

Not all of the above symptoms are seen in all cases.
References: (a) Gross, M. 1982. In *Anorexia nervosa: A comprehensive approach,* ed. M. Gross. Lexington, MA: The Collamore Press. (b) Halmi, K.A., J. Falk, and E. Schwartz. 1981. Binge-eating and vomiting: A survey of a college population. *Psychological Medicine* 11:697–706. (c) Lucas, A.R. 1981. Bulimia and vomiting syndrome. *Contemporary Nutrition* 6(no.4).

Binger/Purgers

More people binge and purge than are involved in any other eating disorder, at least in the college-age population. Thirteen percent of the respondents to a survey of college students admitted to practicing these behaviors (although a small percentage said they binged but did not purge). Female binger/purgers outnumbered males by four to one (Halmi et al., 1981). In a study of urban high school students, eight percent were found to be bingers or binger/purgers (Johnson et al., 1983).

By binging, we mean secretly consuming large amounts of high-energy foods in a short period of time, usually many thousands of kcalories within a couple of hours. The binger feels he or she can't stop voluntarily, and only quits eating when pain, sleep, or somebody else interrupts the eating. Purging is accomplished through vomiting or the use of enemas, laxatives, or diuretics.

Binger/purgers may be underfat, of normal weight, or overfat; however, many have family histories of overfatness. The disorder ordinarily begins during adolescence or early adulthood (Gross, 1982), usually after a period of dieting (Wooley and Wooley, 1984). In the survey of college students just mentioned, 75% of the students were of normal body weight at the time of the survey, whereas approximately 10% of both men and women in the study were overweight or obese. Table 11.1 summarizes their typical living habits, plus the physical signs and symptoms and psychological traits often seen among binger/purgers.

Physicians and mental health workers who treat binger/purgers find that these individuals often feel dominated by food and frustrated by the

binging—secretly consuming large amounts of high-energy foods in a short time, often stopping only when interrupted by pain, sleep, or another person

purging—intentionally clearing food out of the system by vomiting and/or using enemas, laxatives, or diuretics

A starver. A person with a starving eating disorder limits her energy intake to very low levels, although she often pushes herself to do physically demanding solitary athletic activities. Thoughts about eating and not eating occupy a large part of her time. Approximately half of the people who are starvers alternately binge and purge.

control it has over them. Generally they recognize that their eating pattern is abnormal. They feel depressed and of low self-worth after an episode.

Many different kinds of complications can occur: tooth decay (from repeated vomiting of acidic stomach contents), dehydration, menstrual disturbances, and electrolyte imbalances. At worst, death can result from electrolyte imbalances, particularly of potassium, that may cause heart failure.

Starvers

starving—deliberately restricting all food intake to drastically low levels

The typical individual who is deliberately starving is an upper-middle- or middle-class teen-age female; less than 10% of starvers are male. An estimated 1% of teenage girls in North America become starvers. Most of them are of normal weight before they begin this practice (Bruch, 1981), but may lose up to 40% of their body weight with the disorder.

As young children, most starvers were cooperative, thoughtful, and obedient. Their families tend to be so close that it is difficult for each member to develop an individual identity and feel in charge of his or her own behavior; the parents in such families also tend to be overprotective and rigid. Among their peers, starvers tend to be highly competitive and achieving. They make an enormous effort to be outstanding in everything they do (Bruch, 1978a).

Table 11.2 Characteristics Associated with Starving as an Eating Disorder

Living habits	Physical signs and symptoms	Psychological traits
Very low energy intake (500–800 kcal/day)	Loss of 20–40% of original weight	Relentless pursuit of thinness
Slow and ritualistic eating	BMR decreased by up to 40%	Inaccurate body image (supposes higher weight)
Involvement in food-related activities	Amenorrhea (absence of menstruation)	Loss of ability to correctly perceive and interpret body stimuli
Demanding physical activity	Hormonal and other biochemical changes	Lack of independent identity; overly attached to parents
Increasing social isolationism	Delayed gastric emptying and secretions	Sense of ineffectiveness
Perfectionism in studying and other activities	Constipation	View of circumstances as "black or white"
	Brittle hair, hair loss	Out of touch with emotions
	Downy hair, especially on back and face	Denial of condition being a problem
	Abnormal sleep patterns	

Not all of the above symptoms are seen in all cases.
References: (a) Bruch, H. 1981. Developmental considerations of anorexia nervosa and obesity. *Canadian Journal of Psychiatry* 26:212–217. (b) Crisp, A.H. 1980. *Anorexia nervosa: Let me be.* London: Academic Press. (c) Garfinkel, P. E., and D.M. Garner. 1982. *Anorexia nervosa: A multidimensional perspective.* New York: Brunner/Mazel, Publishers. (d) Palazzoli, M.S. 1978. *Self-starvation.* New York: Jason Aronson.

Table 11.2 lists characteristics often seen in starvers. In their pursuit of thinness, they reduce their weight to such low levels that they experience biochemical and hormonal changes. Their body functions slow down: the gastrointestinal tract works more slowly; BMR goes down, as do blood pressure and pulse; and menstruation often stops. The most serious possible consequence of prolonged starvation is death, as described in Chapter 5 (on energy).

Starvers also misinterpret many messages their bodies try to give them regarding hunger, temperature, pain, and fatigue (Bruch, 1981). For example, when they feel the sensation that a healthy person would recognize as hunger, they do not believe it is caused by *needing* something to eat; rather, they might believe that they have a stomach ache from *having eaten* a few carrot sticks many hours ago. Alternatively, they may experience physiological sensations as before, but choose not to respond to the messages:

SLICE OF LIFE:
A Starver Speaks Out

. . . I was going through agony, i.e. my stomach was shrinking and causing pain, also blood pressure went very low, and I passed out when standing up. Heavy nose bleeds were also a feature, but the main problem was trying to keep warm due to loss of weight. I found starving myself a great challenge, as I always loved food and eating, so stopping myself from doing this took a great deal of willpower. [From *Anorexia Nervosa: Let Me Be* (Crisp, 1980)]

While all this is happening, the starver denies that anything is wrong; in fact, she often maintains that she is still overfat and ought to lose more weight. She frequently drives herself to perform demanding physical activities despite her low energy intake, at least in the earlier stages of the disorder.

Throughout this experience, she takes great satisfaction in demonstrating incredible self-control over her studying, exercising, and eating. She avoids eating most foods, even though she is frantically preoccupied with food and eating, and often deliberately puts herself in proximity to food by cooking for other people.

The following Slice of Life describes many of these factors in the words of a starver:

SLICE OF LIFE:
Another Starver Describes Her Condition

I contracted anorexia at about the age of 12½ although it progressed very gradually and I did not believe that there was anything wrong with me. It was my parents who dragged me to the doctors, worried out of their minds. All I remember of that time is that my sole concern was food and what I was not going to eat. My school work did not suffer at first, quite the opposite, as all my energy went into it. I suppose my first realization that there was something wrong with me was when I found it so hard to chat to the other girls at school. I just used to be there, staring at nothing. A friend once told me that I used to be quite popular, as I was always fairly lively and friendly, but now they did not know how to treat me. They could not be themselves with me any more because I had changed so much. I was getting worse and the gap between me and my world and other people was getting wider. [From *Anorexia Nervosa: Let Me Be* (Crisp, 1980)]

In recent years, an analogy has been drawn between starving behaviors in women and compulsive running in men. Some clinicians have noted similar traits in the family background, socioeconomic class, and personality characteristics of the two groups; it has been suggested that compulsive runners might be in search of an identity as well (Yates et al., 1983). Further discussion of this hypothesis would take us afield of our topic, but it is worth reinforcing the idea that what is seen externally—the food avoidance or the running—is a dramatic *symptom*, but not the basic *problem*.

It is important for coaches and trainers to educate themselves about this disorder, since starvers sometimes join athletic teams to support their determination to exercise hard and regularly. A perceptive coach or trainer should recognize a person who is vehement about weight loss and over-

Table 11.3 Characteristics Associated with Combined Starving, Binging, and Purging

Living habits	Physical signs and symptoms	Psychological Traits
Starving alternated with recurrent overconsumption of food (5000–20,000 kcal/day) with intent of purging later	Physical signs and symptoms as seen in starvers (Table 11.2)	Pursuit of thinness
	Tooth decay	Awareness that eating pattern is abnormal
Use of vomiting, enemas, laxatives, or diuretics for weight loss	Swollen glands	Feeling that life is dominated by food
	Irritation of esophagus, stomach	Feelings of depression and self-deprecation after binges
Use of alcohol and/or other drugs	Bloody diarrhea	
	Dehydration	Fear of not being able to stop eating voluntarily
Socially more outgoing and sexually involved than starver	Electrolyte depletion	Mood swings
	Amenorrhea	
Impulsiveness	Abnormal sleep patterns	
Socially unacceptable behaviors		

Not all of the above symptoms are seen in all cases.
References: (a) Beumont, P.J.V., G.C.W. George, and D.E. Smart. 1976. "Dieters" and "vomiters and purgers" in anorexia nervosa. *Psychological Medicine* 6:617–622. (b) Casper, R.C., et al. 1980. Bulimia: Its incidence and clinical importance in patients with anorexia nervosa. *Archives of General Psychiatry* 37:1030–1035. (c) Garfinkel, P. E., H. Moldofsky, and D. M. Garner, 1980. The heterogeneity of anorexia nervosa: Bulimia as a distinct subgroup. *Archives of General Psychiatry* 37:1036–1040.

zealous about exercise, and get her or him in for evaluation.

Not every instance of excessive weight loss among athletes is indicative of a true eating disorder with its psychiatric involvement, though; such weight loss may be a temporary reaction to the extreme pressure athletes undergo to maintain a certain competitive weight. Nonetheless, the athlete should be evaluated, and if there is no eating disorder should receive nutrition counseling and followup monitoring for appropriate food intake. It is a good idea to have someone other than the coach responsible for supervising the weight control of athletes (Smith, 1980).

Combined Starver/Binger/Purgers

The combined starver/binger/purger tends to be a slightly older teen than the starver. Approximately half of the people treated for starving also practice binging/purging (Garfinkel et al., 1980). Again, girls with the disorder greatly outnumber boys.

As a child, the starver/binger/purger was generally well-behaved, outgoing, competitive, and achieving (Casper et al., 1980). She is more likely to have been somewhat overweight before the onset of the disease (Beumont et al., 1976), and her mother is more likely to be obese than the starver's (Garfinkel, 1981).

Table 11.3 lists characteristics likely to be found in a person who starves, binges, and purges. Starver/binger/purgers tend to be somewhat more able to acknowledge and express their emotions than starvers, although they still have considerable difficulty in this regard. They seek out more involvement with others than starvers do, but remain somewhat socially isolated. Mental health workers note that they tend to be more impulsive, and are more likely to engage in socially unacceptable behaviors such as stealing (Casper et al., 1980). They are also more prone to use alcohol and other drugs than starvers are (Garfinkel et al., 1980).

As you would suspect, the physical problems that starver/binger/purgers develop can include those of both groups discussed earlier. In rare cases, stomach distention from binging is so great as to cause tears in the stomach and subsequent death (Saul et al., 1981).

The following slice of life describes what it is like to be a starver/binger/purger in the words of an affected person.

SLICE OF LIFE:
A Starver/Binger/Purger Tells
It Like It Is

Every morning at 6:30 without fail, I would lie in bed planning exactly what I would and would not eat that day, and every night I would lie there and count up the calories of that meagre supply. In short, I was obsessed with food.

During the week I purged myself, starving myself, dreading the weekend ahead when I knew very well I was likely to go on a binge, eating all in sight, shovelling it in, to make up for what I had deprived myself of in the week. The guilt that followed these binges was unbearable. It made me lose any confidence I might have had in myself, and in my strict self-discipline which seemed all important. . . .

My periods had been non-existent for a good two years; my hair was falling out; I had constant indigestion; looked like a bag of bones, and desperately needed help. [From *Anorexia Nervosa: Let Me Be* (Crisp, 1980)

Biological, Personal/Familial, and Societal Factors Have Been Blamed for the Eating Disorders

Nobody really knows why the eating disorders develop, but there is no shortage of theories. The factors thought to prompt them fall under the headings of biological determinants, personal and family interactions, and societal pressures.

Biological Determinants

Some experts propose that endocrine (hormonal) abnormalities are responsible for eating disorders (Lucas, 1981). They point to the fact that many starvers exhibit hormonal irregularities well before they have lost enough weight for malnutrition to be the sole cause (Halmi, 1983b). Others have suggested that damage to the central nervous system, possibly during birth, may be the culprit (Garfinkel and Garner, 1982).

Frontier

Personal and Family Interactions

Researchers have identified the type of family in which a person with an eating disorder is most likely to be found. Generally the structure is very tight, with evidence of overprotectiveness, rigidity, and lack of conflict resolution (Giesey and Strieder, 1982). The family itself is likely to regard this exaggerated control as benevolence. There is often "enmeshment," or inadequate distinction between the roles of family members.

Hilde Bruch, a leading authority on eating disorders, hypothesizes that trouble occurs if children have been consistently denied the opportunity to become autonomous and make their own decisions, even regarding such personal matters as hunger, comfort, and how they feel emotionally (1978b, 1981). They feel a "paralyzing sense of ineffectiveness." Consequently, when the new stresses of the adolescent years confront such a teenager, it may be that the "youngster withdraws to his own body as the only domain for experiencing a sense of control and a limited awareness of selfhood" (Bruch, 1981).

The starver imposes the kind of control over her body that she wishes she had over her life in general. Her emaciation sets her back physically to prepubertal status where she can avoid confronting adulthood. The binger, on the other hand, may be trying to swallow her problems; the purger is thought to be expressing her anger.

Societal Pressures

Society also takes it on the chin for its role in promoting eating disorders. Another expert notes, "There is little doubt that the modern girl is weighed down by a host of cultural and social pressures that tend to aggravate the

Social pressure and eating disorders. Some experts suggest that the current lean ideal, particularly for women, causes many people to continually attempt to restrict their energy intake even if their weight is acceptable from a health perspective. Such ongoing food denial may precede an eating disorder.

inner conflicts. . . ." (Palazzoli, 1978). As girls view the roles of women in their society, they recognize that there will be many pressures on them as adults. Palazzoli points to the multiple demands of career, fashion, love relationship, and parenting, stating, "It is quite obvious that the conflict between so many irreconcilable demands on her time . . . exposes the modern woman to a terrible social ordeal."

Others point out that modern society exerts pressure on females to be abnormally thin, which requires that they almost continually resist eating while being almost constantly hungry. This expectation demands that women repress their nature and being (Chernin, 1981; Orbach, 1977). An eating disorder results when a woman yields to such societal pressure and believes that maintaining thinness is the only important life issue for her.

A healthier attitude was expressed in the following letter to Ann Landers:

SLICE OF LIFE:
A Letter to Ann Landers
(October 26, 1982)

Dear Ann:

Today both men and women are painfully preoccupied with a passion to look thin. We have been bombarded with a hailstorm of diet pills, low-cal drinks and dozens of books on how to shed unwanted pounds while never going hungry.

When will these fools wake up and realize that not everyone can be thin, and not everyone wants to be? It takes all kinds of people to make a world. Personally, I'd like to tell the woman who wrote that I don't mind if she jiggles.

20 and Free
Reprint courtesy of Ann Landers, News America Syndicate,
Wisconsin Sate Journal.

Initiating Incidents

Clinicians who treat people with eating disorders find that their patients often connect specific kinds of incidents with the triggering of their bizarre food habits. Sometimes it is unkind remarks (not necessarily even accurate) about their bodies that the person remembers as provoking the disordered eating behaviors. An isolated remark by itself would not bring about an eating disorder; such problems occur when there is a history of repeated abuse. One patient recalls the verbal abuse she received in the Slice of Life on page 273.

Others have seen that a teenage girl who doesn't go out with boys feels as if she were on the fringe. Often anorexia appears after a film or lecture on sex education which discusses the sexuality typical of her age group in which she is not yet ready to participate. (Bruch, 1978 b).

For many years, through my adolescence and teens, I had been labelled "Tub" by my brother, who would taunt me unmercifully with this nickname. My parents condoned his behaviour, having their own name of "Rhino" for me, on account of my clumsiness. I suppose no malice was intended, but these names hurt during those particularly sensitive years.

I concealed my hurt feelings and rage at being so labelled, but came to be very self-conscious, and to feel that being large or fat was not nice or desirable. This notion was strengthened considerably when at 15 I embarked upon a relationship which was to last four years with a boyfriend who took delight in pointing out and magnifying my physical imperfections once he had discovered this chink in my armour.

And so, at 19, convinced of my unloveliness, I began to shed weight in an effort to change my body. [From *Anorexia Nervosa: Let Me Be* (Crisp, 1980)]

Multiple Causes

Such experiences, played out against a backdrop of restrictive family patterns and societal demands, may together set the stage for an eating disorder. Many experts believe that a disorder is likely to occur when an immediate initiating experience comes together with other longstanding factors.

Specialized Treatment Is Available

True eating disorders are not likely to go away spontaneously: they need treatment. The following guidelines suggest who might need treatment, who provides it, and what forms it might take.

Who Needs Treatment

We do not intend that you should diagnose eating disorders in yourself or others. Only experienced clinicians should assume that responsibility. However, in order to know whether to seek evaluation, it is important to have some kind of self-screening technique. These questions may be helpful:

■ Do you usually eat within 1000 kcalories of your energy needs on a daily basis?

Figure 11.1 The eating behavior continuum. Some experts believe that a person who restrains herself from eating sufficient food to satisfy hunger has crossed the line into abnormal eating behavior. Considerable exaggeration of such behavior may eventually lead to an eating disorder in some cases. A person who senses she is moving to the right along the continuum may warrant professional evaluation.

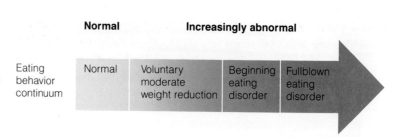

- Does it take you more than half an hour to eat a meal or snack when you are eating alone and are not involved in another activity at the same time?

- Do you have any health problems that can be linked to your eating practices, such as amenorrhea (absence of menstruation) or low body weight?

- Does eating or the anticipation of eating create strong negative feelings in you, such as dread or disgust?

- Do you fear that once you start to eat foods that you enjoy, you will not be able to stop eating?

If you answered "no" to the first question or "yes" to any of the others, it may be reasonable to consider professional evaluation. Remember, *these questions are not the diagnostic criteria for eating disorders;* they are simply designed to help you distinguish between normal and abnormal eating behaviors. Surely, a "wrong answer" to one of the above questions does not mean that a person has a disorder, but a few such answers would make the matter worth checking.

Some clinicians suggest that considering whether eating is primarily regulated internally or externally is a useful indicator of who may be affected. Figure 11.1 shows an eating behavior continuum that may help a person identify where her behaviors fall within the range of possibilities.

If you wonder whether you have an eating disorder, the first step is to consult a medical professional who has had some experience working with people with these conditions. If none is available within a reasonable distance, talk with your general physician or a staff member of your university health center. Ask to be referred to a specialist if he or she thinks it is warranted.

If you think you may have a problem, have a consultation now. The sooner a person with an eating disorder gets treatment, the better the chances of success in dealing with it.

Who Offers Treatment

If treatment is indicated, we strongly suggest that you seek out a clinic that specializes in treating eating disorders; most doctors do not have training that equips them to treat these conditions. Several organizations around the country maintain lists of people and places that offer specialized treatment; you may want to contact them to find out what is available in your area. Two organizations that we have found to be responsive to inquiries are:

- National Anorexic Aid Society, Inc.
  P.O. Box 29461
  Columbus, OH 43229

- American Anorexia Nervosa/Bulimia Association, Inc.
  133 Cedar Lane
  Teaneck, NJ 07666

Types of Treatment Available

There is some variety in the types of treatment available for the eating disorders.

For Disorders That Include Starving. Some clinics treat only the starver; others believe the whole family should be involved, especially when the person with the disorder is quite young and will be living in the household for some time to come. Many treatment teams use both approaches together.

Treatment for starvers involves nutritional rehabilitation, resolution of the disturbed pattern of family interaction, and individual psychotherapeutic help. Generally it is not enough for the person to achieve a normal body weight; without adequate psychotherapy, the disorder will resume as soon as treatment is discontinued. On the other hand, neither does psychotherapy alone usually result in sustained normal body weight. The seriousness of the disorder determines whether hospital care is needed, or whether outpatient treatment will suffice.

Useful therapeutic objectives are for the person to learn to eat appropriately in response to hunger, and to take steps toward doing what she wants to accomplish in life (Satter, unpublished).

For Disorders That Include Binging/Purging. There are also varying approaches to treatment for binging/purging. Except in the most severe cases, this disorder is generally treated on an outpatient basis. Current treatments center on either antidepressant therapy (Hudson et al., 1984), individual psychotherapy, group therapy, behavior modification, or combinations of the above (Fairburn, 1984).

Again, a useful therapeutic objective is for the person to learn to eat appropriately in response to hunger.

Most People Who Are Treated for Eating Disorders Improve

Because criteria for diagnosis and treatment of eating disorders are not well standardized, data regarding the success of different treatment programs are difficult to compare (Vandereycken and Pierloot, 1983). Nonetheless, Hsu undertook the sizeable task of summarizing 16 studies of followup to treatment for over 700 patients whose habits had included starving (1980).

Among all the patients in the studies considered, there was an overall death rate of six percent.

Hsu states, "about three quarters of the patients are better at followup than at initial presentation in terms of body weight. Outcome according to menstrual function is less satisfactory ($\frac{1}{2}$–$\frac{3}{4}$ resumed menstruation), and psychiatric status is even more unsatisfactory. Improvement in these two areas often, but not always, follows an improvement in weight." Many patients experienced social anxieties, with those that remained ill having more problems in that regard. On the other hand, a high proportion were able to maintain full-time employment.

A former patient reflects on what her treatment did for her:

SLICE OF LIFE:
Changes That Resulted from Treatment

After fourteen weeks hospitalization on a strict regime, bed rest and family therapy I am now 28 pounds heavier, happy most of the time, and most important of all I understand myself far better than I ever have done. I can't say I know myself perfectly yet, but being able to answer for my actions and emotions is a much more positive way of going through life than denying my mind and my body.

At last, as well as others valuing my own worth, I do too. I intend to respect both my body and my mind from now on. [From *Anorexia Nervosa: Let Me Be* (Crisp, 1980)]

Data are beginning to be collected on the outcome of treatment for binging/purging. One study notes that depending on how treatment was evaluated, 29–42% of the patients were considered cured after up to six years of treatment (Abraham et al., 1983).

We hope that this discussion of eating disorders has helped you to understand better the nature of these conditions, the difference between normal and abnormal eating behaviors, and what steps to take if a disorder is suspected.

Eating disorders are dangerous because they can wreak nutritional and physiological havoc on bodies that could otherwise be healthy. They are also wasteful in that preoccupation with body weight and eating divert a person's time and creative energies from other important aspects of life.

SUMMARY

■ Eating disorders that involve starving, binging, and/or purging are not primarily *nutritional* problems but *psychological* ones. It is important to understand that everyone occasionally under- or overeats, but that people who have eating disorders do so *frequently, drastically, and involuntarily.* These disorders are serious conditions and require professional treatment.

■ Intense concern about the eating disorders has developed mainly within the past two decades, so their classification and terminology are still being established. You may often see such terms as anorexia nervosa, bulimia, bulimarexia, and dietary chaos syndrome, but they do not all mean the same thing to everyone.

■ Although different combinations of behaviors are seen in different individuals, people with eating disorders tend to have two traits in common: (1) they rely almost totally on eating to provide the satisfactions that other experiences should generate, and (2) they view a particular body weight as being essential to getting what they want out of life. Binging/purging is the most common eating disorder in the college-age population.

■ The various types of eating disorders have potential negative consequences including tooth decay; dehydration; menstrual disturbances; electrolyte imbalances; inability to correctly interpret the body's messages about hunger, pain, and fatigue; and—in the most extreme cases—death.

■ Biological determinants, personal and family interactions, and societal pressures have all been blamed for the eating disorders, but no one really knows why they develop. Some clinicians have found that their patients connect specific incidents with the triggering of their abnormal eating habits. It seems likely that such incidents, in combination with restrictive family patterns and societal demands, may be the cause of these disorders.

■ True eating disorders need specialized professional treatment. You should not attempt to diagnose an eating disorder in yourself or anyone else, but if you suspect abnormal eating behavior, seek professional evaluation immediately. Most people who are treated for eating disorders do improve.

REFERENCES

Abraham, S.F., M. Mira, and D. Llewellyn-Jones. 1983. Bulimia: A study of outcome. *International Journal of Eating Disorders* 2(no. 4):175–180.

Beumont, P.J.V., G.C.W. George, and D.E. Smart. 1976. "Dieters" and "vomiters and purgers" in anorexia nervosa. *Psychological Medicine* 6:617–622.

Bruch, H. 1978a. Anorexia nervosa. *Nutrition Today* 13(no.5):14–18.

Bruch, H. 1978b. *The golden cage: The enigma of anorexia nervosa.* Cambridge, MA: Harvard University Press.

Bruch, H. 1981. Developmental considerations of anorexia nervosa and obesity. *Canadian Journal of Psychiatry* 26:212–217.

Casper, R.C., E.D. Eckert, K.A. Halmi, S.C. Goldberg, and J.M. Davis. 1980. Bulimia: Its incidence and clinical importance in patients with anorexia nervosa. *Archives of General Psychiatry* 37:1030–1035.

Chernin, K. 1981. *The obsession: Reflections on the tyranny of slenderness.* New York: Harper and Row, Publishers.

Crisp, A.H. 1980. *Anorexia nervosa: Let me be.* London: Academic Press.

Crisp, A.H. 1981. Therapeutic outcome in anorexia nervosa. *Canadian Journal of Psychiatry* 26:232–235.

Fairburn, C.G. 1984. Bulimia: Its epidemiology and

management. In *Eating and its disorders*, ed. A.J. Stunkard and E. Stellar. New York: Raven Press.

Garfinkel, P.E. 1981. Some recent observations on the pathogenesis of anorexia nervosa. *Canadian Journal of Psychiatry* 26:218–223.

Garfinkel, P.E., and D.M. Garner. 1982. *Anorexia nervosa: A multidimensional perspective.* New York: Brunner/Mazel, Publishers.

Garfinkel, P.E., H. Moldofsky, and D.M. Garner. 1980. The heterogeneity of anorexia nervosa: Bulimia as a distinct subgroup. *Archives of General Psychiatry* 37:1036–1040.

Giesey, G., and F. H. Strieder. 1982. Attending to family issues in anorexia nervosa. In *Anorexia nervosa: A comprehensive approach*, ed. M. Gross. Lexington, MA: The Collamore Press.

Gross, M. 1982. Bulimia. In *Anorexia nervosa: A comprehensive approach*, ed. M. Gross. Lexington, MA: The Collamore Press.

Halmi, K.A., J. Falk, and E. Schwartz. 1981. Binge-eating and vomiting: A survey of a college population. *Psychological Medicine* 11:697–706.

Halmi, K.A. 1983a. Classification of eating disorders. *International Journal of Eating Disorders* 2(no.4):21–26.

Halmi, K.A. 1983b. Anorexia nervosa and bulimia. *Psychosomatics* 24:111–129.

Hsu, L.K.G. 1980. Outcome of anorexia nervosa: A review of the literature. *Archives of General Psychiatry* 37:1041–1046.

Hudson, J.I., H.G. Pope, Jr., and J.M. Jonas. 1984. Treatment of bulimia with antidepressants: Theoretical considerations and clinical findings. In *Eating and its disorders*, ed. A.J. Stunkard and E. Stellar. New York: Raven Press.

Johnson, C.L., C. Lewis, S. Love, M. Stuckey, and L. Lewis. 1983. In *Understanding anorexia nervosa and bulimia*. Columbus, OH: Ross Laboratories.

Lucas, A.R. 1981. Bulimia and vomiting syndrome. *Contemporary Nutrition* 6(no.4).

Orbach, S. 1977. *Fat is a feminist issue: The anti-diet guide to permanent weight loss.* New York: Paddington.

Palazzoli, M.S. *Self-starvation.* New York: Jason Aronson.

Satter, E. (Unpublished) *Eating disorders: Description, context, and treatment.*

Saul, S.H., A. Dekker, and C.G. Watson. 1981. Acute gastric dilatation with infarction and perforation: Report of fatal outcome in patient with anorexia nervosa. *Gut* 22:978–983.

Smith, N.J. 1980. Excessive weight loss and food aversion in athletes simulating anorexia nervosa. *Pediatrics* 66:139–142.

Vandereycken, W., and R. Pierloot. 1983. Long-term outcome research in anorexia nervosa. *International Journal of Eating Disorders* 2(no.4):237–242.

Wardle, J., and H. Beinart. 1981. Binge eating: A theoretical review. *British Journal of Clinical Psychology* 20:97–109.

Wooley, S.C., and O.W. Wooley. 1984. Should obesity be treated at all? In *Eating and its disorders*, ed. A.J. Stunkard and E. Stellar. New York: Raven Press.

Yates, A., K. Leehey, and C.M. Sisslak. 1983. Running—an analogue of anorexia? *New England Journal of Medicine* 308(no.5):251–255.

PART FOUR

MICRONUTRIENTS: REGULATORS AND
RAW MATERIALS FOR BODIES

12

Vitamins

IN THIS CHAPTER: Vitamins Have Similarities But Differ in Several Ways ▪ The Necessary Amounts of Vitamins Are Available from Foods ▪ Extreme Deficiencies Are Rare in Developed Countries ▪ Large Excesses of Vitamins Are Dangerous ▪ People Take Vitamin Supplements for Many Different Reasons—Some Justifiable, Some Not ▪ You Can Check Your Vitamin Intake Using Assessment Techniques You Have Already Learned

Many people need little convincing that vitamins are important: three-quarters of the Americans surveyed believe that taking extra vitamins beyond those provided by their diets will give them more energy and pep. An FDA study shows that 40–50% of the U.S. population takes vitamin supplements regularly, and it is estimated that $2.6 billion is spent per year on vitamin and mineral supplements.

Although the common assumption that this class of nutrients provides energy is not accurate, it is true that vitamins are essential for the body's functioning. In this chapter, we will describe what vitamins do. Further, we emphasize that a *well-chosen diet can supply all the vitamins that most people need.*

We will also deal with the matter of vitamin supplements, since they are so commonly used. Although supplements can be helpful in some circumstances, many nutritionists believe that the pendulum has swung too far in the direction of their use. This concern is based on the fact that large excesses of some vitamins can cause serious damage; some people take dangerously large doses because of inaccurate claims about the benefits supplemental vitamins can provide.

Many newspapers and magazines contain articles that are excessive in their claims for what vitamins can accomplish and what doses should be taken: "*Miracle vitamin beats tiredness*" one headline claims, and then goes on to recommend levels that are hundreds of times the RDA for certain vitamins. Another article suggests large multivitamin supplements for athletes, the formulation varying with the sport. To many people, such materials convey the impression that you can't get too much of vitamins.

In this chapter, we want to help you find the middle ground: the point at which you take in enough vitamins to carry out the functions that vitamins are needed to perform, but not enough to cause possible damage. We'll start by describing the nature of vitamins—how these substances are alike as a group, and how they differ.

Vitamins Have Similarities but Differ in Several Ways

vitamins—organic compounds present in small amounts in foods, and needed in small amounts by the body as regulators of metabolic functions

The thirteen known vitamins are organic substances that occur in small amounts in foods; they are needed by the human body in minute amounts as regulators of metabolic functions. Vitamins generally do not require digestion but are absorbed intact through the small intestine.

We need relatively little of these substances because vitamins are not used up in one biochemical reaction: one molecule is used repeatedly. Only gradually are vitamins degraded (broken apart) and in need of replacement. Consider vitamin B-12, the vitamin needed in the smallest amount. Just 1 gram of vitamin B-12 can fulfill the RDA of 333,333 people for one day. Even the vitamin we need in the largest amount, vitamin C, has a recommended intake of only 60 mg/day. A gram of it can supply 17 people for one day.

Various Solubilities, Storage Capacities, and Toxicities

Traditionally, the vitamins are subdivided according to whether they are soluble in fat or in water. The fat-soluble-vitamins are A, D, E, and K; the water-soluble vitamins are thiamin, riboflavin, niacin, vitamin B-6, folacin, vitamin B-12, pantothenic acid, biotin, and vitamin C.

The maximum amount of a vitamin that body tissues can maintain is called its saturation level. The saturation levels of various vitamins differ. In general, fat-soluble vitamins can be stored in larger quantities and thus have a greater potential to reach excessive levels and become toxic (harm the body). Vitamin D is regarded as the most toxic of all the vitamins; it is currently suggested that doses for infants should not exceed 2½ times their RDA (DeLuca, 1980). Water-soluble vitamins have generally been thought to have relatively low saturation levels, with the excess being excreted in the urine. However, even they can become toxic, as an increasing number of examples demonstrate (more on this later).

Whether a vitamin is fat-soluble or water-soluble also influences how well it is absorbed, and depends in part on what is in the gut. For example, the presence of fat in the chyme facilitates the absorption of fat-soluble vitamins.

saturation level—the maximum amount of a substance a tissue can maintain

Various Structures, Forms, and Potencies

Aside from the fact that they are all organic, vitamins are otherwise structurally unrelated: there is no characteristic organization of the carbon, hydrogen, and oxygen in a vitamin molecule. Furthermore, some vitamins also contain nitrogen, sulfur, or cobalt in their structures. Figure 12.1 demonstrates these points by showing the dissimilar structures of two vitamins.

Some of the vitamins have several different but closely related chemical forms that can function as that vitamin. These different forms can even occur in the same food at the same time. For example, nicotinamide and nicotinic acid, two forms of niacin, can be simultaneously present in one food. (These compounds are not the same as nicotine in tobacco.)

Sometimes a compound that is rather unlike a nutrient can be converted into one by the body. Such early versions of nutrients are called *precursors*; vitamin precursors are called provitamins. For example, vitamin A has a provitamin called carotene, and the amino acid tryptophan can be a provitamin of niacin.

provitamins—vitamin precursors that the body can convert into the active form of a vitamin

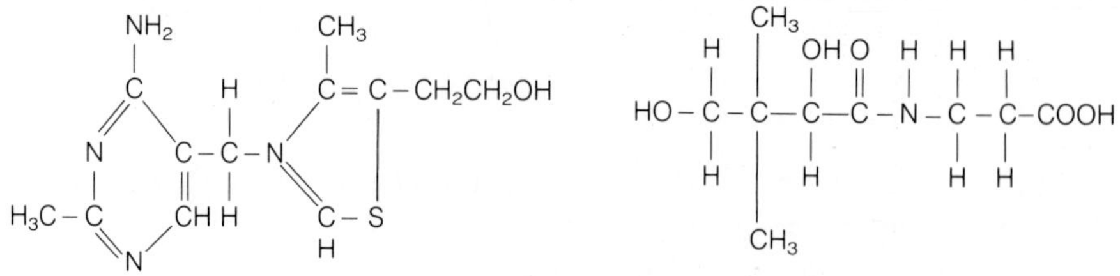

Thiamin

Pantothenic acid

Figure 12.1 The structures of two vitamins. These examples demonstrate that there is no typical structure for vitamins.

Because vitamins and provitamins occur in different forms, a single vitamin can be known by a multitude of chemical names. You might encounter these names on the labels of food products to which vitamins have been added, or on the labels of vitamin supplements. Such names are alternatives to the letter names, or letter/number names, that many vitamins were given when they were first discovered. Often, when vitamins are shown on an ingredient list, the letter/number names accompany the chemical names (Figure 12.2). Some of the more common names/forms for the vitamins are shown in Table 12.1.

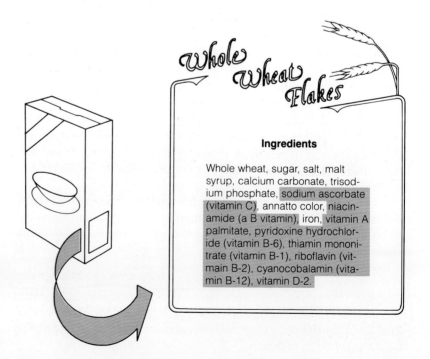

Figure 12.2 How added vitamins are shown on ingredient lists. Labels of foods with added vitamins usually give both the common vitamin name and the name of the specific chemical compound used.

Whole Wheat Flakes

Ingredients

Whole wheat, sugar, salt, malt syrup, calcium carbonate, trisodium phosphate, sodium ascorbate (vitamin C), annatto color, niacinamide (a B vitamin), iron, vitamin A palmitate, pyridoxine hydrochloride (vitamin B-6), thiamin mononitrate (vitamin B-1), riboflavin (vitamin B-2), cyanocobalamin (vitamin B-12), vitamin D-2.

Table 12.1 The Vitamins and a Few of Their Names/Forms

VITAMIN A, retinol, retinal, retinaldehyde, retinoic acid, vitamin A palmitate, carotene

THIAMIN, vitamin B-1

RIBOFLAVIN, vitamin B-2

NIACIN, nicotinamide, nicotinic acid

VITAMIN B-6, pyridoxine, pyridoxamine, pyridoxal, pyridoxol

FOLACIN, folate, folic acid, pteroylglutamic acid

PANTOTHENIC ACID, pantothenate

BIOTIN

VITAMIN B-12, cobalamin, cyanocobalamin

VITAMIN C, ascorbic acid, ascorbate

VITAMIN D, cholecalciferol, ergocalciferol

VITAMIN E, tocopherols (alpha, beta, gamma, and delta), tocotrienols

VITAMIN K, phylloquinone, menadione (a synthetic provitamin)

The form in which a vitamin occurs can influence its potency. For example, among the many forms of vitamin E, some have only 1% to 50% of the potency of the most active form (alpha-tocopherol). Vitamin A is another vitamin for which the potency of different forms varies considerably. Part of the reason for these differences is that various vitamin forms have different levels of absorption. With Vitamin A, a much smaller proportion of the provitamin carotene is absorbed than is retinol, another form of vitamin A.

While discussing forms of vitamins, it is in order to comment on "natural" vs. synthetic vitamins, since some people assume that there are substantial differences between the two. The fact is that "natural" and synthetic vitamin forms are structurally identical: although they have different origins, they are not chemically different. Therefore they function in the body in the same way. The Slice of Life on page 286 points out that even the presumption that "natural" vitamins are extracted from natural sources may not be accurate.

Various Stabilities

Some vitamins are less stable than other nutrients. They can be degraded by oxygen, light, various pH conditions, heat, and/or the passage of time. Because people are greatly concerned with how vitamin losses occur in foods and how to prevent them, much of Chapter 14 (on processing) will deal with this topic.

SLICE OF LIFE:
How Natural Are "Natural" Vitamins?

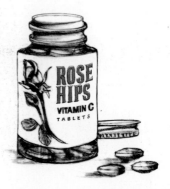

The article from which this was excerpted was written by a pharmacist with the Consumers Co-operative of Berkeley, Inc.

Spurred by our growing sales . . . I visited two manufacturers of "natural" vitamins in Southern California. These companies make capsules, tablets, and other dosage forms sold under some of the most famous brand names found in "health food" stores. . . .

During the visits, it became clear that many vitamin products labeled "natural" or "organic" are not really what I had imagined those terms to mean.

For example, their "Rose Hips Vitamin C Tablets" are made from natural rose hips combined with chemical ascorbic acid, the same vitamin C used in standard pharmaceutical tablets. Natural rose hips contain only about 2% vitamin C, and we were told that if no vitamin C were added the tablet "would have to be as big as a golf ball." A huge stock barrel containing raw material for tablet manufacture was labeled "Rose Hips—Adjusted to contain 50% Ascorbic Acid." Nevertheless, the labels on the bottles read by the consumer were titled simply "Rose Hips Vitamin C." Would you have guessed that the amount of vitamin C coming from rose hips was but a tiny fraction of the amount added as a chemical? . . .

Apparently, [the words "natural" and "organic"] can be used freely because there are no legal definitions of "natural" or "organic." In fact, since the vitamins themselves are identical, no one can tell them apart—either in a test tube or in an animal. A legal distinction could hardly be enforced when no way can be devised to test the difference. [From "How Natural Are Those 'Natural' Vitamins?" (Kamil, 1974)]

Various Units of Measurement

In the past, vitamins were quantified by their mass, which meant that milligrams and micrograms were the usual units of measurement. For a few vitamins, the International Units (IUs) that pharmacists use (which are often directly related to mass) were the standard units.

equivalents—unit now coming into use as an indicator of vitamin activity in the body

Now that scientists are aware that different forms of some vitamins and their precursors have varying potencies, a new unit called equivalents is increasingly being used to reflect as accurately as possible the amount of vitamin *activity* the various forms provide. The 1980 RDA committee made their recommendations for intakes of vitamins A, E, and niacin in equivalents (see inside back cover). However, most food composition tables still express levels of these vitamins in the older units, and until food composition tables can be revised to match the newer equivalent values, comparing such values will be like comparing apples and oranges. Table 12.2 gives an overview of these temporary discrepancies. We will discuss how to deal with them at appropriate points in this chapter.

Table 12.2 Discrepancies in Units of Measurement for Certain Vitamins

Vitamin	Older unit	Newer unit	Comments
A	IU	retinol equivalent (RE)	No simple, accurate mathematical conversion can be made from IUs to REs, since IU values do not take into account—as well as REs do—the varying potencies of different forms. Nonetheless, a very rough estimate of 1 RE = 5 IUs is sometimes used.
E	IU	alpha-tocopherol equivalent	No simple, accurate mathematical conversion can be made from old to new units, since IU values reflect only the alpha-tocopherol present. New units reflect the combined activity of all forms of vitamin E present.
Niacin	mg	niacin equivalent (NE)	New values are figured as follows: 1 mg of niacin = 1 NE 60 mg of tryptophan = 1 NE

The Necessary Amounts of Vitamins Are Available from Foods

Almost all vitamins function in almost all body cells. Therefore, every vitamin has a widespread effect on the body, and body functions are likely to be influenced by many vitamins simultaneously.

As examples, many vitamins are involved at the same time in the processes of energy production, growth, reproduction, and immune function. [One researcher summarized the way in which ten vitamins, through their biochemical activities, are involved in warding off disease (Beisel, 1982).] That concept may be surprising since people usually think that a particular vitamin has very limited functions in only certain tissues—such as associating vitamin A with keeping the skin from getting rough. These associations have come about mainly because symptoms of extreme deficiency or excess are more obvious in some parts of the body sooner than they are in others, due to the specialized functions or unique structures of those tissues or regions. If the malnutrition were allowed to continue (and death did not occur first), other regions would also develop symptoms (Smith et al., 1983).

Each vitamin influences, and is influenced by, many other nutrients. The study of such interactions is another rapidly growing nutrition frontier. We already know that adequate vitamin E intake enhances vitamin A utilization, and that a deficiency of vitamin B-6 can interfere with the conversion of the vitamin precursor tryptophan into niacin. An example of a vitamin interacting with minerals is that vitamin C increases iron absorption, but in large amounts it decreases copper absorption. [Chapter 13 (on minerals) will describe such effects more fully.] Vitamins also interact with macronutrients. For example, the need for vitamin E is greater when there are more polyunsaturated fatty acids in the diet, and the need for several vitamins increases when a high-calorie diet is consumed.

The amounts of vitamins people need to perform metabolic functions are obtainable from food. However, different foods do not contain the same vitamins or the same amounts of vitamins. As we discuss vitamin functions in this section, we will also show the levels of vitamins present in some representative foods from each food group.

The Fat-Soluble Vitamins

Historically, vitamins have been subdivided into two groups according to their solubility. We begin our discussion of functions and sources with the fat-soluble vitamins.

Vitamin A. Vitamin A, although it was the first vitamin discovered, still puzzles scientists who are trying to discover its exact metabolic function in the cell (J. Olson, 1984). It is known, however, to be important for maintaining the health and normal functioning of cartilage, bone, and body coverings and linings (epithelial tissues).

Epithelial tissues include the corneas of the eyes; mucous membranes including the linings of nasal passages, the gastrointestinal tract, and genitourinary tract; and skin. Mucus helps maintain tissue integrity (wholeness), which protects an organism against infection. If vitamin A is not available, the body produces the tough protein keratin instead of mucus. When keratin is produced by epithelial tissue instead of mucus, the keratin detrimentally changes the nature of the surface (a process called *keratinization*). This process makes skin dry and rough, and may subject other mucous membranes to cracking and hemorrhage. The most devastating example of this effect occurs in the cornea of the eye, the clear covering over the front of the eyeball: in severe and prolonged cases of vitamin A deficiency, keratinization can cause blindness. Although this disease is not often seen in the developed countries, it causes blindness in an estimated quarter of a million children annually (McLaren, 1984). The term used to refer to vitamin A deficiency symptoms in the eye is xeropthalmia.

xeropthalmia—vitamin A deficiency disorder of the eye

Vitamin A plays another role in the eye; it is a component of *rhodopsin*, a colored, light-sensitive substance in the retina. When light falls on rhodopsin, it undergoes changes that are translated into messages about what was seen; then it is converted back to its original form. If vitamin A has been deficient in the diet, these conversions occur more slowly than normal, and there is a time lag before the eye can see again. Since this occurs particularly when the eye is trying to adapt from bright light to darkness, the condition is called night blindness.

night blindness—difficulty in adapting from bright light to darkness due to vitamin A deficiency

Vitamin A is known to be important for growth because when animals have been depleted of this nutrient, their bodies cannot accomplish the bone remodeling and synthesizing that adds to length.

The RDA committee has recommended levels of daily vitamin A intake at 1000 retinol equivalents (REs) for men and 800 REs for women. These levels can easily be achieved by including one vitamin A-rich food in the diet each day. Remember that vitamin A values are currently being expressed in both IUs and REs. When comparing food values (still expressed in IUs) to RDA values (now in the more accurate REs), it is necessary to use temporarily as the standard for intake the U.S. RDA of 5000 IUs.

The fruit and vegetable group has the greatest number of outstanding sources of vitamin A, as Table 12.3 shows. Of those foods, the ones that generally have the highest amount of vitamin A are the carotene-containing deep orange and dark green varieties. The best among them are apricots, broccoli, cantaloupe (muskmelon), carrots, pumpkin, winter squash, sweet potatoes, and spinach and other dark, leafy greens. All of these foods furnish 50% to over 100% of the U.S. RDA for vitamin A in a single serving. Another food that provides a large amount of vitamin A in one serving is liver. Dairy products and eggs have lesser amounts.

Because there are few significant sources of vitamin A, a person who does not eat those particular foods is not likely to consume the RDA for vitamin A. [This is the case with many Americans even though the *average* vitamin A intake of Americans does meet the RDA (Science and Education Administration, 1980).] For example, somebody who avoids liver, and who limits his or her fruit and vegetable consumption to only corn, peas, lettuce, apples, and orange juice, is likely to have trouble meeting the recommended level of vitamin A intake.

Vitamin D. The primary roles of vitamin D are to enhance the intestinal absorption of calcium and phosphorus and to promote retention of calcium that might otherwise be lost in the urine. These activities are important for maintaining sufficiently high levels of calcium and phosphorus in the blood to promote their deposition in bone (DeLuca, 1980). If the level of vitamin D is inadequate in the body over a period of time, bones will fail to mineralize or will progressively demineralize, resulting in bone softening. When this occurs in children, the condition is called rickets; it is characterized by abnormal bone development that may result in bowed legs and other deformities. An analogous condition in adults is called osteomalacia.

rickets, osteomalacia—progressive demineralization of bone in children and adults, respectively, caused by a vitamin D deficiency

Because vitamin D is linked closely to bone growth and maintenance, the RDA for this nutrient is highest for people who are growing. For adults above age 22, an intake of 5 μg is adequate.

No foods that people normally eat are naturally very high in vitamin D. The best common source of vitamin D is a product that has had vitamin D added to it—fortified milk. Note from Table 12.4 that two servings will provide the adult RDA. (Because food composition data describe vitamin

Table 12.3   Vitamin A in Some Foods

Food	Household measure	IUs of vitamin A	Percent of U.S. RDA 0 25 50 75 100
Fruits and vegetables			
Apple	1 medium	120	
Apricots, cnd	½ c	2,245	XXXXXXXX
Broccoli, Z, ckd	½ c	2,405	XXXXXXXXX
Cantaloupe, 5 in. diameter	¼ melon	2,310	XXXXXXXX
Carrot, raw	7 ½ in. long	7,930	XXXXXXXXXXXXXXXXXXXX))159%
Corn, cnd	½ c	290	X
Green beans, Z, ckd	½ c	390	XX
Lettuce, iceberg	1 c	180	
Orange juice, Z	½ c	135	
Peach, fresh	1 medium	1,330	XXXX
Spinach, Z, ckd	½ c	8,100	XXXXXXXXXXXXXXXXXXXX))162%
Grain products			
Bread, average	1 slice	tr	
Dry cereal, not fort	1 oz	0	
Pasta, ckd	½ c	0	
Milk and milk products			
Buttermilk from skim milk, not fort	1 c	tr	
Milk, vitamin A-fort	1 c	500	XX
Milk, whole, not fort	1 c	310	X
Cheese, cheddar	1 ⅓ oz	400	XX
Meats and alternates			
Beef, ground, brld	3 oz	20	
Eggs	2	520	XX
Kidney beans, cnd	1 c	10	
Liver, beef, fried	3 oz	45,000[a]	XXXXXXXXXXXXXXXXXXXX))900%
Limited extras			
Butter	1 t	150	X
Carbonated beverages	12 oz	0	
Sugar, honey	1 T	0	

Table 12.4   Vitamin D in Some Foods

Food	Household measure	IUs of vitamin D	Percent of RDA for age 22 and older				
			0	25	50	75	100
Fruits and vegetables							
All types		0					
Grain products							
All types made without milk		0					
Milk and milk products							
Milk, vitamin D- fortified	1 c.	100	XXXXX	XXXXX			
Milkshake, McDonald's	1 average	35	XXXX				
Cottage cheese	2 c	10	X				
Meats and alternates							
Eggs	2 medium	54	XXXXX				
Fish (bass)	3 oz	1					
Meats (muscle types)	3 oz	0					
Liver, beef, fried	3 oz	12	X				

The columns on the right of this chart represent the portions of the RDA of Vitamin D found in the specified servings of food. Each X in the column represents 5% of the adult RDA. The RDA for vitamin D is 5μg (200 IU) for people age 22 and older. Data adapted from Pennington, J.A., and H.N. Church. 1980. *Food values of portions commonly used*. Philadelphia: J.B. Lippincott.

[a]Value varies widely
The columns on the right of this chart represent the portions of the U.S. RDA of vitamin A found in the specified servings of food. Each X in the column represents 5% of the U.S. RDA. The U.S. RDA for vitamin A is 5000 IU.
Abbreviations:
  brld = broiled   cnd = canned   Z = frozen
  ckd = cooked   fort = fortified
Data adapted from: (1) Pennington, J.A., and H.N. Church. 1980. *Food values of portions commonly used*. Philadelphia: J.B. Lippincott. (2) Science and Education Administration. 1981. *Nutritive value of foods*. Home and Garden Bulletin Number 72. Washington, DC: U.S. Department of Agriculture.

Table 12.5 Vitamin E in Some Foods

Food	Household measure	Mg of alpha-tocopherol	Percent of U.S. RDA (10 mg) 0 25 50 75 100
Fruits and vegetables			
Apple	1 medium	0.47	X
Corn, cnd	4 oz	0.06	
Corn, Z, ckd	4 oz	0.21	
Peas, Z, ckd	4 oz	0.28	X
Potato, boiled	1 medium	0.04	
Strawberries, Z	4 oz	0.24	
Tomatoes, fresh	4 oz	0.45	X
Grain products			
Bread, white	1 slice	0.02	
Bread, whole wheat	1 slice	0.09	
Cookie, shortbread	3 small	0.13	
Oat cereal, dry	1 oz	0.17	
Milk and milk products			
Ice cream, vanilla	$1\frac{1}{2}$ c	0.12	
Milk, whole	1 c	0.09	
Meats and alternates			
Beef steak, broiled	3 oz	0.11	
Bologna	3 oz	0.05	
Chicken, Z, fried	3 oz	0.14	
Eggs	2 medium	0.46	X
Haddock, broiled	3 oz	0.51	X
Peanuts, dry roasted	$\frac{1}{2}$ c	9.20	XXXXX XXXXX XXXXX XXX
Pork chops, fried	3 oz	0.14	
Limited extras			
Butter	1 t	0.05	
Margarines made with various oils	1 t	0.65	X
Mayonnaise made with various oils	1 T	0.84 – 3.40	XX–XX XX
Milk chocolate candy	1 oz	0.31	X

The columns on the right of this chart represent the amount of the most active form of vitamin E (alpha-tocopherol) found in the specified servings of food. Each X in the column represents 5% of the adult male RDA for vitamin E. The adult male RDA is 10 mg of alpha-tocopherol equivalent. (Since many other, less active forms of vitamin E are present at the same time, the total vitamin E activity of these foods is likely to be somewhat higher than these figures suggest.)

Abbreviations:

ckd = cooked
cnd = canned
Z = frozen

Data adapted from R.H. Bunnell, J. Keating, A. Quaresimo, and G.K. Parman. 1965. Alpha-tocopherol content of foods. *American Journal of Clinical Nutrition*, 17:1–10.

D in IUs, we are comparing our food sources to the adult RDA of 200 IU, which is equivalent to 5 μg.)

Most people are not reliant on dietary sources for obtaining all of the vitamin D they need. In fact, the RDA committee states that it may not be necessary for adults to take in dietary vitamin D if they are exposed to enough sunlight to convert an adequate amount of the vitamin D precursor 7-dehydrocholesterol in the skin into the active vitamin D form. However, since such conversion depends on the length and intensity of exposure and on the color of the skin, the committee thought it advisable to recommend sufficient dietary vitamin D to meet the needs of people who may not meet optimal conditions. (For most adults, as little as 10 minutes of sun exposure per day on a light-skinned face and hands may be enough to promote the conversion of 7-dehydrocholesterol to the needed vitamin D.)

Vitamin E. Many researchers believe that vitamin E performs primarily as an antioxidant; it prevents the oxygen from combining with other substances and damaging them (Bieri, 1984). For example, the presence of vitamin E is thought to protect vitamin A from being oxidized. Vitamin E also protects polyunsaturated fatty acids (PUFAs) from oxidation; this occurs not only in foods, but also in the body, where PUFAs are part of cell membranes.

antioxidant—substance that prevents the oxygen from combining with other substances to which it might cause damage

Vitamin E deficiency is so rare that for many years this vitamin was said to be "in search of a disease" (Bieri, 1975). This fact seemingly invited nutrition hucksters to make unfounded claims about what diseases it can cure or prevent. (Have you seen ads for vitamin E that suggest it can protect you from heart disease or cancer, or cure you of muscular dystrophy, or improve your sexual or athletic performance? These are examples of unsupported claims.) Although vitamin E deficiency is virtually impossible to induce in healthy subjects, it can occur in premature infants, and it might occur in somebody who is unable over a period of years to absorb fat and fat-soluble vitamins. The RDA recommends 10 mg of vitamin E equivalents for adult males and 8 mg of vitamin E equivalents for adult females.

Among ordinary foods, plant oils, including those in grains, nuts, and seeds, provide the highest levels of vitamin E. Notice in Table 12.5 that the best sources of the most active form of vitamin E (alpha-tocopherol) are products made from plant oils. This means that mayonnaise and other salad dressings, many margarines, and many oils used as ingredients are good contributors of vitamin E.

Two points should be made about these outstanding vitamin E sources. First of all, many of these foods belong to the limited extra group, which makes them exceptions to the general rule that limited extras are low in vitamins. Second, a person's need for vitamin E goes up in direct relationship to the amount of polyunsaturated fat in the diet; since many of the foods that contain high levels of polyunsaturated fats also usually contain high levels of vitamin E, the higher need for the vitamin tends to be automatically satisfied when the fat is eaten.

Aside from its presence in vegetable oils, vitamin E is widely available at low levels throughout the food supply. A factor that makes the vitamin E status of Americans better than Table 12.5 might lead you to believe is that other forms of vitamin E than those shown on this chart occur in food; although they are less potent, they add somewhat to the total vitamin E activity of foods. The RDA committee estimates that the other forms present may raise the diet's vitamin E activity by 20% (National Research Council, 1980).

Vitamin K. Vitamin K, the fourth and last fat-soluble vitamin, is necessary for blood clotting when bleeding occurs; vitamin K helps convert various clotting precursor substances into their active forms (Suttie and Olson, 1984).

The body is not ordinarily at risk for vitamin K deficiency because humans have two means of obtaining it, and it is unlikely that both sources would be interfered with at the same time. Diet is one way of getting it. Leafy vegetables and meats are the leading dietary sources of vitamin K, although lesser amounts are available from other vegetables and milk (Table 12.6). One good or excellent source per day is likely to meet the recommendation for the safe and adequate intake of 70–140 μg for adults.

In addition, vitamin K is produced by intestinal bacteria and absorbed from the gut; most of us meet about half of our needs for vitamin K in this way (National Research Council, 1980). People who are on a program of antibiotic therapy may lose this source, since antibiotics are likely to destroy the helpful vitamin K-producing bacteria in the colon as well as the harmful ones they are intended to destroy.

The Water-Soluble Vitamins

Besides having water-solubility in common, some of these vitamins also perform related biochemical tasks. Several of them serve as parts of coenzymes; that is, these vitamins, joined to other compounds, unite with specific proteins that are enzyme precursors to create active enzymes.

Thiamin, Riboflavin, and Niacin. Thiamin, riboflavin, and niacin all function primarily as parts of coenzymes in energy metabolism. Each has a part in energy-producing biochemical reactions involving carbohydrates, fats, proteins or amino acids, and alcohol. It is logical to discuss these three vitamins together also because they are often found in the same foods. This means that people whose diets are grossly inadequate more often than not develop all three deficiencies at the same time. This is seen especially in the developing parts of the world.

Nonetheless, individual deficiencies are possible. Severe and prolonged thiamin deficiency results in the disease beriberi (literally "I can-

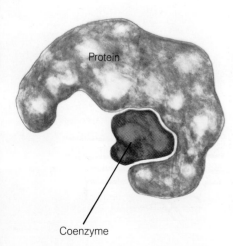

An active enzyme may consist of a protein plus a coenzyme.

coenzymes—vitamin-containing substances that unite with enzyme precursors to create active enzymes

beriberi—disease resulting from thiamin deficiency

Table 12.6 Vitamin K in Some Foods

Food	Household measure	Micrograms of vitamin K	Relative amount per serving Poor (<10 μg)	Fair (10–50 μg)	Good (50–100 μg)	Excellent (>100 μg)
Fruits and vegetables						
Applesauce	$\frac{1}{2}$ c	<10	X			
Asparagus, raw	5–6 spears	57			X	
Banana	1 small	<10	X			
Broccoli	$\frac{1}{2}$ c	126				X
Cabbage, raw	1 c	155				X
Lettuce	1 c	96			X	
Orange	1 small	<10	X			
Peach	1 medium	<10	X			
Peas, green, boiled	$\frac{1}{2}$ c	221				X
Spinach, raw	1 c	48		X		
Tomato, raw	1 medium	7	X			
Grain products						
Bread	1 slice	<10	X			
Milk and milk products						
Milk	1 c	14		X		
Meat and alternates						
Beef, ground, raw	3 oz	59			X	
Liverwurst	2 oz	68			X	
Limited extras						
Coffee	1 c	76			X	

In this chart, the relative vitamin K values of foods are shown by designating them as poor, fair, good, or excellent sources. The RDA safe and adequate intake of vitamin K for adults is 70–140 μg.
Data adapted from: (1) Pennington, J.A., and H.N. Church. 1980. *Food values of portions commonly used*. Philadelphia: J.B. Lippincott. (2) Suttie, J.W. 1982. Vitamin K content of ordinary foods. Lecture resource, University of Wisconsin, Madison WI. Compilation from various sources.

not"). It is characterized by neuromuscular changes that can become so serious that heart failure may result; sometimes edema may occur. Riboflavin deficiency results in skin lesions (breaks in the skin) that are indistinguishable from the lesions caused by several other deficiencies. Niacin deficiency can lead to pellagra, the symptoms of which were historically described by four D's: diarrhea, dermatitis, dementia (mental illness), and death.

pellagra—disease resulting from niacin deficiency

Table 12.7   Thiamin, Riboflavin, and Niacin in Some Foods

Food	Household measure	B vitamins	Percent of U.S. RDA 0	25	50	75	100
Fruits and vegetables							
Banana	1 medium	B-1	T				
		B-2	R				
		Niacin	N				
Lettuce, iceberg	1 c	B-1					
		B-2					
		Niacin					
Peas, frozen, cooked	$\frac{1}{2}$ c	B-1	TTT				
		B-2	R				
		Niacin	N				
Grain products							
Bread, whole wheat		B-1	T				
		B-2					
	1 slice	Niacin	N				
Bread, enriched	1 slice	B-1	T				
		B-2	R				
		Niacin	N				
Bread, not enriched	1 slice	B-1					
		B-2					
		Niacin					
Shredded Wheat (not fortified)	1 large biscuit	B-1	T				
		B-2					
		Niacin	N				
Fortified cereals	1 oz	B-1	(Considerable variation; check labels.)				
		B-2					
		Niacin					
Milk and milk products							
Milk, 2%, no solids added	1 c	B-1	T				
		B-2	RRRRF				
		Niacin					
Cheddar cheese	$1\frac{1}{3}$ oz	B-1					
		B-2	RR				
		Niacin					

continued

Table 12.7   continued

Food	Household measure	B vitamins	Percent of U.S. RDA 0–25	25–50	50–75	75–100
Meats and alternates						
Kidney beans, canned	1 c	B-1	TT			
		B-2	R			
		Niacin	N			
Beef, ground, broiled	3 oz	B-1	T			
		B-2	RR			
		Niacin	NNNNN			
Eggs	2	B-1	T			
		B-2	RRR			
		Niacin				
Peanuts	$\frac{1}{2}$ c	B-1	TTT			
		B-2	R			
		Niacin	NNNNN	NNNNN	NN	
Pork, roasted, lean	3 oz	B-1	TTTTT	TTTTT	TT	
		B-2	RRR			
		Niacin	NNNNN	N		
Limited extras						
Butter	1 t	B-1				
		B-2				
		Niacin				
White sugar	1 T	B-1				
		B-2				
		Niacin				

The columns on the right of this chart represent the portions of the U.S. RDA of thiamin (T), riboflavin (R), and preformed niacin (N) found in the specified servings of food. The niacin values do not account for the presence of the niacin precursor tryptophan. Foods with significant levels of protein (which contains the amino acid tryptophan) therefore have greater niacin activity than these values shown. Each character in the column represents 5% of the U.S. RDA. The U.S. RDA for thiamin is 1.5 mg; for riboflavin, 1.7 mg; and for niacin, 20 mg. Data adapted from: (1) Pennington J.A., and H.N. Church. 1980. *Food values of portions commonly used*. Philadelphia: J.B. Lippincott. (2) Science and Education Administration. 1981. *Nutritive value of foods*. Home and Garden Bulletin Number 72. Washington, DC: U.S. Department of Agriculture.

Of these three, pellagra has probably affected the greatest number of people as an isolated disease. Although the disease (but not its cause) had been known for centuries in other parts of the world, it did not seriously affect the United States until there was an explosive outbreak in the southern states between 1905 and 1910. A scientist noted that the diets of people with pellagra were lacking in meat, milk, and eggs, and that when these foods were given, the patients improved. This finding suggested that pellagra was a nutritional deficiency disease rather than a microorganism-caused disease. The theory was later confirmed when another researcher administered body substances including waste products from pellagrins (those affected with pellagra) to healthy volunteers; the healthy people did not get the disease (McCollum, 1957). (It's doubtful that such a research proposal would be approved today by a committee on the ethical use of human subjects.)

In keeping with their primary roles in energy metabolism, these vitamins should be consumed (according to RDA committee recommendations), in amounts directly proportional to a person's energy intake: the more kcalories a person's diet contains, the higher the intake of these vitamins should be. This is accomplished fairly effortlessly since foods that provide a lot of energy are also likely to provide more of these vitamins (provided they are not mainly low-nutrient-density foods). The RDAs established for the reference man and woman reflect appropriate vitamin intakes for people in the United States with average energy usage. For thiamin and riboflavin, the adult RDAs are between 1 and 2 mg/day; for niacin, they are between 13 and 19 niacin equivalents.

Niacin is one of the vitamins that increasingly is being quantified in equivalents (NE). The older system that described niacin in milligrams took only preformed niacin into account; the newer value of equivalents also takes into account niacin that can be converted from the amino acid tryptophan (60 mg tryptophan = 1 NE).

Generally speaking, thiamin, riboflavin, and niacin occur in highest amounts in foods that are significant sources of protein. Therefore, milk and milk products and meats and alternates are notable sources, as shown in Table 12.7. As you can also see from the table, there are some individual standouts: pork is an exceptional source of thiamin, milk and milk products are excellent sources of riboflavin, and peanuts are high in niacin.

However, the lesser sources—fruits, vegetables, and grain products—are also significant contributors of these three vitamins. Because we usually eat more servings of these sources, their contributions become notable when added together; a survey shows them to be the origin of approximately 40–60% of the intake of thiamin, riboflavin, and niacin of Americans (Science and Education Administration, 1980). Also, grain products make a significant contribution because many of them are enriched or fortified with these vitamins. (More will be said about enrichment and fortification in Chapter 14.)

Vitamin B-6. Vitamin B-6 also serves as a coenzyme, but it is usually not involved directly in energy-producing reactions, as are the B vitamins just discussed. Many reactions involving amino acids, such as the conversion

The produce market. Fresh vegetables and fruits are the best sources of most vitamins.

of essential amino acids to nonessential amino acids, require vitamin B-6. Vitamin B-6 also participates in the production and transformation of many other important body substances. Symptoms seen in association with vitamin B-6 deficiency most often involve nervous system problems such as depression, confusion, and convulsions, which also involve muscles.

Because of its importance in protein metabolism, this vitamin is thought to be needed in direct proportion to the amount of protein in the diet. Therefore, the adult RDAs for vitamin B-6 of 2.2 g/day for men and 2.0 g/day for women are based on average American protein intakes.

Meats and alternates are generally good sources of vitamin B-6; fruits and vegetables are less consistent sources. Grain and milk products provide lesser amounts (Table 12.8). Americans don't do as good a job of getting this vitamin as they do most others: we average 76% of the RDA (Science and Education Administration, 1980). Suggestions for achieving the recommended intake for this vitamin are to include larger servings of nuts, flesh proteins, and/or the better fruit and vegetable sources. Note that bananas are a fairly good, available source. Appendix J is a more extensive table of the vitamin B-6 content of foods.

Folacin and Vitamin B-12. Folacin and vitamin B-12 are discussed together because each is a part of coenzymes involved in DNA and RNA metabolism. Since DNA and RNA are the substances that direct cell division, these

Table 12.8 Vitamin B-6 in Some Foods

Foods	Household measure	Milligrams of vitamin B-6	Percent of U.S. RDA
			0　25　50　75　100
Fruits and vegetables			
Apple	1 medium	0.04	
Banana	1 small	0.51	XXXXX
Green beans, frozen	4 oz	0.08	X
Broccoli, chopped, frozen	4 oz	0.14	X
Cucumber	4 oz	0.04	
Grapefruit	$\frac{1}{2}$	0.03	
Spinach, chopped, frozen	4 oz	0.21	XX
Grain products			
Bread, whole wheat	1 slice	0.04	
Cookies, chocolate chip	2 average	0.01	
Crackers, Saltines	6 squares	0.02	
Tortilla, corn	1 average	0.02	
Popcorn, popped	3 c	0.09	X
Milk and milk products			
Cheese, cheddar	$1\frac{1}{3}$ oz	0.03	
Milk, skim or whole	1 c	0.10	X
Meats and alternates			
Beef, lean, raw	3 oz	0.37	XXXX
Chicken, light meat	3 oz	0.58	XXXXXX
Cod, raw	3 oz	0.19	XX
Eggs	2 medium	0.11	X
Lima beans, canned	4 oz	0.10	X
Peanut butter	4 T	0.20	XX
Tuna, canned	3 oz	0.36	XXXX
Limited extras			
Butter	1 t	tr	
Carbonated beverages	12 oz	0	
Coffee	6 oz	0	

vitamins are especially important during periods of growth. In addition, folacin and vitamin B-12 are important in the metabolism of certain amino acids.

Deficiencies of either of these vitamins produce a form of anemia characterized by large, immature red blood cells, a condition called megaloblastic anemia. In cases where anemia has been produced by an inadequacy of vitamin B-12, treatment with large amounts of folacin will normalize the red blood cells. However, folacin cannot substitute for B-12 in other ways. It cannot prevent the nerve damage that vitamin B-12 deficiency produces, for example. Therefore, although these two vitamins are similar in some ways, they must be examined individually.

People are much more likely to become deficient in folacin than in vitamin B-12. Folacin is suspected to be low in the diets of many Americans (Science and Education Administration, 1980). It is a nutrient whose recommendation you cannot satisfy with a single serving of a food, since levels tend to be modest in any one food. Fortunately, though, some foods in each of the food groups make significant contributions. The only type of basic food notably low in folacin is flesh protein (Table 12.9). The higher contributors of folacin are found among fruits and vegetables (the term *folacin* comes from the same root word as *foliage*), with lesser amounts in grains, legumes, nuts, and dairy products. Appendix I offers a more extensive table. The adult RDA for folacin for both men and women is 400 μg.

The food sources of vitamin B-12 are considerably different from those of folacin. For this vitamin, flesh proteins are among the better contributors. In fact, foods of animal origin are the only reliable sources of vitamin B-12 (Table 12.10). A recent survey shows that, on the average, American intake of vitamin B-12 comfortably exceeds the RDA of 3 μg/day for adults (Science and Education Administration, 1980). However, people who avoid all animal products (vegans) must find another means of obtaining B-12, or deficiency will occur once the body's stores are depleted.

Some merchants promote the alga spirulina as a B-12 source for vegans. Vitamin B-12 can be present in this alga (due to bacterial production), but levels in different samples have been found to vary so widely that spirulina should not be regarded as a reliable source (Herbert and Drivas, 1982). Rather, a vitamin B-12 supplement or a food fortified with vitamin B-12 should be consumed to achieve the recommended level of intake.

megaloblastic anemia—form of anemia characterized by large, immature red blood cells

---

The columns on the right of this chart represent the portions of the U.S. RDA of vitamin B-6 found in the specified servings of food. Each X in the column represents 5% of the U.S. RDA. (Note that many of the values are for uncooked foods; the vitamin B-6 content of the cooked item is likely to be somewhat lower.) The U.S. RDA for vitamin B-6 is 2.0 mg.

Data adapted from: (1) McQuitkin, C., and R.H. Matthews. 1981. *Provisional table on the nutrient content of bakery foods and related items.* Washington, DC: Human Nutrition Information Service, U.S. Department of Agriculture. (2) M.L. Orr. 1969. *Pantothenic acid, vitamin B-6, and vitamin B-12 in foods.* Home Economics Research Report no. 36. Washington, DC: Agricultural Research Service, U.S. Department of Agriculture.

Table 12.9 Folacin in Some Foods

Food	Household measure	Micrograms of folacin	Percent of U.S. RDA (0 25 50 75 100)
Fruits and vegetables			
Banana	1 medium	33	XX
Broccoli, fresh, cooked	1 spear	101	XXXXX
Cabbage, raw	$\frac{1}{2}$ c	59	XXX
Grape juice	$\frac{1}{2}$ c	3	X
Green beans, cooked	$\frac{1}{2}$ c	50	XXX
Lemon	1 medium	9	
Lettuce, head	1 c	20	X
Lettuce, romaine	1 c	98	XXXXX
Orange juice	$\frac{1}{2}$ c	68	XXX
Pear, fresh	1 medium	23	X
Potatoes, mashed	$\frac{1}{2}$ c	21	X
Raisins	2 T	1	
Grain products			
Bread, white	1 slice	10	X
Bread, whole wheat	1 slice	16	X
Cake, chocolate with icing	1 wedge	6	
Cornflakes	1 oz	3	
Rice, brown	$\frac{1}{2}$ c	15	X

continued

intrinsic factor—substance produced by the stomach lining; enhances vitamin B-12 absorption

pernicious anemia—anemia resulting from the inadequate production of intrinsic factor, which leads to the inadequate absorption of vitamin B-12 despite its presence in the diet

The presence of vitamin B-12 in the diet does not guarantee that it will be absorbed. Vitamin B-12 depends for its absorption on the presence of a substance called **intrinsic factor**, which is produced by the lining of the stomach. If intrinsic factor is absent, only about 1% of dietary B-12 is absorbed; but when intrinsic factor is present, amounts up to the RDA may be absorbed from one meal (Herbert et al., 1980). The production of intrinsic factor sometimes decreases in the elderly, so older people may become deficient in the vitamin even if their diets contain RDA levels of it. This deficiency disease is called pernicious anemia; people who have it are usually given periodic injections of vitamin B-12.

Table 12.9 continued

Food	Household measure	Micrograms of folacin	Percent of U.S. RDA 0 25 50 75 100
Milk and milk products			
Milk, whole	1 c	12	X
Cheese, cheddar	$\frac{1}{3}$ oz	7	
Cheese, cottage	2 c	58	XXX
Yogurt	1 c	27	X
Meats and alternates			
Beef, lean, cooked	3 oz	3	
Chicken, dark, cooked	3 oz	6	
Eggs, hard cooked	2 medium	44	XX
Frankfurter	1	2	
Peanuts	$\frac{1}{2}$ c	53	XXX
Pinto beans	$\frac{1}{2}$ c	26	X
Pork, lean, cooked	3 oz	4	
Salmon, canned	3 oz	17	
Sesame seeds	1 T	8	
Walnuts, English	$\frac{1}{2}$ c	33	XX
Limited extras			
Butter	1 t	0	
Mayonnaise	1 T	0	

The columns on the right of this chart represent the portions of the U.S. RDA of folacin found in the specified servings of food. Each X in the column represents 5% of the U.S. RDA. The U.S. RDA for folacin is 400 μg.

Data adapted from B.P. Perloff, and R.R. Butrum. 1977. Folacin in selected foods. *Journal of the American Dietetic Association* 70:161–172.

Pantothenic Acid and Biotin. The vitamins pantothenic acid and biotin are both components of enzymes involved in energy metabolism, and pantothenic acid is also involved in the synthesis of other vital body substances. The Greek word from which *pantothenic* was derived means "from all sides," referring to the widespread distribution and usefulness of this nutrient.

Deficiencies of these vitamins can produce diverse problems such as fatigue, neuromuscular disorders, and dermatitis; however, people are unlikely to experience deficiencies of either one (McCormick and Olson, 1984; R. Olson, 1984). Pantothenic acid is so generally available among

Table 12.10 Vitamin B-12 in Some Foods

Food	Household measure	Micrograms of B-12	Percent of the adult RDA
			0 25 50 75
Fruits and vegetables			
All fruits	$\frac{1}{2}$ c	0	
All vegetables	$\frac{1}{2}$ c	0	
Grain products			
All grain products made without milk and eggs	1 serving	0	
Milk and milk products			
Milk, whole or skim	1c	0.96	XXXXXX
Cheese, cheddar	$1\frac{1}{3}$ oz	0.3	XX
Meats and alternates			
Beef, lean, raw	3 oz	1.5	XXXXXXXXXX
Chicken, light meat	3 oz	0.38	XXX
Codfish, raw	3 oz	0.68	XXXXX
Eggs	2	2.3	XXXXXXXXXXXXXXX
Haddock, raw	3 oz	1.1	XXXXXXX
Legumes, cooked	1 c	0	
Liver, beef	3 oz	67.8	XXXXXXXXXXXXXXXXXX))XX 2260%
Tuna, canned	3 oz	1.86	XXXXXXXXXXXX

The columns on the right of this chart represent the portions of the RDA for adults of vitamin B-12 found in the specfified servings of food. Each X in the column represents 5% of the RDA for adults. The RDA for adults is 3 μg. Data adapted from M.L. Orr. 1969. *Pantothenic acid, vitamin B-6, and vitamin B-12 in foods.* Home Economics Research Report Number 36. Washington DC: U.S. Department of Agriculture.

common foods that scientists have been unable to induce a deficiency experimentally. As for biotin, colonic bacteria are thought to be an additional source of this vitamin. A deficiency could be caused by consumption of large amounts of a compound that could bind the vitamin in the intestine and make it unavailable for absorption. (Raw egg whites contain such a compound, called *avidin*; however, you would have to consume most of your diet as raw egg white to induce such a deficiency.)

Vitamin C. Vitamin C has always generated a lot of interest, probably because its deficiency disease, scurvy, has dramatic symptoms that can be quickly reversed if the affected person is given vitamin C. Early reports of cures were regarded as magical; this was the case in the 1500s when 110 crewmen who had come to America with explorer Jacques Cartier were cured of their scurvy by drinking a brew the Indians had made from the

scurvy—disease resulting from vitamin C deficiency

needles of a type of evergreen tree. The needles, we now know, contained small amounts of vitamin C. Later, in the 1700s, British sailors cured or prevented scurvy by eating limes, earning themselves the nickname of *limeys* (McCollum, 1957).

The extensive research done on vitamin C has yet to reveal exactly what it does at the cellular level (Sauberlich, 1984). Nonetheless, a considerable amount is known about the impact of vitamin C on various structures and functions. It apparently is needed for the formation of collagen, the protein that serves so many connective functions in the body. Among the body's collagen-containing materials and structures are the framework of bone, the gingivae (gums), and the binding materials in skin, muscle, and scar tissue. Vitamin C also seems to be necessary for the production of other substances such as certain hormones and neurotransmitters, and is needed for the metabolism of certain amino acids and vitamins. In addition, it aids blood cells in fighting infection, the liver in detoxifying dangerous substances, and the gut in absorbing iron from foods. With such wide-ranging effects, it is not surprising that symptoms of vitamin C deficiency include generalized feelings of weakness, bleeding gums and loosened teeth, easy bruising and small hemorrhages in the skin, and impaired wound healing.

The adult RDA for vitamin C is 60 mg/day. It is quite easy to get this amount in the diet, since several common foods have such a high content that they can furnish half or more of the RDA in one serving. The citrus fruits have a well-deserved reputation in this regard, but they are not alone: broccoli, cabbage, cantaloupe (muskmelon), cauliflower, green pepper, and strawberries are also excellent sources. Many other fruits and vegetables make lesser but still significant contributions (Table 12.11).

In addition to the many natural sources, vitamin C is added to some food products. As a result, Americans average about 150% of their RDA for vitamin C (Science and Education Administration, 1980).

Table 12.12, pages 308–309, summarizes the major points regarding vitamin needs, functions, and sources.

Nonvitamins

Some substances that are not essential for humans have been touted recently. Although several of these are involved in metabolic reactions, since they are produced in adequate amounts within the healthy body, they cannot be categorized as vitamins. Among these substances are rutin, inositol, para-aminobenzoic acid (PABA), bioflavinoids (dubbed "vitamin P" by some), lipoic acid, and ubiquinone.

Choline is another nonvitamin of particular interest. It is a component of the neurotransmitter acetylcholine, which is present in lower-than-normal levels in people who have certain nervous disorders. For this reason, it is being tested as part of the treatment for those conditions. However, there is no evidence that normally healthy people would benefit in any way from taking supplemental choline. Choline is generally found in foods as a component of the phospholipid lecithin (Chapter 7).

Although these substances are not vitamins, they are nonetheless mar-

Table 12.11 Vitamin C in Some Foods

Food	Household measure	Milligrams of vitamin C	Percent of U.S. RDA (0 25 50 75 100)
Fruits and vegetables			
Apple	1 medium	6	XX
Broccoli, Z, ckd	½ c	53	XXXXX XXXXX XXXXX XXX
Cantaloupe, 5 in. diameter	¼ melon	45	XXXXX XXXXX XXXXX
Cranberry sauce	½ c	3	X
Grapes, green	10	2	X
Green beans, Z, ckd	½ c	4	X
Lettuce	1 c	3	X
Orange juice, Z, diluted	½ c	60	XXXXX XXXXX XXXXX XXXXX
Peas, Z, ckd	½ c	11	XXXX
Pepper, sweet green, raw	1 pod	94	XXXXX XXXXX XXXXX XXXXX X))XX 157%
Potato, white, baked	1 (8 oz)	31	XXXXX XXXXX
Spinach, Z, ckd	½ c	20	XXXXX XX
Strawberries	½ c	44	XXXXX XXXXX XXXXX
Tomatoes, cnd	½ c	21	XXXXX XX
Grain products			
All products, not fortified	1 oz	0	
Cereal, fortified	1 oz	(Check label for level of fortification.)	

continued

keted by some dietary supplement manufacturers, who welcome having another product to sell. For normally healthy people who consume them, the only possible benefit is from the placebo effect—that is, if consumers believe that the substance will make them feel better, there may be some improvement of psychological origin.

Other nonvitamins are more worrisome to scientists because they may actually be harmful in some instances. "Vitamin B-15," also known as "pangamic acid," is an example. There is no scientific proof that its components are either useful or safe for humans, and some compounds marketed as "pangamic acid" actually are known to be toxic (Herbert, 1983).

"B-17," or laetrile, is the last nonvitamin we will mention here. Part of our concern about its use stems from the fact that this substance contains the poison cyanide, making consumption of large amounts dangerous. Laetrile has sometimes been used as a cancer treatment (although scientific tests find it ineffective for this purpose); here the primary concern is that its use may delay or substitute for treatments that *could* slow down or arrest the disease (more on laetrile in Chapter 15).

Table 12.11 continued

Food	Household measure	Milligrams of vitamin C	Percent of U.S. RDA 0	25	50	75	100
Milk and milk products							
Cheese, firm types	$1\frac{1}{3}$ oz	0					
Milk	1 c	2	X				
Meats and alternates							
Eggs	2 medium	0					
Legumes, ckd	1 c	0					
Meats, ckd	3 oz	0					
Pecans, walnuts	$\frac{1}{2}$ c	1					
Limited extras							
Alcoholic beverages	1 serving	0					
Fats, oils	1 T	0					
Sugar, honey	1 T	0					

The columns on the right of this chart represent the portions of the U.S. RDA of vitamin C found in the specified servings of food. Each X in the column represents 5% of the U.S. RDA. The U.S. RDA for vitamin C is 60 mg.

Abbreviations:

ckd = cooked

cnd = canned

Z = frozen

Data adapted from: (1) Pennington, J.A., and H.N. Church. 1980. *Food values of portions commonly used*. Philadelphia: J.B. Lippincott. (2) Science and Education Administration. 1981. *Nutritive value of foods*. Home and Garden Bulletin Number 72. Washington, DC: U.S. Department of Agriculture.

Extreme Deficiencies Are Rare in Developed Countries

Because people in developed countries have access to a wide variety of nutritious foods year round, very few experience extreme deficiencies. Of course, occasional vitamin deficiencies do occur, and this section discusses the circumstances in which they are likely to be seen. In the main, however, vitamin deficiencies occur in the developing countries.

General Causes of Vitamin Deficiencies

Generally, vitamin deficiencies occur when:

1. The diet is limited to only *a few types* of foods.

2. The diet is limited in overall *quantity*.

3. The individual cannot absorb or utilize vitamin(s) to a normal extent

(continued on page 310)

Table 12.12 Key Information about the Vitamins

Vitamin	RDA for healthy adults	Major dietary sources	Major functions	Signs of severe, prolonged deficiency	Signs of extreme excess
Fat-soluble					
A	Females: 800 RE, 4000 IU[a] Males: 1000 RE, 5000 IU[a]	Fat-containing and fortified dairy products; liver; provitamin carotene in orange and deep green produce	Component of rhodopsin (Still under intense study)	Keratinization of epithelial tissues including the cornea of the eye (xerophthalmia); night blindness; dry, scaling skin; poor immune response	Damage to liver, kidney, bone; headache, irritability, vomiting, hair loss, blurred vision from preformed vitamin A. From carotene: yellowed skin
D	5µg (200 IU)	Fortified and full-fat dairy products, egg yolk	Promotes absorption and use of calcium and phosphorus	Rickets (bone deformities) in children; osteomalacia (bone softening) in adults	GI upset; cerebral, CV, kidney damage; lethargy
E	Females: 8 alpha-tocopherol equivalents Males: 10 alpha-tocopherol equivalents	Vegetable oils and their products; nuts, seeds; present at low levels in other foods	Antioxidant to prevent cell membrane damage; still under intense study	Possible anemia	In anemic children, blood abnormalities may develop
K	70–140 µg	Green leafy vegetables; meats	Aids in formation of certain proteins, especially those for blood clotting	Severe bleeding on injury: internal hemorrhage	Liver damage and anemia from high doses of the synthetic form menadione
Water-soluble					
Thiamin (B-1)	Females: 1.1 mg Males: 1.5 mg	Pork, legumes, peanuts, enriched or whole grain products	Component of coenzyme used in energy metabolism	Beriberi (nerve changes, sometimes edema, heart failure)	?
Riboflavin (B-2)	Females: 1.3 mg Males: 1.7 mg	Dairy products, meats, eggs, enriched grain products, green leafy vegetables	Component of coenzyme used in energy metabolism	Skin lesions	?

continued

Table 12.12 continued

Vitamin	RDA for healthy adults	Major dietary sources	Major functions	Signs of severe, prolonged deficiency	Signs of extreme excess
Water-soluble					
Niacin	Females: 14 niacin equivalents Males: 19 niacin equivalents	Nuts, meats; provitamin tryptophan in most proteins	Component of coenzyme used in energy metabolism	Pellagra (diarrhea, dermatitis, dementia, death)	Flushing of face, neck, hands; liver damage
B-6	Females: 2.0 mg Males: 2.2 mg.	High protein foods in general, bananas, some vegetables	Component of coenzyme used in amino acid metabolism	Nervous and muscular disorders	Unstable gait, numb feet, poor hand coordination, abnormal brain function
Folacin	400 μg	Green vegetables, orange juice, nuts, legumes, grain products	Component of coenzyme used in DNA and RNA metabolism	Megaloblastic anemia (large, immature red blood cells); GI disturbances	Masks vitamin B-12 deficiency
B-12	3 μg	Animal products	Component of coenzyme used in DNA and RNA metabolism	Megaloblastic anemia; pernicious anemia when due to inadequate intrinsic factor; nervous system damage	?
Pantothenic acid	4–7 mg	Widely distributed in foods	Component of coenzyme used in energy metabolism	Fatigue, sleep disturbances, nausea, poor coordination	?
Biotin	100–200 μg	Widely distributed in foods	Component of coenzyme used in energy metabolism	Fatigue, depression, muscular pain, dermatitis	?
C	60 mg	Fruits and vegetables, especially broccoli, cabbage, cantaloupe, cauliflower, citrus fruits, green pepper, strawberries	Maintains collagen; is an antioxidant; aids in detoxification; still under intense study	Scurvy (skin spots, bleeding gums, weakness); delayed wound healing; impaired immune response	GI upsets, confounds certain lab tests, poorer immune response

[a]Less accurate than RE values; to be used only until food composition tables are converted to RE values.

References: Chandra, 1983; Dubick and Rucker, 1983; Goodhart and Shils, 1980; Krause and Mahan, 1979; National Nutrition Consortium, 1978; National Research Council, 1980; Sauberlich, 1983; Schaumburg et al., 1983; Scrimshaw and Young, 1976; Weinsier and Butterworth, 1981.

due to inborn problems, disease conditions, or alcohol or other drug use.

4. The requirements for vitamins are unusually high due to rapid growth or disease.

At present, on a worldwide scale, most people who experience vitamin deficiency simply do not get enough to eat. This being the case, they are more likely to have multiple deficiencies than a single, independent vitamin deficiency. The notable exception, perhaps, is vitamin A; in areas of the world where good sources of vitamin A are not commonly consumed, this deficiency does occur.

Signs and Symptoms of Vitamin Deficiencies

As mentioned earlier, each vitamin affects the whole body; many vitamins are simultaneously involved in processes such as energy production, growth, reproduction, and immune function. Therefore, a person who has any vitamin deficiency will generally feel weak, fail to grow or reproduce, and be more susceptible to illnesses.

In addition, some vitamin deficiencies have very obvious effects on specific body tissues. Certain signs and symptoms are associated with particular deficiency diseases. Table 12.12 identifies which symptoms tend to be seen with which deficiencies. Remember, however, that such signs by themselves are not adequate for diagnosing vitamin deficiencies.

Both very serious and less severe deficiencies can be identified by biochemical testing. Marginal multiple vitamin deficiencies can be reflected in such general effects as frequent infectious illnesses (Beisel, 1982) or impaired growth.

Time Frame for a Deficiency

The amount of time it takes to develop a vitamin deficiency varies greatly according to the vitamin. For example, if a person has no intake of vitamin C whatsoever, deficiency symptoms can develop within two months (Hodges, 1980). In contrast, it takes a much longer time to produce a vitamin E deficiency in adults; in a three-year study, men who were vitamin E-depleted did not show deficiency symptoms (Bieri, 1975).

As you might suspect, there is also some variation from one individual to another in the amount of time it takes to develop a particular deficiency. Also, age matters: deficiencies develop more rapidly in children than in adults.

Large Excesses of Vitamins Are Dangerous

As we have stated before, people who ingest very large amounts of vitamins put themselves at risk of developing health problems.

General Causes of Vitamin Excesses

It is possible to take in toxic levels of vitamins by eating too much of a single food that has a very high vitamin density. This is so unusual, though, that the same example is cited over and over: the cases of vitamin A toxicity that occurred when Arctic explorers and their dogs ate polar bear liver, which contains 2600–3600 REs of vitamin A *per gram* (National Nutrition Consortium, 1978). (The male RDA for vitamin A is 1000 REs for a whole *day.*)

More commonly, vitamin toxicity results when people ingest vitamin supplements in excessive quantities for a long period of time. Approximately 4000 people receive treatment annually for vitamin supplement poisoning (Dubick and Rucker, 1983). Many people are unaware that substances that are essential at one level can be harmful at higher doses. One distinguished nutrition scientist has noted that "some food faddists are performing self-experimentation studies with combinations and doses of single nutrients never previously envisioned [by scientists]" (Beisel, 1982). However, even physicians have been known to prescribe irresponsibly large doses of vitamins that were later found to be toxic (Schaumburg et al., 1983).

Signs and Symptoms of Vitamin Excesses

Toxicity symptoms can potentially affect all of the body's tissues and systems, just as deficiencies can. And just as there are classic symptoms of vitamin deficiency, typical indicators of vitamin excesses are increasingly being recognized. For example, a 16-year-old boy developed symptoms of severe headache, stomach pain, nausea and vomiting, and joint pain from a daily vitamin A intake of 50,000 IU for $2\frac{1}{2}$ years, which he used to self-treat his acne (Farris and Erdman, 1982). Table 12.12 gives symptoms of other vitamin toxicities insofar as they are currently known.

The level of toxicity for a given vitamin is influenced by several factors. The storage capacity of the vitamin, its level of intake, its chemical form, and the length of time during which the overdose occurs all play important roles. The water-soluble vitamins have generally been thought to be relatively nontoxic; it has been assumed that excesses are excreted in the urine. However, this is apparently not always the case. Massive doses of vitamin B-6, long believed to be nontoxic, are now known to produce serious neurological symptoms that can result in people needing to use a cane to walk, and losing the normal function of their hands. Such symptoms may take years to disappear completely after the supplement has been discontinued (Schaumburg et al., 1983).

Time Frame for a Toxicity

Theoretically, toxicity can occur within a couple of minutes after a massive vitamin ingestion or over a lifetime from an accumulation of more moderate overdoses. Actually, though, people who incur vitamin toxicities have

megadosing—taking doses of a nutrient at ten or more times the RDA

usually been overdosing at ten or more times the RDA (often referred to as "megadosing") for anywhere from a few months to a few years before they seek help for their vitamin-caused problems.

People Take Vitamin Supplements for Many Different Reasons—Some Justifiable, Some Not

A Food and Drug Administration survey indicates that 43% of Americans take vitamin supplements regularly, with some users taking as many as 14 different preparations (McDonald, Stewart, and Schucker, 1983). As the preceding material suggests, though, we believe it is unnecessary for most people to take supplements in order to meet their need for vitamins. In fact, we are concerned that some people who take vitamin supplements may assume that all their nutritional needs can be met from them, and therefore become careless in their food choices. Since there are approximately 50 essential nutrients, getting an adequate intake of only the 13 vitamins does not constitute good nutrition.

On the other hand, vitamin supplements can be very helpful in certain circumstances. Certainly, for the rare individual with a medically diagnosed vitamin deficiency, supplementation would be in order, along with an improved diet. But most people who take vitamins do so for a variety of other reasons. To help you determine which situations call for vitamin supplementation and which do not, we have grouped these situations according to the degree to which supplementation may be required or advisable. When vitamin supplements are used by a normally healthy person, they should generally be limited to the individual's RDA levels. (This should not be construed as a recommendation to supplement. Rather, since we acknowledge what a common practice it is for healthy people to take vitamin supplements, it is a reasonable guideline for avoiding toxicity.)

When a Vitamin Supplement Is Needed

People who eat no animal products will not get vitamin B-12 in their diets. They must get it in a fortified food product or a supplement, such as fortified soy milk or a vitamin B-12 pill. It may also be difficult for vegans to achieve recommended levels of intake for riboflavin and vitamin D.

When Vitamin Supplements Are Often Useful

At particular times during the life cycle, nutrient needs are higher than can be easily met by ordinary foods. A supplement of 100% of the U.S. RDA for vitamins is likely to meet needs without provoking toxicity. On the other hand, very careful attention to diet can provide the same results.

Pregnancy and Lactation. A woman's need for energy and all nutrients is increased during pregnancy and lactation; however, since the percentage of need for the micronutrients is higher than the need for extra energy, a supplement can be useful and is often recommended by physicians.

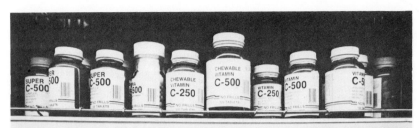

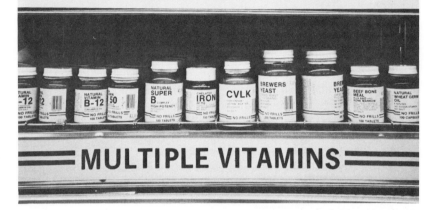

Vitamin supplementation. Approximately 43% of Americans take vitamin supplements routinely. In some instances, modest supplements of up to 100% of the U.S. RDA are useful; however, at high intakes there is danger of overdose.

For example, the RDA for folacin increases by 100% during pregnancy, and is even higher for the mineral iron. Although it is possible to achieve that intake of folacin with a very carefully planned diet, it is often more reliable and convenient to supplement these two nutrients.

Periods of Rapid Growth. During their early years and again during their teens, children experience growth spurts that create an extra demand for all nutrients.

During the first four to six months of life, when infants should receive breast milk or infant formula as their only food, they need few supplemental vitamins. In fact, the only additional vitamin the breast-fed infant needs is vitamin D; the infant receiving commercially prepared infant formula gets all that is needed in the formula. While a baby is learning to eat other foods, his needs may be higher than his or her consumption; many pediatricians justifiably prescribe supplements at this time. During their teens, though, children are usually able to meet their needs through food alone, if they choose well.

Elder Years. It has long been assumed that the elderly use vitamins in amounts no greater than younger adults do. In fact, the Recommended Dietary Allowances state that people over 51 actually need less of some of the B vitamins because they typically expend less energy.

However, the amount of research done on elderly subjects is quite scanty compared with that done on young adults. Some scientists now hypothesize that the needs of the elderly may be slightly higher, due to (possibly) less efficient absorption and utilization (Watkin, 1980). As more research is done with this age group, the RDAs for the elderly will be refined.

Many elderly people have dietary vitamin intakes lower than the RDA because they do not eat enough, or choose food poorly, or both. Also, the elderly often have chronic health problems for which they take medications that can interfere with their nutrition. For these reasons, physicians frequently suggest the elderly take vitamin supplements instead of trying to change their diets. This approach seems reasonable, provided their diets are not seriously inadequate; the approach also allows them to maintain the eating habits they enjoy.

Articles in the popular press sometimes suggest that large doses of vitamins, especially vitamin E, may be able to prevent aging. Although it seems theoretically possible that the antioxidant properties of vitamin E might protect cell membranes and enable cells to survive longer (and therefore people to live longer), animal experiments do not bear out this hypothesis.

When Vitamin Supplements Are Selectively Useful

Vitamin supplements can be useful for dealing with certain medical conditions, depending on individual circumstances. For these situations, the judgment of a health care professional is needed to determine whether supplement usage is indicated.

Acne. Since vitamin A is involved in the health of the skin, it is logical to wonder whether it might relieve various sorts of skin problems. Some forms of vitamin A have been prescribed in the past for people who have acne. However, it has not reliably brought about improvement, and has been the cause of a large proportion of the cases of vitamin A toxicity.

More recently, one form of vitamin A called 13-cis-retinoic acid has been found to be beneficial when used in a lotion or as an ingested medication. Because of the possibility of some undesirable side effects when it is ingested, though, physicians prescribe it for only the most serious cases (Perry and McEvoy, 1983).

Cardiovascular (CV) Disease. Vitamin E has been touted by some as a preventive medication for CV disease. There is little scientific support for this theory. The only circumstance in which vitamin E has been found to help a CV problem has been in some cases of intermittent claudication, a condition in which leg pain occurs in atherosclerotic arteries during exercise (Haeger, 1982).

Drug Usage. Many drugs—whether they are prescription or over-the-counter types—can affect the usual intake, absorption, metabolism, and/or excretion of nutrients. If drugs are taken for only short periods of time (days or a couple of weeks), serious nutritional consequences are not as likely to occur.

Since both prescription and over-the-counter products can affect nutrients, it is your responsibility to tell your primary health care provider what drugs (if any) you routinely take so that your nutritional status can be monitored in light of your drug usage. Long-term drug usage is most common among adults, and Chapter 18 will discuss some common nutrient–drug interactions.

Alcohol Consumption. The ingestion of alcohol affects the usual metabolism of many nutrients, either interfering with or enhancing the body's normal handling of them. Of the vitamins, thiamin, niacin, folacin, and vitamin B-6 are notably affected; it is not uncommon to find deficiencies of these vitamins in long-term, regular consumers of large amounts of alcohol. In such cases, vitamin supplementation is a needed part of treatment.

In light of this, it may seem surprising that we have rated vitamin supplementation for heavy users of alcohol as only *selectively* useful. This is because supplementation is of limited benefit in dealing with the total problem of heavy alcohol use. The physiological damage caused by alcohol has as much to do with direct toxic effects (which vitamins cannot repair) as with nutritional problems. Therefore it is far preferable to decrease alcohol consumption. (Chapter 18 deals with alcohol–nutrient reactions more thoroughly.)

When Vitamin Supplements Are Questionable

We question some circumstances under which vitamins have been used, either because the data suggest that vitamin supplementation is not helpful, or because there are insufficient data on which to make a judgment. Such conditions are described in the following sections.

Colds. It has been suggested that massive doses of vitamin C are able to prevent and/or cure the common cold. This promotion began when Linus Pauling, who won a Nobel Prize in physical chemistry in the mid-1950s, formed the novel hypothesis that humans, because their bodies do not produce ascorbic acid as do those of many other animals, need megadoses of it to achieve the levels produced (and thus assumed to be needed) by these other animals.

Based on observations of animals whose bodies function quite differently from those of humans, he recommended taking as much as several *grams* of vitamin C every day. (The RDA is 60 *mg*.) He claimed there would be many benefits, including fewer colds. Many people, influenced by his excellent reputation and the simplicity of his recommendation, began taking the doses he recommended.

Observations were subsequently made of people who took such supplements. Some people who took megadoses of vitamin C developed certain other medical problems, such as diarrhea (National Research Council, 1980), hypoglycemic effects, impaired immune function, or a certain type of anemia, if they were susceptible to those problems (Sauberlich, 1984). Other effects also occurred. For example, some common medical tests—such as the test a diabetic uses to find out whether there is sugar in his or her urine—yielded inaccurate results in people who had taken megadoses.

When the claims regarding the impact of supplemental vitamin C on the incidence and treatment of colds were tested in double-blind studies involving hundreds of subjects per study, the following results were obtained:

- **Prevention**   There was no statistically significant difference in the incidence of colds between groups that received supplemental vitamin C and those that did not (Anderson, Reid, and Beaton, 1972; Chalmers, 1975; Pitt and Costrini, 1979; Thomas and Holt, 1978). On the other hand, some studies showed a very small decrease in the number of colds among people taking vitamin C in doses of 250, 1000, or 2000 mg per day (Anderson, 1978). Interestingly, the larger supplements were not more effective in this regard than the smaller supplements (Anderson, 1978).

   Another study (Baird et al., 1979) demonstrated that 80 mg of vitamin C from either orange juice or its synthetic counterpart had a slight effect similar to that of the larger doses of purified vitamin C used in some of the earlier studies. Therefore, if more vitamin C slightly reduces a person's likelihood of getting colds, the same benefit can be had from drinking an extra two-thirds of a cup of orange juice per day; larger supplements of vitamin C yield no better results.

- **Treatment**   As far as the treatment of colds is concerned, the evidence is somewhat more positive; vitamin C supplements taken during a cold reduced the severity of the symptoms in some people during the first few days of the cold (Anderson, Reid, and Beaton, 1972, Anderson, 1978; Pitt and Costrini, 1979; Thomas and Holt, 1978). Also, some people taking supplements spent less time at home with the cold—an average of half a day less (Anderson, Reid, and Beaton, 1972). This may be due to the antihistaminic effect that vitamin C sometimes has (Clemetson, 1980).

   Nonetheless, the total number of days that people's colds lasted did not differ from one group to the other (Anderson, 1978).

Cancer. Research attempting to relate the occurrence of cancer to consumption of nutrients is voluminous: both epidemiological and animal studies have contributed to the knowledge about cancer prevention. Yet, many questions remain.

Two vitamins have repeatedly been mentioned in connection with cancer prevention: vitamins A and C. A considerable amount of epidemiological and animal evidence shows an inverse relationship between the risk of cancer and the consumption of diets high in various forms of vitamin A. That is, more vitamin A and its precursors in the diet have been associated with less cancer, especially of the lung, urinary bladder, and larynx in some studies (Committee on Diet, Nutrition, and Cancer, 1982).

Other studies suggest that the consumption of diets containing higher amounts of vitamin C is associated with a lower risk of certain cancers, particularly gastric and esophageal types. This effect is attributed to the fact that vitamin C interferes with the formation of nitrosamine, a potent carcinogen (Committee on Diet, Nutrition, and Cancer, 1982). [More on nitrosamines in Chapter 15 (on toxicants).]

The report cited above emphasizes that often populations with less cancer have eaten *food* that is higher in vitamins A and C, and the report recommendation is to consume *food* sources, since it is possible that some of the protective effect may be due to accompanying substances in the foods rather than to the vitamins themselves. Other researchers are wary of suggesting that consuming food sources of these vitamins will lower cancer risk (Willett and MacMahon, 1984), but the National Research Council and the American Cancer Society promote this practice.

Athletic Activity. Sometimes an athlete takes high doses of vitamins in an attempt to improve performance. Supplemental vitamins cannot improve performance, however, unless the person is vitamin-deficient to begin with.

Some athletes and coaches have presumed that since thiamin, riboflavin, and niacin are needed in proportion to energy usage, athletes who have high energy demands would benefit from vitamin supplements. However, studies have shown that "vitamin intake in combination with large caloric expenditures and intakes (~4,800 kcal/day) were without effect on performance of endurance, speed, coordination, and muscle strength" (Costill and Miller, 1980). The same food sources that should be used to provide the extra energy the athlete needs (high carbohydrate foods) will themselves furnish whatever extra vitamins are needed, provided that most of those foods are minimally processed or are enriched.

Emotional Stress. Popular literature contains recommendations that people take vitamin supplements if they are experiencing psychological stress—and indeed, the vitamin industry has been happy to oblige with various "stress vitamin" preparations. Although it is true that the body's biochemistry is somewhat altered during stress, no research has proved that stress per se warrants an increase in any vitamin in amounts substantially above the RDA (Herbert, 1980).

Of course, from a medical point of view, the term *stress* also refers to the extra demands put on the body by accidental injury, surgery, infection, or chronic illness. In stress of origins such as these, it may be appropriate for a physician to recommend vitamin supplementation (National Dairy Council, 1980).

Mental Illness. Vitamin megadoses have been tried as experimental treatments for mental illnesses of various types, including schizophrenia. Some therapists have written enthusiastically about positive results. However, when these therapies were tested using well-designed studies in both the United States and Canada, the megavitamin doses were not found to be successful (American Psychiatry Association, 1974; Ban, 1981).

Only occasionally have vitamin deficiencies been the cause of serious mental symptoms (as in pellagra); in such cases, supplementation is necessary. However, pellagra is very rare in North America today.

Premenstrual Syndromes (PMS). Within the past few years, the medical community has begun to recognize that some women's bodies undergo substantial changes just before menstruation. The hormonal changes that occur during a woman's cycle may have rather dramatic effects on her sense of physical and mental well-being.

Various nutrition-related treatments have been proposed. Some focus on limiting salt and sugar in the diet. Others suggest taking megavitamin doses and minerals. In the main, such treatments have not been subjected to careful scientific scrutiny. Some of the studies that attempt to support the use of supplements have not been carefully designed. Others have been printed in journals that do not have a rigorous research review process. Therefore, we feel that there is no currently satisfactory or appropriate evidence to support the hypothesis that vitamin and mineral supplements are useful for treatment of PMS.

It is not known at this point whether in the long run supplementation will be helpful or harmful. Some of the instances of vitamin B-6 toxicity that have been reported occurred in women who took megadoses as treatment for PMS; their intakes ranged from from 1000 to 3000 times the RDA per day (Schaumburg et al., 1983).

You Can Check Your Vitamin Intake Using Assessment Techniques You Have Already Learned

In this section, we suggest two types of diet analysis for assessing the adequacy of your vitamin intake. One provides an overview of intake; the second is more specific.

General Check on Vitamin Adequacy

A diet that follows the recommendations of the SANE guide is likely to contain at least two-thirds of the RDA for all of the vitamins, and considerably more for some. Although it is a commendable goal to try to achieve 100% of the RDA levels for vitamin intake, occasional consumption of two-thirds of the RDA is acceptable. (Remember that the RDAs are set substantially higher than the average level of need.) Therefore, the SANE guide offers a reasonable standard for intake. (The use of the SANE guide was described in Chapter 2; an example was shown in Figure 2.10.)

More Specific Check on Vitamin Adequacy

You can use food composition data to get a more accurate picture of your vitamin intake. This method involves keeping a 24-hour food record, and recording the foods' vitamin contents. Figure 12.3 suggests a format and gives an example.

Vitamin values for many foods can be found in resources described in the next paragraphs.

Using Food Composition Tables. Appendix E gives values for vitamin A, thiamin, riboflavin, niacin, and vitamin C that are largely taken from USDA Home and Garden Bulletin Number 72. Appendix F includes similar values for fast foods. Appendix J gives data for vitamins B-6 and B-12, and

Food or beverage	Amount eaten	Vita-min A (IU)	Thiamin (mg)	Ribo-flavin (mg)	Niacin (mg)	Vita-min C (mg)	Vitamin B-6 (mg)	Vitamin B-12 (µg)	Folacin (µg)
Apple	1 medium	120	.04	.03	.1	6	.04	0	13
Quarter pounder w/cheese	1 sandwich	660	.31	.37	7.4	2.7	.23	2.15	20
French fries	Med. serv.	17	.12	.02	2.3	12.5	.22	.03	11
Coke	8 oz.	0	0	0	0	0	0	0	0
Oatmeal-walnut raisin cookie	1 medium	15	.08	.05	.5	tr	.045	0	4
Submarine: Roll	1 large	tr	.54	.32	4.5	tr	.01	0	15
Meat (bologna)	2 oz.	nd	.1	.12	1.4	0	.06	nd	1
Cheese (processed)	3/4 oz.	195	.01	.10	tr	0	.03	.15	2
Mayonnaise	1 T.	40	tr	.01	tr	0	nd	nd	tr
Lettuce, leaf	¼ c.	45	.01	.01	.05	1	.01	0	5
Tomato	¼ c.	493	.03	.02	.4	12	.07	0	27
Onion	2 T.	tr	.01	.02	.1	4	.03	0	4
Pickle	2 T.	nd	nd	nd	nd	nd	tr	0	nd
Coke	8 oz.	0	0	0	0	0	0	0	0
Ale	12 oz.	nd	.01	.11	2.2	nd	.22	0	20
Totals		1585	1.26	1.18	18.95	37.2	.965	2.33	122
Your RDA		*5,000	1.5	1.7	19	60	2.2	3.0	400
% of your RDA		32%	84%	69%	100%	62%	44%	78%	31%

*Use the IU value from the RDA table, since food composition data are expressed that way.

Figure 12.3 One-day diet analysis using food composition tables to determine vitamin adequacy. This food record and analysis were done by a 21-year-old man. When no data were available for a food or its components, "nd" was entered.

Figure 12.4 Converting nutrition label values for vitamins into weight units. A nutrition label for instant oatmeal gives this information. The colored area shows that by multiplying the label percentages by the appropriate values from the U.S. RDA, you can get the approximate amounts of vitamins per serving. (The U.S. RDA is shown in Table 1.2.)

Nutrition information per serving
Serving size = 1 ounce

Calories	110
Protein	4 grams
Carbohydrate	18 grams
Fat	2 grams

Percentage of U.S. RDA

		Times U.S. RDA		Equals
Protein	6%			
Vitamin A	20%	x 5,000 I U ‡	=	1,000 I U
Vitamin C	*			
Thiamin	20%	x 1.5 mg	=	.3 mg.
Riboflavin	10%	x 1.7 mg	=	.17 mg
Niacin	15%	x 20 mg	=	3 mg
Calcium	10%			
Iron	20%			
Vitamin D	*			
Vitamin B-6	20%	x 2.0 mg	=	.4 mg
Folacin	20%	x .4 mg	=	.08 mg
Phosphorus	6%			

*Contains less than 2% of the U.S. RDA for this nutrient

‡Since RDA's were expressed in the IUs when these standards were developed, the RDA values in IUs must be used in these calculations.

Appendix I gives data for folacin. Data may be missing in these tables for some of the foods you have eaten, since reliable data for some foods and vitamins have not yet been published. For this reason, your totals for those vitamins are likely to be lower than your actual intake.

Using Nutrition Labels. Another source of food composition information is nutrition labels. Not all foods carry this information since it is required only on foods for which a nutritional claim has been made or to which nutrients have been added. (For other items, inclusion of this information is optional.)

The bottom part of a nutrition label is required to state what percentages of the U.S. RDA for vitamins A and C, thiamin, riboflavin, and niacin occur in one serving of the food. (Protein and the minerals calcium and iron must also be listed; beginning in July of 1985, the sodium value must be listed as well.) In addition, values for vitamins D, E, B-6, folacin, vitamin B-12, biotin, and/or pantothenic acid may be shown, as well as values for the minerals phosphorus, iodine, magnesium, zinc, and copper.

Since these values are percentages and not absolute quantities, you must convert the percentages to weight units by multiplying them by their U.S. RDA values in order to determine the amount of each vitamin per serving. Figure 12.4 shows an example.

Using the Data. Once you have the food composition data assembled and recorded, then:

- Total the columns.

- Fill in your RDA for the vitamins.

- Calculate what percentage of the RDA you took in for each vitamin.

Remember that even this method gives only an approximation of your vitamin intake. Your calculated intake of some vitamins may be lower than your actual intake if you were unable to find the vitamin values of some foods you ate. However, your calculated intake could be higher than your actual intake, if poor food handling or storage practices brought about substantial vitamin degradation. [More about this in Chapter 14 (on processing).]

In summary, vitamins play an essential role in reproduction, growth, and the maintenance of health. They are unevenly but widely distributed among the foods of the basic food groups. Prolonged inadequate intake produces deficiency diseases, and prolonged excessive intake produces toxic effects. Although vitamin supplementation is useful in some instances, the regular intake of vitamin supplements is not recommended for most people.

SUMMARY

- Most people need little convincing that vitamins are important, but not everyone realizes that a well-chosen diet can supply all the vitamins that most people need, or that vitamin supplements taken in very high doses can be dangerous.

- Vitamins are regulators of metabolic functions; they are needed only in minute amounts. Vitamins A, D, E, and K are fat-soluble; thiamin, riboflavin, niacin, B-6, folacin, B-12, pantothenic acid, biotin, and vitamin C are water-soluble. In general, the body can accumulate more of the fat-soluble vitamins: thus they have more potential to accumulate in harmful amounts.

- The vitamins are structurally unrelated to each other, and some occur in several slightly different chemical forms that can all function in the body as that vitamin. The body can also convert vitamin precursors called provitamins into active forms. The form in which a vitamin occurs can affect its potency, but there is *no* difference between "natural" and synthetic vitamins—the body uses both in exactly the same way.

- Several units of measurement are used to quantify vitamins. Now that scientists are aware of the varying potencies of different forms of some vitamins and their precursors, a unit called equivalents is coming into common use to reflect as accurately as possible the amount of vitamin *activity* the various forms provide.

- Almost all vitamins are at work in almost all body cells, so every vitamin has a widespread effect on the body, and body functions (such as energy production, growth, reproduction, and immune function) are influenced by many vitamins simultaneously. Tables 12.3–12.11 list common food sources of vitamins, and Table 12.12 summarizes their major functions and signs of deficiency or excess.

■ Some substances that have recently been touted as vitamins are in fact produced in adequate amounts by healthy people; thus they are not technically vitamins and certainly need not be supplemented in the diet. Other nonvitamins are toxic and can cause harm to people who consume them.

■ Extreme vitamin deficiencies are rare in the developed countries but still occur in many parts of the world. Such deficiencies usually arise when food is limited in type and/or quantity, when the individual cannot absorb or utilize vitamins to a normal extent, and in individuals whose need for vitamins is high due to rapid growth or disease. Worldwide, most people who have vitamin deficiencies simply do not get enough to eat, and are likely to have multiple deficiencies rather than a shortage of a single vitamin. There is considerable variation in both the signs and symptoms of deficiencies and the time it takes for a particular deficiency to develop.

■ Large excesses of vitamins are dangerous, though it is rare for an individual to consume harmful amounts of any vitamin in ordinary foods. Vitamin toxicity is more often the result of ingesting vitamin supplements in excessive quantities over a long period of time. The level of toxicity for a given vitamin is influenced by several factors including storage capacity in the body, level of intake, chemical form, and the length of time in which the overdose occurs. People who suffer the ill effects of toxicity have usually been taking vitamin megadoses for anywhere from a few months to a few years.

■ Most healthy people do not need to take vitamin supplements at all. Vegetarians who do not eat any animal products do need supplemental vitamin B-12, and supplements can be helpful during pregnancy and lactation, periods of rapid growth, and the elder years. Vitamin supplements may also have limited use in the management of acne or CV disease, and in individuals who are taking certain kinds of drugs or using alcohol heavily. Vitamin doses above the RDAs have not been shown to be effective in preventing colds or cancer, in enhancing athletic performance, or in relieving emotional stress, mental illness, or premenstrual syndrome.

REFERENCES

American Psychiatry Association Task Force on Vitamin Therapy in Psychiatry. 1974. Megavitamin and orthomolecular therapy in psychiatry. *Nutrition Reviews* (Supplement 1) 32:44–48.

Anderson, T.W. 1978. Vitamin C and the common cold. *Contemporary Nutrition* 3(no.10).

Anderson, T.W., D.B.W. Reid, and G.H. Beaton. 1972. Vitamin C and the common cold: A double-blind trial. *Canadian Medical Association Journal* 107:503–508.

Baird, I.M., R.E. Hughes, H.K. Wilson, J.E. Davies, and A.N. Howard. 1979. The effects of ascorbic acid and flavonoids on the occurrence of symptoms normally associated with the common cold. *American Journal of Clinical Nutrition* 32:1686–1690.

Ban, T.A. 1981. Megavitamin therapy in schizophrenia. In *Nutrition and behavior*, ed. S.A. Miller. Philadelphia: The Franklin Institute Press.

Beisel, J. 1982. Special supplement on nutrition and immune response. *American Journal of Clinical Nutrition* 35(vol.2): 417-468.

Bieri, J.G. 1975. Vitamin E. *Nutrition Reviews* 33:161–167.

Bieri, J.G. 1984. Vitamin E. In *Present knowledge in nutrition*, ed. R.E. Olson et al. Washington, DC: The Nutrition Foundation, Inc.

Bunnell, R.H., J. Keating, A. Quaresimo, and G.K. Parman. 1965. Alpha-tocopherol content of foods. *American Journal of Clinical Nutrition* 17:1–10.

Campbell, G.D., Jr., M.H. Steinberg, J.D. Bower. 1975. Ascorbic acid induced hemolysis in G-6-PD deficiency. *Annals of Internal Medicine* 82:810.

Chalmers, T.C. 1975. Effects of ascorbic acid on the common cold. *The American Journal of Medicine* 58:532–536.

Chandra, R.K. 1983. Nutrition, immunity, and infection: Present knowledge and future directions. *The Lancet* 1(no. 8326):688–691.

Clemetson, C.A. 1980. Histamine and ascorbic acid in human blood. *Journal of Nutrition* 110:662–668.

Committee on Diet, Nutrition, and Cancer. 1982. Diet, nutrition, and cancer. Washington, DC: National Academy Press.

Costill, D.L., and J.M. Miller. 1980. Nutrition for endurance sport: Carbohydrate and fluid balance. *International Journal of Sports Medicine* 1:2–14.

DeLuca, H.F. 1980. Vitamin D. In *Modern nutrition in health and disease*, ed. R.S. Goodhart and M.E. Shils. Philadelphia: Lea and Febiger.

Dubick, M.A., and R.B. Rucker. 1983. Dietary supplements and health aids—a critical evaluation. Part 1–Vitamins and minerals. *Journal of Nutrition Education* 15(no.2):47–53.

Farris, W.A., and J.W. Erdman. 1982. Protracted hypervitaminosis A following long-term, low-level intake. *Journal of the American Medical Association* 247:1317–1318.

Fraser, D.R. 1984. Vitamin D. In *Present knowledge in nutrition*, ed. R.E. Olson et al. Washington, DC: The Nutrition Foundation, Inc.

Goodhart, R.S., and M.E. Shils, ed. 1980. *Modern nutrition in health and disease*. Philadelphia: Lea and Febiger.

Haeger, K. 1982. Long-term study of a-tocopherol in intermittent claudication. *Annals of the New York Academy of Sciences* 393:369–374.

Herbert, V. 1980. The vitamin craze. *Archives of Internal Medicine* 140:173–176.

Herbert V. 1983. Separating nutrition facts from nutrition quacks. Guest lecture. University of Wisconsin, Madison WI, October 7, 1983.

Herbert, V., and G. Drivas. 1982. Spirulina and vitamin B-12. (Letter.) *Journal of the American Medical Association* 248:3096–3097.

Herbert V., N. Colman, and E. Jacob. 1980. Folic acid and vitamin B-12. In *Modern nutrition in health and disease*, ed. R.S. Goodhart and M.E. Shils. Philadelphia: Lea and Febiger.

Hodges, R.E. 1980. Ascorbic acid. In *Modern nutrition in health and disease*, ed. R.S. Goodhart and M.E. Shils. Philadelphia: Lea and Febiger.

Kamil, A. 1972. How natural are those natural vitamins? *Co-op News* 25(no. 11):3.

Krause, M.V., and L.K. Mahan. 1979. *Food, nutrition, and diet therapy*. Philadelphia: W.B. Saunders Company.

McCollum, E.V. 1957. *A history of nutrition*. Boston: Houghton Mifflin Company.

McCormick, D.B., and R.E. Olson. 1984. Biotin. In *Present knowledge in nutrition*, ed. R.E. Olson et al. Washington, DC: The Nutrition Foundation, Inc.

McDonald, J.T., M.L. Stewart, and R.E. Schucker. 1983. Assessment of vitamin and mineral supplement usage by means of a telephone survey. (Abstract.) *Federation Proceedings* 42:530.

McLaren, D.S. 1984. Vitamin A deficiency and toxicity. In *Present knowledge in nutrition*, ed. R.E. Olson et al. Washington, DC: The Nutrition Foundation, Inc.

McQuitkin, C., and R.H. Matthews. 1981. *Provisional table on the nutrient content of bakery foods and related items*. Washington, DC: Human Nutrition Information Service, U.S. Department of Agriculture.

National Dairy Council. 1980. Nutritional demands imposed by stress. *Dairy Council Digest* 51(no.6):31–35.

National Nutrition Consortium. 1978. *Vitamin-mineral safety, toxicity, and misuse*. Chicago: The American Dietetic Association.

National Research Council, National Academy of Sciences (NAS). 1980. *Recommended dietary allowances*. Washington, DC: NAS.

Olson, J.A. 1984. Vitamin A. In *Present knowledge in nutrition*, ed. R.E. Olson et al. Washington, DC: The Nutrition Foundation, Inc.

Olson, R.E. 1984. Pantothenic acid. In *Present Knowledge in nutrition*, ed. R.E. Olson et al. Washington, DC: The Nutrition Foundation, Inc.

Orr, M.L. 1969. *Pantothenic acid, vitamin B-6, and vitamin B-12 in foods*. Home economics research report no. 36. Washington, DC: Agricultural Research Service, U.S. Department of Agriculture.

Pennington, J.A., and H.N. Church. 1980. *Food values of portions commonly used*. Philadelphia: J.B. Lippincott Company.

Perloff, B.P., and R.R. Butrum. 1977. Folacin in selected foods. *Journal of the American Dietetic Association* 70:161–172.

Perry, M.D., and G.K. McEvoy. 1983. Isotretrinoin: New Therapy for Cystic Acne. *Clinical Pharmacy* 2(no. 1:12-19).

Pitt, H.A, and A.M. Costrini. 1979. Vitamin C prophylaxis in Marine recruits. *Journal of the American Medical Association* 241:908–911.

Sauberlich, H.E. 1983. Clinical aspects of vitamin B-6 (pyridoxine) metabolism. *Nutrition and the M.D.* 9:1–2.

Sauberlich, H.E. 1984. Ascorbic acid. In *Present knowledge in nutrition*, ed. R.E. Olson et al. Washington, DC: The Nutrition Foundation, Inc.

Schaumburg, H., J. Kaplan, A. Windebank, N. Vick, S. Rasmus, D. Pleasure, and M.J. Brown. 1983. Sensory neuropathy from pyridoxine abuse: A new megavitamin syndrome. *New England Journal of Medicine* 309:445–448.

Science and Education Administration. 1980. *Food and nutrient intakes of individuals in 1 day in the United States*, Spring 1977. Washington, DC: United States Department of Agriculture.

Science and Education Administration. 1981. *Nutritive value of foods*. Home and garden bulletin No. 72. Washington, DC: U.S. Department of Agriculture.

Scrimshaw, N.S., and V.R. Young. 1976. The requirements of human nutrition. *Scientific American* 235:51–64.

Smith, E.L., R.L. Hill, I.R. Lehman, R.J. Lefkowitz, P. Handler, and A. White. 1983. *Principles of biochemistry: Mammalian biochemistry*. New York: McGraw-Hill.

Suttie, J.W. 1982. Vitamin K content of ordinary foods. Lecture resource, University of Wisconsin, Madison WI. Compilation from various sources.

Suttie, J.W., and R.E. Olson. 1984. Vitamin K. In *Present knowledge in nutrition*, ed. R.E. Olson et al. Washington, DC: The Nutrition Foundation, Inc.

Thomas, W.R., and P.G. Holt. 1978. Vitamin C and immunity: An assessment of the evidence. *Clinical and Experimental Immunology* 32:370–379.

Watkin, D.M. 1980. Nutrition for the aging and the aged. In *Modern nutrition in health and disease*, ed. R.S. Goodhart and M.E. Shils. Philadelphia: Lea and Febiger.

Weinsier, R.L., and C.E. Butterworth. 1981. *Handbook of clinical nutrition*. St. Louis: The C.V. Mosby Co.

Willett, W.C., and B. MacMahon. 1984. Diet and cancer—an overview. *New England Journal of Medicine* 310:697–701.

13

Minerals

IN THIS CHAPTER: Minerals Are Elements ▪ Varying Bioavailability Makes Mineral Needs Difficult to Establish ▪ The Necessary Levels of Essential Minerals Are Available from Foods ▪ Mineral Intake Should Be Neither Too Low Nor Too High ▪ You Can Assess Your Mineral Status As You Did for Vitamins

13 Minerals

Many consumers think of minerals as almost indistinguishable from vitamins. Frequent references are made to *vitamins and minerals* together, as though they were one large nutrient group.

It is true that a number of similarities exist between these two groups: they are both types of micronutrients whose importance to humans has been appreciated mainly in this century. Like vitamins, minerals are widespread in basic foods, but are nonetheless aggressively produced, promoted, and sold by the supplement industry. Professional nutritionists are concerned that some advertising claims for the benefits of mineral supplements are misleading, or even blatantly false, and may encourage the intake of toxic levels.

However, there are also differences between the two groups. The major distinction between vitamins and minerals is that vitamins are organic compounds, whereas minerals are inorganic. The chapter begins by explaining this chemical difference.

Minerals Are Elements

minerals—the chemical elements (other than carbon, hydrogen, oxygen, and nitrogen) that make up the body

Minerals are the chemical elements other than carbon, hydrogen, oxygen, and nitrogen that make up the body. Whereas carbon, hydrogen, oxygen, and nitrogen account for 96% of body weight, minerals constitute only about 4%.

Minerals in the body make up in number what they lack in gross weight: at least 20 are commonly found in humans, and perhaps as many as 60 have been identified in living organisms (Li and Vallee, 1980).

Categories

Minerals are generally divided into two categories. Those present in the human body in amounts greater than 0.01% of body weight (or needed in the diet in amounts of 100 mg or more per day) are called macro- or major minerals. They are: calcium, phosphorus, magnesium, sulfur, potassium, sodium, and chloride.

macro- or **major minerals**—those present in the body in amounts greater than 0.01% of body weight

The macrominerals present in your body in the largest amounts are calcium ($\sim 2\frac{1}{2}$ pounds) and phosphorus ($\sim 1\frac{1}{2}$ pounds). Figure 13.1 shows the amounts typically present in an adult male.

The minerals that are present in your body in smaller quantities than 0.01% of body weight are called trace minerals. They include: iron, iodine, fluoride, zinc, selenium, copper, chromium, manganese, molybdenum, cobalt, arsenic, nickel, and vanadium.

trace minerals—those present in the body in amounts less than 0.01% of body weight

Iron and zinc are the most prevalent trace elements in your body, which probably contains 2 to 4 grams of each of them. Most of the other trace minerals are present in much smaller quantities—perhaps just a thousandth as much.

To help you visualize how small the amounts of trace elements in your body are, imagine that your normal body weight is one ton (2000 pounds). Assuming normal trace mineral composition, you would contain only 1.8 oz of iron, 1.1 oz of zinc, 0.05 oz of copper, 0.01 oz of iodine, 0.003 oz of chromium, 0.001 oz of cobalt, and 0.0004 oz of vanadium.

Relative Importance

At this time scientists do not think that the body requires all the chemical elements it contains: only some of the minerals found in the human body have been found essential for growth, reproduction, and health maintenance. Although you might expect that the distinction between essential and nonessential minerals should be easy for scientists to make, they do not unanimously agree on the status of some of the minerals.

A major reason why essentiality is not always clear-cut is that the necessary tests for some trace minerals are very difficult to conduct. A traditional test of essentiality is to show that serious negative consequences result when animals' diets contain very low levels of the test nutrient for a certain period of time; however, it is extremely difficult to keep all traces of some trace minerals out of test diets. Therefore, it's very difficult to

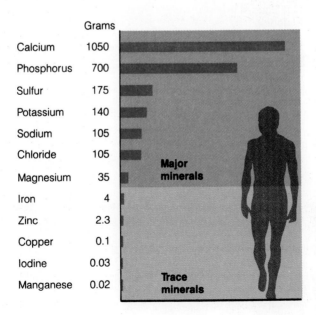

	Grams
Calcium	1050
Phosphorus	700
Sulfur	175
Potassium	140
Sodium	105
Chloride	105
Magnesium	35
Iron	4
Zinc	2.3
Copper	0.1
Iodine	0.03
Manganese	0.02

Major minerals

Trace minerals

Figure 13.1 Some of the minerals in a 70-kg man. Amounts of the major minerals and a few of the essential trace minerals are shown. Other trace minerals occur in the body in even smaller amounts than the ones in this figure.

design a study in which the effects of a specific trace mineral deficiency can be demonstrated in the traditional way.

Disagreements among scientists about the essentiality of particular minerals also reflect differences in judgment. For example, some scientists regard fluoride as essential, while others do not. These differing judgments arise from two facts: (1) that the presence of fluoride in the diet significantly discourages tooth decay, and (2) that poor growth and death do not result from lack of fluoride. Table 13.1 identifies the minerals thought by some mineral experts to be essential for animals, and therefore likely to be needed by humans as well. The fact that this table does not agree completely with the RDA listing of essential minerals underscores these differences in judgment.

The importance of a given mineral to your health is not necessarily proportional to the amount in your body. For example, the human body probably contains more aluminum, which is not believed to be essential to health, than it does chromium, manganese, and some other essential trace minerals. Moreover, the consequences of essential *trace* element deficiency can be just as severe as those of a deficiency of a *major* essential mineral.

Table 13.1   Minerals—Essential and Nonessential

Minerals believed essential for animals

Calcium	Arsenic	Manganese
Phosphorus	Chromium	Molybdenum
Sulfur	Cobalt	Nickel
Potassium	Copper	Selenium
Sodium	Fluoride[a]	Silicon
Chloride	Iodine	Vanadium
Magnesium	Iron	Zinc

Minerals not proved to be required for animals

Aluminum	Germanium	Strontium
Antimony	Gold	Thallium
Barium	Lanthanum	Titanium
Beryllium	Mercury	Uranium
Bismuth	Niobium	Zirconium
Boron	Radium	Cadmium[b]
Bromine	Rubidium	Lead[b]
Cesium	Ruthenium	Lithium[b]
Gallium	Silver	Tin[b]

Laboratory tests have demonstrated that the minerals in the top group are needed to support life processes in animals (presumed to include humans). Those in the lower group have not been shown to be necessary. (Some scientists disagree with these lists in a few particulars.)

[a]Scientists have not demonstrated that fluoride is essential for life itself, but it is well documented that its presence in the diet has a beneficial effect on dental health.

[b]Scientists have shown these elements to be essential in isolated studies. These data need to be confirmed by other investigators before these minerals are classified as essential.

References: (1) Mertz, W. 1981. The essential trace elements. *Science* 213:1332–1338. (2) Li, T.K., and B.L. Vallee. 1980. The biochemical and nutritional roles of other trace elements. In *Modern nutrition in health and disease,* ed. R.S. Goodhart and M.E. Shils. Philadelphia: Lea and Febiger.

As with other essential nutrients, mineral intakes in excess of need can be dangerous. For example, the minerals zinc and iron are essential for life, but if they are ingested in very large quantities they are toxic.

Varying Bioavailability Makes Mineral Needs Difficult to Establish

A key concept regarding minerals is that the bioavailability (usefulness to the body) of a given ingested mineral varies a great deal depending on the circumstances. Many factors influence mineral bioavailability, some decreasing and others increasing it.

bioavailability—degree to which the body is able to use a substance in the form or amount actually present

Although healthy people generally absorb more than 90% of the protein, carbohydrate, and fat in their diets, they do not generally absorb minerals as efficiently. In fact, in controlled studies, adults have been found to absorb an average of only about 5% of the manganese, 10% of the iron, 10–20% of the zinc, and 30–40% of the magnesium and calcium in their diets.

The different foods and medications that people consume can cause large variations in the bioavailability of minerals in their diets. For example, healthy adults have been found to absorb anywhere from 1% to over 35% of their dietary iron intake, depending on the composition of the diets (Monsen et al., 1978); the same range of absorption values applies for zinc. And studies have shown the absorption of calcium to range from less than 5% to more than 60% of what was ingested. Bioavailability of minerals can also be influenced by other factors, such as urinary excretion and an individual's health.

This section will discuss in more detail specific factors that influence bioavailability. Let's first examine the dietary factors that improve mineral bioavailability.

Dietary Factors That Improve Mineral Bioavailability

Few dietary factors actually improve the body's use of minerals. Much of this discussion centers on iron, since more is known about the bioavailability of this mineral than about that of others.

The iron in your diet can be classified into two categories: heme iron and nonheme iron (Monsen et al., 1978). Heme iron, as the name implies, is found in the hemoglobin of blood and in the myoglobin of animal flesh—meat, fish, and poultry—although nonheme iron also occurs in these foods. All the iron in eggs, milk, and plant foods is considered nonheme iron. This classification system is important because scientists have found that people generally absorb 15–35% of the heme iron in their diets but only 2–20% of the nonheme iron.

heme iron—a special form of iron present in meat, fish, and poultry, in which the iron is part of a protein (hemoglobin or myoglobin)

nonheme iron—iron present in the diet other than heme iron (includes milk, eggs, and plant products)

What does all this mean in practical terms? Let's assume that you consumed equal amounts of iron in two meals. However, in one meal the iron was provided by a piece of meat, and in the other meal it was provided by cereal. You would absorb more iron from the meal containing the meat.

There are at least two ways to improve the absorption of nonheme iron; they are discussed in the upcoming sections. Vegetarians are often particularly interested in this matter, although it warrants more general concern since nonheme iron accounts for over 80% of the iron in the diets of most North Americans (Monsen et al., 1978).

Ascorbic Acid and Iron. One way to improve the absorption of nonheme iron is to increase the vitamin C in the diet. Scientists have found that adding 75 mg of ascorbic acid to a meal can increase more than twofold the absorption of nonheme iron from that meal. This means that adding a 6-oz glass of orange juice to a breakfast of toast and eggs can result in the bioavailability of the iron in the toast and eggs being more than doubled. Similarly, adding canned tomatoes to a rice casserole can improve the bioavailability of the iron in the rice. (Unfortunately, ascorbic acid has not been found to improve the absorption of other minerals in humans.)

Unidentified Meat Factor and Iron. A second dietary factor that can increase the absorption of nonheme iron is known as the unidentified meat factor.

Although scientists do not know what substance in meat is responsible for this effect, they do know that adding 3 ounces of meat, fish, or poultry to a meal can increase more than twofold the absorption of the nonheme iron in the meal. In other words, adding ham or tuna to a macaroni and cheese casserole increases the bioavailability of the iron in the macaroni and cheese. At the same time, the heme iron in the meat or fish is absorbed with characteristic efficiency.

It is important to be aware of one other fact when you use these principles: ascorbic acid and/or unidentified meat factor must be consumed *at the same meal as the nonheme iron* in order to increase its bioavailability. The orange juice or sausage you consume at breakfast will not influence the absorption of the nonheme iron eaten at supper. Rather, a moderate amount of vitamin C or meat added to each meal will probably improve your utilization of iron more than eating a large amount of those foods at just one meal during the day.

Dietary Factors and Other Minerals. Although less research has been done regarding the bioavailability of other minerals, it is known that an adequate supply of vitamin D, either in the diet or synthesized in response to sunlight, is needed for optimal absorption of calcium and phosphorus (Allen, 1982). Also, the presence of lactose in foods appears to facilitate calcium and magnesium absorption. And investigators have observed that zinc is absorbed more efficiently when the dietary level of protein is increased (Greger, 1983).

Nutritionists have found that infants absorb the iron and zinc in breast milk more efficiently than the iron and zinc in cow's milk or infant formulas. The exact reason for this phenomenon is not known (Saarinen and Siimes, 1979; Hurley and Lonnerdal, 1982). However, this is one good reason why breast milk is superior to cow's milk for infants. (There will be more discussion of this topic in Chapter 16, which deals with the nutrition of mothers and infants.)

Unfortunately, scientists do not yet know as much about the mineral forms or dietary factors that improve the absorption of other minerals, but research is in progress.

unidentified meat factor—substance present in meat that can increase the bioavailability of nonheme iron consumed at the same meal

Figure 13.2 Various compounds in foods can decrease mineral bioavailability. Although whole grains and legumes contain fairly large amounts of minerals, they also include fiber and phytate, which reduce mineral bioavailability.

Factors That Depress Mineral Bioavailability

A number of factors also decrease the bioavailability of minerals.

Dietary Fiber and Related Compounds. Dietary fiber and some organic compounds found in foods with fiber decrease the absorption of minerals. Probably the most important of these substances is phytate, an organic compound that contains phosphorus. Fiber and phytate are commonly found in whole grains, bran, and soy products (Figure 13.2).

Human and animal studies have shown that adding phytate either alone or with fiber to a meal can decrease the absorption of zinc, calcium, magnesium, and sometimes iron. The phosphorus that is included in the phytate structure is generally not well absorbed either.

Because phytate and fiber decrease the absorption of calcium, it might seem logical to supplement with calcium diets containing lots of phytate, but the addition of calcium to a high phytate diet causes a further decrease in zinc absorption. The phytate–zinc complexes are fairly insoluble in the gut, but the phytate–calcium–zinc complexes are even less soluble.

Live yeast as an ingredient in food breaks down phytate (Reinhold et al., 1974). For this reason, the minerals in a whole grain, yeast-leavened bread may have a higher bioavailability than those in a whole grain unleavened bread or cereal.

Most Americans probably do not consume enough fiber and phytate to decrease their absorption of minerals significantly, but some do. For example, vegetarians may consume considerable amounts of fiber and phytate; this is of particular concern because their intake of some minerals, especially calcium and zinc, may be rather low to begin with. (This is also characteristic of people in developing countries.) Individuals who regularly supplement their diets with generous portions of bran may also decrease their absorption of minerals. Over a long period, this could lead

phytate—phosphorus-containing organic compound found in some plant materials; decreases mineral absorption to mineral deficiencies, particularly if the dietary intake is inadequate or even marginal.

tannins, oxalates—naturally occurring compounds that can depress absorption of some minerals in some cases

Tannins. Tannins are other compounds that can inhibit the absorption of minerals. They are the organic compounds that give tea its astringent quality; they are also found in certain grains such as sorghum. Investigators have found that adding a cup of tea to a meal depresses the absorption of the nonheme iron in the whole meal by almost two thirds, an effect ascribed to the tannins (Morck, Lynch, and Cook, 1983).

Other Dietary Components. Many other factors naturally present in foods can depress the absorption of minerals in certain situations (Solomons, 1982; Allen, 1982). For example, oxalates (organic acids found in spinach, rhubarb, and chocolate) depress the absorption of some minerals. Large amounts of ascorbic acid can decrease copper absorption.

Competition for Absorption. Minerals can also compete with each other for absorption. Scientists have found that when people's diets are supplemented with iron, zinc absorption is often depressed. This effect might occur when the amount of iron consumed from foods and supplements is several times the intake of zinc (Solomons, 1982). This is a common occurrence among pregnant women who take iron supplements.

Similarly, it has been found that the supplementation of human diets with zinc can depress the absorption of copper (Sandstead, 1982). Many other interactions of this sort exist among the trace minerals, such as between vanadium and chromium, and manganese and iron. Consumers must be aware that supplementation of diets with trace minerals "just to be sure" can sometimes create problems instead of solving them.

pica—the ingestion of nonfood substances such as clay, laundry starch, or chalk

Practicing Pica. Some people eat items that most individuals in our society would not consider to be food, such as clay, laundry starch, fireplace ashes, newspaper, or paint chips. (Supposedly the paint chips taste sweet!) These practices are called pica, and are most often found among women and children in certain cultures. Although some physicians have hypothesized that individuals who are deficient in minerals such as iron are more apt to practice pica, this has not been proved (Lackey, 1983). The custom generally seems to be taught within certain cultures.

Pica can affect in two ways the mineral nutriture of people who practice it. First, toxic substances may be present in the items consumed. For example, repeated ingestion of chips of lead-based paints is likely to result in lead toxicity. This type of pica is seen primarily among young children. Second, the items eaten may contain substances that inhibit mineral absorption. For example, the special types of clay that are consumed by some women in the southern part of the United States, in the Middle East, and in other parts of the developing world often contain compounds that interfere with iron and zinc absorption. The effect is accentuated if energy and mineral intakes are low.

Although we have emphasized the negative aspect of minerals' preventing each other's absorption, this phenomenon can be beneficial at times. Researchers have shown that calcium and iron can depress the bioavailability of lead; therefore, children absorb less toxic lead from paint chips or other sources when they have consumed adequate amounts of calcium and iron. Similarly, mercury in fish is less toxic when adequate dietary selenium has been consumed (Underwood, 1977).

Influences on Excretion. As mentioned earlier, absorption is not the only stage at which mineral utilization can be modified. For example, high levels of dietary protein tend to increase the urinary excretion of calcium, resulting in a net loss of that mineral. On the other hand, although high dietary levels of phosphorus decrease calcium absorption, they also depress urinary excretion of calcium, sometimes to a greater extent. The importance of dietary phosphorus levels on calcium utilization by humans is, therefore, a confusing and controversial topic (Greger and Krystofiak, 1982).

Table 13.2 summarizes the major dietary factors that affect the bioavailability of minerals.

Table 13.2 Major Dietary Factors Affecting the Bioavailability of Minerals

Mineral affected	Factors that improve bioavailability (and some sources)	Factors that decrease bioavailability (and some sources)
Calcium	Vitamin D (fortified dairy products, sunlight on skin) Lactose (milk and some dairy products)	Fiber, phytate (whole grains and soybeans) Oxalate (spinach, rhubarb, chocolate)
Phosphorus	Vitamin D (fortified dairy products, sunlight on skin)	Fiber, phytate (whole grains and soybeans)
Magnesium	Lactose (milk and some dairy products)	Fiber, phytate (whole grains and soybeans)
Iron	Unidentified meat factor (meat, fish, poultry) Ascorbic acid (certain fruits and vegetables) Unidentified factors (breast milk)	Tannins (tea, sorghum) EDTA (food additive) Certain forms of phosphorus (food additives, egg yolk)
Zinc	Protein (high protein foods)	Fiber, phytate (whole grains and soybeans) Excess calcium, especially in presence of phytate (calcium supplements) Excess iron (iron supplements)
Lead[a]	Unknown	Calcium (dairy products) Iron (other high protein foods)

[a]In this instance, decreasing the bioavailability is a benefit, since lead is toxic.

Medications. The interactions between medications and nutrients are many and complex. Consumers should be aware that medications—even over-the-counter drugs—can affect the utilization of and requirements for dietary minerals, just as they can for vitamins. For example, aluminum-containing antacids can decrease the absorption of dietary phosphorus and fluoride (Roe, 1976). These antacids are commonly available; some people eat them as freely as candy without realizing their possible negative nutritional effects.

The opposite is also true: not only can drugs influence the utilization of minerals, but minerals can influence the utilization of drugs. If you take the antibiotic tetracycline with a glass of milk, the calcium in the milk will bind to the tetracycline; neither will be absorbed.

Physiological Factors. Your physiological status also plays a role in how well your body absorbs the minerals you consume. For example, scientists know that people who have low body reserves of iron absorb both heme and nonheme iron more efficiently than individuals who have larger body stores: in other words, the individuals who have greater need for the iron absorb a higher proportion of it. Similar observations have been made in regard to calcium, phosphorus, magnesium, and zinc.

It's a happy thought that the bodies of healthy individuals can make remarkable adjustments to different diets and to the total environment—but, of course, there are limits to this.

From this discussion, you can see that innumerable factors influence the bioavailability of minerals, and that minerals probably never function independently in the body. Knowing this, we can now examine each mineral individually—a convenient although not particularly realistic way of describing the roles minerals play in the body.

The Necessary Levels of Essential Minerals Are Available from Foods

Different minerals have different biochemical functions, which can be grouped into four general categories:

1. They form part of tissue structure.

2. They help maintain water and acid–base balance.

3. They form components of important organic molecules that regulate body processes, such as enzymes and hormones.

4. They facilitate nerve impulse transmission and muscle contraction.

Let's look at these mineral functions, requirements, and sources in more detail. First, the macrominerals.

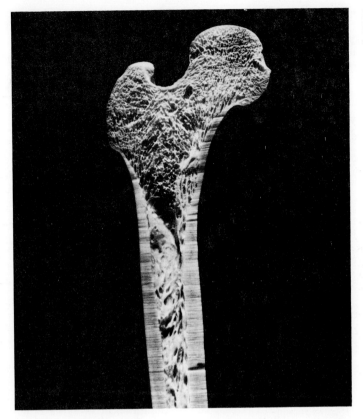

Figure 13.3 Cross section of bone. The lacy interior of bone shows how minerals are crystallized around a protein matrix (network).

Calcium and Phosphorus

Calcium and phosphorus deserve early attention both because they are present in the body in greatest weight and because they have many functions.

Functions. Calcium and phosphorus are well known for their contributions to body structure. In fact, 99% of the calcium and 85% of the phosphorus in the human body are found in bones and teeth, where they are part of hydroxyapatite, a hard compound that is a combination of calcium, phosphorus, oxygen, and hydrogen. Other minerals add to the high concentration of ash (total mineral content) of bones and teeth, but their functions there are less clear.

Although bones contain a large proportion of minerals, these structures are not like rocks, which are solid minerals. First of all, bones are living tissues. Their cells produce and secrete collagen, a special protein that forms the framework of connective tissue and bone. Calcium and phosphorus are incorporated into bone when they crystallize in and around this matrix (framework). Figure 13.3 shows a cross section of a bone; you can see that it is not a solid mass of minerals.

Bones also differ from rocks in that the bones in living animals are

hydroxyapatite—hard compound found in bones and teeth; consists of calcium, phosphorus, oxygen, and hydrogen

ash—the total mineral content of a tissue

Table 13.3 Calcium and Phosphorus in Some Foods

Foods	Household measure	Percent of the adult RDA — Calcium (100 75 50 25 0)	Phosphorus (0 25 50 75 100)
Fruits and vegetables			
Apricots, raw or dried	3 whole		P
Beans, green snap, cooked	½ c	C	
Corn, cooked	½ c		PP
Peas, cooked	½ c		PP
Spinach, cooked	½ c	CC	P
Turnip greens, cooked	½ c	CCC	P
Grain products			
Bread, whole grain	1 slice	C	P
Bread white enriched	1 slice	C	P
Cereal, sweetened puffed wheat	1 oz		P
Cereal, shredded wheat	1 oz		PPP
Spaghetti, cooked noodles	½ c		P
Milk and milk products			
Milk	1 c	CCCCCCC	PPPPPP
Yogurt, plain	1 c	CCCCCCCCC	PPPPPPPP
Cheese, cheddar	1⅓ oz	CCCCCCC	PPPPP
Cheese, cottage	2 c	CCCCCC	PPPPPPPPPPPPPPP
Ice cream	1½ c	CCCCCC	PPPPP
Meats and alternates			
Beans, canned with tomato sauce and pork	1 c	CCC	PPPPPP
Beef, ground, broiled	3 oz		PPPPP
Eggs, fried	2	C	PPPP
Liver, beef, cooked	3 oz		PPPPPPPPP
Peanut butter	¼ c	C	PPPPPP
Salmon including bones, canned	3 oz	CCCC	PPPPPP
Salmon, no bones, cooked	3 oz		PPPPPP
Shrimp	3 oz	CC	PPPPPP
Walnuts, English, chopped	½ c	CC	PPPPPP
Limited extras			
Beer	12 oz		PPP
Butter, margarine	1 t		
Candy, milk chocolate	1 oz	CC	PP
Carbonated cola beverage	12 oz		P
Honey, white sugar	1 T		

always being remodeled; for example, bones must be enlarged as a person grows. During this process, cells in the bone continually dissolve some of the minerals, which are then carried away in the blood. Simultaneously, calcium, phosphorus, and various other minerals are brought from the blood into bone, where they are deposited to form part of its structure. When the amounts of minerals leaving and entering the bones are equal, a state of homeostasis or dynamic equilibrium is said to exist. This is the desirable situation in fully grown, healthy adults.

Phosphorus is also present in cell membranes as part of phospholipids. It is present, too, in many other important body substances: DNA and RNA; coenzymes with a wide variety of functions; and adenosine triphosphate (ATP), a chemical involved in the release of energy in the body. In addition, it functions in acid–base balance. Calcium also performs additional critical functions: it is involved with other elements in nerve transmission, and with vitamin K in blood clotting.

Recommended Intakes and Sources. The RDAs for both calcium and phosphorus are 800 mg (about $\frac{1}{6}$ teaspoon each) daily. Experts recommend that teenagers and pregnant women consume the larger amount of 1200 mg daily to provide materials for their own growth or the growth of their fetuses. Lactating women should also consume 1200 mg per day for milk production.

Just as some minerals are concentrated in specific tissues of your body, so are certain minerals concentrated in particular foods. According to a recent survey by the USDA, almost half of the calcium consumed by Americans is supplied by milk and milk products (Science and Education Administration, 1980a). Table 13.3 shows what a rich source of calcium milk is. A cup of milk provides about 300 mg of calcium; to get an equivalent amount from other dairy products, you would have to consume $1\frac{1}{3}$ ounces of most hard cheeses, 2 cups of cottage cheese, $1\frac{1}{2}$ cups of ice cream, or 2 ounces of processed cheese food. You might recognize these as the serving sizes of dairy products in the SANE guide, which were portioned that way to provide similar amounts of calcium. If you consume the two servings of milk or milk products recommended per day by the SANE guide, you will ingest almost 600 mg of calcium, just 200 mg short of the RDA. That amount is relatively easy to obtain from other foods.

Low calcium intakes are more likely among people who don't drink milk, so suggestions are in order for other ways to get calcium. Those people might: 1) try different milk products such as yogurt or cheese; (2)

The columns on the right of this chart represent the portions of the adult RDA of calcium (C) and phosphorus (P) found in the specified servings of food. Each character in the column represents 5%. The adult RDA is 800 mg for each of these minerals.

Adapted from: Pennington, J.A.T., and H.N. Church. 1980. *Food Values of portions commonly used.* Philadelphia: J.B. Lippincott Company; Science and Education Administration. 1981. *Nutritive value of foods.* Home and garden bulletin no. 72. Washington, DC: U.S. Department of Agriculture; U.S. Department of Agriculture. *Nutritive content of foods* series. Agriculture handbooks no. 8-1, 8-4, 8-5, and 8-7. Washington, DC: USDA.

learn to include milk and cheeses in sauces, casseroles, and desserts; and (3) consume some of the vegetable products such as leafy green vegetables, legumes, and nuts that are good sources of calcium. Fish products in which the soft bones are eaten are also good sources. These suggestions may be particularly attractive to people who are lactose intolerant.

One advantage of getting calcium from dairy products is that it tends to be highly bioavailable. Some of the calcium in vegetable products and legumes, on the other hand, is likely to be made unavailable by phytate and oxalates.

If for some reason you cannot tolerate good food sources of calcium, you may benefit from a calcium supplement. It is best to get professional advice about which kind to use, because the health risks and benefits of available products vary considerably. For example, bone meal (finely ground animal bones) contains all the typical bone minerals, but may also contain lead that accumulated in the animal's bones throughout its lifetime. Taken over a period of time, this could result in lead poisoning (Dubick and Rucker, 1983). Pregnant women and young children especially should be discouraged from using bone meal.

Many foods that are good sources of calcium are also good sources of phosphorus, as Table 13.3 shows: milk and other dairy products, legumes, and nuts are good examples. The reverse is not necessarily true; although meat, fish, poultry, and eggs are very rich sources of phosphorus, they generally contain little calcium. It's easy for most people to take in the Recommended Dietary Allowance of phosphorus from ordinary dietary sources.

Rather than being concerned about people not getting enough phosphorus, some nutritionists have been concerned that the ratio of phosphorus to calcium in the diets of North Americans is too high. However, in controlled human metabolic studies, no adverse effects were seen when

SLICE OF LIFE:
Serious Problems from Bone Meal Intake

This incident was described in *Health Quackery*, by the editors of *Consumer Reports* Books (1980):

[An] incident reported in *JAMA* involved a California woman whose acting career ended when she developed an incapacitating illness. After more than twenty physicians failed to find the cause, . . . an investigation of the medical literature convinced her that she was suffering from lead poisoning. Subsequent testing revealed that she was right.

The source of the lead was a bone-meal supplement that the woman had been taking for six years. Analysis showed significant levels of lead in the health food product, which was made from horse bones. The bone meal contained 190 parts per million of lead, more than twenty times the average content that the FDA has found in similar products made from cattle bones.

the levels of phosphorus in the diet exceeded the level of calcium threefold (Greger and Krystofiak, 1982).

Bone Disorders. Since calcium is an important component of bone, you would expect a dietary deficiency of calcium to affect the skeleton. However, it has been difficult to find a consistent correlation between a person's calcium intake and the occurrence of the common bone diseases. Let's review some of these diseases. Rickets and osteomalacia (also discussed in Chapter 12) are skeletal conditions in which more mineral salts leave the bone than are replaced. This leads to "softening" of bones and skeletal deformities. However, even though these conditions involve calcium, they are not caused by low calcium intake; rather, inadequate vitamin D status or physiological problems that impair calcium and phosphorus absorption and retention are likely to be at fault (Sandstead, 1980).

Osteoporosis is another bone disease. In this condition, both the protein matrix of bone and its mineral deposits are gradually lost, decreasing the total amount of bone and weakening the skeleton. This condition is four times more prevalent in women than in men, and usually begins in the 30s. Disability results if the weakened bones break, which is most likely to happen in the vertebrae, arms, and hips.

In the United States, nearly 4% of people over 85 years of age sustain a serious fracture each year; over $1 billion is spent annually in this country just on the acute care of hip fractures, most of which are due at least in part to osteoporosis (Heaney et al., 1982).

Although it has been theorized that osteoporosis may be a calcium deficiency disease, its actual causes are still debatable. However, scientists have learned that women, especially after menopause, often require a dietary intake of 1.5 grams of calcium to achieve calcium balance—almost double the current RDA (Heaney et al., 1982). Exercise also has been found to delay some of the loss in bone mineral associated with aging (Montoye, 1984).

A number of methods have been tried to halt the progress of existing osteoporosis and to prevent it in younger women. These include exercise regimens, supplements of calcium and fluoride, and estrogen (female hormone) therapy. Although experiments show some benefit from each of these methods, at this time scientists know of neither a sure cure nor a guaranteed preventive treatment for osteoporosis (Heaney et al., 1982). Nonetheless, some physicians promote exercise regimens and daily intakes of calcium in the 1200-1500 mg range for all of their female patients over age 35.

Another effect you might expect from low calcium intake is interference with blood clotting and nerve transmission, since this mineral plays roles in those body processes. However, if dietary intake of calcium is not sufficient to keep blood calcium at normal levels, several hormones work together to withdraw calcium from the bone as needed in the bloodstream. Therefore, blood calcium levels are largely unaffected by dietary calcium intake.

osteoporosis—disease in which bone tissue is gradually lost, weakening the skeleton

Frontier

Magnesium

Like calcium and phosphorus, magnesium also has diverse functions. It, too, is a component of bone. It is a component of many enzymes as well, often catalyzing reactions in which phosphorus is involved. Along with calcium, it is necessary for the transmission of nerve impulses, thereby influencing the contraction and relaxation of muscles. It also helps stabilize DNA and RNA, the substances that direct cell division.

The recommended adult intake for magnesium is a little less than half of the RDA for calcium: 300 mg for women and 350 mg for men. The richest sources of dietary magnesium are nuts, legumes, seafood, and certain leafy green vegetables (Table 13.4). Whole grain products, meats, and milk also contribute significant amounts of magnesium to the diets of Americans.

Even though legumes, nuts, and products made from them are rich sources of magnesium, only 5% of the magnesium that the average American consumes is from these sources. This means that a food is not a major source of magnesium if it is not consumed in significant quantities. On the other hand, grain products provide 21% of the average American intake of magnesium; this amount is more than is contributed by any other group of foods (Science and Education Administration, 1980a). Of the grain products, whole grains contain significantly more magnesium than refined items do; therefore an easy way to increase your magnesium intake is to consume a couple of servings of whole grain products daily. This can be useful information for Americans, since their average intake is below the adult RDA for magnesium (Science and Education Administration, 1980a).

Sulfur

Sulfur is a component of two vitamins: thiamin and biotin. The majority of the sulfur in your body, though, is found in three amino acids: methionine, cystine, and cysteine. These amino acids are part of cellular proteins and are present in foods of both plant and animal origin. Thus, if the diet is adequate in protein, it will also be adequate in sulfur.

A compound consisting of sulfur combined with oxygen (sulfate) plays a role in acid–base balance.

Sodium, Potassium, and Chloride

Sodium, potassium, and chloride are grouped together because they are electrolytes that perform similar types of functions.

electrolytes—substances that carry an electrical charge when dissolved in water

Functions. An important function of sodium, potassium, and chloride is water balance. In Chapter 4 we discussed the role of dissolved mineral ions and soluble proteins in controlling the movement of water from one region of the body to another. Recall that water diffuses through a membrane from the side with the greater concentration of water toward the side with the lesser concentration of water (or greater concentration of particles). The electrolytes are the minerals most involved in water bal-

Table 13.4 Magnesium in Some Foods

Food	Household measure	Poor (<10 mg)	Fair (10–50 mg)	Good 50–100 mg	Excellent (>100 mg)
Fruits and vegetables					
Many fruits	$\frac{1}{2}$ c		X		
Most vegetables	$\frac{1}{2}$ c		X		
Lettuce	1 c	X			
Spinach, cooked	$\frac{1}{2}$ c			X	
Grain products					
Bran cereal	1 oz				X
Bread, whole grain	1 slice		X		
Bread, unenriched	1 slice	X			
Milk and milk products					
Milk	1 c		X		
Meats and alternates					
Most meats, fish, poultry	3 oz			X	
Almonds	$\frac{1}{2}$ c				X
Legumes, cooked	1 c				X
Peanut butter	$\frac{1}{4}$ c				X
Shrimp	3 oz		X		
Tofu	6 oz				X
Walnuts, pecans	$\frac{1}{2}$ c			X	
Limited extras					
Alcoholic beverages	1 serving	X			
Candy, milk chocolate	1 oz		X		
Fats, oils	1 T	X			
Sugars	1 T	X			

In this chart, the relative magnesium values of foods are shown by designating them as poor, fair, good, or excellent sources. The U.S. RDA for magnesium is 400 mg.

Adapted from: Pennington, J.A.T., and H.N. Church. 1980. *Food Values of portions commonly used*. Philadelphia: J.B. Lippincott Company; U.S. Department of Agriculture. *Nutritive content of foods* series. Agriculture handbooks no. 8-1, 8-4, 8-5, and 8-7. Washington, DC: USDA. Agricultural Research Service, 1963. *Composition of foods*. Agricultural Handbook No. 8. Washington, D.C.: USDA.

ance. Potassium (K^+) is the electrolyte found in the highest concentration within body cells; magnesium, phosphates, and sulfates are also found here. Sodium (Na^+) and chloride (Cl^-) are found in highest concentration in extracellular fluids such as blood plasma. On each side of the membrane, the sum of the negatively charged ions is about equal to the total of positively charged particles. Chloride also functions in the body in a buffering system that compensates for excess acid or alkali.

Estimated Safe and Adequate Daily Dietary Intakes. For some minerals, instead of designating RDAs, the 1980 RDA committee suggested ranges of intakes that were "estimated safe and adequate." They did this because human data regarding these minerals were then too limited for them to make more definite statements about human needs; revisions in these estimates can be expected in future editions.

The range of daily intake recommended as safe and adequate for potassium is between 1875 and 5615 mg daily. For sodium, the range is 1100–3300 mg, and for chloride, the suggested intake is 1700–5100 mg; that's equivalent to 2.7–8.2 grams of salt (NaCl) daily, or about $\frac{1}{2}$ to $1\frac{3}{4}$ teaspoons.

The recommended intake of sodium is an important but confusing and controversial issue. First, it's easy to confuse the terms *sodium* and *salt*; however, since salt is only 40% sodium, the terms cannot be used interchangeably, especially when quantities are being considered.

Sodium intake is important because some scientists believe that high sodium consumption may be related to the development of essential hypertension, or unexplained high blood pressure, which is a major risk factor for cardiovascular disease. (Overfatness is another possible cause of high blood pressure; when weight gain is the cause, weight loss is the best means of lowering it.) In 1979, the American Society for Clinical Nutrition convened a symposium on dietary factors related to health. The summary report noted that 9% to 20% of the American population is genetically susceptible to developing essential hypertension. Among these individuals, "a lifelong modest restriction of salt intake to levels less than 1380 mg/day in adults will probably prevent the onset of hypertension" (Tobian, 1979).

Compare that to the average North American salt intake of 10,000 to 12,000 mg per day, which contains 3900 to 4700 mg of sodium (Institute of Food Technologists' Expert Panel on Food Safety and Nutrition, 1980). A healthy adult who is not exercising actively and thus not losing large amounts of sodium in sweat, probably requires a minimum of only 200 mg of sodium daily—the amount in 500 mg of salt.

Other experts do not endorse the moderate restriction of sodium because they doubt that such restriction will prevent the onset of hypertension in all susceptible individuals (White and Crocco, 1981). Unfortunately, there is no certain technique for identifying which individuals might benefit from sodium restriction. They question the purpose of putting people to the considerable effort of making this substantial change if it is not guaranteed to protect against hypertension.

Frontier

Still other scientists have suggested that sodium may not be the primary mineral involved in hypertension after all; some old and new research casts doubt on sodium having a major role in this condition. Some scientists believe that the intake of adequate amounts of other minerals, particularly potassium and perhaps calcium, can reduce the incidence of hypertension (White and Crocco, 1981; McCarron, et al., 1984). Further investigation is under way to clarify the role of minerals in the origin, prevention, and treatment of the disease.

The electrolytes are of particular interest to athletes and others who exert themselves physically because these minerals are lost in perspiration. Sodium and chloride are the two primary electrolytes lost in sweat; potassium and magnesium are lost to a much lesser degree (Costill and Miller, 1980). Therefore, people who perspire heavily should be concerned about the status of these essential nutrients, especially sodium and chloride.

It's important to keep in mind that the solution of sodium and chloride that leaves the body as perspiration is only about one-third as concentrated as the solution of those same electrolytes in your normal body fluids. Therefore, when you perspire, you are losing relatively more water than electrolytes, and the sodium and chloride left in your body actually become more concentrated within the remaining body fluids as perspiration continues (Costill and Miller, 1980). For this reason, it is important to restore water losses first; after that, most people adequately replace electrolytes by eating according to their hunger. Only people who have perspired so copiously as to lose 6–8% or more of body weight need to consciously increase sodium chloride intake (Costill, 1979). This can easily be accomplished by adding a little extra salt to food. Potassium losses, which are much smaller, can also be restored easily from a normal diet; your body will retain a higher proportion of the electrolytes you consume.

Some people take salt tablets in a well-intentioned effort to replace sodium and chloride. We do not recommend this practice because it can result in an overdose, especially if rehydration has not been accomplished first. In addition, ingested salt tablets may resist being dissolved, sticking to the lining of the stomach where they can cause irritation.

Several "sport drinks" are marketed that contain nutrients of concern to athletes and others who engage in demanding physical performance. However, just as we did not endorse their use earlier because of their inappropriately high carbohydrate content, we are similarly disenchanted with the high concentration of electrolytes that many of them contain.

In general, we believe that people can meet their needs better by using water and food as their sources of these nutrients. If people want to use the sport drinks, they should be diluted, depending on the contents of the particular product. A sports physiologist or nutritionist who specializes in working with athletes can suggest the appropriate proportions.

Sources. Foods produced by nature contain only modest amounts of sodium, with animal products having more than plant foods. Processing often adds more sodium to a food than was there to begin with: pickles, salty snack foods, processed cheeses, and smoked meats and sausages often contain

Table 13.5 Sodium in Some Foods

Food	Household measure	Milligrams of sodium			
		0	500	1000	1500
Fruits and vegetables					
Apple	1 medium				
Banana	1 medium				
*Beans, green, cooked without salt	$\frac{1}{2}$ c				
*Beans, green, canned with salt	$\frac{1}{2}$ c	xxxxx			
*Cucumber	1 large				
*Dill pickle	1 large	xxxxxxxxxxxxxxxxxxxxxxxxxxxxxx			
Orange juice	$\frac{1}{2}$ c				
*Peach, fresh	1 medium				
*Peaches, canned	$\frac{1}{2}$ c				
*Potato, baked	1 average				
*Potato chips	10 chips	xxxx			
Grain products					
Bread	1 slice	xx			
Macaroni, cooked without salt	$\frac{1}{2}$ c				
Milk and milk products					
Milk	1 c	xx			
*Cheese, cheddar	$1\frac{1}{3}$ oz	xxxxx			
*Cheese, processed	$1\frac{1}{3}$ oz	xxxxxxxx			
Yogurt, plain	1 c	xx			

continued

several hundred milligrams of sodium per serving. Experts believe that about 40% of the sodium ingested in foods by most Americans was added during processing (Council on Scientific Affairs, 1983). Table 13.5 enables you to compare the sodium contents of processed and unprocessed foods.

Consumers often increase the sodium content of their foods even further when they get to the table by adding salt or other flavor enhancers, such as soy sauce or monosodium glutamate. About 30% of the sodium consumed by Americans is believed to be added in this way by consumers themselves. If you are concerned about your sodium intake, the best and easiest way to reduce it is to make less use of the salt shaker and sodium-rich flavor enhancers.

Sodium is also present in the water supplies of many cities. Home water softeners can add even more of this mineral to water, since the

Table 13.5 continued

Food	Household measure	Milligrams of sodium 0	500	1000	1500
Meats and alternates					
*Beef, ground, cooked without salt	3 oz	x			
*Frankfurter	3 oz	xxxxxxxxxxxxxxxxx			
Peanut butter	¼c	x			
*Salmon, fresh	3 oz	x			
*Salmon, canned with salt	3 oz	xxxxxxxxx			
Walnuts, chopped	½c				
Limited extras					
Beer	12 oz	x			
Butter	1 t	x			
Salt	1 t	xxxxxxxxxxxxxxxxxxxxxxxxxxxxxxxxxxxxxxxxxx			
Soy sauce	1 T	xxxxxxxxxxxxxxxx			
Sugar	1 T				

The columns on the right of this chart represent the amount of sodium found in specified servings of food; each X represents 50 mg. The broken vertical line indicates the beginning of the safe and adequate range for daily intake (1100–3300 mg). For comparison, pairs of unprocessed processed foods are marked with an asterisk (*) and bracket.

Data sources: Pennington, J.A.T., and H.N. Church. 1980. *Food Values of portions commonly used*. Philadelphia: J.B. Lippincott Company; Science and Education Administration. 1980b. *The sodium content of your food*. Home and garden bulletin no. 233. Washington, DC: U.S. Department of Agriculture; U.S. Department of Agriculture.

softening process substitutes sodium for the calcium and magnesium that made the water hard. Even so, water is usually only a minor source of sodium intake; if drinking water contains 20 mg per quart, which is not uncommon, the average individual will ingest from this source less than 100 mg of sodium daily, based on amounts typically used in food preparation and as a beverage (Safe Drinking Water Committee, 1980).

Foods are not the only sources of sodium. Many medications, including over-the-counter drugs, contain more than 200 mg per dose of sodium.

Chloride ions are almost as generously obtainable from food sources as sodium, since chloride constitutes the other half of the table salt molecule. Potassium is also not usually regarded as a problem nutrient to obtain; usual intakes of this mineral are within the safe and adequate range for adults. Furthermore, potassium is widespread in the food supply, with many fruits, vegetables, milk and yogurt, meats, legumes, and nuts being especially good sources (Table 13.6).

Table 13.6 Potassium in Some Foods

Food	Household measure	Milligrams of potassium				
		0	500	1000	1500	2000
Fruits and vegetables						
Apple	1 medium	xx				
Banana	1 medium	xxxxxxx				
*Beans, green, cooked without salt	$\frac{1}{2}$ c	xx				
*Beans, green, canned with salt	$\frac{1}{2}$ c	xx				
*Cucumber	1 large	xxx				
*Dill pickle	1 large	xxxx				
Orange juice	$\frac{1}{2}$ c	xxxxx				
*Peach, fresh	1 medium	xxxx				
*Peaches, canned	$\frac{1}{2}$ c	xxxx				
Potato, baked	1 medium	xxxxxxxxxx				
Potato chips	10 chips	xxxxx				
Grain products						
*Bread, whole grain	1 slice	xx				
*Bread, enriched	1 slice	x				
Macaroni, cooked	$\frac{1}{2}$ c	x				
Milk and milk products						
*Milk	1 c	xxxxxxx				
*Cheese, cheddar	1 $\frac{1}{3}$ oz	x				
*Cheese, processed	1 $\frac{1}{3}$ oz	x				
*Yogurt, plain	1 c	xxxxxx				

continued

Iron

Now for discussion of the trace minerals; the first is iron.

Functions. Iron, like many other minerals, is a component of many enzymes. It is also a part of the carrier proteins hemoglobin (found in blood) and myoglobin (its counterpart in muscle). Although iron accounts for less than 1% of the weight of these proteins, it enables them to perform the essential ongoing tasks of transporting oxygen and carbon dioxide to and from all body cells.

hemoglobin, myoglobin—oxygen-carrying proteins found in blood and muscle, respectively

Table 13.6 continued

Food	Household measure	Milligrams of potassium				
		0	500	1000	1500	2000
Meats and alternates						
*Beef, ground, cooked	3 oz	xxxxxxxxxx				
*Frankfurter	3 oz	xxxx				
Peanut butter	$\frac{1}{4}$ c	xxxxxxxxxx				
*Salmon, fresh sockeye	3 oz	xxxxxxx				
*Salmon, canned	3 oz	xxxxxx				
Walnuts, chopped	$\frac{1}{2}$ c	xxxxx				
Limited extras						
Beer	12 oz	xx				
Butter	1 t					
Salt						
Soy sauce	1 T	x				
Sugar	1 T					

The columns on the right of this chart represent the amount of potassium found in specified servings of food; each X represents 50 mg. The broken vertical line indicates the beginning of the safe and adequate range for daily intake (1875–5624 mg). For comparison, pairs of unprocessed/processed foods are marked with an asterisk (*) and bracket.

Data sources: Pennington, J.A.T., and H.N. Church. 1980. *Food Values of portions commonly used*. Philadelphia: J.B. Lippincott Company; Science and Education Administration. 1981. *Nutritive value of foods*. Home and garden bulletin no. 72. Washington, DC: U.S. Department of Agriculture; U.S. Department of Agriculture. *Nutritive content of foods* series. Agriculture handbooks no. 8-1, 8-4, 8-5, and 8-7. Washington, DC: USDA.

Recommended Intake. Iron is an exception to the general rule that RDA values are higher for adult males than for adult females. Males, on the average, have larger bodies and more lean body mass, and thus require more nutrients. However, the adult male RDA for iron is 10 mg, and that for females is 18 mg. Women require more dietary iron because of losses of iron during menstruation and childbirth.

The RDA for iron for adolescent males and females is also 18 mg daily. These high iron recommendations reflect physiological changes that occur during the teen years. For teenaged males, the extra iron is used primarily to form additional lean body mass; for females, it is used to replace that lost in menstruation.

The recommended intakes of iron during pregnancy and lactation are the highest of all due to the demands of growing fetal, placental, and maternal tissues. Because it is almost impossible to meet these needs through diet alone during pregnancy, the 1980 RDA committee recommended for

Table 13.7   Iron in Some Foods

Food	Household measure	Milligrams of iron per serving		
		0	(RDA/men) 10	(RDA/women) 18
Fruits and vegetables				
Apricots, raw	2–3 medium	X		
Apricots, dried	3 large halves	XX		
Beans, green snap, cooked	$\frac{1}{2}$ c	X		
Broccoli, chopped, cooked	$\frac{1}{2}$ c	X		
Corn, cooked	$\frac{1}{2}$ c	X		
Lettuce, Iceberg	$\frac{1}{6}$ head	X		
Orange juice	$\frac{1}{2}$ c			
Peas, green, cooked	$\frac{1}{2}$ c	XXX		
Potatoes, mashed with milk	$\frac{1}{2}$ c	X		
Raisins	2 T	X		
Spinach, chopped, cooked	$\frac{1}{2}$ c	XXXX		
Turnip greens, chopped, cooked	$\frac{1}{2}$ c	XXX		
Grain products				
Bread, whole grain	1 slice	XX		
Bread, white enriched	1 slice	X		
Bread, unenriched	1 slice			
Cereal, bran flakes	1 oz	XXXXXXXXX		
Cereal, wheat flakes, iron-fortified	1 oz	XXXXXXXXX		
Cereal, shredded wheat	1 oz	XX		
Spaghetti, enriched	$\frac{1}{2}$ c	X		
Milk and milk products				
Milk	1 c			
Cheese, cheddar	$1\frac{1}{3}$ oz	X		

continued

this group 30–60 mg of supplemental iron daily. Iron needs during lactation are not substantially different from those of nonpregnant women, but continued supplementation of the mother for 2–3 months after delivery is advisable to replenish stores depleted by the pregnancy.

Sources. Foods contain very uneven quantities of iron. Table 13.7 lists the iron content of common foods. High levels of iron are found in meats and alternates, such as fish, poultry, eggs, legumes, and nuts. Meat, fish, and

Table 13.7 continued

Food	Household measure	Milligrams of iron per serving		
		0	(RDA/ men) 10	(RDA/women) 18
Meat and alternates				
Almonds	$\frac{1}{2}$ c	XXXXXX		
Beans, canned with tomato sauce and pork	1 c	XXXXXXXXX		
Beef, ground, broiled	3 oz	XXXXXX		
Chicken breast, cooked	3 oz	XXX		
Eggs, hard boiled	2	XXXX		
Liver, beef, cooked	3 oz	XXXXXXXXXXXXXX		
Peanut butter	$\frac{1}{4}$ c	XX		
Shrimp, canned	3 oz	XXXXX		
Tuna, canned	3 oz	XXX		
Walnuts, chopped	$\frac{1}{2}$ c	XXXX		
Limited extras				
Beer	12 oz			
Butter, margarine	1 t			
Carbonated beverages	12 oz			
Honey	1 T			
Molasses, light	1 T	XX		
Sugar, white	1 T			

The columns on the right of this chart represent the amount of iron in the specified servings of food as compared to the adult RDAs; each X represents 0.5 mg. Since the RDAs for men and women differ markedly for iron, both values are shown here. Remember that the amount of iron absorbed may be substantially less than the amount present, depending on bioavailability.

Data sources: Pennington, J.A.T., and H.N. Church. 1980. *Food Values of portions commonly used*. Philadelphia: J.B. Lippincott Company; Science and Education Administration. 1981. *Nutritive value of foods*. Home and garden bulletin no. 72. Washington, DC: U.S. Department of Agriculture; U.S. Department of Agriculture. *Nutritive content of foods* series. Agriculture handbooks no. 8-1, 8-4, 8-5, and 8-7. Washington, DC: USDA.

poultry are superior sources because the heme iron and unidentified meat factor they contain make the iron in those foods very bioavailable. Whole grain and enriched cereal products can also contribute significant amounts of iron to the diet. Certain vegetables, such as peas and deep green leafy vegetables, are other sources of iron, although they are less bioavailable.

Several foods are questionable sources of iron. For example, certain dried fruits, such as raisins and apricots, contain significant amounts of iron only if eaten in large amounts. (The drying process doesn't add iron to these foods, it just concentrates the iron and all other substances that were in the fresh product by removing most of the water.)

Molasses contains more iron than refined sugar does, but since it is very energy-dense, it is not suitable as a regular source of iron for most

Meat, fish, and poultry as sources of needed minerals. Iron and zinc are two minerals often found in short supply in the diets of Americans. Meat is one of the best sources of both. Furthermore, meat furnishes a form of iron that is absorbed better than that found in other foods.

people—you would get a lot of kcalories with a little iron. Furthermore, it is not known how bioavailable the iron in molasses is.

Generally, milk and milk products, most fruits, fats, oils, refined unenriched grain products, and sugars are poor sources.

The daily iron consumption of Americans presents an ironic situation. The average man takes in about 16 mg, in comparison to his RDA of 10 mg; however, the average woman gets approximately 11 mg, in contrast to her RDA of 18 mg. Men tend to have higher iron intakes mainly because they consume a larger quantity of food (Science and Education Administration, 1980a).

Anemia. When humans consume amounts of iron that are inadequate to meet their needs, they become anemic. However, iron deficiency is not the only cause of anemia.

anemia—general term indicating that blood hemoglobin levels are low, or that the concentration of red blood cells is lower than normal

Anemia is a general term indicating that blood hemoglobin levels are low, or that the concentration of red blood cells is lower than normal. When this condition occurs, body cells receive less oxygen, and carbon dioxide wastes are removed less efficiently. These compromised functions cause an individual to feel tired or "run down."

Anemia can result from a number of causes: loss of blood due to surgery, accidents, or disease; genetic conditions; and various vitamin or mineral deficiencies. But the most common cause of anemia in North America and in the world in general is iron deficiency. The age groups most apt to develop anemia are children aged 1 to 5, adolescents, young adult women, and the elderly. Pregnant women are also at risk, as was discussed earlier. Individuals whose family incomes are below the poverty level are more apt to have low hemoglobin levels than members of more affluent families, and blacks are more apt to have low hemoglobin levels than whites (National Center for Health Statistics, 1974).

A temporary "sports anemia" sometimes develops among physically untrained people as they begin an intensive training program. However, this condition seems to be transient; blood iron levels usually rise spontaneously in a couple of weeks and then stabilize within the normal range. Since the condition corrects itself in such a short period of time, no treatment is usually necessary, other than to encourage intake of a diet that supplies RDA levels of protein and iron (Buskirk, 1981).

Among well-trained athletes, the incidence of anemia is similar to that in the general population. Females are more likely to be anemic than males, and dietary methods are recommended as a first approach to treatment (Pate, 1982). Iron supplements are recommended only if changes in diet do not succeed in curing the anemia.

Studies have been done to determine whether iron supplements can improve the performance of athletes whose blood values for iron are already within normal ranges. Two such studies have been done on female athletes who had normal blood hemoglobin values when the studies began. Although they took supplemental iron throughout the season, no significant change was noted in their blood iron values. Therefore, it is not beneficial for athletes to routinely take iron supplements (Pate, 1982).

Iodine

Iodine makes its principal contribution to human function as a component of thyroxin, a hormone produced by the thyroid gland. The minute amount of thyroxin within each body cell acts as a metabolic accelerator, controlling the rate at which energy is produced within the cells' mitochondria.

Sources. Traditionally, the best dietary sources of iodine were ocean fish, other seafoods, and crops that had been grown on land near the ocean. To supplement the diets of Americans who did not live near salt water, iodine began to be added to table salt, making iodized salt the major source of iodine for many Americans, especially those living in the Midwest.

Seafoods and iodized salt are, however, no longer the major sources of iodine in America; recent surveys indicate that milk and grain products are now the major sources (Harland et al., 1980). This has come about because dairy cows are being fed more iodine, iodine-containing compounds are being used as disinfectant washes on cows' udders, and iodine-containing dough conditioners are now being used in commercially baked breads.

Because of these new sources of iodine, adult Americans may have consumed levels of iodine during the 1970s that were more than five times the amount suggested in the RDAs (Harland et al., 1980). The Food and Drug Administration has successfully encouraged the dairy industry to reduce the use of iodine-containing compounds in recent years, out of concern that dietary intakes might become too high for some Americans.

goiter—enlargement of the thyroid gland, resulting primarily from iodine deficiency

cretinism—irreversible condition involving both mental and physical growth retardation; can result from iodine deficiency in the mother's diet during pregnancy

Deficiency and Toxicity. Goiter, or enlargement of the thyroid gland, is the most obvious symptom of iodine deficiency (Figure 13.4). When iodine is inadequate in the diet, the thyroid gland does not have enough of this mineral to produce a normal amount of the hormone thyroxin; in order to allow for a greater production of the hormone, therefore, the thyroid gland enlarges. However, even with a larger mass of thyroid tissue, the gland is unable to produce enough additional thyroxin.

In the early part of the twentieth century, goiters were very common in inland areas, especially in the Midwest. After iodized salt was accepted as a public health measure designed to increase iodine intake to recommended levels, the incidence of goiters dropped markedly. However, they are still common in inland areas of South America, Africa, and Asia (Cavalieri, 1980).

Iodine deficiency is not the only cause of goiter. Dietary factors and drugs that prevent the normal incorporation of iodine into thyroxin can also promote the development of goiters. This effect is accentuated in people who have low or marginal intakes of iodine.

If iodine is deficient in the diets of pregnant women, there is the possibility of an additional penalty: the child may be born a cretin. Cretinism is an irreversible condition characterized by both mental and physical growth retardation.

People who chronically ingest very high amounts of iodine may also develop a thyroid enlargement. (This is an example of deficiency and excess both causing similar symptoms.) This condition is common in certain areas of Japan where residents consume large amounts of iodine-rich seaweed (Cavalieri, 1980).

Fluoride

Fluoride functions in teeth and bones by becoming part of hydroxyapatite crystals and making them larger and even harder. A certain minimal level of fluoride in the diet, therefore, increases resistance to dental caries. Also, it has been suggested, although not proved, that adequate fluoride may delay the onset or severity of osteoporosis.

The estimated adult safe and adequate intake range for fluoride is 1.5 to 4 mg. The major source of fluoride in most people's diets is water. Fluoride is present naturally in the water supplies of some areas. Where it is not, public health agencies encourage that it be added at the level of 1 part per million, which is equivalent to 1 ounce of fluoride in over 7750 gallons of water. This small concentration of fluoride is associated with a reduced rate of dental caries (Leverett, 1982). People whose water is fluoridated are likely to consume anywhere from 2–3.5 mg of fluoride daily (Safe Drinking Water Committee, 1980). Tea and the soft edible bones of fish are also rich sources of fluoride.

Although small amounts of fluoride can lower the incidence of dental caries, people who habitually drink water that contains four times or more the recommended level may develop slight mottling (spotty discoloration) of their teeth. When the water supply contains eight times the recommended level, fluorosis may develop; this is a condition characterized by

Figure 13.4 Goiter. Severe, long-term iodine deficiency results in enlargement of the thyroid gland, which you can see in the women in this photograph.

severe mottling of the teeth and eventual degenerative and crippling bone and joint disorders (Underwood, 1977).

Zinc

Zinc makes its contribution to human health as a component of over 70 enzyme systems with a wide variety of functions. It is also necessary for adequate immune functions. If zinc is deficient in the diet, diverse symptoms occur, including loss of appetite, failure to grow, skin changes, impaired healing of wounds, and decreased taste acuity.

The adult RDA for zinc is 15 mg. The average North American consumes only about two-thirds of the adult RDA of zinc daily (Solomons, 1982).

Until about 25 years ago, it was thought that people would never develop deficiencies of trace minerals in ordinary living situations. However, although it is unusual for otherwise healthy people to develop such deficiencies, a team of scientists discovered that it can occur. In some villages in Iran and Egypt, they found adults who were unusually short and sexually immature, whose abnormalities were corrected by zinc supplementation. It is not surprising, in retrospect, that the deficiency occurred: the local staple diet was low in zinc; the bioavailability of the small amount of zinc present was poor; and general infections and gut infestations resulted in high excretion of zinc (Prasad, 1979). Zinc deficiency is not limited to the Middle East, however. Its symptoms of poor growth in children, poor

Table 13.8 Zinc in Some Foods

Food	Household measure	Relative amount per serving			
		Poor (<0.2mg)	Fair (0.3–0.6 mg)	Good (0.6–1.0 mg)	Excellent (>1.0 mg)
Fruits and vegetables					
Most fruits	½c	X			
Many vegetables	½c		X		
Grain products					
Bread, white	1 slice	X			
Bread, whole grain	1 slice		X		
Macaroni	½c		X		
Milk and milk products					
Milk	1 c			X	
Meats and alternates					
Beef, pork, turkey, veal	3 oz				X
Chicken, dark meat	3 oz				X
Chicken, light meat	3 oz			X	
Eggs	2			X	
Cooked legumes	1 c				X
Nuts	½c				X
Peanut butter	¼c				X
Seafood	3 oz				X
Fish	3 oz			X	
Limited extras					
Fats, oils	1 T	X			
Sugar, candies	1 oz	X			

In this chart, the relative zinc values of foods are shown by designating them as poor, fair, good, or excellent sources. The U.S. RDA for zinc is 15 mg.

Data source: Murphy, E.W., B.W. Willis, and B.K. Watt. 1975. Provisional tables on the zinc content of foods. *Journal of the American Dietetic Association* 66:345–355.

wound healing in adults, a scaly dermatitis, and impaired resistance to infections have also been seen in other parts of the world.

Because severe zinc deficiency was found to prevent sexual maturation and therefore impair performance, some supplement promoters have suggested that normally healthy men can improve their sexual performance by taking zinc supplements. However, excessive zinc adds nothing to performance beyond what is possible for the well-nourished individual.

Table 13.8 shows that the best dietary sources of zinc are seafood, red meats, nuts, and legumes. Other meat products, milk, and whole grain products also contribute significant amounts to the diet. Of course, the bioavailability of zinc from some of these products—especially whole grains, legumes, and nuts—is lessened by the fiber and phytate they contain.

Selenium

Selenium is a trace mineral that has come into the limelight in this decade. It is known to be interdependent with vitamin E, and in some instances a low level of one nutrient can be partly compensated for by the presence of the other.

Selenium is a component of an important enzyme that helps prevent damage to cell structures. For this reason, it has been suggested as a factor for cancer prevention. Some animal studies show that selenium has a protective effect (Willett and MacMahon, 1984). However, more studies are necessary to determine whether there is a cause-and-effect relationship in humans.

Another important issue, if selenium proves to be useful in human cancer prevention, will be the amount to recommend. According to the Committee on Diet, Nutrition, and Cancer, "increasing the selenium intake to more than 200 μg/day by the use of supplements has not been shown to confer health benefits exceeding those derived from the consumption of a balanced diet" (1982). However, because of its potential for toxicity, intake beyond the RDA safe and adequate range should be avoided (National Dairy Council, 1983).

The safe and adequate daily intake recommended by the 1980 RDA committee for adults is 0.05–0.2 mg. Selenium is obtained primarily from grains although meats, fish, and poultry are also substantial contributors (Pennington et al., 1984). However, the selenium content of grains is quite variable, depending in part on the selenium content of the soil, which varies considerably.

Because the selenium content of grains varies according to the soil, the selenium content of diets in various regions of the world can also differ widely. In a large area of western China, for example, selenium intake is very low. In the same region, a potentially fatal condition called Keshan disease, which is characterized by heart damage, is seen in some children. To determine whether the deficiency is the cause of the heart damage, selenium supplements were given to thousands of children for four years.

During that time, the incidence of Keshan disease dropped to about 5% of the rate in controls (Keshan Disease Research Group et al., 1979).

Despite this impressive response to raising the level of selenium intake, Keshan disease is probably a more complex problem than simple selenium deficiency. This belief is based on the fact that in other places in the world that also have low selenium intake, Keshan disease is not found.

Other Trace Minerals: Copper, Cobalt, Chromium, Manganese, and Molybdenum

The estimated safe and adequate daily dietary adult intake ranges for copper and manganese range up to 5 mg at most, and for chromium and molybdenum they are less than one-half of a milligram each. The fact that they are needed in such small amounts does not diminish their importance, however.

Functions. These minerals have a variety of functions. Copper is a component of many enzymes, and is important in the synthesis of collagen and in normal immune function. Since its presence influences iron metabolism, copper deficiency can result in anemia.

The only known function of cobalt is as a component of vitamin B-12. Therefore, an adequate intake of this vitamin, easily obtainable from foods of animal origin, ensures an adequate intake of cobalt.

Chromium aids in normal glucose metabolism, apparently by working with insulin. Since chromium levels decrease as people age, and since low chromium levels are often noted in diabetic populations, some scientists have suggested that low chromium levels may be a factor in adult-onset diabetes in some individuals.

Manganese and molybdenum, like many other minerals, are best known as components of enzymes with a variety of functions.

Sources. It is not possible, for several reasons, to give reliable data for the copper, chromium, manganese, and molybdenum content of foods. First, the analyses for some of these minerals are difficult to perform, and therefore those that have been done have resulted in only a limited amount of usable information. Second, the amounts of trace minerals in many foods are extremely variable, depending on the minerals' concentration in the soil, water, and/or in the fertilizer involved in food production. The amounts of certain trace minerals in root vegetables can vary by severalfold (Underwood, 1977); the trace mineral content of seafood is also affected by environmental conditions. Therefore, no single value can be regarded as representative of any of these minerals in a particular food.

Despite analytical problems and natural variation, however, trace minerals are thought to be widely distributed in foods as they come from nature; people who eat a wide variety of foods are likely to get what they need. Furthermore, since the foods available in any given part of North America have come from many different regions, the likelihood is increased that at least some good sources of these minerals will be present.

Because refinement processes generally remove much of the trace mineral content of foods, you will get more trace minerals from minimally processed items such as whole grains; you will get very little from such foods as white flour, sugars, and fats. But it is a mistake to think that food processing always decreases the trace mineral content of foods; remember that iodine is added to some dough products during processing. Also, foods can accumulate trace minerals *unintentionally* during processing. Canned foods, for example, sometimes take on small amounts of iron and non-essential minerals like tin and lead from the cans (Greger and Baier, 1981; Schaffner, 1981). We'll talk more about the effects of processing on minerals in Chapter 14.

Table 13.9 summarizes much of the information presented here about essential minerals.

Mineral Intake Should Be Neither Too Low Nor Too High

We have mentioned that different mineral deficiencies have different results; for example, low iron intakes can lead to a type of anemia; low iodine can result in goiter; and prolonged low calcium intakes may be part of the cause of osteoporosis. Does this mean that mineral deficiencies are rampant in developed countries?

Deficiencies

Generally speaking, deficiencies are more likely to occur if several precipitating factors are present at the same time. Such a grouping of factors is less likely to happen in developed countries than in developing countries. Iron deficiency is an exception: it is a familiar problem in virtually all parts of the world. The following factors are likely to precede mineral deficiencies:

1. The diet is limited in overall quantity, resulting in low intakes of minerals and all other nutrients.

2. The diet is poorly selected for mineral content due to lack of knowledge, unavailability of certain foods, or poverty.

3. Bioavailability of minerals is low, for any of the many reasons discussed earlier.

4. The individual cannot absorb, utilize, or maintain minerals normally due to inborn metabolic problems, disease conditions, or alcohol or other drug use.

5. Requirements for minerals are unusually high due to rapid growth or disease.

Given these factors, it's not hard to predict which categories of people will be most at risk of mineral deficiency. For example, some elderly individuals may have limited food intake due to medical, social, or psycho-

Table 13.9 Key Information about Many Essential Minerals

Mineral	RDA for healthy adults	Major dietary sources	Major functions	Signs of severe, prolonged deficiency	Signs of extreme excess
Major minerals					
Calcium	800 mg	Milk, cheese, dark green vegetables, legumes	Bone and tooth formation; blood clotting; nerve transmission	Stunted growth; maybe bone loss	Depressed absorption of some other minerals
Phosphorus	800 mg	Milk, cheese, meat, poultry, whole grains	Bone and tooth formation; acid–base balance; component of coenzymes	Weakness; demineralization of bone	Some forms depress absorption of some minerals
Magnesium	Females: 300 mg Males: 350 mg	Whole grains, green leafy vegetables	Component of enzymes	Neurological disturbances	Neurological disturbances
Sulfur	(Provided by sulfur amino acids)	Sulfur amino acids in dietary proteins	Component of cartilage, tendon, and proteins; acid–base balance	(Related to protein deficiency)	Excess sulfur amino acid intake leads to poor growth; liver damage
Sodium	1100–3300 mg[a]	Common salt, soy sauce, cured meats, pickles, canned soups, processed cheese	Body water balance; nerve function	Muscle cramps; reduced appetite	High blood pressure in genetically predisposed individuals
Potassium	1875–5625 mg[a]	Meats, milk, many fruits and vegetables, whole grains	Body water balance; nerve function	Muscular weakness; paralysis	Muscular weakness; cardiac arrest
Chloride	1700–5100 mg[a]	Common salt, many processed foods (as for sodium)	Plays a role in acid–base balance; formation of gastric juice	Muscle cramps; reduced appetite; poor growth	Vomiting

continued

[a]Estimated safe and adequate daily dietary intake

References: (1) Shils, M.E. 1980. Magnesium. In *Modern nutrition in health and disease*, ed. R.S. Goodhart and M.E. Shils. Philadelphia: Lea and Febiger. (2) National Research Council, National Academy of Sciences (NAS). 1980. *Recommended dietary allowances*, 9th ed. Washington, DC: NAS. (3) Scrimshaw, N.J., and V.R. Young. 1976. The requirements of human nutrition. *Scientific American* 235:50–64. (4) Underwood, E.J. 1977. *Trace elements in human and animal nutrition*. New York: Academic Press.

Table 13.9   continued

Mineral	RDA for healthy adults	Major dietary sources	Major functions	Signs of severe, prolonged deficiency	Signs of extreme excess
Trace minerals					
Iron	Females: 18 mg Males: 10 mg	Meats, eggs, legumes, whole grains, green leafy vegetables	Component of hemoglobin and enzymes	Iron deficiency anemia, weakness, impaired immune function	Acute: shock, death Chronic: liver damage, cardiac failure
Iodine	0.15 mg	Marine fish and shellfish; dairy products; iodized salt; some breads	Component of thyroid hormones	Goiter (enlarged thyroid)	Iodide goiter
Fluoride	1.5–4.0 mg[a]	Drinking water, tea, seafood	Maintenance of tooth (and maybe bone) structure	Higher frequency of tooth decay	Mottling of teeth; skeletal deformation
Zinc	15 mg	Meats, seafood, whole grains	Component of enzymes	Growth failure; reproductive failure; impaired immune function	Nausea; vomiting; diarrhea; adversely affects copper metabolism
Selenium	0.05–0.2 mg[a]	Seafood, meat, whole grains	Component of enzyme; functions in close association with vitamin E	Muscle pain; maybe heart muscle deterioration	In animals: liver damage; depressed growth
Copper	2–3 mg[a]	Seafood, nuts, legumes, organ meats	Component of enzymes	Anemia; bone changes	Liver and neurological damage
Cobalt	(Required as vitamin B-12)	Vitamin B-12 (animal products)	Component of vitamin B-12	Not reported except as vitamin B-12 def.	Diseases of red blood cells
Chromium	0.05–0.2 mg[a]	Brewers' yeast, liver, seafood, meat, some vegetables	Involved in glucose and energy metabolism	Impaired glucose metabolism	Lung, skin, and kidney damage (occupational exposures)
Manganese	2.5–5.0 mg[a]	Nuts, whole grains, vegetables and fruits	Component of enzymes	Abnormal bone and cartilage	Neuro-muscular effects
Molybdenum	0.15–0.5 mg[a]	Legumes, cereals, some vegetables	Component of enzymes	Disorder in nitrogen excretion	Inhibition of enzymes; adversely affects cobalt metabolism

logical problems; they may consume foods with poor mineral bioavailability; they may suffer from a variety of conditions that cause minerals to be used inefficiently; and they may use a variety of medications that interfere with mineral utilization. Similarly, a pregnant vegetarian woman has a high requirement for minerals, but may be consuming a diet with low levels of some minerals or with poor mineral bioavailability. Keep in mind that being "at risk" does not *guarantee* that a person will develop a deficiency, but that he or she is more *apt* to do so.

As with vitamin deficiencies, mild mineral deficiencies are likely to result in certain common consequences such as a decline in reproductive performance and compromised ability to deal with stresses such as injury or infection.

Excesses

The old saying, "If a little is good, more is better," is not true for any nutrients, including minerals—especially trace minerals. It is definitely possible to ingest too much; a respected trace minerals researcher states that ingesting unbalanced amounts of individual trace minerals "is not only unscientific but also potentially dangerous" (Mertz, 1984). Finding the range between too little and too much is the key to good mineral nutrition.

Interference with Other Minerals. We have already mentioned one way in which a mineral excess may be damaging: a large amount of one mineral in the diet, such as iron, can depress the absorption of another mineral, such as zinc. And if the person's intake of zinc is already low, the excess of iron will make zinc status even worse. Although the amount of iron may not be toxic per se, it can interfere with the status of the zinc.

Such imbalances rarely occur when people get their minerals in food, but they can occur fairly easily if people supplement their diets with individual minerals. Consumers should be very cautious about taking a mineral supplement to ensure their health; they may do more harm than good.

Toxicities. There are two general types of toxicities: acute and chronic. An *acute* toxicity occurs when a person consumes a single large dose of a mineral; the effects are rapid and severe. This may occur, for example, when picnickers store acidic lemonade in galvanized (zinc-coated) containers, or when a child consumes a bottle of his mother's iron supplements. Acute poisonings of this sort usually cause nausea, vomiting, and diarrhea; they can be fatal. About 12 children die annually in the United States due to acute iron poisoning (Committee on Medical and Biological Effects of Environmental Pollutants, 1979). Adults must remember that mineral supplements, like all other medications, should be kept out of the reach of small children.

Most cases of mineral toxicity occur more gradually and are due to *chronic* exposure to lower-level excesses of the mineral. Two examples—iodine and fluoride—have already been discussed.

Some minerals are well known for their toxicity; these include lead, cadmium, and mercury. Although many of the reported cases of such toxicities were due to industrial exposure, occasionally these minerals enter the food supply in sufficient quantities to be toxic. This topic will be discussed further in Chapter 15.

People vary in their sensitivity to excess amounts of minerals. For some rare individuals, even moderate intakes of certain minerals can be toxic; this is the result of genetic predisposition, and requires medical treatment. In general, children are more sensitive than adults to toxic doses of minerals.

There are risks associated with consuming either too little or too much of any single mineral. You can obtain the right balance of minerals by making varied selections from each of the four basic food groups of the SANE guide. The use of mineral supplements is not recommended for most people.

You Can Assess Your Mineral Status As You Did for Vitamins

Because we have discussed the difficulties in setting nutritional requirements and determining some mineral contents of foods, you might think there is no way to evaluate whether your intake is adequate or not. Actually, we do have enough information to estimate the mineral adequacy of diets with some accuracy.

General Check on Mineral Adequacy

A diet that follows the recommendations of the SANE guide is likely to contain at least one-half to two-thirds of the recommended levels of the essential minerals. The SANE guide is somewhat less useful for promoting adequate intakes of this nutrient group than others.

The greater the variety of foods you consume from the four basic food groups, the greater the likelihood that you will take in the 20 or more minerals you need. Further, foods that are less processed usually furnish more minerals than the more processed items.

More Specific Check on Mineral Adequacy

Just as for vitamins, you can determine the mineral status of your diet yourself by using food composition tables, at least for those minerals for which reliable data exist. Appendix E gives the values for calcium, phosphorus, iron, and potassium; Appendix K gives sodium values; and Appendix L gives values for zinc.

In summary, minerals are a diverse group of nutrients, of which more than 20 are essential for reproduction, growth, and maintenance of health. The field of mineral research, especially regarding trace minerals, is currently very active.

SUMMARY

■ Both vitamins and minerals are important micronutrients widespread in basic foods; the main difference between them is that vitamins are organic (carbon-containing) and minerals are inorganic, being simply individual chemical elements. Depending on the amounts present, essential minerals are categorized as either major or trace. Some minerals present in the body are needed for growth, reproduction, and maintenance of health, and are considered essential. Minerals are not present in proportion to their importance; trace and major mineral deficiencies both can be damaging to health.

■ Many factors can influence the bioavailability of minerals, making specific intake recommendations difficult to establish. For example, both vitamin C and unidentified meat factor can increase the absorption of nonheme iron in the diet; and vitamin D is needed for optimal absorption of calcium and phosphorus. On the other hand, dietary fiber, phytate, tannins, and oxalates can depress the absorption of minerals, and minerals can compete with each other for absorption. Medications and physiological factors can also affect mineral absorption and effects within the body. Supplementing a diet with individual minerals may create nutritional problems instead of solving them. Table 13.2 summarizes major dietary factors that affect mineral bioavailability.

■ Minerals have four general types of functions in the body: (1) they form part of tissue structure, (2) they help maintain water and acid–base balance, (3) they form components of enzymes and hormones, and (4) they facilitate the function of nerve and muscle cells. Tables 13.3–13.8 list food sources for essential minerals, and Table 13.9 summarizes key information about their RDAs, major functions, and signs of deficiency or excess.

■ Mineral deficiencies are most likely to arise when the following combination of circumstances exists: (1) the overall diet is limited in quantity, (2) the diet is poorly selected for mineral content, (3) mineral bioavailability is low, and (4) mineral requirements are unusually high due to rapid growth or disease. Although all of these factors are less likely to occur simultaneously in the developed countries than in less developed parts of the world, iron deficiency is fairly common almost everywhere.

■ It is definitely possible to consume mineral overdoses; overdoses can both interfere with the absorption of other minerals and cause either acute or chronic toxicity symptoms, depending on the type and duration of exposure. The minerals necessary to health can be obtained in almost all cases by simply eating a balanced and varied diet; mineral supplements are not necessary for most people.

REFERENCES

Allen, L.H. 1982. Calcium bioavailability and absorption: A review. *American Journal of Clinical Nutrition* 35:783–808.

Buskirk, E.R. 1981. Some nutritional considerations in the conditioning of athletes. *Annual Reviews of Nutrition* 1:319–350.

Cavalieri, R.R. 1980. Trace elements. In *Modern nutrition in health and disease*, ed. R.S. Goodhart and M.E. Shils. Philadelphia: Lea and Febiger.

Committee on Diet, Nutrition, and Cancer. 1982. *Diet, nutriton, and cancer*. Washington, DC: National Academy Press.

Committee on Medical and Biological Effects of Environmental Pollutants. 1979. *Iron*. Baltimore: University Park Press.

Costill, D.L. 1979. *A scientific approach to distance running*. Los Altos, CA: Tafnews Press.

Costill, D.L., and J.M. Miller. 1980. Nutrition for endurance sport: Carbohydrate and fluid balance. *International Journal of Sports Medicine* 1:2–14.

Council on Scientific Affairs. 1983. Sodium in processed foods. *Journal of the American Medical Association:* 249:784–789.

Dubick, M.A., and R.B. Rucker. 1983. Dietary supplements and health aids—a critical evaluation. *Journal of Nutrition Education* 15:47–53.

The editors of *Consumer Reports* Books. 1980. *Health quackery.* New York: Holt, Rinehart & Winston.

Greger, J.L. 1983. Nutrient interactions involving iron and zinc. *Food and Nutrition News* 55:13–16.

Greger, J.L., and M. Baier. 1981. Tin and iron content of canned and bottled foods. *Journal of Food Science* 46:1751–1754, 1765.

Greger, J.L., and M. Krystofiak. 1982. Phosphorus intake of Americans. *Food Technology* 36:78–80, 82, 84.

Harland, B.F., R.D. Johnson, E.M. Blindermann, et al. 1980. Calcium, phosphorus, iron, iodine and zinc in the "Total Diet." *Journal of the American Dietetic Association* 77:16–20.

Heaney, R.P., J.C. Gallagher, C.C. Johnson et al. 1982. Calcium nutrition and bone health in the elderly. *American Journal of Clinical Nutrition* 36:986–1013.

Hurley, L.S., and B. Lonnerdal. 1982. Zinc binding in human milk; citrate vs. picolinate. *Nutrition Reviews* 40:65–71.

Institute of Food Technologists' Expert Panel on Food Safety and Nutrition. 1980. Dietary salt. *Food Technology* 34:85–91.

Keshan Disease Research Group of the Chinese Academy of Medical Science, Beijing; Antiepidemic Station of Sichuan Province, Chengdu; Antiepidemic Station of Xichang District of Sichuan; and Antiepidemic Station of Mianning County, Sichuan. 1979. Observations on effect of sodium selenite in prevention of Keshan disease. *Chinese Medical Journal* 92:471–476.

Lackey, C. 1983. Pica during pregnancy. *Contemporary Nutrition* 8(no. 11).

Leverett, D.H. 1982. Fluorides and the changing prevalence of dental caries. *Science* 217:26–30.

Li, T.K., and B.L. Vallee. 1980. The biochemical and nutritional roles of other trace elements. In *Modern nutrition in health and disease*, ed. R.S. Goodhart and M.E. Shils. Philadelphia: Lea and Febiger.

McCarron, D.A., C.D. Morris, H.J. Henry, and J.L. Stanton. 1984. Blood pressure and nutrient intake in the United States. *Science* 224:1392–1398.

Mertz, W. 1981. The essential trace elements. *Science* 213:1332–1338.

Mertz, W. 1984. Foods and nutrients. *Journal of the American Dietetic Association* 84:769–770.

Monsen, E.R., L. Hallberg, M. Layrisse, et al. 1978. Estimation of available dietary iron. *American Journal of Clinical Nutrition* 31:134–141.

Montoye, H.J. 1984. Exercise and osteoporosis. In *Proceedings of the American Academy of Physical Education.* Champaign-Urbana: Human Kinetics Publications, Inc.

Morck, T.A., S.R. Lynch, and J.D. Cook. 1983. Inhibition of food iron absorption by coffee. *American Journal of Clinical Nutrition* 37:416–420.

Murphy, E.W., B.W. Willis, and B.K. Watt. 1975. Provisional tables on the zinc content of foods. *Journal of the American Dietetic Association* 66:345–355.

National Center for Health Statistics. 1974. *Preliminary findings of the first health and nutrition examination survey*, U.S. Department of Health, Education, and Welfare (DHEW) Publication (HRS) 74-1219-1, 1971-2. Washington, DC: DHEW.

National Dairy Council. 1983. Diet, nutrition, and cancer. *Dairy Council Digest* 54(no.6):31–36.

National Research Council, National Academy of Sciences (NAS). 1980. *Recommended dietary allowances*, 9th edition. Washington, DC: NAS.

Nourse, A.E. 1971. *The body.* New York: Time-Life Books.

Pate, R.R. 1982. Sports anemia and its impact on athletic performance. In *Nutrition and athletic performance*, ed. W. Haskell, J. Scala, and J. Whittam. Palo Alto: Bull Publishing Company.

Pennington, J.A.T., and H.N. Church. 1980. *Food values of portions commonly used.* Philadelphia: J.B. Lippincott Company.

Pennington, J.A.T., D.B. Wilson, R.F. Newell, B.F. Harland, R.D. Johnson, and J.E. Vanderveen. 1984. Selected minerals in foods surveys, 1974 to 1981/82. *Journal of the American Dietetic Association* 84:771–780.

Prasad, A.S. 1979. *Zinc in human nutrition.* Boca Raton, FL: CRC Press, Inc.

Reinhold, J.G., A. Parsa, N. Karimian, J.W. Hammick, and F. Ismail-Beigi. 1974. Availability of zinc in leavened and unleavened wholemeal wheaten breads as measured by solubility and uptake by rat intestine in vitro. *Journal of Nutrition* 104:976–982.

Roe, D.A. 1976. *Drug-induced nutritional deficiencies.* Westport, CT: AVI Publishing Co., Inc.

Saarinen, U.M., and M.A. Siimes. 1979. Iron absorption from breast milk, cow's milk, and iron-supplemented formula: An opportunistic use of changes in total body iron determined by hemoglobin, ferritin, and body weight in 132 infants. *Pediatric Research* 13:143–147.

Safe Drinking Water Committee. 1980. *Drinking water and health,* Vol. 3. Washington, DC: National Academy of Sciences.

Sandstead, H.H. 1980. Clinical manifestations of certain classical deficiency diseases. In *Modern nutrition in health and disease,* ed. R.S. Goodhart and M.E. Shils. Philadelphia: Lea and Febiger.

Sandstead, H.H. 1982. Copper bioavailability and requirements. *American Journal of Clinical Nutrition* 35:809–814.

Schaffner, R.M. 1981. Lead in canned foods. *Food Technology* 35:60–64.

Science and Education Administration. 1980a. *Food and nutrient intakes of individuals in 1 day in the United States, Spring 1977.* Nationwide food consumption survey 1977–78; preliminary report no. 2. Washington, DC: U.S. Department of Agriculture.

Science and Education Administration. 1980b. *The sodium content of your food.* Home and garden bulletin no. 233. Washington, DC: U.S. Department of Agriculture.

Science and Education Administration. 1981. *Nutritive value of foods.* Home and garden bulletin number 72. Washington, DC: U.S. Department of Agriculture.

Scrimshaw, N.S., and V.R. Young. 1976. The requirements of human nutrition. *Scientific American* 235:50–64.

Shils, M.E. 1980. Magnesium. In *Modern nutrition in health and disease,* ed. R.S. Goodhart and M.E. Shils. Philadelphia: Lea and Febiger.

Solomons, N.W. 1982. Biological availability of zinc in human nutrition. *American Journal of Clinical Nutrition* 35:1048–1075.

Tobian, L.J. 1979. The relationship of salt to hypertension. *American Journal of Clinical Nutrition* 32:2739–2748.

Underwood, E.J. 1977. *Trace elements in human and animal nutrition.* New York: Academic Press.

United States Department of Agriculture (USDA). 1976. *Nutritive content of foods: Dairy and egg products.* Agricultural handbook no. 8-1. Washington, DC: USDA.

United States Department of Agriculture (USDA). 1979. *Nutritive content of foods: Fats and oils.* Agricultural handbook no. 8-4. Washington, DC: USDA.

United States Department of Agriculture (USDA). 1979. *Nutritive content of foods: Poultry products.* Agricultural handbook no. 8-5. Washington, DC: USDA.

United States Department of Agriculture (USDA). 1980. *Nutritive content of foods: Sausages and luncheon meats.* Agricultural handbook no. 8-7. Washington, DC: USDA.

United States Department of Agriculture (USDA). 1982. *Nutritive content of foods: Breakfast foods.* Agricultural handbook no. 8-8. Washington, DC: USDA.

United States Department of Agriculture (USDA). 1982. *Nutritive content of foods: Fruits and fruit juices.* Agricultural handbook no. 8-9. Washington, DC: USDA.

White, P.L., and S.C. Crocco. 1981. Hypertension: A sodium related problem. *Cereal Foods World* 26:61–63.

Willett, W.C., and B. MacMahon. 1984. Diet and cancer—an overview. *New England Journal of Medicine* 310:697–701.

PART FIVE

A TASTE OF FOOD SCIENCE

14

Effects of Food Processing on Micronutrients

IN THIS CHAPTER: Food Production and Processing Have a Language of Their Own ▪ Factors in Food Production Influence the Micronutrient Content of Foods ▪ Food Handling Affects Nutrients in Several General Ways ▪ Fresh Storage Results in Losses that Can Be Controlled ▪ Nutrient Losses from Processing Can Be Minimized by Consumer Handling and Selection ▪ Various Food Preservation Methods Result in Different Levels of Micronutrient Losses ▪ Cooking Losses Can Be High, But Vary with the Method Selected ▪ Assess Your Intake for Nutrient Retentiveness

You may have the impression from previous chapters that vitamin and mineral values of foods are fixed at the levels shown in food composition tables, and that you get exactly those amounts of micronutrients when you eat the foods. That's not necessarily true.

Many factors can cause changes in the nutritional value of a food. Take as an example the vegetable you had as part of your dinner last night. Let's say it was green beans. The variety of those green beans (Kentucky Wonder? Blue Lake?); the conditions under which they were grown and harvested (what kind of soil? picked ripe?); and the way they were stored, processed, and cooked are some of the factors that could have influenced their nutritional value at the dinner table.

This chapter deals with some of the changes that occur in vitamin and mineral content during the production, storage, and processing of foods. These changes can make a significant difference—positive as well as negative—in the nutrient content of our diets, because so much of the food we eat has been processed in some way.

Estimates of the proportion of the United States food supply that has been processed before purchase range from 44% (Traub and Odland, 1978) to 55% (Clydesdale, 1982). Processing continues after we bring food home: the various changes we make in food before we eat it—such as peeling it, cutting it up, cooking it, perhaps freezing it, and then heating it again before serving—all cause nutritional changes.

The information presented here about nutrient changes in food holds true whether the production and processing were done commercially or at home. Although some consumers believe that the food industry is uniquely responsible for nutrient losses, such destruction occurs universally no matter who carries out the process. In fact, commercial processors have developed techniques for maintaining both aesthetic and nutritional quality that are unavailable to the typical householder, so it is possible that commercially processed foods may have higher nutrient values than similar foods less carefully processed at home.

Another important concept is that even though processing often decreases the vitamin and/or mineral content of foods, it is not our intent to dissuade you from using processed foods. They are here to stay, and we are the benefactors. Processing and preservation technologies give us greater food safety and availability all year round, which is a nutritional advantage. We can minimize the losses by choosing those foods that have been handled in the most nutrient-conservative ways.

Furthermore, processing can actually improve the nutrient content of foods when commercial processors add certain nutrients to their products. A serious public health problem—called *goiter*—was virtually eliminated in the United States several decades ago, when iodine began to be added to salt. Therefore, the nutritional benefits of food processing should also be recognized.

Food Production and Processing Have a Language of Their Own

Some terms with which you may already be familiar mean quite different things to the general public than they do to people familiar with food laws.

"Health Food" and "Natural Food"

The terms health food and natural food have not been legally defined, even though many people assume that foods so labeled contain "fewer chemicals" and are somehow better than other foods (Figure 14.1). These terms, in truth, guarantee nothing about the nature of the products they are applied to. An investigation of health food stores by the New York City Department of Consumer Affairs showed that "health foods do not differ significantly from conventional foods in terms of nutritional value, pesticide residue, appearance, and taste. The major difference the Department found between health foods and conventional foods is the much higher cost of the former" (Gourdine, et al., 1983).

health food, natural food— these terms have no legal definition, and guarantee nothing about the products to which they are applied

"Organic Food"

The term organic farming has been defined by the United States Department of Agriculture as "the production of food which avoids or largely excludes the use of synthetically compounded fertilizers, pesticides, growth regulators, and livestock feed additives" (Price and Brown, 1981).

However, attempts to pass federal legislation detailing standards for "organic foods" have not been successful. Therefore the term "organic" on a label does not have a specific meaning, except in a few states that have their own legal definitions. There are also private, voluntary organic farming organizations that encourage their members to adhere to certain standards, but such arrangements are not legally binding.

organic food—product that may or may not have been grown by organic farming methods; the term has no legal definition except in a few states

Figure 14.1 Terms that have no legal definition. Although many people like what the words "natural," "health," and "organic" imply, these adjectives have no federal legal definitions. Therefore, they can be used without challenge by food processors—and they guarantee nothing.

Figure 14.2 Imitation foods.
Foods that simulate another food but have less of an essential nutrient, or contain a substitute ingredient, need to be labeled "imitation."

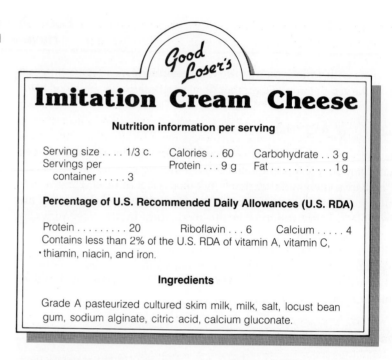

> *Good Loser's*
>
> # Imitation Cream Cheese
>
> ### Nutrition information per serving
>
> Serving size . . . . 1/3 c.   Calories . . 60   Carbohydrate . . 3 g
> Servings per   Protein . . . 9 g   Fat . . . . 1 g
>   container 3
>
> ### Percentage of U.S. Recommended Daily Allowances (U.S. RDA)
>
> Protein 20   Riboflavin . . . 6   Calcium 4
> Contains less than 2% of the U.S. RDA of vitamin A, vitamin C, thiamin, niacin, and iron.
>
> ### Ingredients
>
> Grade A pasteurized cultured skim milk, milk, salt, locust bean gum, sodium alginate, citric acid, calcium gluconate.

Nonetheless, food producers know that there are some people for whom the terms "health food," "natural food," and "organic food" have very positive connotations, so you will often see products labeled in this way.

Imitation Food

imitation food—product that has less of an essential nutrient than the food it imitates, or that contains substitute ingredients

Imitation food, on the other hand, is legally defined. When a food has less of an essential nutrient than the food it resembles in taste and appearance, it must carry the term "imitation" on the label. A food product must also be labeled "imitation" if it includes some substitute ingredients (such as vegetable oil in "filled" milk).

An imitation food, although it is lower in some nutrients than the reference food, can still have considerable nutritional value. There may be little detectable difference in sensory properties, and the food may be available at lower cost. For these reasons, imitation cheese is often used on frozen pizzas, for example. There are even some cases in which you may value the fact that the imitation food is lower in some nutrients, such as the lower amount of fat in imitation cream cheese (Figure 14.2).

Engineered, Fabricated, or Formulated Food

engineered, fabricated, or **formulated food**—food industry terms for extensively processed foods made from highly refined ingredients

Engineered, fabricated, or formulated food, although not legal terms used in labeling, are food industry terms for extensively processed foods made from highly refined ingredients. For example, fruit drink crystals are made from sweeteners, flavorings, colorings, and sometimes added nutrients.

Other fabricated foods are cakes, cookies, or beverage powders that are marketed as complete meals for weight reduction purposes; there are many others.

Such foods are no better nutritionally than the ingredients from which they were made. This is an important concept, because the levels of many trace minerals are low in highly refined ingredients, and are therefore also low in fabricated food products. Such products are often low in fiber as well. People who make use of these foods should be aware of their shortcomings and may want to compensate for them elsewhere in their diets.

Food industry futurists maintain that engineered foods that satisfy all known human needs can be produced. Read the opinion of Merritt L. Kastens, a management consultant and food industry publication editor, in the following Slice of Life.

SLICE OF LIFE:
The Food of the Future?

. . .there is an unusual change in life style which is radically altering what, where, and when people eat. . . . They would like to have a proper diet, but it is too much trouble keeping track of the four food groups and counting calories. It is just too complicated. . . .

What is needed is assured nutrition that is easy to understand, easy to obtain, and that is adaptable to current life styles and tastes good. The practical alternative to fighting the lost cause of "eat your spinach, darling, it's good for you," is to make what you *want* to eat "good for you." It is certainly possible to make some highly palatable food products that are completely balanced with good nutrition. The food industry has been doing it with dog food for years. Recently, things have progressed to the point where the industry offers alternative nutritional balances for dogs of different ages, and states of health. There is no reason that similar approaches can't be used for human food.

How do you feel about this idea? Your attitude is important, because the food industry is likely to pursue this course only if the general public seems receptive to it.

Factors in Food Production Influence the Micronutrient Content of Foods

Although it is not the aim of this chapter to deal extensively with food production, it is worth noting that such factors as the plant variety, season of production, climatic conditions, and maturity at harvest can have a great impact on the micronutrient content of foods (Institute of Food Technologists, 1974). For example, tomatoes that are vine-ripened out-of-doors in summer sunlight have twice as much vitamin C as tomatoes grown in greenhouses in winter (Agricultural Research Service, 1977). Plants that are harvested before they are ripe, or after they are past their prime, often do not have as high a vitamin value as their just-mature counterparts. Analysis of food samples has shown that the amount of carotene in different carrots can vary by as much as 12-fold, and the vitamin C in tomatoes can vary by as much as 5-fold (Bender, 1978). The content of certain minerals in produce can vary considerably with the mineral content of the soil, as discussed in Chapter 13.

Food Handling Affects Nutrients in Several General Ways

The goals of food handling in the time between production and consumption are to keep food safe to eat, to maintain (or sometimes improve) its nutritional quality as much as possible, and/or to improve convenience. In the course of trying to accomplish these goals, nutrient changes may occur.

A huge body of scientific literature has been generated about the effects of processing on nutrients, from which we can make certain generalizations:

- Increases in micronutrients occur primarily when nutrients are deliberately added to foods (although other processing techniques such as sprouting and fermentation also increase certain nutrients).

- Vitamin losses may occur due to changes in pH (acidity or alkalinity); chemical degradation reactions resulting from exposure to such factors as oxygen, light, or heat; the passage of time; and/or physical separation. Destruction occurs if one or more of these factors cause a change in the vitamin structure that makes it impossible for the resulting chemical compound to perform the vitamin's functions. Not all vitamins are equally vulnerable to these factors. For example, vitamin C is very vulnerable to destruction by oxygen, but several of the B vitamins are relatively stable in the presence of oxygen.

- The two least stable vitamins are probably vitamin C and thiamin. Because vitamin C is sensitive to so many different conditions, it is often monitored in studies designed to assess vitamin destruction from food processing.

- Minerals tend to be relatively stable in the face of pH changes, oxidation, light, heat, and time; they are more likely to be lost from foods by physical separation. Examples of physical separation are removing portions of the edible product, as occurs in milling grain and peeling fruits; and leaching, which is the dissolving of minerals into fluid that may later be discarded. In general, mineral losses tend to be lower than vitamin losses, largely because there are fewer ways in which minerals can be lost.

leaching—dissolving of nutrients into a surrounding fluid

■ Nutrient losses are cumulative. The more processes used on a food, the greater the potential for nutrient destruction.

We should mention that some nutrients have been studied less thoroughly than others. In part, this is because scientists are less concerned about nutrients of which there are no apparent shortages in typical diets and because of analytical problems. Therefore, when you read that vitamin "X" is affected by a particular process, it does not necessarily mean that all others are unaffected. It may mean that others were not included in the study.

Fresh Storage Results in Losses that Can Be Controlled

When fresh fruits and vegetables are not consumed immediately after harvesting, progressive vitamin degradation will occur as time passes. The fat-soluble vitamins and vitamin C are particularly vulnerable in typical oxygen-containing environments (Institute of Food Technologists, 1974).

Storage temperature makes a difference in the rate of vitamin loss: the higher the temperature, the greater the losses will be. At room temperature for one day, losses of vitamin C in various vegetables are usually from 30 to 40%; at temperatures near freezing, losses are typically less than 10% in the same time. Similarly, the faster a product loses moisture during storage, the greater the vitamin losses will be (Fennema, 1977). In general, the vitamins in vegetables are more subject to degradation during fresh storage than the vitamins in fruits and meats (Fennema, 1977).

Riboflavin loss from milk in the grocery store. Milk is an excellent source of riboflavin, which is vulnerable to light. The current practice of packaging milk in waxed cardboard cartons or plastic jugs limits the amount of light that reaches the milk, and therefore minimizes riboflavin loss.

When you become aware of the opportunities for vitamin loss in fresh vegetables, the optimal situation becomes apparent: you retain vitamin values best by putting vegetables into an airtight package and chilling them immediately after harvest. The conscientious home gardener can accomplish this. So can most commercial processors, who have developed their techniques for harvesting and holding fresh vegetables (just hours before canning or freezing them) with these principles in mind. Unprocessed vegetables bought at the grocery store may have lower vitamin values, especially if they were picked before their prime and stored for days under less-than-optimal conditions.

Fluid milk can lose riboflavin, which is vulnerable to light, if it is improperly stored. In the days when milk was delivered to the doorstep in clear glass bottles, as much as 50% of its riboflavin was destroyed in two hours of exposure to sunlight. Current methods of packaging fluid milk in waxed cardboard or plastic containers are much more conservative of riboflavin. Under supermarket conditions, no more than 7% of the riboflavin is lost from milk in plastic containers, and less than 4% is lost from milk in paper containers in 24 hours (Bender, 1978).

Nutrient Losses from Processing
Can Be Minimized by Consumer Handling and Selection

Various processing techniques that promote or retard nutrient losses might be done either commercially or at home.

Trimming

Removing edible parts of plant foods results in nutrient losses. This occurs partly because some of the food is thrown away and partly because the rest is exposed to oxygen. Sometimes it is also the case that the vitamin values of the discarded parts are higher (per weight unit) than those of the parts kept to eat. For example, the vitamin C in potatoes is present in highest concentrations in the layer just beneath the skin; vitamin C losses from peeled potatoes may therefore range from 12 to 35% (LaChance, 1975).

Tests on cabbage have shown that the outer, darker green leaves have more carotene, vitamin K, and vitamin C than the inner leaves have (Bender, 1978), and that the outer layers of spinach and lettuce contain more of vitamins B and C than the inner ones do (Muller and Tobin, 1980). The leaves of spinach may contain 20 times as much vitamin C as the stems, and iron is two to four times more concentrated in the leaves. Broccoli buds have more vitamin C than the stalks (LaChance, 1975).

To avoid these losses, the message is clear: eat the edible skins and peels of fruits and vegetables; try to salvage the darker, outer leaves of vegetables; and be sure to eat the other parts you know to be of high nutrient density.

Dividing

Any vitamins that are vulnerable to oxygen will be partially destroyed when food is cut or chopped. Dividing food into smaller pieces produces a larger total surface area; consequently, more oxygen exposure and vitamin destruction occur. Cantaloupe cut into slices and refrigerated for 24 hours lost 35% of its vitamin C. Tomato pulp lost 40% of its vitamin C in a day (LaChance, 1975).

On the other hand, oxygen exposure does not always result in such rapid vitamin destruction. Orange juice can be kept in the refrigerator for several days before significant vitamin C is lost (Agricultural Research Service, 1977) because the acidity of the juice helps protect the vitamin. This holds true for any form of orange juice, whether it is freshly squeezed, canned, or reconstituted from frozen concentrate.

Soaking

Soaking brings about micronutrient losses because water-soluble vitamins and minerals leach into the water. When peeled potatoes were soaked for approximately a day at room temperature, the amount of many water-soluble vitamins decreased by approximately 10%. Refrigeration can make a difference: very little vitamin C was lost when peeled potatoes were stored in water and refrigerated for almost a day (LaChance, 1975).

Milling and Refining of Flour

Grains in their whole form have three major portions. The tough, darker, outer layers are the bran layers; the region toward one end of the kernel from which sprouting occurs is the germ; and the lighter, larger, inner starchy portion is the endosperm. Figure 14.3 shows these areas in a kernel of wheat.

Milling is the grinding of grain into flour. The bran layers and the germ do not break down as readily as the endosperm does, which makes them relatively easy to separate from the powdered endosperm early in the milling process. Such separation is called refinement.

Different types of flour are produced by controlling the relative proportions of powdered endosperm, ground bran layers, and germ. Whole wheat flour contains all parts of the grain; refined white flours have had some or all of the bran and germ sifted out. This has nutritional significance since the germ and bran layers contain most of the vitamins, minerals, and fiber that are in the grain, whereas the endosperm is largely starch.

Figure 14.4 shows the percentages of micronutrients found in white flour compared with whole wheat flour. You can see from this illustration why the SANE guide promotes the idea that at least two of the grain product servings consumed per day should be whole grain products. Commonly available whole grain products are whole wheat or graham flour, brown rice, dark rye flour, and rolled oats.

bran—tough, darker, outer layers of grain kernels in their whole form

germ—region toward one end of the grain kernel, from which sprouting occurs

endosperm—lighter, larger, inner starchy portion of the grain kernel

milling—the grinding of grain into flour

refinement—separation of the bran and germ from the endosperm early in the milling process

Figure 14.3 A kernel of wheat.
The three parts of a wheat kernel have different nutritional characteristics. The endosperm contains most of the starch and protein; the bran and germ contain most of the fiber and micronutrients.

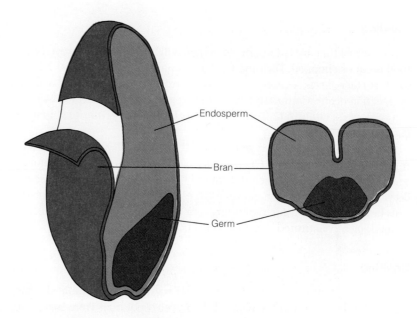

Fortification

fortification—any addition of nutrients to foods in the course of processing

Fortification, as the United States government now uses the term, refers to any addition of nutrients to foods (Quick and Murphy, 1982). [Many people continue to define this term by its earlier meaning, which is the addition of unusually large levels of nutrients to foods (Leveille, 1984). In this section, we are assuming the newer government definition.]

In the United States, fortification has made a substantial contribution to the total nutrient intake of the population: in 1970, it accounted for 40% of the thiamin, 25% of the iron, 20% of the niacin, and 15% of the riboflavin consumed (Quick and Murphy, 1982). Other nutrients were contributed at lower levels.

Nutrients cannot be added to foods in unlimited amounts. Food and Drug Administration (FDA) regulations restrict the amount of any nutrient that can occur in a single serving of any fortified food to 150% of the U.S. RDA. If more than that amount is contained in a food after nutrients are added, the item ceases to be regarded as a food and is classified as a drug.

Two types of fortification, enrichment and restoration, have more specific meanings and applications.

enrichment—the addition of nutrients *already present* in a food, raised to levels that meet a specific FDA standard

Enrichment. Enrichment is the addition of nutrients *already present* in a food, raised to levels that meet a specific FDA product Standard of Identity (Quick and Murphy, 1982). In the United States, refined grain products such as wheat flours, bread, rolls and buns, farina, cornmeal, corn grits, macaroni and noodle products, and rice are commonly enriched. The FDA standards call for thiamin, riboflavin, niacin, and iron to be added to specific levels in these products.

Figure 14.4 compares enriched wheat flour with refined and whole wheat flours. It shows that enriched products are clearly second best to whole grains, because only thiamin, riboflavin, niacin, and iron are added.

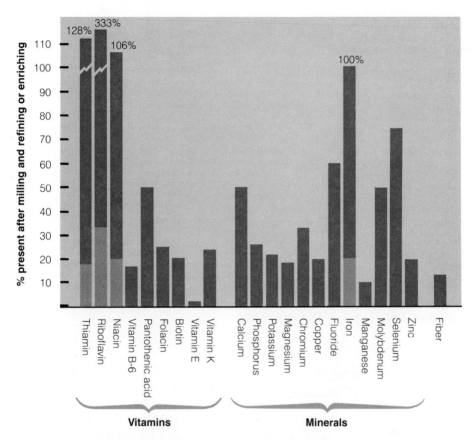

Figure 14.4 Proportions of some nutrients present in wheat flour after refinement and enrichment. On this graph, 100% represents the nutrients found in whole wheat. The most commonly used refined flour (darker bars) contains less than half the amount of many nutrients present in whole wheat. Enriched flour (lighter extension of bars) has had only four nutrients added: thiamin, riboflavin, niacin, and iron. (Data from Davis, D. R. 1981. Wheat and nutrition. *Nutrition Today* 16:16–21.)

However, enriched products are a nutritional improvement over refined products, which have less than half the level of most nutrients that are present in whole wheat.

Restoration. Restoration is the adding back to preprocessing levels of nutrients that were lost during processing. For example, vitamin A is often restored to dried skim milk (Quick and Murphy, 1982).

restoration—the addition back to preprocessing levels of nutrients that were lost from a food during processing

Refining of Sugars

Most sugars are produced from the juices of certain plants, such as sugar cane, sugar beets, and the maple tree. Sugars are also produced commercially when cornstarch is converted into corn syrup. Honey is the only notable concentrated sugar source of animal origin.

Table 14.1   Nutritional Content of One Tablespoon of Various Concentrated Sweets

Food (1 T.)	Nutrients	% of the U.S. RDA			
		0	25	75	100
White sugar	Calcium				
	Iron				
	Thiamin				
	Riboflavin				
	Niacin				
Dark brown sugar	Calcium	▪			
	Iron	▪			
	Thiamin				
	Riboflavin				
	Niacin				
Light molasses	Calcium	▬			
	Iron	▬▬			
	Thiamin	▪			
	Riboflavin	▪			
	Niacin				
Blackstrap molasses	Calcium	▬▬▬▬▬			
	Iron	▬▬▬▬▬▬			
	Thiamin	▪			
	Riboflavin	▪			
	Niacin	▪			
Honey	Calcium	▪			
	Iron				
	Thiamin				
	Riboflavin	▪			
	Niacin	▪			
Maple syrup	Calcium	▬			
	Iron	▪			
	Thiamin				
	Riboflavin				
	Niacin				

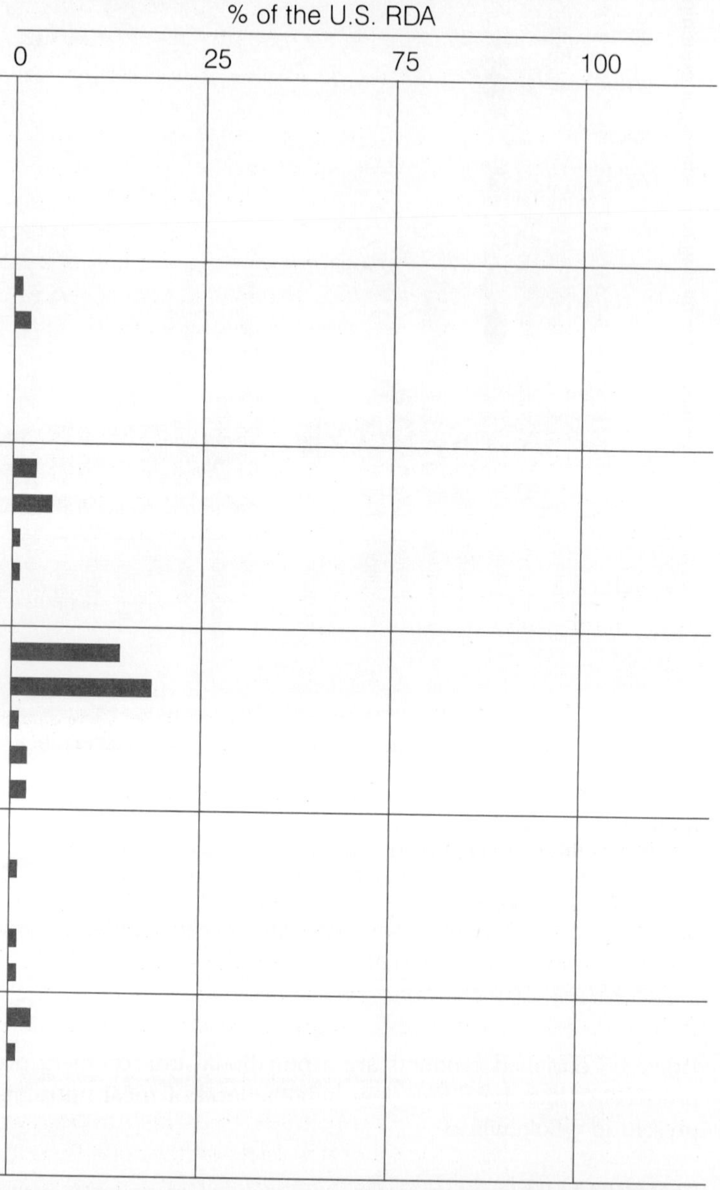

Of the foods commonly used as sweeteners, only blackstrap molasses appears to contribute an appreciable amount of any of the nutrients shown above; however, since the bioavailability of its calcium and iron is not known, its nutritional usefulness is uncertain. None of the sweeteners are significant sources of protein, vitamin A, or vitamin C—but they all contain from 42 to 65 kcalories per tablespoon.

Data sources: (1) Pennington, J.A.T., and H.N. Church. 1980. *Food values of portions commonly used*. Philadelphia: J.B. Lippincott Company. (2) Science and Education Administration. 1981. *Nutritive value of foods*. Home and Garden Bulletin No. 72. Washington, DC: United States Department of Agriculture.

Refining (in the case of sugars) consists of squeezing the juices from the plants, removing impurities, and evaporating most or all of the water. In this process, the low levels of other nutrients that were present in the plant juices are often lost, leaving the final product nutritionally significant only for its energy value. Sugars provide a lot of kcalories and not much else.

Some people believe that the "less refined" or "more natural" sources of sugars are substantially more nutritious. Table 14.1 compares some key nutrients in white sugar, brown sugar, honey, maple syrup, and molasses with the U.S. RDA for those nutrients. Although this illustration shows that there are minor differences in the nutritional values of various sweeteners, it more emphatically points out that none is a particularly good source of nutrients in comparison with the day's needs.

Sprouting

Sprouting occurs when seeds of peas or beans are kept moist so that they begin to grow. Some vitamin C is produced (Bender, 1978), but not in very large amounts. Raw mung bean sprouts, for example, have approximately 12 mg of vitamin C per cup—not exactly a potent source, considering the U.S. RDA of 60 mg (Pennington and Church, 1980).

Table 14.2 summarizes how to purchase, store, and prepare foods to keep vitamin losses to a minimum.

sprouting—process that occurs when seeds of peas or beans are kept moist so that they begin to grow

Various Food Preservation Methods Result in Different Levels of Micronutrient Losses

Food preservation techniques also produce micronutrient changes.

Drying and Dehydration

The removal of moisture from food, called drying or dehydration, is the oldest method of food preservation known. Thousands of years ago, it involved drying foods in the sun for several days. Now, although sun-drying is still practiced both at home and by the food industry, most commercial techniques rely on faster means of moisture removal such as oven drying, freeze-drying, or spray-drying.

Vitamins A (as carotene), C, and thiamin have been found to be affected by drying methods. The extent to which they are destroyed depends on the amount of time the process is used and the conditions involved, so there is great variation in losses when considering all types of drying practices. The ranges of reported losses have been 10–50% for vitamin C (Bluestein and Labuza, 1975); 5–70% for thiamin; and 5–40% for carotene (Muller and Tobin, 1980). These figures may also include losses from pretreatments such as blanching (described on p. 381). The greatest losses occur with sun-drying, and the least with freeze-drying.

Storage of dried items also influences vitamin value. Nutrient retention is better when exposure to oxygen and moisture are minimized, and products are held at temperatures close to freezing (Kramer, 1974).

drying, dehydration—removal of moisture from food (can be accomplished by several techniques)

Table 14.2 Ways to Get and Maintain Better Micronutrient Levels in Foods

Foods	When Purchasing	During storage	During preparation
In general	Very fresh products have highest micronutrient values, followed by frozen, rapidly dehydrated, canned, and slowly dehydrated foods.	Whether fresh or preserved, vitamin content is higher if food is used sooner and stored cooler Frozen foods retain vitamins best at 0°F and below	If cutting up, delay until necessary. If cooking, heat only long enough to be "done" If cooking in water, use minimal amount
Fruits and vegetables		Wrap tightly to exclude air if item doesn't have protective peeling Keep whole Keep cold	Use edible parts known to have high micronutrient content If cooking, cook for shortest possible time in least possible water
Grain products	Whole grains have higher micronutrient levels than refined products Enriched products are better than refined Fortified cereals have variable micronutrient contents		Cook cereals and rice in just enough water to be absorbed
Dairy products	Plastic and cardboard containers conserve nutrients better than clear glass ones do Restored dried skim milk has more vitamin A than the unrestored version	Keep cold Keep covered Keep away from strong light	
Meats	Fresh meats have a higher vitamin content than smoked ones Expense does not correspond to nutrient value	Keep cold	Use meat drippings (not the melted fat)

Canning

canning—process in which a food and its rigid container are heated sufficiently to kill harmful microorganisms

Canning is making foods "commercially sterile" by heating both the food and its rigid container sufficiently to kill harmful organisms that might otherwise have grown during storage.

Figure 14.5 compares losses of some vitamins in canned fruits to losses incurred from freezing and drying. (The foods analyzed were typical grocery store samples.) Overall, vitamin losses from canning are higher than those from the other processes. Only about half the amounts of these vitamins found in fresh fruits or fresh-cooked vegetables remain in the canned products.

The water-soluble vitamins in a canned product usually become distributed between the food and the fluid in which it is packed. If the fluid

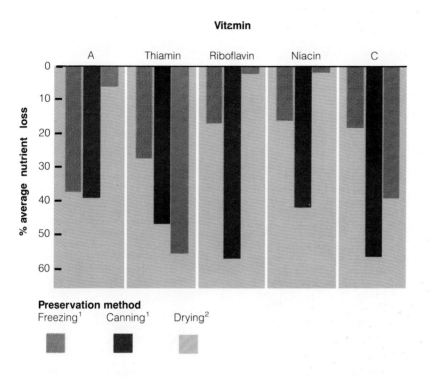

Figure 14.5 Vitamin losses in fruits during freezing, canning, and drying. [1]Fruits analyzed were apples, apricots, blueberries, pie cherries, orange juice, peaches, raspberries, and strawberries. [2]Fruits analyzed were apples, apricots, orange juice, and peaches. (Adapted from Roberts, T. 1983. Food preservation and nutrition. *National Food Review* 20:2–6.)

is discarded, up to 30–40% of the water-soluble vitamins may be lost (Hagen and Schweigert, 1983).

Vitamin retention in stored canned goods is also an issue. If stored for a year, vitamins in canned goods will be better preserved at temperatures in the range of 50–65°F. Lower temperatures are recommended for longer storage (Kramer, 1974).

Blanching

Blanching involves heating foods for just long enough (usually a few minutes) to destroy many of the enzymes that affect color, flavor, texture, and nutritive value. This process is used prior to freezing of vegetables and sometimes before canning, dehydration, or irradiation. (If freezing were done without blanching, nutrient losses would be even greater, and aesthetic quality would be poor.)

The extent of nutrient loss varies with the blanching method used and the nature of the product (Lund, 1975). When vegetables are blanched in boiling water, 10–35% of the vitamins are lost; when they are steamed, only up to 10% are sacrificed. Microwave blanching may result in the lowest losses of all (Bender, 1978).

blanching—heating a food for just long enough to destroy many of the enzymes that affect its palatability and nutritive value

Freezing

Freezing involves lowering the temperature of foods so far that enzymes and microorganisms are made virtually inactive. However, they can become more active again when the temperature rises. Nutritional value, sensory

freezing—lowering the temperature of a food so far that enzymes and microorganisms are virtually inactivated

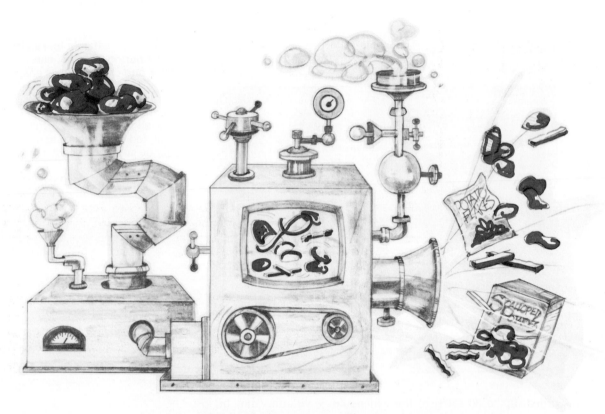

Food processing can turn a simple food item—such as pota-toes—into a large number of food products.

characteristics, and safety of frozen foods all deteriorate rapidly after thawing; thawed food should be used immediately.

Freezing itself is a very nutrient-conservative process, although there is some destruction of vitamins E and C. Figure 14.5 shows that frozen fruits from the typical marketbasket have usually lost less than 30% of their vitamins, compared with their fresh forms. Nutrient retention is better in fruits than in vegetables. In frozen vegetables, more of this vita-min destruction results from the blanching that precedes freezing than from the freezing itself. Despite such losses, frozen fruits and vegetables can have higher nutrient levels than poorly handled grocery store "fresh" foods.

Several studies have demonstrated the effects of freezing temperature and length of storage on various frozen products. For best vitamin reten-tion, frozen foods should be maintained at 0°F or less. If temperatures are higher by 20°, losses of vitamin C may be ten times as great or more (Fennema, 1977). In one study that assessed vitamin content after 6–12 months of storage at 0°F, average losses for vegetables were about 50% (Fennema, 1977). For fruits, losses were not over 30%, and for concentrated juices, less than 5%.

Vitamin E content has not been assessed in most of these studies on the effects of freezing. However, other studies have determined that vita-min E losses from french-fried frozen items amounted to approximately 65% in two to three months (Bunnell et al., 1965).

Fermentation and Pickling

Fermentation involves allowing microorganisms to partially metabolize components of a food; the resulting metabolites that accumulate in the food discourage the growth of undesirable microorganisms.

Fermented dairy products such as buttermilk and yogurt have approximately the same vitamin and mineral values as the products from which they originated. Foods that are fermented in a salt solution (pickled) usually lose water-soluble vitamins by leaching into the brine, while sodium increases in the product (Jones, 1975).

In fermented soy and grain products such as tofu and tempeh, niacin and riboflavin actually increase due to bacterial production (Muller and Tobin, 1980). Wines have lower levels of most nutrients than the juices from which they were made; the content of some of the B vitamins in beer increases slightly during the brewing process (Jones, 1975).

fermentation—process in which microorganisms metabolize components of a food, changing the composition and taste of the food

Smoking

Among the approximately 300 chemicals in smoke, there are several compounds that kill bacteria and protect against oxidation of food components. (There are also compounds in smoke about which health concerns have been raised; these will be discussed in the next chapter.) Decreases in nutrients from the smoking process do not usually exceed 20%.

Pasteurization

Pasteurization consists of heating a food at a temperature below its boiling point for under a minute to kill pathogens (disease-causing organisms) that might be present, while doing the least possible damage to nutrients. However, not all microorganisms or their spores (resting forms) are killed, so other methods of preservation, such as refrigeration, must be used in conjunction with pasteurization (Muller and Tobin, 1980).

Milk is the most commonly pasteurized food. The process kills a broad range of organisms, from those that can cause gastrointestinal infections of several days' duration to those that can cause tuberculosis. Other foods that are sometimes pasteurized are fruit juices, egg products, pickles, beer, and wine (Lund, 1975).

Nutrient losses from pasteurization are small, as the developers of this method intended. The greatest loss is of vitamin C, but since most pasteurized foods are not good sources of vitamin C to begin with, this is not significant.

pasteurization—heating a food at a temperature below its boiling point for less than a minute to kill pathogens while doing the least possible damage to nutrients

UHT Processing

UHT is the abbreviation for ultra-high temperature processing. The procedure resembles pasteurization except that it is accomplished at a higher temperature over an even shorter period of time. The benefits are greater destruction of microorganisms with less destruction of nutrients (Institute of Food Technologists, 1974). This process enables milk to be stored safely in

ultra-high temperature processing (UHT)—process that resembles pasteurization, but is done at a higher temperature for a shorter period of time

Table 14.3 The Extent of Vitamin Losses Caused by Various Food Preservation Methods		
Small losses (0–10%)	**Moderate losses (up to 30%)**	**Largest losses (up to 50%)**
Irradiation	Blanching and freezing	Canning
Freeze-drying	Smoking	Sun-drying
Pasteurization		
Rapid dehydration		
UHT processing		

its unopened package at room temperature for a couple of years (Arnold and Roberts, 1982).

Although the marketing of UHT milk in the United States has not been a great commercial success thus far, UHT processing has considerable potential for other products and/or other locales.

Irradiation

irradiation, cold sterilization— using gamma rays, X rays, or electrons to kill microorganisms that cause food spoilage

Irradiation or cold sterilization involves using gamma rays, X rays, or electrons to kill microorganisms that cause spoilage. Since there is only a small temperature rise when this process is used, changes in nutritional and physical characteristics are minimal (Institute of Food Technologists, 1983), and the shelf life of fresh products may be tripled.

This process can inhibit sprouting in root crops; kill insects or fungi that destroy grains, fresh fruits, or vegetables; and reduce pathogenic organisms. However, even though irradiation has been accepted for use in several foods by a committee of the United Nations, thus far the United States has approved it only for potatoes and wheat (Arnold, 1983), and more recently for spices (Labuza and Erdman, 1984). Even for these products, it has not been commonly used to date because there was expected to be negative public reaction to irradiated food; furthermore, there were alternative preservation methods that could be employed. Now that the safety of some of the alternative methods (such as the addition of the chemical ethylene dibromide or EDB) has been questioned, government regulatory agencies and the food industry are reevaluating the practicality of irradiation.

Adding Chemicals

Chemicals added to foods may have protective, destructive, or no effects on the nutrients in the foods. Sulfites, which are used in some foods to maintain freshness, exemplify this variation: they destroy thiamin, but protect vitamin C against oxidation. BHA and BHT are other commonly used chemicals that protect vitamins vulnerable to oxygen. Baking powder and baking soda, when used to leaven baked goods, can destroy thiamin in the products they are part of (Matz, 1975). Concerns about the safety of chemical additives will be discussed in the next chapter.

Table 14.3 summarizes the losses that can result from various food preservation methods.

Cooking Losses Can Be High, But Vary with the Method Selected

Cooking of food, like other types of food processing, is a mixed blessing. On the one hand, it can make food more palatable and digestible. It can also reduce the levels of some potentially harmful substances that may be present in food, such as microorganisms, enzymes that degrade vitamins, and substances that interfere with nutrient absorption. In general, then, cooking is important for making certain foods safe, nutritious, palatable, and digestible.

On the other hand, cooking also has nutritional penalties. Table 14.4 shows how severe the losses of some vitamins can be. It is important to remember, however, that cooking losses can be extremely variable: they will differ not only with the stability of the nutrients, but also with the type of food, the amount of water used in its preparation, the cooking time, the size of the food pieces, and the particular process being used (Harris and Karmas, 1975). Heating particularly affects the fat-soluble vitamins (especially vitamin A), vitamin C, and thiamin. Final cooking before serving tends to moderate some of the variation in nutrient contents

Table 14.4   Possible Losses of Vitamins from Cooking

Vitamin	Range of cooking losses (%)
Vitamin A	0–40
Carotene	0–30
Vitamin D	0–40
Vitamin E	0–55
Thiamin	0–80
Riboflavin	0–75
Niacin	0–75
Vitamin B-6	0–40
Vitamin B-12	0–10
Vitamin C	0–100

In many cases, vitamin destruction from cooking may cause the largest losses of all. These losses can be minimized by choosing from among the more nutrient-conservative cooking methods.

Adapted from NUTRITIONAL EVALUATION OF FOOD PROCESSING, 2nd Edition, Second Printing, 1977. Harris and Karmas, AVI Publishing Company, Westport, Connecticut.

among foods preserved in different ways. Frozen vegetables as purchased have considerably better vitamin retention than canned vegetables have; however, once each type of processed product has been cooked or heated, these differences in nutritional values are smaller (Bender, 1978).

As you might expect, heating causes less loss of minerals than of vitamins, unless foods are cooked in a large amount of water that is later discarded. Studies on the effect of processing on the mineral content of many foods show little if any difference among foods prepared from raw, frozen, or canned products (Hagen and Schweigert, 1983).

The following sections focus on the relative vitamin losses that can result from different cooking processes. This information is not designed to discourage you from cooking foods (keep in mind the benefits of doing so), but rather to help you make wise choices among methods.

Boiling

boiling—cooking foods in water at a temperature of 212°F (100°C)

Boiling—cooking foods in water at a temperature of 212°F—can cause significant nutrient losses. Minerals are lost when large amounts of water encourage leaching. In a study that tested calcium losses in many vegetables, 25% of the mineral was lost when the vegetables were covered with water during cooking, and less was lost when less water was used (LaChance, 1975).

When vegetables are cooked in water to cover, they lose an average of about 45% of their vitamin C and 20% of their carotene. However, if only ½ cup of water is used, losses are almost 10% less; if cooking is waterless, losses are yet another 10% less (LaChance, 1975).

Cooking time also makes a significant difference in vitamin loss. Best retention is possible when vegetables are cooked for the shortest possible time. Many vegetables, such as green or wax beans, spinach, green peas, and broccoli should be boiled for less than ten minutes. Starchier vegetables such as carrots, potatoes, and legumes need more time.

The best way to boil vegetables is to cook them only until crisp-tender in just enough water to prevent scorching in a pan with a tight-fitting lid. This combines the most nutrient conservative way of boiling with the benefits of steaming.

Steaming

steaming—using the vapor from heated water to cook foods

Steaming is using the vapor from heated water to cook foods. When vitamin C is measured as the test nutrient, it is apparent that steaming causes much lower nutrient losses than boiling does. Studies done on various vegetables show the extent of vitamin C losses to be in the 15–20% range (Bender, 1978). Mineral losses from steaming average approximately half of what they would have been for boiling (LaChance, 1975).

Microwave Cooking

microwave cooking—using short electromagnetic waves to cook foods quickly

Microwave cooking involves exposing foods to short electromagnetic waves. You would expect more nutrients to be retained during microwave cooking than other cooking processes, because the time involved is short and the use of water is usually minimal. However, tests done on the nutrient content of microwave-cooked foods do not uniformly show its nutritional superiority over foods cooked by more conventional means. Whereas some researchers have found that microwave cooking results in considerably greater vitamin retention than boiling, pressure cooking, or oven heating do, other studies have not always supported this generalization (Bender, 1978). Until more definitive work is done, we can safely say only that retention of nutrients during microwave cooking is at least as good as with more conventional cooking methods.

Pressure Cooking

Pressure cooking uses superheated steam under pressure in an airtight utensil to cook foods quickly. This method draws favorable reviews for its nutrient retention. Since processing time is short and there is usually little loss of nutrients by leaching, retention of vitamin C is generally better than with either boiling or steaming without pressure (LaChance and Erdman, 1975).

pressure cooking—using superheated steam under pressure in an airtight utensil to cook foods quickly

Roasting, Frying, and Grilling

Vitamin losses from roasting, frying, or grilling meats are approximately 20%. Stewing or boiling the same products would cause double these losses (Muller and Tobin, 1980). However, for vegetables, roasting (baking) leads to greater losses of some vitamins than boiling does (LaChance, 1975).

Steam Table Holding

Many institutional and restaurant kitchens rely on steam tables to keep cooked products hot and ready to serve. Although steam tables meet these two objectives very well, they may also be responsible for considerable vitamin loss. Losses of vitamin C ranged all the way up to 94% in various products held over three hours, with 50% loss being fairly common. Losses of other vitamins were not as great (LaChance, 1975). For this reason as well as for aesthetic ones, many facilities that must prepare food in quantity have pressure steamers to cook small batches of food (especially vegetables) that can be served and replaced quickly.

Suggestions for minimizing vitamin losses during cooking of foods are included in Table 14.2.

Assess Your Intake for Nutrient Retentiveness

You can evaluate whether you are achieving maximal nutrient retention in foods that you purchase and prepare by using a form similar to that shown in Figure 14.6. List the foods you consumed in one day, the forms in which they were purchased, the conditions of their storage, the processing they received, and the methods of cooking used.

Food	Form of purchase		Conditions of home storage		Home processing		Method of cooking	
	Used	*Better*	*Used*	*Better*	*Used*	*Better*	*Used*	*Better*
Cantaloupe	fresh, whole		sat on counter	refrigerator	cut just before eating	—	—	—
Puffed wheat	not enriched	enriched wheat cereal	cupboard	—	—	—	—	—
Cheese	natural	—	wax paper wrapping	tight plastic wrap	—	—	—	—
Crackers	enriched	whole wheat	cupboard		—		—	—
Apricots	dried	fresh *	cupboard	refrigerator	—	—	—	—
Green pepper	fresh, whole		refrigerator	—	cut in strips in a.m.	delay or don't cut	—	—
Ice cream cone	frozen	—	—					
Chicken	whole, frozen	—	freezer & refrigerator	—	—	—	stew	roast
Rice	enriched	brown **	cupboard	—	—	—	boiled in large pot of water	simmered in minimal water
Green beans	canned	frozen	cupboard				boiled 1 hr. in juice	short heating
Celery	hearts	whole stalk	refrigerator shelf	air tight wrapping freezer	cleaned & cut just before eating	—	—	—
Orange juice	frozen	—	refrigerator	freezer	added water	—	—	—

* not in season, so not practical
** don't like it, so not reasonable

Figure 14.6 One-day self-evaluation for ways to improve nutrient retention in foods. The woman who analyzed this day's intake had a stove top and oven, and a refrigerator with a small freezer space.

In the adjacent columns, identify (if possible) a method that would have been more nutrient-conservative. The method should also be one that is possible for you to use, given your current constraints and food preferences. There is no point in deciding to buy all frozen foods if you have only enough freezer space for two ice cube trays; and don't expect to grow all your own fresh produce if you don't have space or time to garden. If you've always cooked your vegetables by simmering them for several hours, don't expect to adjust immediately to eating all tender-crisp vegetables. As with other behavior modification efforts, you can best achieve success here by having reasonable goals that you work toward in easily attainable steps.

SUMMARY

■ The vitamin and mineral values of foods are not necessarily exactly as indicated on food composition tables, since food production, storage, and processing can all cause nutrient changes. Not all of these changes are for the worse, since nutrients can be added to foods as well as removed from them, and processing and preservation technologies give us greater food safety and availability all year round. Consumers can minimize nutrient losses in the foods they eat by making informed choices about selection, storage, and preparation.

■ Food production and processing have their own terminology. Health food and natural food have no legal definitions; nor does organic food except in a few states. Engineered, fabricated, and formulated foods are industry terms for extensively processed products made from highly refined ingredients. If foods contain less nutrients than the products they resemble, they may be defined as imitation food.

■ Many food production factors (such as plant variety, climate, and maturity at harvest) can influence the micronutrient content of foods. Food handling also affects nutrients in several general ways. Vitamin losses, particularly of vitamin C and thiamin, can result from many causes including pH changes, oxidation, exposure to light or heat, the passage of time, and/or physical separation. Minerals tend to be more stable than vitamins; they are most likely to be lost by physical separation. Generally the more processes a food undergoes, the greater the potential for nutrient destruction. However, micronutrient losses also occur during fresh storage, especially if temperature and exposure to light and oxygen are not controlled.

■ Nutrient losses from processing can be minimized by consumer handling and selection. Trimming, dividing, and soaking plant foods can all cause avoidable losses. The milling and refining of flour can result in losses of nutrients contained in the bran and germ of all grain kernels. Many types of refined food products are also fortified, enriched, or restored by the deliberate addition of new or already-present nutrients.

■ Various food preservation methods result in different levels of micronutrient losses. Most of these processes are intended to kill or inactivate potentially harmful microorganisms and increase the product's shelf life while doing as little aesthetic and nutritional damage as possible. Freezing, UHT processing, and irradiation tend to be the most nutrient-conservative preservation techniques. Dehydration, canning, blanching, fermentation, smoking, and pasteurization all have important roles in food preservation as well, and can be controlled to minimize nutrient losses.

■ Micronutrient losses from cooking can be high, but can also be controlled to some extent. Boiling and steam table holding can cause considerable losses; steaming, microwave cooking, and pressure cooking tend to be more nutrient-conservative.

■ Using the information in this chapter, you can evaluate whether you are retaining reasonable levels of nutrients in the foods you purchase and prepare.

REFERENCES

Agricultural Research Service. 1977. *Conserving the nutritive values in foods.* Home and Garden Bulletin No. 90. Washington, DC: United States Department of Agriculture.

Arnold, S., and T. Roberts. 1982. UHT milk: Nutrition, safety, and convenience. *National Food Review* 18:2–5.

Arnold, S.R. 1983. Food irradiation hinges on approval, feasibility, and acceptance. *National Food Review* 20:7–10.

Bender, A.E. 1978. *Food processing and nutrition.* New York: Academic Press.

Bluestein, P.M., and T.P. LaBuza. 1975. Effects of moisture removal on nutrients. In *Nutritional evaluation of food processing*, eds. R.S. Harris and E. Karmas. Westport, CT: The AVI Publishing Company, Inc.

Bunnell, R.H., J. Keating, A. Quaresimo, and G.K. Parman. 1965. Alpha-tocopherol content of foods. *American Journal of Clinical Nutrition* 17:1–10.

Clydesdale, F.M. 1982. Nutrition/technology transfer: Positive or negative? In *Published papers from the Stokely-VanCamp Symposium*, Knoxville, Tennessee, May, 1981.

Davis, D.R. 1981. Wheat and nutrition. *Nutrition Today* 16:16–21.

Fennema, O. 1977. Loss of vitamins in fresh and frozen foods. *Food Technology* 31:32–36.

Gourdine, S.P., W.W. Traiger, and D.S. Cohen. 1983. Health food stores investigation. *Journal of the American Dietetic Association* 83:285–290.

Hagen, R.E., and B.S. Schweigert. 1983. Nutrient contents of table-ready foods: Cooked, processed and stored. *Contemporary Nutrition* 8(no.2). Minneapolis: General Foods.

Harris, R.S., and E. Karmas, eds. 1975. *Nutritional evaluation of food processing*. Westport, CT: The AVI Publishing Company, Inc.

Institute of Food Technologists' (IFT) Expert Panel on Food Safety and Nutrition and the Committee on Public Information. 1974. *The effects of food processing on nutritional values: A scientific status summary*. Chicago: Institute of Food Technologists.

————. 1983. Radiation preservation of foods. *Food Technology* 37:55–60.

Jones, I.D. 1975. Effects of processing by fermentation on nutrients. In *Nutritional evaluation of food processing*, eds. R.S. Harris and E. Karmas. Westport, CT: The AVI Publishing Company, Inc.

Kastens, M.L. 1982. Revolution in the food system. *Food Engineering* 54:105–108.

Kramer, A. 1974. Storage retention of nutrients. *Food Technology* 28:50–60.

Labuza, T.P., and J.W. Erdman, 1984. *Food science and nutritional health: An introduction*. St. Paul, MN: West Publishing Company.

LaChance, P.A. 1975. Effects of food preparation procedures on nutrient retention with emphasis upon food service practices. In *Nutritional evaluation of food processing*, eds. R.S. Harris and E. Karmas. Westport, CT: The AVI Publishing Company, Inc.

LaChance, P.A., and J.W. Erdman. 1975. Effects of home food preparation practices on nutrient content of foods. In *Nutritional evaluation of food processing*, eds. R.S. Harris and E. Karmas. Westport, CT: The AVI Publishing Company, Inc.

Leveille, G.A. 1984. Food fortification—Opportunities and pitfalls. *Food Technology* 38:58–63.

Lund, D.B. 1975. Effects of blanching, pasteurization, and sterilization on nutrients. In *Nutritional evaulation of food processing*, eds. R.S. Harris and E. Karmas. Westport, CT: The AVI Publishing Company, Inc.

Matz, S.A. 1975. Effects of baking on nutrients. In *Nutritional evaluation of food processing*, eds. R.S. Harris and E. Karmas. Westport, CT: The AVI Publishing Company, Inc.

Muller, H.G., and G. Tobin. 1980. *Nutrition and food processing*. Westport, CT: The AVI Publishing Company, Inc.

Pennington, J.A.T., and H.N. Church. 1980. *Food values of portions commonly used*. Philadelphia: J.B. Lippincott Company.

Price, C.C., and J. Brown. 1981. Organic certification programs. *National Food Review* 15:31–32.

Quick, J.A., and E.W. Murphy. 1982. *The fortification of foods: A review*. Agriculture Handbook Number 598. Washington, DC: United States Department of Agriculture.

Roberts, T. 1983. Food preservation and nutrition. *National Food Review* 20:2–6.

Science and Education Administration. 1981. *Nutritive value of foods*. Home and Garden Bulletin No. 72. Washington, DC: United States Department of Agriculture.

Traub, L.G., and D.D. Odland. 1978. Convenience foods as home prepared: Cost, yield, and quality. *National Food Review* 4:30–33.

15

Beyond Nutrients: What Else Is in Your Food?

IN THIS CHAPTER: Toxicology Offers a Perspective on Harmful Substances in Food ▪ Microorganisms Affect More People Than Any Other Foodborne Problem ▪ Environmental Contaminants Are Common But Not Always Harmful ▪ Naturally Occurring Substances Can Be Toxic ▪ Additives Pose Risk to Only a Small Number of People ▪ Simple Strategies Help You Avoid Problems from Contaminants, Toxicants, and Additives in Food

Along with the growing public interest in the nutritional value of food, there has been increasing concern about aspects of food that may be harmful. Many people express this as a fear of "chemicals in our food." As you know from preceding chapters, such a generalized fear about chemicals is unwarranted, since the essential nutrients themselves are chemicals. So are thousands of other substances that occur naturally in foods, and most of these chemicals are harmless in the amounts typically consumed.

Nonetheless, it is true that there are also potentially harmful substances in foods that we would be better off to avoid. Some of these substances occur naturally in foods as they grow, others find their way into the food supply unintentionally, and a few others may be added to foods deliberately to accomplish some other desired effect.

It would be convenient and reassuring if we could simply produce two lists of chemicals—harmful and not harmful—and note the foods in which they occur. Then we could easily avoid the harmful chemicals or foods, and the matter would be closed. However, this is not possible, since many factors influence the ability of a substance to cause harm.

This point is well made in the following definition of food by food scientist Paul LaChance: "Food is composed of known chemicals plus unknown chemicals, which may be modified by intentional additives and/or contaminants, which may be modified by maturation, storage, processing, and preparation, which may be modified by digestion, absorption, and metabolism—the net result of which may have good, bad, or no effects upon the body cells and tissues."

This introduction should forewarn you that the matter of harmful substances in food is not a particularly straightforward topic. Keep in mind, too, that even though there are many types of potential food-related dangers, the food supply in North America is generally the safest in the world; the purpose of this discussion is to suggest ways in which you can make it even safer for yourself, in light of what is currently known.

Toxicology Offers a Perspective on Harmful Substances in Food

toxicology—the scientific study of harmful substances, including their detection and actions

Toxicology is the scientific study of harmful substances (that occur in both food and nonfood items) and their detection, actions, and the treatment of conditions they produce. Some terms commonly used in toxicological discussions are:

safety—a practical certainty that a substance will not cause injury

hazard—a source of danger; the *probability* that injury will result from use of a substance

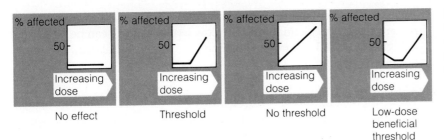

Figure 15.1 Possible forms of the dose response curve. (Adapted from: Murphy, S.D. Toxicological assessment of food residues. Reprinted from Food Technology. 1979. 33(6):35–42. Copyright © by Institute of Food Technologists.)

toxicity—the capacity of a substance to produce injury at some level of intake

toxicant, toxin, poison (used almost synonymously)—a substance with the capacity to harm

detoxification—the process of converting a dangerous substance into a harmless one

mutagen—a type of toxicant that causes a change in the cell's genetic material (these changes are called *mutations*)

carcinogen—a type of mutagen that allows a cell to multiply out of control, eventually resulting in cancer (even if the risk of cancer is small—such as one case resulting per million exposures—a substance that has this effect is still called a carcinogen)

A key concept is that *all substances are toxic at a certain level of intake, but most are not hazardous under normal conditions of use.*

The types of problems that the relatively few hazardous chemicals may cause range from such minor symptoms as a slight, short-term skin rash, to permanent damage of the nervous system, kidneys, or liver.

Possible Relationships between Dosage and Effect

Toxicologists view substances as having one of the four following effects:

no effect—there is no negative effect at any practical level of intake

threshold effect—the substance can be ingested without effect up to a certain amount; after that, negative effects increase with increasing amounts of intake

no threshold—all levels of intake produce harm; the greater the intake, the greater the harm

low-dose beneficial threshold—low levels of intake produce desirable effects; increasing levels eventually cause negative effects
Figure 15.1 illustrates these four possibilities, which are called dose-response curves.

dose-response curve—graph that shows the relationship between the dosage of a substance and its effect

Many nutrients have a low-dose beneficial threshold: vitamins and minerals that are essential for life at low levels of intake can be very toxic at higher levels. A large number of food toxicants are substances that show a threshold effect.

Factors that Influence Toxicity

A number of factors influence the activity and effects of food toxicants.

Detoxification. One reason that low levels of some toxicants cause no harm is that the body has a means of detoxifying small amounts of them. The liver is most directly involved in changing toxicants into harmless metabolites.

Time. The liver is able to detoxify substances at only a limited rate. As an extreme example, we can safely ingest 10,000 mg of the toxicant solanine, which is present in the 120 pounds of potatoes the average American consumes annually, provided the consumption is spread out over a year. The same amount of solanine in one dose, on the other hand, would be enough to kill a horse (Institute of Food Technologists, 1975).

Storage. Toxicants that cannot be degraded easily by the body can slowly accumulate in the liver, bones, or adipose or other tissues over many years until eventually they are present in large enough amounts to cause serious problems. Cadmium and PCBs are examples of toxicants the body stores.

Nutritional Status. A person whose diet is deficient in either energy intake or specific nutrients (for instance, vitamin C) has an impaired ability to deal with toxicants (Bidlack, 1982).

Growth and Body Size. Pregnancy and rapid growth in children can increase the body's absorption of some toxicants. Furthermore, when a given amount of toxin is ingested by two people of different body sizes, the toxin will have a greater effect on the smaller person because there is more toxin present per unit of body weight.

Interactions among Substances. The toxicities of individual substances are generally not additive; that is, if you ate $\frac{1}{100}$ of the lethal dose of each of 100 different toxic food components, the mixture would probably be harmless.

antagonist—a substance that can render a toxicant ineffective

Some toxicants have antagonists that render the toxicants ineffective. For example, the presence of selenium in fish tends to decrease the potential toxicity of any mercury present (Ganther, 1980). And the addition of calcium, iron, and other trace elements to the diet has been found to depress the absorption and therefore the toxicity of cadmium and lead (Fox, 1983; Mahaffey, 1983).

anticarcinogen—a compound in food that can counteract the effect of cancer-causing substances

There are also compounds in food that counteract the effect of cancer-causing substances. These are called anticarcinogens; one of the goals of current cancer research is to identify these compounds and learn how they work (Ames, 1983). For example, foods of the cabbage family are believed to contain anticarcinogens.

Ranking of Food-Related Problems

A practical ranking of major food-related public health problems, based on the number of people affected by them, was suggested by a recent director of the FDA's Bureau of Foods. Problems caused by microorganisms head the list, with environmental contaminants and naturally occurring food toxicants near the middle, and food additives—interestingly enough—at the bottom (Wodicka, 1977). Let's look at these factors in that order.

Microorganisms Affect More People Than Any Other Foodborne Problem

The Centers for Disease Control (CDC) report that of the tens of thousands of foodborne disease cases reported to them annually, over half are caused by microorganisms (1983). Since it is likely that only about ten percent of such cases ever get reported to the CDC, the actual number of cases is estimated to be over two million each year (Zottola, 1977). (As high as this number is, it means that in the United States only a very small proportion of the food eaten each year contains enough microorganisms to produce illness.)

In one recent year, restaurant food was the cause of outbreaks in 43% of the reported cases, with the most common contributing factor being improper storage (Centers for Disease Control, 1983). Usually the foods involved had already been cooked, but were improperly handled before they were consumed (Schweigert, 1982).

Common Foodborne Infections and Bacterial Intoxications

The greatest number of foodborne illnesses are caused by bacteria commonly found in the environment. They can cause problems in either of two ways. One is that they reproduce in food in *large numbers* if environmental conditions are favorable, surpassing the threshold that people can tolerate. The resulting illnesses are called foodborne infections. The bacteria that most often cause these illnesses are organisms of the salmonella and shigella groups, and *Campylobacter fetus* and *Escherichia coli* (Harvard Medical School Health Letter, 1984).

foodborne infection—illness produced by food containing large numbers of bacteria

Bacteria may also cause illness by producing *toxins*, the effects of which make you sick. These illnesses are called foodborne bacterial intoxications, and are most often caused by *staphylococcus aureus* organisms. *Clostridium perfringens* is a common organism that causes foodborne illness having the characteristics of both infection and intoxication (Zottola, 1977).

foodborne bacterial intoxication—illness produced by food containing bacterial toxins

These organisms are widespread, occurring in such diverse places as the intestinal tracts of people and other animals, on skin, in nasal passages, and in the soil. From such origins they have spread throughout the environment. They thrive in any setting that provides their essential nutrients (high-protein foods in particular); moisture; oxygen (or absence of oxygen, depending on their particular needs); and suitable temperature (especially 40–140°F).

The illnesses they cause may occur any time from a few hours after the infected food was eaten to a few days later. Symptoms may include nausea, vomiting, diarrhea, and/or intestinal cramps; fever; headache; and general weakness. Although these illnesses tend to be short-term and are not usually severe, they occasionally cause the death of a person in already very weakened physical condition.

An Uncommon, Serious Food Intoxication: Botulism

The *Clostridium botulinum* organism, when it produces its toxin in food, may cause the sometimes fatal disease botulism. Even though botulism is not common, it deserves discussion because of its serious consequences.

This organism is found in soil and in the sediments of many freshwater lakes and rivers. The organism by itself is not hazardous: probably everybody has consumed it at one time or another without dire consequences. Problems occur when it is present in an environment where circumstances allow it to thrive: anaerobic conditions (no oxygen), the presence of low-acid foods, and room temperature. In time the bacteria, or their protected resting forms called spores, become active and produce the potentially deadly toxin. The affected food will not necessarily look or smell unusual, making the toxin impossible to detect (Muller and Tobin, 1980).

Low-acid canned foods that have been improperly processed are most often the cause of botulism. Foods with a pH higher than 4.6 are regarded as low-acid; Figure 15.2 shows the acidity of various foods.

Symptoms of botulism usually occur within two days after eating an infected food. The disease affects the nervous system, its symptoms often beginning with double vision and progressing to inability to swallow, speech difficulty, and paralysis of the respiratory system, which results in death.

Although experts say that botulinum toxin can be destroyed by boiling food hard for 20 minutes (Agricultural Research Service, 1975), many people prefer the still safer method of discarding any food suspected to be contaminated.

Special precautions should be taken to protect babies less than a year old from botulism. Unlike an adult's mature gastrointestinal tract, a baby's digestive system seems to provide the conditions that allow this organism to produce toxin. Certain samples of honey and corn syrup have been found to contain botulinum spores, so these foods should not be given to children less than one year of age. These products have been suspected of causing some cases of infant botulism and subsequent death (Centers for Disease Control, 1978).

Prevention Strategies

In general, the ways to avoid foodborne infections and intoxications are to use clean food, avoid contaminating it, and discourage the growth of microorganisms and production of toxins by making food conditions inhospitable.

Start with Clean Food. Choose food that looks clean. Soil that is clinging to food contains many microorganisms. Similarly, organic animal waste that may have been used as fertilizer is a common source of foodborne disease (Jukes, 1981).

botulism—an uncommon but sometimes fatal food intoxication

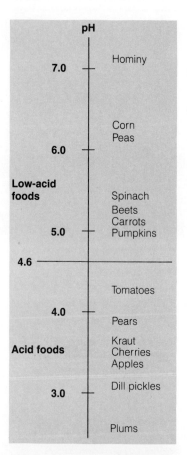

Figure 15.2 The pH values of various canned foods. Low-acid foods must be processed under pressure at temperatures greater than 212°F to ensure the destruction of *Clostridium botulinum.* Reference: Leveille, G.A., and M.A. Uebersax. 1979. Fundamentals of food science for the dietitian: Thermal processing. *Dietetic Currents* 6(no.3). Columbus, OH: Ross Laboratories.

Foods that are good hosts for microbial growth should be well wrapped or in closed containers at the time of purchase. Food cans should not show evidence of leaky seams or bulging ends. Milk should have been pasteurized; eggs should not have cracks in them.

Keep Food Clean. The next challenge is to keep food clean. Be sure that all the equipment that comes in contact with food is clean; wash knives and cutting boards between their use for raw foods and cooked foods to avoid cross-contamination between the two.

Be sure that you are not a source of contamination yourself. Wash your hands before you start handling food, and rewash them after you have touched yourself in any way—after smoking, using the bathroom, blowing your nose, or covering a sneeze. People with cuts or sores on their hands should not prepare food unless they wear plastic or vinyl gloves.

Keep Food Out of the Temperature Danger Zone. The temperature range most conducive to the reproduction of microorganisms that cause foodborne illnesses is called the *danger zone.* For storage and holding purposes, 40–140°F is the range to avoid. Figure 15.3 shows the effects of different

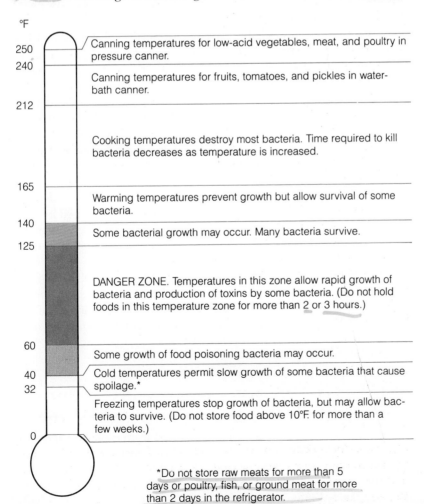

Figure 15.3 Effects of temperature on microorganisms.
Source: Agricultural Research Service. 1975. *Keeping food safe to eat.* Home and Garden Bulletin No. 162. Washington, DC: United States Department of Agriculture.

temperatures on microorganisms. During cooking of meats, internal temperatures should reach at least 140°F to kill existing pathogens. Refer to a cookbook to find temperature standards for various meats.

Between preparation and consumption, food should be kept either hotter than 140°F or colder than 40°F. When cooling large amounts of cooked foods for cold storage, it is best to spread the food out in thin layers, which allows faster cooling. Of course, there are times when foods do sit out at room temperatures, such as when they are on the table during meals or are part of a buffet. If you have the right equipment, it is possible to maintain safe temperatures in these situations by using ice-lined bowls for cold food, and using warmers for hot food.

Most often, though, people do not use such precautions, and foods are exposed to danger zone temperatures for a while. It is impossible to know exactly how long they are safe to eat, but two to three hours has been suggested as a practical limit of safety for foods kept between 60° and 125°F. (Agricultural Research Service, 1975). After that time, it is sensible to throw them away. Keep in mind the old adage, "When in doubt, throw it out."

Follow Canning Instructions to the Letter. If you are canning foods at home, be sure to use methods recommended in the brochures published by the United States Department of Agriculture. This is particularly important for protection against botulism. Such brochures are available through the extension system in your state. If you have information from a previous year, check to be sure that it is still current; important changes are made in the instructions from time to time. It is critical to use the right method for each product you are preserving. Recommended substances to add to the product, processing times, and whether to heat in boiling water or in a pressure cooker may seem like picky details, but may literally make the difference between life and death.

This section has emphasized the harm that can be caused by some bacteria present in food. It is only fair to point out that certain microorganisms can also play a positive role and are deliberately and safely added during processing. Bacteria are used to make yogurt, some cheeses, vinegar, and wine; yeast is used to make beer; and specific molds are cultured on certain varieties of cheese. Keep in mind, though, the important difference in safety: the time-tested, deliberate use of microorganisms in food processing is likely to be safe, but random or accidental introduction of microorganisms into food is more likely to create hazards.

Environmental Contaminants Are Common But Not Always Harmful

Environmental contaminants can get into food from cookware and other food containers; vehicular wastes such as auto exhaust; industrial products and wastes; and agricultural products and wastes such as fertilizers, pesticides, and antibiotics.

Environmental contaminants vary greatly in their composition. Minerals, organic compounds, and even radioactivity can all contaminate the food supplies of people and animals, but only a relatively small number of these contaminants ever enter the food and water supply in sufficient quantities to be of practical significance.

Mineral Contaminants from Cookware and Other Food Containers

Minerals such as lead, aluminum, tin, and iron can migrate into foods in varying amounts from food preparation equipment and metal storage containers.

Lead.   Lead can leach into foods from the solder used to seal the side seams of cans and to close the hole in the top of evaporated milk cans. It was estimated in 1981 that approximately 14% of the lead taken in by the average adult comes from such solder (Schaffner, 1981); the proportion is likely to decrease with improvements in packaging techniques.

Another possible source of lead is pottery glazes. Some historians have suggested that lead toxicity from lead-lined cooking pots and lead water pipes may have been one of the factors preceding the decline of the Roman Empire (Jueneman, 1983). Lead is no longer used in glazes on commercially produced dishes in the United States because of this hazard. However, there is no way to assure the safety of homemade pottery or items made in other countries (Henderson, 1982).

Lead can also get into food by way of the local soil and water, which in turn can accumulate it from such sources as paint chips from buildings being demolished, solid waste sludges used as fertilizers, and airborne products of fuel combustion (Mielke et al., 1983). As the use of vehicles requiring leaded gasoline declines, human accumulation of lead appears to be declining as well (Annest et al., 1982).

There is particular concern about the amount of lead children ingest. They can be harmed by lower levels of intake because they absorb a higher percentage of the lead they take in, and because they have smaller body sizes. Data on lead levels in children from a recent Health and Nutrition Examination Survey (HANES—a major study of nutritional status in the United States) are shown in Table 15.1. A significant number of black children, especially from low-income urban homes, had high enough levels of lead in their blood that medical treatment was advisable. Experts currently consider 30 micrograms of lead per 100 ml of blood to be the amount that indicates excessive exposure.

In recent years, the FDA has encouraged the food industry to develop ways to reduce lead intake from containers. The industry has responded by reducing the amount of solder used to weld some seams, by welding other seams without the use of solder, by developing a two-piece can with no side seam, and by packaging more foods in glass. All baby foods are now sold in glass containers (except formula preparations), and people who make their own baby food are advised to avoid making it from canned food.

Table 15.1   Percent of American Children with Elevated Lead Levels in Blood

	% of children	
	White	Black
Annual family income		
Under $6,000	5.9	18.5
$6,000–14,999	2.2	12.1
$15,000 or more	0.7	2.8
Degree of urbanization of place of residence		
Urban, 1 million persons or more		
Central city	4.5	18.6
Non–central city	3.8	3.3
Urban, fewer than 1 million persons	1.6	10.2
Rural	1.2	10.3

This table gives the percentage of children ages 6 months to 5 years who have blood lead levels of 30 micrograms or more per 100 ml (1976–1980). This is the amount currently considered by experts to indicate excessive exposure.

Adapted from Annest, J.L. et al. 1982. Blood lead levels for persons 6 months–74 years of age: United States, 1976–80. *NCHS Advance Data* 79:1–24.

As a result of those measures, children's lead intake fell to the level the FDA had set as a goal for this age group (Bander et al., 1983). Similarly, between 1974 and 1980 the lead levels in common adult foods were reduced by almost half, putting intake within the range regarded as safe by the FDA (Schaffner, 1981).

Aluminum. Some people have recently become concerned that the use of aluminum cookware will lead to toxicity. In fact, aluminum is one of the most common elements in the earth's crust, and is therefore naturally present in plant foods. Although some aluminum enters the diet as a component of additives in certain processed cheeses and certain baked goods, people who routinely take aluminum-containing medications can achieve higher aluminum intakes than anybody could obtain through food.

Last on the list of contributors to aluminum intake is cooking equipment and foil. Only a very small amount of the aluminum estimated to be in the average adult American diet can be attributed to cooking in aluminum cookware or contact of food with aluminum foil. Some of the mineral will be picked up from aluminum containers if food is stored in them.

Tin. Tin is the coating on "tin cans" (which are really mainly steel). Little tin is introduced to food from other sources. Studies that have assessed the migration of tin from containers into foods show that tin content tends to be higher in food when the cans have not been lacquered inside. In fact, foods from lacquered cans contain virtually undetectable levels of tin.

The length of storage time is another important factor: certain canned foods stored on the shelf for four months nearly double their earlier tin content in some cases. When opened and refrigerated in the can for one week, tin levels rose to as high as six times the original levels in cans that were only partially or not at all lacquered (Greger and Baier, 1981).

What is the practical significance of this information? Actually, people in North America very rarely experience obvious problems from tin intake from cans. Occasionally, the higher temperature in warm climates can promote a greater reaction between the can and its contents in improperly handled foods, and some people have experienced nausea and vomiting from high tin intakes (Benoy et al., 1971). In North America, a more practical concern is that tin is able to interfere with the absorption of zinc. For this reason, it is a good idea to remove any unused food portion from its can and store it in a glass or plastic container.

Iron. Iron may also get into food from cans and kettles. Since this nutrient is low in many people's diets, there is generally little reason to worry about increased intake from this source. In fact, some nutritionists promote the practice of cooking in iron cookware as a means of increasing iron intake; but since iron from this source is believed to be very poorly utilized (Hallberg et al., 1983), we do not predict much nutritional benefit from this practice.

Mineral Contaminants from Other Sources

Mineral contaminants other than those found in food containers can also enter the food supply in various ways.

Mercury. Mercury is a naturally occurring element that appears to be present in all biological tissues (Underwood, 1977). The burning of fossil fuel and the production of compounds including industrial chemicals, electrical apparatus, dental preparations, pharmaceuticals, and paper can add considerable amounts of mercury to the environment.

There are a number of reports in the scientific literature of mercury toxicity among industrial workers. (In fact, the phrase "mad as a hatter" is derived from the symptoms shown by hat-makers who treated furs with mercury during the 1700s and 1800s.) Now there are government standards mandating that industries reduce or eliminate exposure of their workers and the general population to mercury wastes.

Fortunately, most industrial mercury wastes that find their way into the environment do not enter the food supply. Problems occur when microorganisms in soil and water add organic compounds to inorganic mercury, thereby producing an organic form known as methyl mercury, which is much more toxic to biological systems (Underwood, 1977). The ingestion of methyl mercury in sufficient quantities can cause progressive loss of coordination, vision, and hearing; mental deterioration; and death. Infants born to mothers who ingested large amounts of methyl mercury during pregnancy suffer from a variety of neurological disorders.

methyl mercury—an organic form of mercury, highly toxic to biological systems

One severe outbreak of methyl mercury poisoning that has received wide publicity occurred about 25 years ago in Japan among the people living near Minamata Bay. Unknown to most of the residents, industrial wastes containing mercury were dumped into the bay. Fish and people who ate these fish accumulated methyl mercury in their bodies. The problem was not identified until many severe cases of methyl mercury poisoning had occurred (Figure 15.4).

Cadmium. There are many environmental sources of cadmium. It enters the environment through its use in the manufacture of batteries, plastics, and paints. It is a common contaminant of phosphate fertilizers and sewage sludge. Cigarette smoke can be a major source of cadmium for some individuals.

Most foodstuffs contain little cadmium naturally (Fox, 1983). However, oysters and other seafood, especially those grown in industrially contaminated water, can contain very high levels of cadmium. Some vegetable crops can also accumulate cadmium when grown in soil to which phosphate fertilizers or sewage sludge have been heavily applied (Underwood, 1977).

Some scientists have found that exposure to low levels of cadmium causes hypertension in rats (Kopp et al., 1982). The significance of this observation for humans needs to be investigated.

Organic Contaminants

Agricultural and other industrial technologies add many different organic contaminants to the food supply. Some can be toxic in certain situations.

Antibiotics. In addition to their use in treating human infections, antibiotics are used to treat animal infections and to increase the weight gain of food-producing animals. This makes it possible to produce greater quantities of meats, milk, and eggs at lower cost.

However, for many years some scientists have been concerned that antibiotic residues are not completely metabolized by animals and can remain in their tissues (Food and Drug Administration, 1974). People consuming meat or milk from such animals could have allergic reactions to the antibiotic residues. The more real problem is that the presence of antibiotics in food can contribute to a buildup of antibiotic-resistant bacteria in the intestinal tract of consumers (Holmberg et al., 1984).

To prevent such occurrences, the federal government has restricted the use of antibiotics in animal feed to particular types and levels. Furthermore, producers are supposed to discontinue the use of antibiotics at specified times prior to selling livestock. The adequacy of these regulations is now doubted because of the buildup of antibiotic-resistant bacteria.

Organic Chlorinated and Brominated Compounds. Polychlorinated biphenyls (PCBs), polybrominated biphenyls (PBBs), and a variety of other organic compounds with attached chloride or bromide ions have been

polychlorinated biphenyls (PCBs), polybrominated biphenyls (PBBs)—types of industrial compounds, some of which have entered the food supply by accident and are of concern because they may accumulate in biological tissues over time

Figure 15.4 The effects of methyl mercury intoxication. The woman in this photograph ate fish contaminated with methyl mercury from Minamata Bay, Japan, when she was pregnant with her daughter; the girl is severely and permanently handicapped as a result.

used extensively for a variety of industrial purposes. Through pollution and accidents, many of these compounds have entered the environment and our food system. Not many of these compounds are likely to cause acute toxicity (Kimbrough, 1974). However, since the bodies of animals are unable to metabolize them easily and because these chemicals are soluble in body fat, they can accumulate in tissues over time from very low levels of repeated exposure. This accumulation makes their potential for chronic toxicity a real concern.

Some of these compounds are toxic to the liver and can thus adversely affect the metabolism of some nutrients, drugs, and other toxicants. PCBs and related compounds have also been found to produce skin lesions and to adversely affect animals' nervous systems and immune systems, potentially making them more susceptible to carcinogens.

Real alarm over PCBs in foodstuffs occurred in the 1970s. Scientists reported that not only did some fish from industrially polluted waters contain high levels of these chemicals in their tissues, but that the milk of mothers who had consumed these fish also contained high levels of PCBs (Rogan et al., 1980). Many programs have been initiated by federal and state agencies to limit further pollution with PCBs, to monitor lakes and fish for PCB contamination, and to advise residents in affected areas. Women who live in these areas and who have routinely consumed fish caught in PCB-polluted waters are often advised to consider feeding commercial formula rather than their own milk to their infants.

An example of a single accident causing widespread concern occurred in 1973, when 500–1000 pounds of a fire retardant containing PBB were accidentally substituted for a nutritional supplement in the diets of dairy cattle in Michigan (Reich, 1983). By the time the mistake was discovered, "virtually every resident of the lower peninsula of Michigan from 1973 to 1975 had some exposure to PBB" (Schwartz and Rae, 1983).

A massive cleanup effort was launched, and numerous studies attempted to measure the impact of PBB on health. Like PCBs, PBB accumulates in the tissues of affected individuals and is excreted in breast milk. The symptoms that followed exposure to PBB, such as tiredness, headaches, and dizziness (Weiss, 1981), were difficult to link causally to PBB. Therefore the scientific and political debate over this contaminant goes on.

Radioactivity

More than 40 naturally occurring kinds of radioactive atoms have been identified in rocks and soil. Many of these occur in the cells of plants and animals as well.

Of course, there are now sources of radioactivity other than nature. Fallout from tests of nuclear weapons, mining of certain ores, nuclear fuel processing, reactor installations, and applications of radioisotopes in medicine, industry, and agriculture can also contribute radioactivity to the environment.

Table 15.2 puts the various sources into perspective. Despite the many new sources of radioactivity, natural sources are still responsible for the vast majority of radiation exposure.

Table 15.2 Radiation in the United States (Whole Body Dose) Estimated from Different Sources

| Source | Millirem[a]/Person/Year | |
	1970	Projected for 2000
Natural	130	130
Fallout	4	4.99
Nuclear reactors	0.002	0.174
Other sources	0.046	0.265
AEC installations	0.012	0.012
Total all sources	134.060	135.441

[a]Millirem = standardized measure of radioactivity.

Adapted from Comar, C. L. and Thompson, J. C., Jr.: Radioactivity in Foods. In Modern Nutrition in Health and Disease, 6th edition. R. S. Goodhart and M. E. Shils, eds. Lea & Febiger, Philadelphia, 1980.

Figure 15.5 The prevalence of naturally occurring toxicants.
The top series of pictures shows many ordinary foods. If all foods
that contained naturally occurring toxicants were removed, the
foods in the bottom series would remain.

Naturally Occurring Substances Can Be Toxic

Among the myriad of natural chemicals present in almost any foodstuff
there are potentially toxic substances. Figure 15.5 makes the point graphically by picturing some common foods, and then showing how few are
completely free of naturally occurring toxicants. However, because people
usually consume only low levels of these compounds, they are not generally
regarded as a problem.

Nonetheless, there are certain situations in which injury can be caused
by ingestion of compounds that occur naturally in plant and animal materials. Injuries can occur if toxicant-containing foods are consumed in
abnormally large quantities; if foods contaminated with highly toxic substances from fungi or algae are consumed; if "food look-alikes" containing
highly toxic substances are consumed; and if toxicants are consumed by
individuals who are unusually sensitive to their effects for some reason.

Consumption of Abnormally Large Quantities of Natural Toxicants

If people eat large amounts of a single food (especially if they eat less of
other foods at the same time), they may experience effects from naturally
occurring toxicants. This can happen if individuals deliberately emphasize

just a few foods in their diets, or it can occur in large numbers of people during a famine, when minor foodstuffs may of necessity become major dietary components. Certain naturally occurring toxicants have caused problems at times, but there are often ways to avoid such problems, as the rest of this section explains.

methylxanthines—group of compounds that occur naturally in many plant species, with coffee, tea, and cola beverages being common sources

Caffeine and Related Compounds. Caffeine, theophylline, and theobromine are members of a group of compounds known as methylxanthines. They occur naturally in about 63 species of plants (Institute of Food Technologists, 1983). Products containing these compounds are used daily in almost all cultures worldwide (IFT, 1983). The most common sources of these compounds are coffee, tea, chocolate, cola beverages, and a variety of over-the-counter prescription drugs (Roberts and Barone, 1983; IFT, 1983). Caffeine has been the most thoroughly studied of these compounds. Tables 15.3 and 15.4 indicate the amounts of caffeine in many commonly used substances.

Caffeine is a drug. It is well documented that low doses of it enhance alertness and therefore increase the amount of time it takes for a person

Table 15.3 Caffeine Content of Selected Food Products

Product	Amount	Range (mg)	Average (mg)
Roasted and ground coffee (percolated)	5 oz.	39–168	74
Roasted and ground coffee (drip)	5 oz.	56–176	112
Instant coffee	5 oz.	29–117	66
Roasted and ground coffee, decaffeinated	5 oz.	1–8	2
Instant coffee, decaffeinated	5 oz.	2–8	3
Tea	5 oz.	8–91	27
Instant tea	5 oz.	24–31	28
Cocoa	5 oz.	2–7	4
Milk chocolate	1 oz.	1–15	6
Chocolate milk	8 oz.	2–7	5
Baking chocolate	1 oz.	18–118	60
Soft drinks	12 oz.		
Regular colas		30–46	—
Decaffeinated colas		trace	
Diet colas		2–58	—
Decaffeinated diet colas, orange, lemon-lime, root beer, tonic, ginger ale, club soda		0–trace	

Adapted from Roberts, H.R., and J.J. Barone. Caffeine Content of Food Products. Reprinted from *Food Technology*. 1983. 37(9):32–39. Copyright © by Institute of Food Technologists.

Table 15.4   Caffeine Content of Selected Over-the-Counter Drug Preparations

Classification	Mg per tablet or capsule
Stimulants	
NoDoz tablets	100
Vivarin tablets	200
Pain relievers	
Anacin	32
Excedrin	65
Midol	32
Plain aspirin, any brand	0
Vanquish	33
Diuretics	
Aqua-Ban	100
Cold remedies	
Coryban-D	30
Dristan	16
Triaminicin	30
Weight-control aids	
Dexatrim	200
Dietac	200
Prolamine	140

Adapted from Institute of Food Technologists' Expert Panel on Food Safety and Nutrition. Caffeine. Reprinted from *Food Technology*. 1983. 37(4): 87–91. Copyright © by Institute of Food Technologists.

to fall asleep (Von Borstel, 1983). It can also aid performance in prolonged, exhaustive exercise. Endurance was shown to be almost 20% greater when 330 mg of caffeine had been ingested an hour before exercising on an exercise bicycle (Costill, et al., 1978).

The average adult American consumes 3 mg of caffeine per kilogram of body weight daily (Roberts and Barone, 1983), a level of consumption that can produce noticeable effects. Doses of 3–5 mg of caffeine per kg of body weight per day can produce mild anxiety, respiratory stimulation, cardiovascular effects, diuresis (increased urine production), and increased gastric secretions. Long-term intake of more than 600 mg per day may lead to chronic insomnia, persistent anxiety, paranoia, depression, and stomach upset (Gilbert, 1981). The magnitude of these effects depends in large part on previous consumption. You can develop a tolerance to methylxanthines if you consume them consistently over a period of time (Von Borstel, 1983). Higher doses of caffeine can accentuate the symptoms.

Many studies have been done to test the effects of caffeine or coffee on risk factors for cardiovascular disease. Caffeine causes blood pressure to rise slightly (Lane, 1983); high coffee consumption appears to be associated with higher blood cholesterol levels (Thelle et al., 1983); and large intakes of coffee may cause irregularities in heartbeat (Dobmeyer et al., 1983). Nonetheless, epidemiological studies have shown no significant increase in heart disease or heart attacks among coffee consumers (MacCornack, 1977).

Studies attempting to link coffee consumption and cancer have yielded mixed results. Whereas one study found an association between coffee intake and pancreatic cancer (MacMahon et al., 1981), later research did not find an association (Wynder et al, 1983). It is important to keep in mind that studies done on *coffee* are not necessarily indicative of the effects of *caffeine*, since there are many other compounds present in coffee, some of which are thought to have toxic effects (Gilbert, 1981).

There's been more bad press for the methylxanthines. Some physicians have suggested that caffeine and related compounds may promote symptoms of cyclical fibrocystic breast disease in women who are susceptible to it. This condition involves the development of hard, nonmalignant breast lumps that become enlarged and painful premenstrually. Early studies suggested that discontinuing the use of methylxanthines could relieve the discomfort of cyclical fibrocystic breast disease in a high percentage of cases (Minton et al., 1979); however, later studies have shown less dramatic results (Institute of Food Technologists, 1983). More work is in progress.

Caffeine has also been suspected of causing birth defects. This is because birth defects have been noted in the young of animals that were fed caffeine in doses providing the human equivalent of more than 50 cups of strongly brewed coffee per day during pregnancy (Institute of Food Technologists, 1984). However, data involving humans show no evidence that *moderate* consumption of caffeine by pregnant women produces birth defects (Rosenberg et al., 1982).

To protect against excessive intake of methylxanthines, it is best to follow the basic rule of consuming all foods and beverages in moderation. Becoming dependent on large amounts of them is dangerous. On the other hand, for most individuals, a few cups of coffee or tea during a day cannot be considered a real threat to health.

Tannins. Tannins are a diverse group of complex chemicals found in a variety of plant materials and foods derived from them, including tea, sorghum, apples, cider, grapes, and wine. Tannins impart astringency to foods. Gourmets say that tannins give "body and fullness of flavor" to foods (Meyer, 1960). If you've ever tasted Chianti wine, you've been exposed to tannins.

In Chapter 13 (on minerals) we mentioned that tannins in tea are believed to decrease the bioavailability of dietary iron. Another negative effect is that they may be carcinogens when ingested in high doses. The incidence of esophageal cancer is very high among people in South Africa who consume large amounts of high-tannin sorghum. Of course, other substances in the diets of these people may be enhancing the effects of the tannins or may even be carcinogens themselves (Singleton and Kratzer, 1973).

Nitrates, Nitrites, and Nitrosamines. Elemental nitrogen and oxygen combine in various proportions to form nitrates **and** nitrites. Both occur *naturally* in foods and in your body, where some interconversions occur between them. (The major difference between these compounds is that nitrates have more oxygen in their structure.) Nitrites are also used as a food additive to cure meats and prevent the growth of *Clostridium botulinum*. These compounds can react with other substances in food or in your body to form other compounds called nitrosamines.

Levels of nitrates and nitrites vary widely among foods (Table 15.5). A number of factors including agricultural practices and storage conditions can affect the nitrate levels in food. In the average diet, vegetables contribute 87% of the *nitrates* ingested.

Nitrites, on the other hand, are found in vegetables, baked goods and cereals, and cured meats. Although many people assume that all the nitrite in foods is added during food processing, only about 34% of the nitrite in the United States food supply is added intentionally, as it often is to cured meats (Committee on Nitrite and Alternative Curing Agents in Food, 1981). The rest of this amount is naturally occurring.

Nitrosamines can also be formed in some foods, both in nature and during processing. However, the amount of nitrosamines the average person consumes in food is less than a typical cigarette smoker gets from that habit.

There is concern about the association of repeated, low-level ingestion of nitrates, nitrites, and nitrosamines with cancer. In fact, there has been so much interest in this issue that in 1981 the National Academy of Sciences appointed the Committee on Nitrite and Alternative Curing Agents in Food to examine it. After an exhaustive review of the scientific literature, the committee filed a 500-page report. They stated that epidemiological studies have implicated nitrates, nitrites, and nitrosamines in the development of cancer, particularly of the stomach and esophagus. Animal studies, on the other hand, have not provided sufficient evidence to conclude that nitrates and nitrites are themselves carcinogens, but most nitrosamines are. The committee also pointed out that enhancers and inhibitors influence whether cancer occurs. For example, the presence of vitamin C, alphatocopherol, and other antioxidants (substances that prevent reactions between oxygen and certain food constituents) can inhibit the activity of carcinogens by blocking the formation of nitrosamines.

The controversy is complex, and is confounded by the fact that much remains to be learned. Even the experts do not always interpret the available data in the same way or reach the same conclusions regarding how people should eat. To appreciate this point, compare the recommendations on nitrite use that come from the committee just mentioned with the recommendations from another committee of the National Academy of Sciences:

- The Committee on Nitrite and Alternative Curing Agents in Food endorses the continued use of nitrite, due to its effectiveness in discouraging the growth of *Clostridium botulinum* (1981).

nitrates, nitrites—compounds of nitrogen and oxygen that occur naturally in many foods, and can also be added during processing

nitrosamines—chemical products of certain reactions involving nitrates or nitrites

Cancer

Frontier

■ The Committee on Diet, Nutrition and Cancer suggests that the consumption of food preserved by salt-curing (including salt-pickling) or smoking be minimized (1982). [This point was made in the report summary; the body of the report stated that much of the evidence relating to these products does not prove them to be hazardous as they are normally produced and consumed in the United States (USDA, 1983).]

More recently, an unexpected potential source of nitrosamines has come to light: rubber baby bottle nipples may contain unacceptable levels of nitrosamines. To reduce this risk, the FDA recommends boiling new nipples five or six times (using fresh water each time) before use (Harvard Medical School Health Letter, 1984).

The ingestion of large amounts of nitrates is sometimes a health concern for another reason. It can cause a condition called *methemoglobinemia,* which involves the production of abnormal hemoglobin unable to carry the usual amount of oxygen. This condition is most likely to occur in infants, who may become cyanotic (turn blue from lack of oxygen) if they consume well water contaminated with high levels of nitrates (Committee on Nitrite and Alternative Curing Agents in Food, 1981). In most states, there are county and/or state facilities that can test well water for its nitrate content.

Polycyclic Aromatic Compounds. One difficulty in assessing the cancer risk from exposure to nitrates and nitrites in food is that these compounds do not necessarily occur in isolation. Other potential carcinogens and other mutagens may also be present.

For example, some carcinogens may be introduced into foods by normal cooking procedures. Two common classes of mutagens produced in foods by cooking are polycyclic aromatic hydrocarbons and polycyclic aromatic amines. Both are complex organic structures that are also found in some uncooked foods.

Polycyclic aromatic hydrocarbons are most likely to be produced in high-protein foods such as meats, particularly when they are pan-fried or broiled, and especially if charring occurs. Some experts believe consumers should think twice before ordering well-done charbroiled meats on a very frequent basis (Bjeldanes, 1983).

The way to enjoy a smoky taste without incurring the risk mentioned above is to use a "liquid smoke." Liquid smokes are produced by capturing smoke that was created in a limited amount of air, condensing the smoke, and filtering it. This removes most of the benzopyrene, which is a polycyclic aromatic hydrocarbon (Bjeldanes, 1983).

Cyanogenic Glycosides. Cyanogenic glycosides are compounds found in some foods that can release hydrogen cyanide in certain situations. This well-known poison is a potent respiratory inhibitor, and in large quantities can cause death (Conn, 1973). Chronic consumption of smaller quantities of cyanogenic glycosides can affect the nervous system, vision, and hearing.

polycyclic aromatic hydrocarbons, polycyclic aromatic amines—common classes of mutagens produced in foods by certain types of dry heat cooking, especially if charring occurs

cyanogenic glycosides—compounds that can release the poison hydrogen cyanide; found in many types of fruit pits

Table 15.5 Estimates of the Average Concentrations of Nitrate and Nitrite in Vegetables

| Vegetable | Concentration, mg/kg (fresh weight) | |
	Nitrate	Nitrite
Artichoke	12	0.4
Asparagus	44	0.6
Beans: green	340	0.6
lima	54	1.1
dry (navy)	13	nd
Beet	2,400	4.0
Broccoli	740	1.0
Brussels sprouts	120	1.0
Cabbage	520	0.5
Carrot	200	0.8
Cauliflower	480	1.1
Celery	2,300	0.5
Corn	45	2.0
Cucumber	110	0.5
Eggplant	270	0.5
Endive	1,300	0.5
Kale, collard	800	1.0
Lettuce	1,700	0.4
Melon	360	nd
Mushroom	160	0.5
Okra	38	0.7
Onion	170	0.7
Parsley	1,010	nd
Peas	28	0.6
Pepper: sweet	120	0.4
Potato: white	110	0.6
sweet	46	0.7
Pumpkin and squash	400	0.5
Radish	1,900	0.2
Rhubarb	2,100	nd
Spinach	1,800	2.5
Tomato	58	nd
Turnip	390	nd
Turnip greens	6,600	2.3

nd = No data reported

Adapted from "*The Health Effects of Nitrate, Nitrite and N–Nitroso Compounds,*" 1981, with the permission of the National Academy Press, Washington, D.C.

Cyanogenic glycosides are found in the pits of almonds, apples, apricots, cherries, peaches, and other fruits. People are generally not harmed by these items because they do not typically consume fruit pits—or at least not in large quantities. Furthermore, the cyanide is not usually released from intact pits. Lima beans can also contain significant amounts of these compounds, but breeding programs have reduced the levels in commercially available lima beans in North America (Institute of Food Technologists, 1975).

Laetrile, also called amygdalin, is a controversial source of concentrated cyanogenic glycoside. Many claims have been made for the effectiveness of laetrile as a cancer cure, but none has been substantiated in controlled clinical trials (Herbert, 1979). In fact, some patients who have undertaken laetrile therapy have developed blood levels and symptoms of cyanide toxicity (Moertel et al., 1982).

Consumption of Toxins of Fungi and Algae

Toxins produced by fungi (such as molds) and algae can find their way into plants and animals, which in turn affect humans who consume them. This type of microbial food contamination is much less common and has different consequences than the bacterial problems discussed earlier in this chapter.

Mycotoxins. Mycotoxins are toxins produced by fungi; people have been afflicted in certain situations for centuries. Some molds of the genus *Aspergillus* produce a series of mycotoxins called aflatoxins, which many experts believe to be the most potent liver toxins and carcinogenic agents known. Although aflatoxins have been found in many different foods, they most commonly contaminate peanuts, grains, and vegetables. Because of the potential toxicity of aflatoxins, many government, university, and industrial scientists have studied them. They have developed sensitive tests that are used routinely in North America to monitor peanuts and grains for aflatoxin concentration; therefore, exposure from commercially processed foods is believed to be low here. However, aflatoxin contamination is thought to be more prevalent in developing countries. Cassava, a food staple used in some of these countries, is susceptible to aflatoxin contamination.

aflatoxins—a group of mycotoxins (fungal toxins) believed by some to be the most potent liver toxins and carcinogenic agents known

Some other mycotoxins, many of which have not been thoroughly studied, are also believed to be very toxic. It is often best to simply discard food that has become moldy. Although people are sometimes tempted to trim off the mold and use the remaining product, some of the toxin that has already penetrated the food may remain, making the food dangerous to eat (Wilson and Hayes, 1973).

Seafood Toxicants. Sometimes shellfish (such as oysters and clams) contain toxins that were produced by algae they consumed. A variety of serious symptoms, including liver damage, muscle incoordination, respiratory failure, and death can occur in individuals who consume the contaminated shellfish (Schantz, 1973).

Generally the shellfish in any one area are contaminated only during part of the year, so instances of poisoning are sporadic. Government agencies monitor many shellfish beds for contamination, especially during May through October, when the problem is most likely to occur (Schantz, 1973).

Consumption of Toxic Substances in "Food Look-Alikes"

Sometimes people misidentify nonfood materials as foods. Young children are the most common victims of poisoning by nonfood materials. If you've ever watched a baby or toddler explore his or her environment by seeing, touching, and tasting everything, this will not surprise you.

In recent years, state health departments and the Centers for Disease Control (CDC) have also received data on a number of adults who have been poisoned by natural products. Such cases often reflect consumer interest but lack of knowledge about "natural" or "herbal" foods and cures. In 1977, the CDC reported four cases of poisoning, three of which were fatal, caused by teas that had been made from poisonous plant materials (CDC, 1977). Poisonings due to the consumption of toxic mushrooms that were mistakenly identified as edible also occur occasionally (Lampe, 1983).

Those of you who are interested in collecting and consuming natural products should obtain authoritative information from the experts in state hygiene laboratories and state horticultural extension offices concerning which wild foods are safe to eat. If there is any doubt about a plant you are considering for use as food, do not consume it.

Although people who experiment with using nontraditional plants as teas or foods are generally more at risk than people who consume widely marketed products, even nationally distributed items occasionally contain hazardous substances

---

SLICE OF LIFE:
Unwanted Effects from Herbs

In an *FDA Consumer* article entitled *"Herbs Are More Often Toxic Than Magical,"* author Tim Larkin cites an example of a dangerous herbal product (1983):

. . . FDA recently took action against an herbal product, Herbalife Slim and Trim Formula. Advertisements for this product claim that it offers a "safe, sensible, all natural Health and Nutrition Program that gets us back to the Natural way of being Slim and Healthy using herbs." Among the herbs listed for one of the diet formulas are mandrake and pokeroot. Mandrake, whether the American...or European...variety, is highly toxic, as is pokeroot.... Indeed, mandrake was once used by American Indians as a suicide drug. This diet aid claims that it will "keep the weight off indefinitely," which may well prove all too true for those unfortunate enough to consume too much of it.

Treatment of people who ingest toxic plant material is often difficult because the poisonous substances in plants and the symptoms they produce vary so greatly. Some substances may irritate the gastrointestinal tract and rapidly induce nausea and vomiting; others damage the liver or central nervous system. This variety of consequences makes diagnosis difficult. If somebody starts to become ill after consuming an unusual natural product, call your local poison control center immediately. It is likely to be listed with other emergency telephone numbers on the first page of the phone book. If you are advised to go to the hospital emergency room, take along a sample of the plant material if you have it; this will aid in diagnosis and treatment.

Additives Pose Risk to Only a Small Number of People

The Food and Drug Administration defines additives as "substances added directly to food, or substances which may reasonably be expected to become components of food through surface contact with equipment or packaging materials, or even substances that may otherwise affect the food without becoming a part of it" (Jukes, 1981). The discussion that follows concerns substances that are directly and deliberately added to food.

Government Monitoring

The federal government has concerned itself with food additives since 1906. In that year, the Pure Food Law and the ensuing regulations that were drawn to enforce it provided the first means for protection of American food consumers. These documents established some early product and packaging standards, called for truth in labeling, and prescribed the testing methods to be used for evaluating the wholesomeness of foods. It also gave the government the authority to seize and destroy hazardous foods.

A primary concern at that time was to rid the food supply of foreign or misrepresented substances that some food processors were using in lieu of the pure, more expensive product they claimed to be marketing. For example, pepper sometimes was polluted with ground wood, raspberry jam with alfalfa seeds, ground mustard with flour, and candy with plaster of paris (Garard, 1974).

In 1938, the **Federal Food, Drug, and Cosmetic Act** improved on the earlier law, with stronger and more specific prohibitions against adulteration and misbranding. It also contained a method for establishing federal food standards, which identify the ingredients that must be present in particular foods. Over 200 such *standards of identity* exist for products including ice cream, catsup, and mayonnaise, to name a few common examples. Products for which standards exist are not required to carry ingredient lists on their labels, but those without standards of identity must.

In 1958 and 1960, with hundreds of additives already in use, the Food, Drug, and Cosmetic Act was amended in several important ways:

- Proof of safety had to be presented to the FDA by any company wanting to use a new food additive. The additive could not be used until the FDA gave its approval.

- A listing was made of approximately 700 additives already in use that were generally recognized as safe (GRAS), based on their innocuous presence in the food supply for many years. A list of prior sanctioned substances was also prepared, consisting of additives that FDA or USDA had approved before 1958. [The status of additives on these lists can be challenged by new evidence; some substances have lost their places on the original lists in that way (Lehmann, 1979).]

  GRAS list—list of about 700 additives in current use that are generally recognized as safe, based on their longstanding innocuous presence in the food supply

- A margin of safety was established. For most additives, there is an acceptable daily intake of $\frac{1}{100}$ of the amount thought to be hazardous.

- The Delaney Clause specified that no substance could be added to the food supply if it had been shown to cause cancer in people or animals. (Now that sensitive testing can identify minute, probably inconsequential levels of carcinogens in common foods, modifications of the Delaney Clause are being discussed.)

  Delaney Clause—law specifying that no substance can be added to the food supply if it has been shown to cause cancer in people or animals

Purposes and Prevalence of Additives

Additives must have purposes that will benefit the consumer. Four broad categories of legitimate use are to maintain product quality, to help in processing or preparation, to make food more appealing, and to maintain or improve nutritional value (Lehmann, 1979).

There are currently over 2800 additives approved for use in the United States. The average American consumes approximately 160 pounds of additives per year: over 140 pounds of sweeteners including sucrose, 15 pounds of sodium chloride (table salt), and 5–10 pounds of all the others. This means that all the flavorings, colorings, and preservatives ingested by Americans comprise less than 0.6% of the estimated 1670 pounds of food we each consume in a year (Welsh and Marston, 1982). Appendix M lists some of the more commonly used additives and their functions.

Additives That Maintain Product Quality. We benefit from the addition to foods of substances that eliminate or control microorganisms and other living contaminants, and substances that prevent oxidation of food compounds. For example, nitrites are added to cured meats in order to discourage the growth of *Clostridium botulinum*. Examples of other additives used to inhibit the growth of different bacteria, yeasts, and molds are sodium and calcium propionate, sodium benzoate, potassium sorbate, and sulfur dioxide, which are used in baked goods and other products.

Ethylene dibromide (EDB) is an example of a compound used in the United States to control insect infestation in stored grain and citrus fruit (Sun, 1984). However, after forty years of use, new information caused the status of this additive to be changed. Originally this compound was assumed to dissipate quickly after application, making it completely safe for use; but recent evidence has shown that residues last for many months in agricultural products and foods made from them, and that the residues may be carcinogenic. Therefore beginning in 1984, the federal government began to change regulations governing EDB use (Tufts University Diet and Nutrition Letter, 1984). In this issue as in so many others, scientific judgment, political considerations, and consumer responses together have played roles in determining the new regulations; several states created more stringent regulations than the federal government finally settled on.

Another important group of additives that preserve product quality are *antioxidants*, which prevent chemical reactions between oxygen in the air and various constituents of foods. The additives BHA (butylated hydroxyanisole), BHT (butylated hydroxytoluene), and propyl gallate protect against oxidation of fats (rancidity). They are often used in baked products. Antioxidants often function by being easily oxidized themselves, thereby sparing other compounds in the food.

Other additives are used to inhibit the enzymes that cause browning reactions in fruits and vegetables. Vitamin C is sometimes used for this purpose, especially to prevent the browning of fruits. Sulfites—sulfur dioxide, sodium sulfite, sodium or potassium bisulfites, and metabisulfites—are also used on fresh produce for this purpose (Hecht and Willis, 1983). Some people experience life-threatening allergic reactions to sulfites, so pressure is now being exerted to have sulfites removed from the GRAS list. In the meantime, restaurants are encouraged to advise their customers whether sulfites have been used to treat salad items.

Additives That Aid in Processing or Preparation. Leavening agents, anti-caking agents, emulsifiers, stabilizers, thickeners, pH control agents, humectants (moisturizers), maturing and bleaching agents, and dough conditioners are all examples of additives used to achieve processing or preparation benefits.

Sodium bicarbonate, the chemical name for baking soda and also an ingredient in baking powder, is a leavening agent. So are calcium phosphate and sodium aluminum phosphate. Such leavening agents are used in all baked products that are raised without yeast, such as biscuits, muffins, cornbread, and cakes.

Calcium and aluminum silicate and iron-ammonium citrate are anticaking agents used in salts and many powdered products. Many emulsifiers, such as mono- and diglycerides, lecithin, carrageenan, and polysorbates, are used in salad dressings, processed cheese, and ice cream. Various gums, pectin, and alginates are used to thicken jellies, candies, and ice cream.

Acidity is adjusted in such foods as pickles and carbonated beverages by using acetic acid, citric acid, lactic acid, phosphates and phosphoric acid, and sodium acetate.

Additives That Make Food More Appealing. Any additive that makes food more pleasing to taste or look at is a member of this group. *Flavorings* include condiments, spices, concentrated fruits and juices, process flavors (such as "roasted"), or flavor elements concentrated from the above (Lindsay, 1984). Whether such compounds have been extracted from food sources

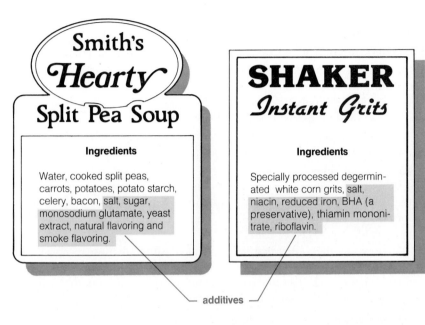

Figure 15.6 Examples of additives in two processed foods.

(natural flavorings) or produced in the laboratory (artificial flavorings), they are often chemically identical (Committee on Food Protection, 1973). In such cases, they are also indistinguishable in terms of their safety (Smith, 1981). Figure 15.6 shows examples of additives as they might appear on the labels of processed foods.

Examples of *flavor enhancers* are monosodium glutamate (MSG) and hydrolyzed vegetable protein. Although they do not have flavors of their own, they help heighten existing flavors in foods.

Sweeteners include a wide variety of substances. The concentrated sugars all qualify here: beet and cane sugars, syrups, honey, and molasses. So do the purified sweet carbohydrates they contain, such as sucrose, glucose, fructose, sorbitol, and mannitol. All these sweeteners offer energy as well as flavor. Sweet additives that provide little or no energy are saccharin and aspartame.

Saccharin has had a checkered past. Although it was included on the GRAS list in 1958 because of its longstanding use without apparent problems, its status was challenged in 1977 by evidence that it caused bladder cancer in rats (Lecos, 1981). Such evidence should be enough to require the removal of saccharin from the food supply, according to the Delaney Clause.

However, saccharin is still on the market as of this writing. Each time the FDA proposes a ban on its use, Congress declares a moratorium on the ban in response to public pressure to keep it available (Lecos, 1981). This has occurred because of saccharin's widespread popularity, and because the studies regarding its effect on humans do not unanimously find it carcinogenic.

Nonetheless, Robert Hoover, Director of the Environmental Epidemiology Branch at the National Cancer Institute, rendered this opinion:

Frontier

"When all the evidence is weighed against the lack of objective evidence of benefit, any use [of saccharin] by nondiabetic children or pregnant women, heavy use by young women of childbearing age, and excessive use by anyone are ill-advised and should be actively discouraged by the medical community" (Lecos, 1981).

Some of the public pressure to allow continued use of saccharin may ease off now that aspartame, another sugar substitute, is on the market.

Aspartame is a sweet dipeptide whose component amino acids are metabolized like those naturally occurring in food (O'Brien and Gelardi, 1981). Aspartame was approved for certain uses in the United States in 1974, but before it entered the market, the FDA stayed the approval because the validity of several toxicological studies was questioned. Subsequent reviews of the data and additional studies cleared the way for eventual approval in 1981 (Lecos, 1981).

However, the controversy has not ended. Although more recent studies continue to support its safety when consumed in moderation (Steginck et al., 1983), some scientists and consumer groups continue to question whether there may be some risks if the product becomes as popular as anticipated.

Aspartame clearly constitutes a hazard for people with the condition phenylketonuria (PKU). This disorder, which is usually diagnozed shortly after birth, is characterized by an inability to metabolize one of the amino acids in aspartame (phenylalanine); phenylalanine builds up in the blood of these individuals, causing neurological damage and subsequent mental retardation in children. For this reason, a warning must appear on aspartame and all products that contain it, to alert people with PKU of the danger.

Colorings are the final group of additives that improve sensory appeal. There are approximately 30 food colorings approved for use in the United States, and some others that can be used in specified circumstances (Lehmann, 1979).

There have been more questions raised about the safety of colorings as a group than about most other categories of additives. Many synthetic dyes that were formerly used in foods are no longer allowed, in some cases because they were found to be carcinogenic. Future use of other synthetic dyes is uncertain and will hinge on individual tests (Jukes, 1981). Natural colorings are not as popular with the food industry, because they do not generally hold up as well in foods as the synthetic colorings do (Meggos, 1984).

Just as with some other scientific quandaries, the experts disagree over how to interpret studies on food coloring. For example, at about the same time that the FDA banned Red No. 2 and suggested using Red No. 40 as a substitute, Canada banned Red No. 40 and in its place used Red No. 2 (Institute of Food Technologists, 1980).

Tartrazine, or Yellow No. 5, is a food coloring of current interest. It has been found to produce hives, itching, runny nose, and/or asthma in some people. The federal government requires tartrazine to be mentioned specifically on food labels when it is used, a regulation that makes it unique among food colorings.

Simple Strategies Help You Avoid Problems from Contaminants, Toxicants, and Additives in Food

It is virtually impossible for consumers to be aware of all the toxic substances in food and the conditions under which harm would be likely, and to plan their food intakes on that basis. Fortunately this is unnecessary, because a few general guidelines can help you avoid most problem substances:

1. Eat a wide variety of foods, and avoid consistently large intakes of any one item. This makes it less likely that you will take in a hazardous amount of any toxicant.

2. Consume a diet that supplies adequate levels of all nutrients. Good nutrition helps the body deal with the stresses induced by toxicants. (Taking the opposite approach of trying to avoid all foods that contain potentially harmful substances could lead to so limited a diet that undernutrition might result.)

3. Follow carefully the instructions for use on the labels of pesticides, fertilizers, and all other household and yard chemicals to keep them out of your food supply.

4. Keep informed about public health matters. The print and electronic media are major sources of information about food recalls and food handling practices.

SUMMARY

■ Thousands of substances besides nutrients occur naturally in foods, and most are harmless in the amounts typically consumed. Among those substances that do have the potential to cause harm, some occur naturally, others find their way into the food supply by accident, and still others may be added on purpose to achieve some other desired effect. Unfortunately, it is not possible to simply make lists of harmful and unharmful chemicals and avoid the former, because so many factors can influence the ability of any substance to cause harm.

■ Toxicology is the scientific study of harmful substances. Common toxicological terms are safety, hazard, toxicity, toxicant (also toxin or poison), detoxification, mutagen, and carcinogen. It is important to remember that all substances comprising foods are toxic at a certain level of intake, but most are not hazardous under normal conditions of use.

■ Dose-response curves illustrate the relationship between the dosage of a substance and its effect. Some substances have no effect; others have a threshold effect or no threshold (are harmful at all levels of intake). Most nutrients have a low-dose beneficial threshold. Many factors influence toxicity, including detoxification processes, time, storge in the body, nutritional status, growth and body size, and interactions among substances.

■ Microorganisms are responsible for the majority of food-related public health problems. Foodborne infections (caused by large numbers of bacteria in food) and intoxications (caused by bacterial toxins) can be very unpleasant but are not usually severe; botulism, a less common intoxication, can be fatal. Simple strategies for avoiding these problems involve using clean food and utensils, keeping food out of the temperature danger zone, and following canning instructions precisely. This does not mean all microorganisms are harmful. Certain microorganisms have played useful roles in food processing for centuries.

■ Environmental food contaminants are common but not always harmful. Minerals such as lead, aluminum, tin, and iron can migrate into food from metal food preparation equipment and storage containers, but this is not a hazard under normal circumstances. Other mineral contaminants such as mercury and cadmium can also enter the food supply in various ways, the harm they produce depending on many factors including chemical form and dosage. Organic contaminants such as antibiotics, PCBs, and PBBs can be toxic in certain situations, and there is concern about the tendency for some of these to accumulate in animal tissues over time.

■ Many naturally occurring substances can also be toxic. Problems can arise if an individual consumes abnormally large quantities of such substances as methylxanthines (including caffeine), tannins, nitrosamines and related compounds, polycyclic aromatic hydrocarbons and amines, and cyanogenic glycosides such as laetrile. Consuming even small amounts of fungal aflatoxins can have dire consequences, as can ingesting algal and seafood toxicants. Poisonings resulting from the ingestion of nonfood items such as misidentified mushrooms and certain herbal teas also occur periodically.

■ Food additives pose relatively little risk to consumers, especially now that government monitoring of the North American food supply is routine and ongoing. Federal laws regulate the introduction of new additives and their margin of safety. The GRAS list includes about 700 additives that are generally recognized as safe, and the Delaney Clause specifies that substances shown to cause cancer in animals or humans cannot be added to the food supply.

■ Additives must benefit food consumers in at least one of the following ways: (1) maintaining product quality (controlling microorganisms, preventing oxidation); (2) aiding in processing or preparation (leavening, emulsifying, thickening); (3) making food more appealing (flavoring, sweetening, coloring); or (4) maintaining or improving nutritional value.

■ Rather than trying to avoid all potentially toxic substances in foods (an impossibility), it makes more sense to take a few reasonable precautions: (1) eat a wide variety of foods, (2) consume adequate levels of all nutrients, (3) use household and yard chemicals safely, and (4) stay informed about public health issues. The North American food supply is generally the safest in the world, and by exercising good judgment you can make it even safer for yourself.

REFERENCES

Agricultural Research Service. 1975. *Keeping food safe to eat*. Home and Garden Bulletin No. 162. Washington, DC: United States Department of Agriculture.

Ames, B.N. 1983. Dietary carcinogens and anticarcinogens. *Science* 221:1256–1264.

Annest, J.L., K.R. Mahaffey, D.H. Cox, and J. Roberts. 1982. Blood lead levels for persons 6 months–74 years of age: United States, 1976–80. *NCHS Advance Data* 79:1–24.

Bander, L.K., K.J. Morgan, and M.E. Zabik. 1983. Dietary lead intake of preschool children. *American Journal of Public Health* 73:789–794.

Benoy, C.J., P.A. Hooper, and R. Schneider. 1971. The toxicity of tin in canned fruit juices and solid foods. *Food Cosmetology and Toxicology* 9:645–656.

Bidlack, W.R. 1982. Toxicant metabolism and the role of nutrients. *Food Technology* 36:106–113.

Bjeldanes, L.F. 1983. Hazards in the food supply: Lead, aflatoxins and mutagens produced by cooking. *Nutrition Update* 1:105–119.

Centers for Disease Control (CDC). 1977. Poisoning associated with herbal teas—Arizona, Washington. *Morbidity and Mortality Weekly Report* 26(no.32):257–259.

————. 1978. Honey exposure and infant botulism—California. *Morbidity and Mortality Weekly Report* 27:249.

————. 1983. Foodborne disease outbreaks: Annual summary 1981. Atlanta, GA: U.S. Department of Health and Human Services, Public Health Service.

Comar, C.L., and J.C. Thompson, Jr. 1980. Radioactivity in foods. In *Modern nutrition in health and disease*, eds. R.S. Goodhart and M.E. Shils. Philadelphia: Lea and Febiger.

Committee on Diet, Nutrition and Cancer. 1982. *Diet, nutrition and cancer.* Washington, DC: National Academy Press.

Committee on Food Protection, National Academy of Sciences (NAS). 1973. *The use of chemicals in food production, processing, storage, and distribution.* Washington, DC: National Academy of Sciences.

Committee on Nitrite and Alternative Curing Agents in Food. 1981. *The health effects of nitrate, nitrite, and N–nitroso compounds.* Washington, DC: National Academy Press.

Conn, E.E. 1973. Cyanogenic glycosides. In *Toxicants occurring naturally in foods.* Committee on Food Protection. Washington, DC: National Academy of Sciences.

Costill, D.L., G.P. Dalsky, and W.J. Fink. 1978. Effects of caffeine ingestion on metabolism and exercise performance. *Medicine and Science in Sports* 10:155–158.

Dobmeyer, D.J., R.A. Stine, C.V. Leier, R. Greenberg, and S.F. Schaal. 1983. The arrhythmogenic effects of caffeine in human beings. *New England Journal of Medicine* 308:814–816.

Food and Drug Administration (FDA). 1974. *Antibiotics and the foods you eat.* U.S. Department of Health, Education, and Welfare Publication No. (FDA)74:6011.

Fox, M.R.S. 1983. Cadmium bioavailability. *Federation proceedings* 42:1726–1729.

Ganther, H.E. 1980. Interactions of vitamin E and selenium with mercury and silver. *New York Academy of Sciences* 355:212–216.

Garard, I.D. 1974. *The story of food.* Westport, CT: The AVI Publishing Company, Inc.

Gilbert, R.M. 1981. Caffeine: Overview and anthology. In *Nutrition and behavior*, ed. S.A. Miller. Philadelphia: The Franklin Institute Press.

Greger, J.L., and M. Baier. 1981. Tin and iron content of canned and bottled foods. *Journal of Food Science* 46:1751–1765.

Hallberg, L., E. Bjorn-Rasmussen, L. Rossander, R. Suwanek, R. Pleehachinda, and M. Tuntawiroon. 1983. Iron absorption from Asian meals containing contamination iron. *American Journal of Clinical Nutrition* 37:272–277.

Harvard Medical School Health Letter. 1984. High-tech hazards to babies. *Harvard Medical School Health Letter* 9(no.6):6.

————. 1984. Food poisoning: Worse than ants at a picnic. *Harvard Medical School Health Letter* 9(no.8):5–6.

Hecht, A., and J. Willis. 1983. Sulfites: Preservatives that can go wrong. *FDA Consumer* 17(no.7):11.

Henderson, D. 1982. Cookware as a source of additives. *FDA Consumer* 16:11–13.

Herbert, V. 1979. Laetrile: The cult of cyanide. Promoting poison for profit. *American Journal of Clinical Nutrition* 32:1121–1158.

Holmberg, S.D., M.T. Osterholm, K.A. Senger, and M.L. Kohn. 1984. Drug-resistant salmonella from animals fed antimicrobials. *The New England Journal of Medicine* 311:617–622.

Institute of Food Technologists' (IFT) Expert Panel on Food Safety and Nutrition and the Committee on Public Information. 1975. *Naturally occurring toxicants in foods.* Chicago: Institute of Food Technologists.

————. 1980. *Food colors.* Chicago: Institute of Food Technologists.

————. 1983. Caffeine. *Food Technology* 37(no. 4):87–91.

————. 1984. Caffeine. *Contemporary Nutrition* 9(no.5).

Jueneman, F.B. 1983. A lead-pipe cinch. *Industrial Research and Development* 25(no.7):19.

Jukes, T.H. 1981. Organic foods and food additives. In *Controversies in nutrition*, ed. L. Ellenbogen. New York: Churchill Livingstone.

Kimbrough, R.D. 1974. The toxicity of polychlorinated

polycyclic compounds and related chemicals. *CRC Critical Reviews of Toxicology.* Boca Raton, FL: CRC Press.

Kopp, S.J., T. Glonek, H.M. Perry, Jr., M. Erlanger, and E.F. Perry. 1982. Cardiovascular actions of cadmium at environmental exposure levels. *Science* 217:837–839.

Lampe, K.F. 1983. Mushroom poisoning. In *CRC handbook of naturally occurring food toxicants,* ed. M. Rechcigl, Jr. Boca Raton, FL: CRC Press.

Lane, J.D. 1983. Caffeine and cardiovascular responses to stress. *Psychosomatic Medicine* 45:447–451.

Larkin, T. 1983. Herbs are often more toxic than magical. *FDA Consumer* 17(no.8):5–11.

Lecos, D. 1981. The sweet and sour history of saccharin, cyclamate, aspartame. *FDA Consumer* 15(no.7):8–11.

Lehmann, P. 1979. More than you ever thought you would know about food additives. *FDA Consumer* Reprint: Health and Human Services Publication No. (FDA)79–2115.

Leveille, G.A., and M.A. Uebersax. 1979. Fundamentals of food science for the dietitian: Thermal processing. *Dietetic Currents* 6(no.3). Columbus, OH: Ross Laboratories.

Lindsay, R.C. 1984. Flavor ingredient technology. *Food Technology* 38(no.1):76–81.

MacCornack, F.A. 1977. The effects of coffee drinking on the cardiovascular system: Experimental and epidemiological research. *Preventive Medicine* 6:104–119.

MacMahon, B., S. Yen, D. Trichopoulos, K. Warren, and G. Nardi. 1981. Coffee and cancer of the pancreas. *New England Journal of Medicine* 304:630–633.

Mahaffey, K.R. 1983. Biotoxicity of lead: Influence of various factors. *Federation Proceedings* 42:1730–1734.

Meggos, H.N. 1984. Colors—key food ingredients. *Food Technology* 38(no.1):70–74.

Meyer, L.H. 1960. *Tannin in food chemistry.* New York: Reinhold Book Corp.

Mielke, H.W., J.C. Anderson, K.J. Berry, P.W. Mielke, R.L. Chaney, and M. Leech. 1983. Lead concentrations in inner-city soils as a factor in the child lead problem. *American Journal of Public Health* 73:302–313.

Minton, J.P., M.K. Foecking, D.J.T. Webster, and R.H. Matthews. 1979. Caffeine, cyclic nucleotides, and breast disease. *Surgery* 86:105–109.

Moertel, C.G., T.R. Fleming, J. Rubin, L.K. Kvols, G. Sarna, R. Koch, V.E. Currie, C.W. Young, S.E. Jones, and J.P. Davignon. 1982. A clinical trial of amygdalin (laetrile) in the treatment of human cancer. *New England Journal of Medicine* 306:201–206.

Muller, H.G., and G. Tobin. 1980. *Nutrition and food processing.* Westport, CT: The AVI Publishing Company, Inc.

Murphy, S.D. 1979. Toxicological assessment of food residues. *Food Technology* 33:(6)35–42.

Nutrition Foundation's Expert Advisory Committee. 1982. *Assessment of the safety of lead and lead salts in food.* New York: The Nutrition Foundation.

O'Brien, L., and R.C. Gelardi. 1981. Alternative sweeteners. *Chemtech* 11:274–278.

Reich, M.R. 1983. Environmental politics and science: The case of PBB contamination in Michigan. *American Journal of Public Health* 73:302–313.

Roberts, H.R., and J.J. Barone. 1983. Biological effects of caffeine: History and use. *Food Technology* 37:32–39.

Rogan, W.J., A. Bagniewska, and T. Domstra. 1980. Pollutants in breast milk. *New England Journal of Medicine* 302:1450–1453.

Rosenberg, L., A.A. Mitchell, S. Shapiro, and D. Slome. 1982. Selected birth defects in relation to caffeine-containing beverages. *Journal of the American Medical Association* 247:1429–1432.

Schaffner, R.M. 1981. Lead in canned foods. *Food Technology* 35:60–64.

Schantz, E.J. 1973. Seafood toxicants. In *Toxicants occurring naturally in foods.* Committee on Food Protection. Washington, DC: National Academy of Sciences.

Schwartz, E.M., and W. Rae. 1983. Effect of polybrominated biphenyls (PBB) on developmental abilities in young children. *American Journal of Public Health* 73:277–281.

Schweigert, B.S. 1982. Perspectives of food science and nutrition in the 1980's. *Food and Nutrition News* 53(no.3):1–3. Chicago: National Livestock and Meat Board.

Singleton, V.L., and F.H. Kratzer. 1973. Plant phenolics. In *Toxicants occurring naturally in foods*. Committee on Food Protection. Washington, DC: National Academy of Sciences.

Smith, M.V. 1981. Regulation of artificial and natural flavors. *Cereal Foods World* 26:278–280.

Steginck, L.D., L.J. Filer, Jr., and G.L. Baker. 1983. Plasma amino acid concentrations in normal adults fed meals with added monosodium L–glutamate and aspartame. *Journal of Nutrition* 113:1851–1860.

Sun, M. 1984. EDB contamination kindles federal action. *Science* 223:464–466.

Thelle, D.S., E. Arnesen, and O.H. Forde. 1983. The Tromso heart study. *New England Journal of Medicine* 308:1454–1457.

Tufts University Diet and Nutrition Letter. 1984. EDB—What do the guidelines mean? Tufts University Diet and Nutrition Letter 2(no.2):7–8.

Underwood, E.J. 1977. *Trace elements in human and animal nutrition*. New York: Academic Press.

United States Department of Agriculture (USDA). 1983. Response to the report, "Diet, nutrition, and cancer," of the Committee on Diet, Nutrition, and Cancer, Assembly of Life Sciences, National Research Council, 1982. Washington, DC: USDA.

Von Borstel, R.W. 1983. Biological effects of caffeine: metabolism. *Food Technology* 37:40–43.

Weiss, B. 1981. Behavior as a common focus of toxicology and nutrition. In *Nutrition and behavior*, ed. S.A. Miller. Philadelphia: The Franklin Institute Press.

Welsh, S.P., and R.M. Marston. 1982. Review of trends in food use in the United States, 1909–80. *Journal of the American Dietetic Association* 81:120–125.

Wilson, B.J., and A.W. Hayes. 1973. Microbial toxins. In *Toxicants occurring naturally in foods*. Committee on Food Protection. Washington, DC: National Academy of Sciences.

Wodicka, V.O. 1977. Food safety—rationalizing the ground rules for safety evaluation. *Food Technology* 31:75–79.

Wynder, E.L., N.E.L. Hall, and M. Polansky. 1983. Epidemiology of coffee and pancreatic cancer. *Cancer Research* 43:3900–3906.

Zottola, E.A. 1977. Food-borne disease I. *Contemporary Nutrition* 2(no.9).

PART SIX

NUTRITION THROUGH YOUR LIFE

16

Nutrition for Pregnancy and Lactation: Mothers and Infants

IN THIS CHAPTER: Nutrition Plays a Critical Role during Pregnancy ▪ Rapid Growth during Infancy Calls for High Nutrient Intake ▪ Both Breast Feeding and Bottle Feeding Have Certain Advantages ▪ Older Infants Need the Nutrients That Solid Foods Provide

"You're *what*? You're *pregnant*?"

Take a few moments to speculate on the rest of this scenario. A happy young husband could be responding to the news from his elated wife, both delighted that their plans for starting a family are on target. Or a couple could be facing the news with mixed reactions—anticipating that parenthood will enrich their lives, but wondering how much they will need to change their career-oriented lifestyle. A teenage boy could be recoiling in fright and anger at the news from his panicky girlfriend. Or an older father who has enjoyed his parenting role but is now looking forward to having the children go out on their own could be reacting in shock to the announcement of his equally astounded middle-aged wife.

Pregnancy has a considerable emotional impact on the lives of the prospective mother and father and the people close to them. It also has a substantial effect on nutritional needs. During pregnancy all the raw materials for the development of what becomes the baby must be taken from the supply of nutrients circulating in the mother's bloodstream. Protein for the newly forming organs and muscles, for example, and minerals for the bones and teeth are supplied from the mother's food intake and body stores. (For a newborn baby, the phrase "You are what you eat" may be more appropriately stated "You are what your mother ate.") At the same time, the mother must meet all her own nutritional needs. During pregnancy, then, the mother is truly eating for two. She will be reminded of this by her increased hunger, but she may need information about what foods will best satisfy her greater nutrient needs.

The decision whether to breast- or bottle-feed is an important one that the mother and father must make before delivery. After birth, breast-fed infants continue to rely on their mothers' bodies as their main source of nourishment. Bottle-fed babies consume substitutes for breast milk in the form of various specially designed formulas created by modern technology.

The questions of when to start adding other foods and what these other foods should be are also important parental considerations. In the past, most parents simply adopted the usual practices of their culture, but now we have scientific data to help shape our thinking about the best way to feed babies. This chapter deals with all of these topics.

Nutrition Plays a Critical Role during Pregnancy

A great deal of new tissue develops during pregnancy. Some of it becomes the baby itself, and some becomes materials that are essential for the baby's survival and that leave the mother's body at the time of delivery.

The rest of the new tissue is part of the mother: it helps her body handle the increased metabolic activity pregnancy generates, and produces reserves for later lactation.

Prenatal Development

The growth that takes place between conception and birth is truly phenomenal. A single fertilized egg cell is so small and multiplies so rapidly that after only four weeks it is 7000 times larger than its original size, yet is only one-fifth of an inch long and still less than an ounce in weight (Berger, 1980). By the time the baby is born, he or she will be about 20 inches long and weigh around 7 pounds.

Stages of Development. This growing mass of cells is given different names as it progresses through the phases from fertilization to birth. During the first two weeks after conception, the fertilized egg is called a zygote. Approximately two weeks after fertilization, the zygote attaches itself tightly to the wall of the uterus, the chamber in which it will grow until delivery. At this stage it is called an embryo. In the area of attachment, an organ called the placenta develops; this organ contains the network of blood vessels that allows for the exchange of oxygen, nutrients, and waste products between the blood supplies of the the mother and developing baby. Eight weeks after fertilization, when the future infant's organs are beginning to develop and tissues are assuming distinct functions, the organism is called a fetus, the term that is used until birth. Figure 16.1 pictures these stages of development.

zygote—the name given to a fertilized egg during the first two weeks after conception

embryo—a zygote that has attached to the wall of the uterus

placenta—organ that forms at the site of embryo attachment and contains the blood vessel network that supports the developing baby

fetus—a developing baby from eight weeks after egg fertilization until birth

Importance of Critical Periods. The sequence and rate of tissue formation in the fetus is intricate and methodical. In normal development, the basic tissue structure is established by cells first dividing rapidly. Next, cell division and increases in cell size occur simultaneously. Finally, increases in cell size predominate. Some experts believe that extremely inadequate or extremely excessive maternal intake of nutrients or toxicants, respectively, is more likely to have serious consequences during the stages of rapid cell division; they refer to these as the critical periods. [Although some recent questions have been raised about the sequence of these events (Dobbing, 1984), this theory still has many adherents.]

Examples of the effects of malnutrition during critical periods have been demonstrated in animals. If a pregnant rat is placed on a diet devoid of zinc during certain periods of gestation (pregnancy), distinct abnormalities such as cleft palate will occur in the offspring. If the deficiency occurs at a different stage of pregnancy, different abnormalities may occur (Hurley, 1980). The form of abnormality is determined by the timing of the deficiency (Worthington-Roberts et al., 1981). Depending on when and for how long the deficiency occurs—perhaps just a few days, for example—it might be possible to make up for it and prevent the negative effects.

The concept of critical periods applies to the possibility of malformations resulting from the mother's use of prescription, over-the-counter,

critical periods—developmental stages involving rapid cell division, during which maternal nutrient intake can have the greatest consequences for the baby

gestation—development of the future baby from fertilization to birth

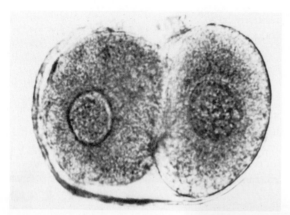
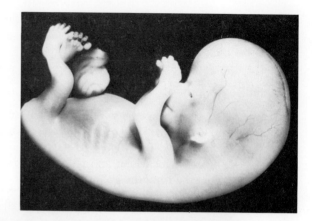
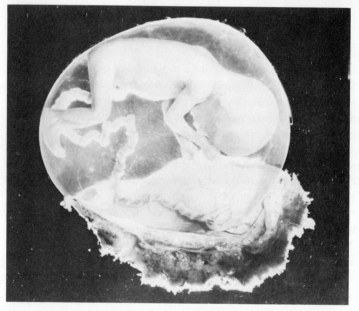

Figure 16.1 Stages of development between conception and birth. The zygote has just begun the process of cell division. The organism pictured on the upper right is eight weeks old, ending the embryonic phase. The lower photo was taken during the fetal stage.

teratogens—factors (including drugs, radiation, and disease) that can cause birth defects

or recreational drugs; her exposure to radiation and pollutants; and the occurrence of diseases such as rubella. These factors are called teratogens (factors that can cause birth defects). Most teratogens are much more likely to cause specific birth defects if the mother is exposed to them during particular weeks of pregnancy (Berger, 1980). Figure 16.2 shows when various body tissues are most vulnerable to damage.

Impact of Birth Weight. The weight of a baby at birth is a strong indicator of the baby's physical condition. Babies weighing less than 2500 grams (about $5\frac{1}{2}$ pounds) at birth are referred to as low-birth-weight babies, and have significantly increased chances of experiencing health problems in the first few months of life. They are also 20 times more likely to die in their first year than babies of higher birth weight (Public Health Service, 1979).

low-birth-weight babies—infants weighing less than about $5\frac{1}{2}$ pounds at birth and having a high risk of health problems

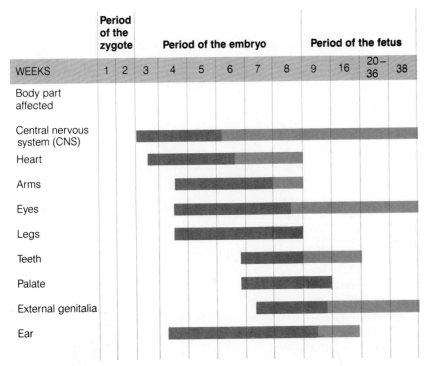

WEEKS	Period of the zygote		Period of the embryo						Period of the fetus			
	1	2	3	4	5	6	7	8	9	16	20–36	38
Body part affected												
Central nervous system (CNS)												
Heart												
Arms												
Eyes												
Legs												
Teeth												
Palate												
External genitalia												
Ear												

Figure 16.2 Vulnerable periods for various parts of the developing body. Different tissues, organs, and systems develop at different times during pregnancy. The critical period theory of development states that injury from nutritional extremes or teratogenic agents is more likely to occur during these periods of rapid development. The darker parts of the bars indicate when damage is likely to be more severe than when the bars are lighter. (Adapted from Moore, KL: *The Developing Human*, 3/e. Philadelphia: W.B. Saunders Co., 1982. Reprinted by permission.

The effects of low birth weight can persist in later years. The health of the next generation can even be affected: a study has shown that the babies of mothers who had weighed 2000 grams or less *when they themselves were born* were more likely to have problems than the babies of mothers who had weighed more at birth. The babies of these low-birth-weight mothers were more likely at birth to require intensive care, to have respiratory difficulties, and to die (Hackman et al., 1983).

Changes in the Mother's Body

The fetus is not the only organism experiencing rapid development. The pregnant woman is also undergoing significant changes.

Weight Gain from Tissue Growth. The most obvious change in the mother is the gain in weight. Figure 16.3 shows the components accounting for the weight added during a normal pregnancy. Notice that the total desirable gain is approximately 25 pounds, and that most of this will occur during the last two-thirds of pregnancy.

When the baby is born, the typical mother loses less than half the weight she gained during a normal, healthy pregnancy. During labor and delivery, materials that leave the mother's body besides the baby are amniotic fluid (liquid that surrounded the fetus in the uterus) and the placenta. The rest of the gained weight is in maternal tissues, such as the mother's increased blood supply and tissue fluid, and breast enlargement, which occurs in preparation for lactation after delivery. Therefore the new mother

Figure 16.3 The components of weight gain during pregnancy. (Adapted from *Maternal Nutrition in the Course of Pregnancy*, 1970, with the permission of the National Academy Press, Washington, D.C.)

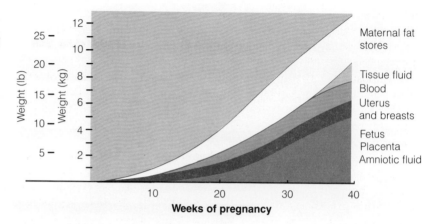

who weighs more after delivery than she did when she became pregnant truly is the "right" weight for that time.

Twenty years ago it was common to restrict the weight gain of a pregnant woman to about 10 pounds so that the baby would be small and easy to deliver. This helped prevent the need for some Cesarean section deliveries, which were very dangerous at that time. It also meant that after the birth of the baby the mother would have less weight to lose to return to her prepregnant weight.

We now know that the healthiest babies are born to mothers who gain 22 to 28 pounds during pregnancy. Therefore, severe restriction of weight gain is no longer recommended. Even women who are already overweight should gain at least 16 pounds during pregnancy (National Research Council, 1970). Pregnancy is *not* the time to shed excess weight.

Other Changes. About one-third of pregnant women experience some degree of "morning sickness." Many women who are troubled by this problem report relief from their nausea if they keep some food in their stomachs at all times. They do this by eating small, frequent meals; by drinking fluids between meals rather than with them; and by eating something bland like a few crackers or toast before getting out of bed in the morning (Satter, 1983).

Constipation is another common problem accompanying pregnancy. It may occur because the gastrointestinal tract works more slowly during pregnancy. In addition, the crowding of the colon by the fetus—especially late in pregnancy—can make elimination more difficult. It is important to consume adequate sources of fiber and fluid at this time to help relieve the problem. Exercising also helps.

Nutrient Needs during Pregnancy

Changes in the fetus and the mother lead to an increased need for nutrients.

Recommended Dietary Allowances for Pregnancy. The Recommended Dietary Allowances for all nutrients increase during pregnancy, but the allowances for some nutrients increase more than for others (Figure 16.4). Those that increase by 50% or more are protein, vitamin D, folacin, iron, calcium, phosphorus, and magnesium. The needs for others increase from 15% to 50%.

Almost 1000 grams of protein are deposited in the fetal and maternal tissues during the course of a typical pregnancy. The 1980 RDA committee suggests that an extra 30 grams of protein per day be added to the pregnant woman's diet; this amount more than meets the demands of the pregnancy.

The increasing amount of proteinaceous tissue causes the mother's basal metabolic rate (BMR) to increase, and she therefore uses extra kcalories to maintain BMR. However, if she becomes less physically active during this period, the increased energy needs for BMR are somewhat offset by energy savings from physical activity. An extra energy intake of 300 kcalories per day is recommended in the second and third trimesters (three-month periods) of pregnancy (National Research Council, 1980). Obviously, "eating for two" does not give license to double the amount of food eaten.

The extra energy utilization also increases the need for several of the B-vitamins. Essential nutrients such as calcium, iron, sodium, potassium, folacin, and vitamin B-12 are important for the development of bones, blood, and other tissues. It is especially important that these substances be provided in adequate but not excessive amounts because excessive amounts of one nutrient can sometimes suppress the bioavailability of another nutrient. For example, excessive iron supplements can depress zinc absorption.

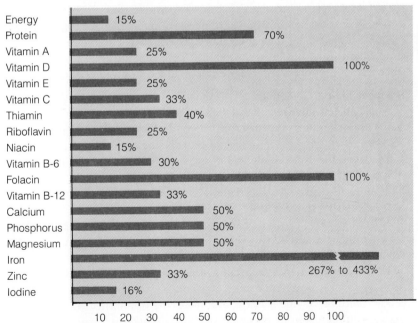

% above recommendations for nonpregnant adult female

Figure 16.4 Increased nutrients recommended for adult pregnancy (and lactation). During pregnancy, nutrient intakes should increase above prepregnancy recommendations, as shown in the chart. During lactation, recommended intakes for most nutrients are even higher than during pregnancy; the exceptions to this are protein, vitamin B-6, folacin, and iron. (Data from National Research Council. 1980. Recommended Dietary Allowances. Washington, DC: National Academy Press.)

preeclampsia—a serious complication of pregnancy involving sudden, drastic fluid retention and hypertension

In the past, sodium was commonly restricted during pregnancy in the belief that this would help women avoid certain problems that might occur during pregnancy and delivery, such as preeclampsia. Preeclampsia (less accurately called "toxemia") is a serious complication of pregnancy that is characterized by sudden and drastic fluid retention (edema) and hypertension. Since excess sodium can cause edema in persons with poor kidney function, excess sodium was thought to be a factor in preeclampsia as well; for this reason, sodium intake of pregnant women was kept to a minimum. We now know that severe sodium restriction can interfere with the development of the fetus and that it is not effective in preventing preeclampsia, so sodium intake during pregnancy is no longer restricted to abnormally low levels (National Research Council, 1980).

Supplements for Pregnancy. The requirements for some nutrients increase substantially during pregnancy. Folacin and iron are especially important for the normal development of the fetus: folacin for cell division, and iron for expanding the blood volume, developing the placenta and other tissues, and building a reserve for blood that may be lost during delivery.

The National Academy of Sciences recommends supplements of 30 to 60 milligrams of iron per day during pregnancy, and for the first two or three months after birth to restore the mother's iron reserves. Supplements of folacin at approximately the RDA level (800 µg per day) are often recommended during pregnancy, especially for women with low dietary intakes (National Research Council, 1980).

Pregnant women can meet their needs for other nutrients by eating a balanced and varied diet. They need other supplements only if they have very restrictive dietary patterns or higher-than-normal needs for some reason. Many physicians nonetheless recommend that all their pregnant patients take a multivitamin and mineral supplement. This is not hazardous unless the amounts of nutrients are excessive or unbalanced. Such a supplement must not be regarded as a replacement for a balanced diet, since many essential nutrients are not included in supplements.

Practical Eating Guidelines for Pregnancy. The principles of adequacy, balance, and variety that characterize a good diet for any person are even more important for the pregnant woman. So is nutrient density, since recommended intakes of nutrients increase by anywhere from 15% to 100% (more for iron), while energy is increased by only 15%. This means that the 300 extra kcalories added to the diet per day should come from high-nutrient-density foods; pregnancy is a time to limit the intake of low-nutrient-density items to only occasional use.

To meet the increased energy and nutrient recommendations, pregnant women are advised to eat extra servings of foods from the SANE guide, as summarized in Table 16.1. Note that increases above the usual adult intakes are suggested in almost every category. The recommended minimal intake of milk and milk products doubles, meats and alternates should increase by one serving, and a serving of another vitamin C-rich food should be eaten. A pregnant woman's hunger and satiety cues may lead her to eat other amounts than these minimal recommendations suggest. Although hunger and satiety signals are often useful guidelines for

Table 16.1 SANE Guide for Pregnancy and Lactation

Food group	Minimum servings daily	
	Nonpregnant adults	Pregnant and lactating females
Fruits and vegetables	4[a]	5[b]
Grain products	4	4 or more
Milk and milk products	2	4[c]
Meats and alternates	2	3

[a]Includes one vitamin C–rich and one vitamin A (carotene)–rich food daily.
[b]Includes two servings of vitamin C–rich and one vitamin A (carotene)–rich food daily.
[c]For pregnant teenagers, increase to at least five servings daily.

intake, if the resulting weight gain is either seriously inadequate or grossly excessive, more deliberate diet planning is necessary.

Vegetarians should be especially careful to take in *enough* energy, protein, vitamins, and minerals during pregnancy. Total vegetarians (vegans) may have difficulty meeting their high nutrient needs and promoting mineral absorption. Because some vegans impose additional restrictions on themselves such as limiting the variety of foods they eat and/or avoiding fortified or enriched foods or appropriate vitamin/mineral supplements, pregnant vegans have a greater risk of deficiency (Dwyer, 1979). Therefore, they should seek the advice of a qualified nutritionist for planning a diet that is nutritionally adequate.

A Special Program for High-Risk Pregnant Women. The Women's, Infants' and Children's Program (WIC) is a nationwide, federally funded program that provides special foods, nutrition education, and medical referral services to low-income women who have high-risk pregnancies. The birth weight of infants and the iron status of mothers who received WIC Program services and foods have been found to be better than those of infants and women not on the program (Hicks et al., 1982).

Women's, Infants' and Children's Program (WIC)— national federally funded program that provides nutritional and medical support for low-income women who have high-risk pregnancies

Concerns about Dietary Toxicants during Pregnancy

Just as it is important to provide enough of the essential nutrients for fetal development, it is also critically important to avoid dangerous levels of substances that could interfere with it. As mentioned earlier, prescription, over-the-counter, and recreational drugs can have teratogenic effects. Alcohol has also been implicated for its ability to cause harm.

Alcohol. Like many other substances, alcohol in the mother's bloodstream will cross the placenta and circulate in the baby's bloodstream. At some level, alcohol interferes with the growth processes in the embryo or fetus, possibly by reducing the supply of oxygen flowing through the placenta and/or by blocking the activity of essential nutrients.

The effects of alcohol are thought to increase in severity in proportion to the amount of alcohol consumed, and to vary in effect depending on the stage of pregnancy. Excess alcohol during the first three months of pregnancy is thought to be most often associated with the development of physical abnormalities. Animal studies and observations of humans indicate that one or more episodes of binge drinking during the early stages of pregnancy are most likely to produce low-birth-weight babies and children with impaired mental functions (Wright et al., 1983). Alcohol in the second three months can increase the risk of miscarriage. And during the third trimester, alcohol abuse is most likely to reduce the rate of growth of the fetus (American Medical Association, 1983). Even heavy alcohol use before conception has been associated with low birth weight (Little et al., 1980).

In the 1960s the name fetal alcohol syndrome (FAS) was given to the set of abnormalities seen among some children of women who consumed large amounts of alcohol during pregnancy. FAS is now considered the third most common cause of mental handicap and the most common preventable cause of mental impairment in the United States (Little and Streissguth, 1981). The typical abnormalities of FAS include unusual facial features (Figure 16.5), poor growth before and after birth, and central nervous system disorders including mental retardation (American Medical Association, 1983).

Although experts agree that frequent heavy drinking during pregnancy is dangerous to the developing fetus, studies regarding the effect of light-to-moderate use of alcohol have produced conflicting results, partly because of the difficulty in separating the effects of alcohol from other factors such as smoking and poor diet. Thus, no threshold level has been defined; that is, there is no level of alcohol consumption known to be completely risk-free during pregnancy. The American Medical Association advises: "Physicians should be explicit in reinforcing the concept that, with several aspects of the issue still in doubt, the safest course is abstinence" (American Medical Association, 1983).

Caffeine.   Caffeine is a drug naturally present in coffee, tea, and chocolate. It is also added to colas and other soft drinks and to certain medications (see Chapter 15).

Because caffeine is a stimulant that crosses the placenta and circulates in the fetal bloodstream, there has been concern that its use during pregnancy may have detrimental effects on the fetus. Animal studies using *very* high levels of caffeine have shown that it can cause abnormalities.

Several studies have been conducted to determine whether these effects can occur in humans as well; the results have generally been negative. It has been shown that women who consume relatively large amounts of caffeine during pregnancy have smaller, less healthy babies; but this may actually result from other factors common in the same women, such as smoking and alcohol use (Linn et al., 1982).

Most experts believe that alcohol and smoking cause more damage to unborn children than caffeine, but the potential for adverse effects of

fetal alcohol syndrome (FAS)—condition occurring in some children of alcoholic mothers, involving certain characteristic abnormalities

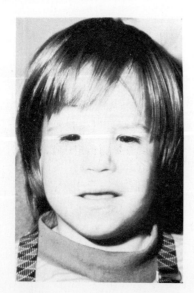

Figure 16.5 A child with fetal alcohol syndrome (FAS). This child shows several characteristic symptoms of FAS: wide space between the eyes, small nose, and long upper lip.

high doses of caffeine still exists during pregnancy. Therefore, the Food and Drug Administration and the National Academy of Sciences recommend that pregnant women avoid high intakes of caffeine from food and drugs during pregnancy (National Research Council, 1980; Lecos, 1980).

Pica. Another dietary practice thought to be potentially dangerous during pregnancy is pica. Pica is the ingestion of substances that are not food, such as clay, laundry starch, or chalk. It is practiced by some members of certain socioeconomic and racial groups, especially black women from the rural South (National Research Council, 1970). Some people believe that pica is a response to a deficiency of iron or other nutrients, but this theory has not been scientifically proved.

> **pica**—the ingestion of nonfood substances such as clay, laundry starch, or chalk

The nutritional significance of pica depends on the type and amount of the nonfood items consumed. Some items (such as starch) are significant because they provide empty kcalories and displace foods that could have provided additional nutrients. Other substances (such as clay) can bind dietary minerals into a nonabsorbable form. Clay and chalk may also contain dangerously high levels of lead.

Interactions of These and Other Factors

Nutrient deficiencies and intake of toxic substances rarely occur as isolated factors. Usually other things influence the developing embryo/fetus, many of which are not directly related to diet. Maternal immaturity (being younger than 17), a large number of previous pregnancies, low socioeconomic status, low physical activity, infections, and certain diseases can also increase the risk of prenatal (before birth) complications.

Interactions between various dietary and nondietary hazards may be especially dangerous to the developing fetus. For instance, the combination of smoking and drinking alcohol is likely to be more dangerous than either practice by itself (Wright et al., 1983). Therefore pregnancy calls for an evaluation of many lifestyle factors, not only nutritional ones.

Rapid Growth during Infancy Calls for High Nutrient Intake

During the first year of life, growth in both length and weight is more rapid than at any other period of life outside the womb. A normal infant doubles his or her birth weight by about four months, and triples it by the end of the first year. The child's height at one year is usually 150% of his or her birth length. This rapid growth causes infants to have the highest nutrient needs per unit of body weight of any age group. The decision of what to feed a baby is thus an important matter.

Continuing Growth

The growth taking place in the infant involves all types of tissue. A lack of nutrients during the first few months after birth can result in a slowing of growth. If adequate feeding is restored later in the first year, part of that deficit can usually be made up. Sometimes, but not always, catch-up growth is complete.

Body growth is important for its own sake, but is also critical because of its relationship to brain growth. In fact, one expert states that the most that can be done nutritionally to promote good *brain* growth is to encourage optimal *body* growth from pregnancy until the second or third birthday (Dobbing, 1984).

Physical Status

At the time of birth, there are no microorganisms in the infant's colon. Vitamin K cannot be produced in the gut until intestinal bacteria become established, which begins to occur as the infant starts taking nourishment.

The newborn's kidneys are not fully developed at the time of birth, so they do not have the ability to concentrate urine as the older child's and adult's kidneys can. Therefore infants require about $1\frac{1}{2}$ ml of water per kcalorie ingested to remove waste products from the body. The gastrointestinal tract is also immature. Gastric secretions, stomach acid, and the production of certain enzymes may be low. These factors suggest that it is wise to limit the infant's intake during the first four to six months of life to appropriately dilute fluids that are easy to digest, such as breast milk or formula.

extrusion reflex—reflex reaction in young babies, in which the tongue is pushed forward and solid food is rejected

Another clue that infants are not prepared for solid foods is the reaction that occurs when solids are put into a baby's mouth; a reflex reaction called the extrusion reflex pushes the tongue forward and ejects the food. However, the infant is adept at sucking and swallowing liquids, the skills needed for delivering milk from the breast or bottle to the stomach.

Nutritional Status

A healthy full-term infant (one who was born to a well-nourished mother after nine months of normal gestation) has built up a reserve supply of some nutrients. For example, iron stored in the newborn's liver can meet his or her needs for several months while the child is on a low-iron diet of breast milk.

However, a steady supply of most nutrients is essential for proper growth and development. These nutrients are especially critical for babies who are born without adequate reserves; low-birth-weight babies are usually more susceptible to the effects of poor diet and disease.

Both Breast Feeding and Bottle Feeding Have Certain Advantages

Against this backdrop, let's look at what breast milk and formulas have to offer the infant.

What Breast Milk Has to Offer the Infant

It is amazing how perfectly human milk matches the human baby's needs. In terms of the nutrients it contains, other benefits it confers, and the amount that is produced, breast milk meets the infant's needs as no other substance or source can.

Nutrients and Immune Factors in Colostrum. Colostrum is the watery liquid produced by the breasts during the first few days after birth. It is higher in protein and some minerals than mature breast milk. It also contains antibodies and special cells that increase the baby's immunity to several diseases.

colostrum—watery liquid produced by the breasts of mothers during the first few days after birth

Nutrients and Immune Factors in Mature Milk. Colostrum is replaced by mature breast milk about four or five days after delivery. Mature breast milk, too, provides unique benefits for the infant.

- *Lactobacillus bifidus* (the bifidus factor) is a beneficial microorganism found in breast milk that prevents the growth of dangerous bacteria in the intestine. Lactoferrin, an iron-containing protein in breast milk, also discourages the growth of potentially harmful bacteria (Winick, 1982).

- The proteins in breast milk are mostly lactalbumins, which are easier for the infant to digest than the casein proteins of non–heat-treated cow's milk.

- Lactose is the main carbohydrate in human and animal milks. It is present at a higher level in human milk than in cow's milk, and it promotes the absorption of calcium and some other minerals.

- Breast milk also has some unique lipids. Fats supply about half of the kcalories in breast milk, and the structure of the triglycerides makes them highly absorbable (Filer et al., 1969).

- The mineral content of breast milk is likewise well suited to the infant's needs. The ratio of calcium to phosphorus is approximately 2:1, which facilitates absorption. Although the iron content is low, it is very readily absorbed by the infant.

- If the mother is well nourished, the vitamin content of her milk will be adequate for the baby's needs, but inadequacies in the mother's diet will be reflected in lower quantities of some vitamins in her milk. This has been shown for B-6 and B-12; it may be true for others as well.

Composition Changed during the Feeding. The composition of mother's milk changes somewhat within a feeding period. The water content of breast milk is initially high; thus, the baby gets relatively dilute milk at the beginning of the feeding session when he or she is very thirsty. As the feeding continues, the fat content increases, the milk is more concentrated, and the baby's hunger is satisfied more quickly (Winick, 1982).

Volume Influenced by the Baby's Intake. The amount of milk the lactating mother produces changes in response to the baby's needs. As the baby grows and requires more milk, he signals his need by more thoroughly emptying his mother's breasts and by wanting to eat more often. Emptying the breasts causes them to make more milk. Conversely, decreased emptying of the breasts causes them to make less milk. That's why a mother who feeds her young infant with formula in place of breast milk on frequent occasions may find that her supply of milk decreases so much that it becomes difficult to resume more regular breast feeding later.

Volume Influenced by the Mother's Diet. In some instances the mother may not produce enough milk to satisfy her baby's needs. If her energy intake is inadequate (due to poor eating habits, dieting to lose weight, or being "too busy to eat"), her milk output may be low despite her infant's deliberate message about wanting more (Satter, 1983). This is less of a problem in the developed countries than in the developing countries, where food shortages and poverty can compromise the ability of some mothers to nourish their children adequately by breast feeding.

Less-Likely Allergy. The newborn infant's immature intestine allows the passage of some whole proteins into the bloodstream. You already know a benefit of this: the infant can absorb antibodies from breast milk. However, this ability to absorb whole proteins also allows other foreign proteins to get into the baby's bloodstream, setting the stage for an allergic reaction (see Chapter 8, on proteins). Since the proteins in human milk do not provoke allergies as often as the proteins in other milks or foods, infants fed exclusively on breast milk in the first months of life are less prone to allergies.

What Formulas Have to Offer the Infant

Various formulas have different characteristics, and some are nutritionally satisfactory substitutes for breast milk for most infants. Be aware, though, that formula cannot provide immunological factors or reduce the likelihood of allergies, as breast milk can.

Cow's Milk Formulas. Most infant formulas are made from cow's milk that has been modified to resemble breast milk as closely as possible. However, the major protein in cow's milk—casein—is difficult for a baby to digest: it makes a tough curd in the stomach. For that reason, most milk-based formulas have been heat-treated in a way that makes the casein easier to digest. The butterfat is replaced by polyunsaturated vegetable oils that are more readily absorbed. Additional lactose or other carbohydrate is incorporated; vitamins and most minerals are also added to resemble the levels in human milk.

One mineral about which there is some debate is iron. Some experts believe that because a normally healthy newborn has enough iron stored in the liver to last for approximately six months, no extra iron is needed in infant formula. They suggest that extra iron may actually have a negative effect. Their thinking has come from two different types of observations. One is that some infants who have been fed iron-fortified formula experience gastrointestinal distress from it. The other is that high iron

Infant feeding—breast or bottle?—Before delivery of the baby, parents must choose between breast and bottle feeding. Nutritional and immunological factors are important, but many other considerations enter into this decision as well (see text).

intakes seem to encourage the growth of pathogenic organisms in some infants. This latter observation has been seen in developing countries, where iron deficiency is often accompanied by low-grade infections; when iron was supplemented, the infections worsened. Other experts believe that infants benefit from iron-supplemented formula: if babies get iron in their diets, they will not deplete their own stores. Because these different points of view exist, most infant formula producers make two types of product—one fortified with iron and one not fortified. A pediatrician's advice can be helpful in deciding which to choose.

Another choice to make in buying formula involves its dilution. Most formulas are available as a powder, a liquid concentrate, or a ready-to-use beverage. The first two need to be reconstituted with appropriate amounts of water before use, which affects both convenience and cost.

Soy Formulas. Some infant formulas are made from the protein of soybeans. Such formulas tend to have a slightly higher protein level and a slightly lower carbohydrate level than cow's milk formulas. Also, mineral bioavailability is likely to be lower, since these products are of plant origin. Due to such differences, these products should be used only on a pediatrician's advice.

Soy formulas may be recommended for infants who are potentially allergic to milk or milk formulas, and for the management of conditions in which lactose must be avoided. However, soy formulas are not recommended for infants who have already shown signs of allergy. Soy pro-

Bonding.—Close interaction between parent and child produces a closeness known as bonding.

tein, like cow's milk protein, is a common allergen. An infant who has reacted strongly to cow's milk protein is also likely to react strongly to soy protein. Colic (persistent abdominal pain in young infants) is seldom relieved by switching to soy formula, so its use in these cases is questionable (American Academy of Pediatrics, 1983c).

Other Formulas. Whole cow's milk or formulas made from it at home are not recommended for the first six months of life. After the baby drinks from a cup and consumes a significant proportion (about one-third) of kcalories from solid foods that provide iron, vitamin C, and carbohydrate, whole cow's milk may begin to replace breast milk or formula. Before that time, using whole milk may result in inadequate intake of some nutrients. Furthermore, some young infants become anemic on cow's milk because it may cause low-level intestinal bleeding (American Academy of Pediatrics, 1983a).

Low fat milks (2%, 1%, or skim) are not recommended for use in the first year, because they do not provide sufficient essential fatty acids. Furthermore, they have larger amounts of electrolytes and proteins that cannot easily be handled by immature kidneys (Fomon, 1974).

Other Factors in the Breast vs. Bottle Decision

Besides the very important matter of what nutrients breast milk and formulas provide, other factors often influence the breast-feeding vs. bottle-feeding decision as well. These include cultural trends, psychological factors, convenience, economy, safety, health of the mother, anticipated effects on the weight status of both mother and infant, effect on fertility, and fear of failure.

Even though breast feeding is the better alternative from nutritional and immunological perspectives, each case must be decided individually. No single decision is right for all families.

Trends in Infant Feeding. At the turn of the century, breast milk was the major source of nutrients for babies throughout infancy. The percentage of mothers who breast-fed their babies began to decline in the early years of this century; by the 1950s, only 20% of women in the United States chose to breast-feed (Beal, 1984). During the 1970s, breast feeding became more popular; by 1980, about 60% of newborn infants were breast-fed (American Academy of Pediatrics, 1982). Nowadays the most common practice is to breast-feed for the first few months, and then switch to a commercial infant formula until whole milk is used later in the first year (Hendershot, 1980).

A Psychological Factor. The healthy physical and mental development of an infant is thought to be promoted by the special feeling of love and attachment called bonding that can occur between parent and baby (Ansfield and Lipper, 1983). Although many different types of interaction can encourage bonding, breast feeding is an ideal situation for fostering it. Bottle feeding can also lead to bonding if the parent holds and interacts with the baby during feeding.

> **bonding**—special feeling of love and attachment that can occur between parent and baby

Convenience. Many mothers find breast feeding to be more convenient than bottle feeding because the milk is already sanitary and at the proper temperature, and because there is no need to purchase, clean, and tote special materials.

However, breast feeding may be inconvenient for some women, especially if they return to work outside the home and the employer does not offer a conveniently close child-care facility. In this case, the mother must choose among these options: coming home for feedings; pumping her breasts beforehand and refrigerating the milk so that somebody else can give it to the baby in her absence; or breast feeding the baby when she is at home, and leaving formula when she is away.

Economy. The nursing mother should consume about 500 more kcalories daily than she did before she was pregnant. The cost of the extra food is the major expense of lactation. Breast feeding can be much less expensive than formula feeding, but the savings are variable, depending on the foods selected by the nursing mother and the type of formula used for bottle feeding (Satter, 1983).

Safety. Breast milk is free of harmful bacteria when consumed directly by the baby. Formula is also clean and sanitary when it is prepared and stored according to the manufacturer's instructions. The sanitation of formula is not a common concern when it is prepared and stored properly, but this is difficult if not impossible in some situations.

In developing countries where water supplies are contaminated and refrigeration is not available, breast feeding is a much safer alternative. In families where poverty and lack of education are problems, parents may try to dilute the formula with extra water to save money or because they cannot read and understand the directions. Here, too, breast feeding is much safer.

Women who have been exposed to high levels of toxic substances may excrete a portion of these materials in their milk. This is especially true of contaminants such as PCBs and certain insecticides that are deposited in the mother's fatty tissues. If a woman suspects that she has been exposed to high levels of such substances, her physician may recommend that her milk be tested to determine if contaminants are present at hazardous levels (Rogan et al., 1980).

A woman who is taking medications or using any sort of drugs should check with her physician about the safety of breast feeding. Many drugs are secreted in breast milk, and some can have harmful effects on the baby (American Academy of Pediatrics, 1983b). If the mother takes oral contraceptive agents (OCAs), some of the hormone will get through to the baby. The potential long-term adverse effects on a baby are debated, but we do know that taking OCAs may decrease the breast milk supply (Satter, 1983).

Alcohol should be used in only small amounts, if at all, because it too is partly secreted in the milk. Smoking causes nicotine and other substances to enter the milk. Caffeine is also partially secreted in milk, so the lactating mother should moderate her use of coffee and other foods or drugs that contain caffeine.

Health of the Mother. If the mother has a chronic illness, she should discuss with her physician whether breast feeding is advisable. With some conditions, the baby may be put at risk; in other cases, breast feeding might cause too much physical stress for the mother; or it may be fine.

Nursing Bottle Caries. If a baby intermittently and over a number of hours sucks on a bottle of milk, formula, juice, or any other liquid containing fermentable carbohydrates, she is at risk of developing nursing bottle caries, or rampant tooth decay. It is especially risky to give a bottle of sugary liquids to a baby when she goes to bed, for a combination of reasons. The production of saliva decreases when a baby sleeps; the liquid may pool in the baby's mouth during sleep; and the baby may suck on the bottle frequently during the night, whenever she is partially awake. These factors all favor the production of acid by bacteria in the mouth, which can lead to extensive tooth decay.

Nursing bottle caries are not a problem for breast-fed babies. They need not be a problem for bottle-fed babies, either, if parents are aware of the risk and act to avoid it.

nursing bottle caries—tooth decay resulting from the prolonged exposure to fermentable carbohydrates, as when fed in baby bottles

Anticipated Weight Gain of the Baby. Caregivers may encourage babies to finish a bottle to avoid wasting formula. Original research has shown that this can lead to overconsumption and higher weights in bottle-fed infants, whereas the problem doesn't arise in breast-fed infants, since the child's appetite is more likely to control his or her intake.

This does not mean that bottle-fed babies are doomed to being over-fat. If parents are aware of the risk of overfeeding, they can watch for the child's satiety signals and let the baby determine the volume of intake. A more recent study has shown that at age 4, the weights of children who were bottle-fed and breast-fed were very similar (Wolman, 1984).

Weight Status of the Mother. A woman who breast feeds her infant often loses the fat she added during pregnancy within six months of delivery, especially if she resumes her prepregnancy level of physical activity. Women who do not breast feed are not as likely to lose the surplus fat, unless they deliberately restrict their food intake and exercise more.

Likelihood of Baby Illnesses. Babies who are breast-fed not only have fewer allergies, but also have less difficulty with colic, diarrhea, and constipation than bottle-fed infants. They have fewer serious illnesses and infections, partly because of the temporary immunities they acquire through breast milk (Nutrition Foundation, 1980). The fact that there are fewer infections in breast-fed infants is not solely a matter of cause and effect, however. Other factors such as the education of the mother have been found to account in part for such differences (Holmes et al., 1983).

Contraception. Breast feeding women do not resume ovulation and menstruation as quickly as women who bottle feed their babies. In populations where breast feeding is the norm, the average time between children is lengthened (Young et al., 1982). This can be an important advantage in developing countries, where bearing children at close intervals can place excessive strain on the family's resources.

However, it is important to be aware that *lactation is not a reliable means of birth control.* Parents who want to avoid another pregnancy must use contraceptive practices that are more reliable.

Fear of Failure. Some women, for various reasons, fear that they will not be successful at breast feeding. Fear of failure can be a stumbling block: anxiety can interfere with the normal hormonal processes that allow milk to be let-down from where it is produced in breast glands to the nipples.

If a prospective mother or new mother has such fears but nonetheless wants to breast feed, she should seek out a health care professional who is known to be supportive of breast feeding. An experienced and caring professional can help a woman understand the normal process of lactation, learn some helpful techniques, and get a perspective on her feelings.

Most new parents experience some anxiety. Nonetheless, the vast majority of women who choose to breast feed are successful at it.

Mother's Nutrient Needs during Lactation

Just as production of new tissues during pregnancy calls for additional energy and nutrients, so does production of milk.

Recommended Dietary Allowances for Lactation. A breast-feeding mother needs, on the average, 500 kcalories more each day than she needed before pregnancy. Note that this is even more energy than is needed for the latter part of pregnancy itself by 200 kcalories more per day. Her needs for protein, vitamins, and minerals also increase; recommended intakes of many nutrients go up anywhere from 25% to 100% above the amounts needed before pregnancy.

Supplements for Lactation. As mentioned earlier, it is reasonable for lactating women to continue with iron supplementation for several months after delivery to replenish their own stores. Strict vegetarians need vitamin B-12 supplements as well, and possibly vitamin D and riboflavin. Other needs can be met through a well-chosen diet.

Practical Eating Guidelines for Lactation. During lactation, the recommended *minimal* intake of foods according to the SANE guide is similar to that for pregnancy (Table 16.1). A lactating mother can increase her energy intake beyond what the minimum provides by adding extra foods from whichever groups she prefers.

A nursing mother must drink extra liquids daily to make up for what she secretes in her milk. An extra four or more cups of water or other fluids each day is recommended for lactation. Many women, prompted by thirst, automatically consume this amount. Others use a more deliberate approach, drinking a glass of milk or water every time they nurse the baby; this is an easy way to ensure adequate water intake.

Supplements for Infants

Healthy infants whose only food is breast milk or infant formula need few supplements to this, although there are some exceptions and qualifications. Most infants are given an injection of vitamin K at birth, since they have no gut bacteria to produce it initially. Having vitamin K in the system could be important—for example, if a baby experiences an injury that makes blood clotting necessary. The breast-fed infant also needs supplemental vitamin D. Fluoride supplements should be given to breast-fed infants, and to infants whose formula is prepared with water that has less than 0.3 part per million of fluoride.

The pros and cons of iron fortification of infant formulas were discussed earlier. There is a similar debate about whether the breast-fed infant should be given iron supplements as a hedge against later anemia. On this matter, take the advice of a trusted pediatrician.

Water should be given to infants during hot weather, or if they have diarrhea or have been vomiting.

Older Infants Need the Nutrients That Solid Foods Provide

Introducing Solid Foods

Thinking has changed in recent years concerning when babies should be started on solid foods. Several decades ago, when convenient baby foods were new on the market, proud parents looked on a baby's early eating of solid foods as a sign of accelerated intellectual and physical development. (It was also believed that eating solid foods would encourage a baby to sleep through the night—a theory that has not been substantiated by many babies.) However, getting solid foods into a young child was found to be no proof that he or she was ready for them. Some parents actually resorted to using "feeders," which squirted food into the back of the mouth because the baby was unable to move it there.

Now we believe that the introduction of solids to infants' diets should be based on when they are physically ready to handle those foods, and on when they need the nutrients that such foods can provide. These two conditions occur at approximately the same time—four to six months of age.

Nutritional Need. At four to six months of age, the infant's iron stores are likely to be running low, especially if the baby has not received iron supplements. In addition, the rapidly growing infant can benefit from eating some solids, which tend to be more concentrated in energy than breast milk or formula.

Physical Readiness. Physical development is the most reliable indicator of a child's readiness for solid foods. Somewhere between four and six months of age, many changes occur that enhance a baby's ability to handle solid foods. First, a baby learns to swallow solids at about this time. His kidneys can concentrate urine more efficiently. He can sit in a high chair. He can show his eagerness for more food when he is hungry, and turn his head away or otherwise refuse food when his hunger is satisfied. It is important to respect these cues in order to avoid overfeeding. All of these indicators show that he is physically ready to eat foods from a spoon.

Sequence and Timing. Because iron stores are largely depleted at six months, it is a good idea to feed iron-fortified infant cereals as the first solid food. Some pediatricians recommend that rice or barley cereals be used until seven to nine months of age since they are less likely to provoke an allergic response than wheat cereals.

Once cereals have been successfully incorporated into a child's diet and the infant has mastered the skill of getting semisolid food from a spoon and swallowing it, he or she is ready for more challenging textures. Cooked, fork-mashed, or diced fruits and vegetables fed by spoon or self-fed by fingers offer a developmentally and nutritionally logical next step.

Adding solid foods to an infant's diet. The appropriate time to begin giving solid food to infants is between four and six months of age, when they are physically ready and need the nutrients.

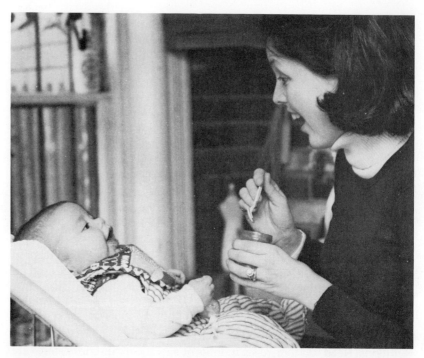

The addition of meat can be postponed until a child begins eating from the table, somewhere near the end of the first year.

When a new food is added to an infant's diet, it should be included in small amounts for several days before another new food is tried. In this way, if there are allergic reactions, the offending food can easily be identified.

When solid foods represent a large part of the child's food intake, caregivers should offer extra liquids, since solid foods contain less water than the breast milk or formula that they are partially replacing.

Table 16.2 summarizes the recommendations for the introduction of solid foods to the infant diet. This table does not need to be followed slavishly, because normal babies develop at different rates. The important consideration is to match the diet to the baby's nutritional needs and developmental readiness.

Commercial vs Homemade Baby Foods. Many parents rely on commercial baby foods until the child can eat with the rest of the family. Others prefer to prepare their own baby foods.

The commercially prepared foods are convenient and safe, but are often more expensive than their home-prepared counterparts. Furthermore, because of their smooth texture, they don't offer much developmental challenge to the child who is ready to progress to a more mature eating style.

Many people believe that commercially prepared baby foods are high in sugar, salt, and preservatives, but most manufacturers now use little

Table 16.2	Recommendations for Feeding Infants		
Age	Foods to introduce	Physical development	Comments
Birth	Breast milk or formula.	Baby can suck liquids from birth, but thrusts tongue forward to push solids from mouth (extrusion reflex). Kidneys cannot concentrate urine. Digestive secretions produced at low levels. Little control of head and neck.	Breast-feeders should be given supplemental fluoride and vitamin D. Formulas are usually adequate in Vitamin D, although fluoride may need to be supplemented (see text).
4–6 months	Iron-fortified cereal[a] mixed with formula or breast milk.	Baby learns to swallow solids. Control of head and neck allow child to sit up for eating, and to indicate hunger and satiety. Kidneys are able to concentrate urine.	Allow 3–4 days between introduction of new items. Delay wheat cereals until 7–9 months if there is family history of allergies.
8 months (or 6 weeks after cereal)	Strained, mashed, or diced fruits and vegetables. Either bottled baby foods or table foods prepared without sugar, honey, or seasonings.		Babies at this age readily accept many tastes, and can learn to appreciate a variety of textures.
9 months	Juices from a cup. Finger foods, whole pieces of soft fruits and vegetables. Pureed, milled, or finely chopped meats. Eggs. Casseroles from family table. Bread and crackers.	Chewing pattern has begun. Whole hand grasp enables child to pick up and hold large items. Child can drink from cup.	This is a transitional period from soft, mushy foods to table foods. Older babies usually prefer to feed themselves and to examine their food by handling it.
12 months	Table foods. Finely cut meats. Most finger foods, except items that are hard to chew such as popcorn, nuts, and raisins, or small, slippery, rounded foods (such as hot dogs, grapes, and candy), due to risk of choking.	Biting, chewing, and swallowing are well developed. Pincer grasp (thumb and fingers) enables child to pick up small objects. Good spoon control begins.	Delay use of honey and corn syrup until after 12 months: they may cause infant botulism.

[a]Continue iron-fortified infant cereal until at least one year of age, to help restore dwindling iron reserves.

References: Alford, B.B., and M.C. Bogle. 1982. *Nutrition during the Life Cycle*. Englewood Cliffs, NJ: Prentice-Hall.
Berger, K.S. 1980. *The Developing Person*. New York: Worth Publishers.
Fomon, S.J. 1974. *Infant Nutrition*. Philadelphia: W.B. Saunders Co.
Food and Nutrition Service. 1981. *"What shall I feed my baby?" A month-by-month guide*. Program aid no. 1281. Washington, DC: U.S. Department of Agriculture.
Satter, E. 1983. *Child of Mine*. Palo Alto, CA: Bull Publishing Company.

or none of these ingredients in their basic pureed foods. If you make your own baby food out of foods being prepared for the rest of the family, you can take out the baby's portion before adding seasoning or sauces. In this way, you will minimize the level of sugar, salt, and spices that the baby receives. Do not make baby food from canned food: canned vegetables and meats contain added salt, and canned fruit has added sugar. Furthermore, canned foods may contain lead if lead solder was used in making the can (see Chapter 15).

A good rule of thumb for those who buy baby food is to stick to simple, single-ingredient items in glass jars. Foods like strained chicken are cheaper and more concentrated in nutrients than fancier combination foods like chicken dinners.

Safety. Baby foods prepared from the family's meals can be just as nutritious as commercial types, but special care is required to make them as safe. One problem is microorganisms. The safest approach to avoiding microorganisms is to make and serve the baby's food on the spot, from what is being served to the rest of the family. Family fare can be changed to baby food by grinding, fork-mashing, or dicing. Baby food that is pureed or ground in quantity ahead of time is a perfect medium for bacterial growth because of its large surface area. Make sure that all equipment used in preparation is scrupulously clean; keep hot foods hot and cold foods cold until they are ready to serve. Do not reheat leftover baby foods more than once, and if a baby food has been at room temperature for more than half an hour, throw it away.

A reminder is in order about the risk from two commercial products sometimes given to infants. Honey and corn syrup have been found to contain spores of *Clostridium botulinum* (see Chapter 15). Since the infant's immature gastrointestinal tract in some cases allows the spores to become active and produce their lethal toxin, these products should not be given to children under one year of age.

A final safety issue has to do with the form of the food served to young children. Data have recently been collected on children who choked to death on food. In a study of over 100 cases involving babies through nine-year-olds, the most common offending foods were hot dogs, candy, nuts, grapes, cookies, meats, and carrots (in that order). This indicates that small, slippery, and thin or rounded foods are risky for the young child (Harris et al., 1984). Caregivers must be especially attentive while children are eating such foods.

Self-feeding. Another milestone in a baby's development is usually reached between seven and nine months, when the baby starts to feed herself. Self-feeding begins with easy-to-hold foods like teething biscuits, and progresses to soft foods like pieces of cooked vegetables.

At about this time, the baby can also begin to drink liquids from a cup. Many experts recommend waiting until this stage to give the baby fruit juices, because fruit juices from a bottle are a possible cause of nursing bottle caries (American Academy of Pediatrics, 1980).

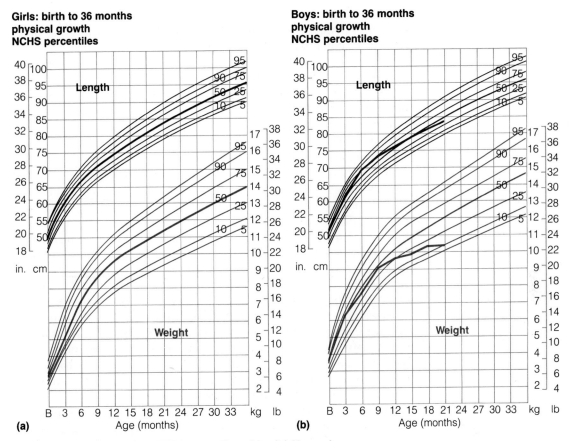

Figure 16.6 (a) Normal growth curves for girls. (b) Normal growth curves for boys. The data shown on (b) are an example of poor growth. (Adapted from National Center for Health Statistics: NCHS Growth Charts, 1976. Monthly Vital Statistics Report Vol. 25, No. 3, Supp. (HRA)76-1120. Health Resources Administration, Rockville, Maryland, June 1976. Data from The Fels Research Institute, Yellow Springs, Ohio. © 1976 Ross Laboratories, Columbus, Ohio 43216.)

How Much Is Enough?

Parents are chronic worriers about whether their baby is getting enough or too much to eat. This can be a particular concern when there is strong influence from grandparents, who are more likely to believe that a fat baby is a healthy baby. On the other hand, a new generation of health care providers and parents want to keep their children too slender.

The soundest approach is to abandon preconceived ideas about how thin or fat a particular child should be, and to provide from the beginning appropriate food in response to the child's hunger and satiety messages. For example, when a baby cries persistently and chews on her hands or other objects, she probably needs to eat. It is equally important for caretakers to stop feeding a child when he or she is satisfied; the child may show this by spitting food out, playing with it, or acting otherwise disinterested. Children who are fed in response to their hunger and satiety signals are likely, it is believed, to attain their individually appropriate weights. The risk in overfeeding or restricting food during infancy is that children may learn not to trust their internal messages and may govern their eating by external controls, resulting in bodies that are overfat or underfat (see Chapter 10).

Babies differ in the quantity of food they require for normal growth, and in the frequency with which they demand to be fed. Many newborns need to be fed every two to three hours until their stomach capacities increase enough to have fewer and larger feedings. A month-old infant will take about 20 ounces of formula or breast milk each day. This often increases to more than a quart per day by around four to six months, the time at which a few teaspoons of solid food are added to the diet. By the time a child is a year old, a variety of table foods accounts for a large part of the diet, and milk intake should have decreased to about 20–32 ounces per day (Satter, 1983).

The best way to check whether a baby's intake of food has been appropriate is to measure his or her growth in length and weight. The charts from the National Center for Health Statistics (Figure 16.6) show the standard for American children. The 50th percentile for weight is the point at which half of the infants weigh more and half weigh less. The 90th percentile is the point at which 10% weigh more, and so on. An individual baby's measurements can then be compared to norms for the population. [See Figure 16.6(b).]

Babies are very individual in the rates at which they grow and in the eventual body size they achieve. You needn't be alarmed if a child does not keep up exactly with the growth of a neighbor child of the same age. You should, however, keep note of how recent growth compares to the pattern established previously. You should call to the health care provider's attention a sudden or dramatic change in the pattern.

SUMMARY

■ Nutrition plays a critical role during pregnancy because so much new tissue is formed at this time. Some of the new tissue becomes the baby, which progresses through several developmental stages. For the first two weeks it is called a zygote, and then an embryo once it becomes implanted in the uterine wall. The term fetus refers to the developing baby from eight weeks after fertilization until birth. Other types of new tissue, such as the placenta, support and nourish the embryo and fetus, and still others become part of the mother.

■ Certain stages of gestation are characterized by rapid cell division; it is during these critical periods that the mother's nutrient intake and exposure to other substances (including teratogens) can have the most dramatic consequences.

■ The weight of both the mother-to-be and the new

baby are important; total desirable gain for the mother is about 25 pounds, although a fairly wide range can be normal. The birth weight of the baby should be at least $5\frac{1}{2}$ pounds. The foods eaten to achieve these weight gains should be chosen for nutritional adequacy, balance, and variety, since the need for many nutrients is especially high at this time. A carefully planned diet can meet these needs, and while vitamin/mineral supplements are advised in some cases, the principle of adequate but not excessive intake should be kept in mind.

■ Pregnant women should be careful to avoid ingesting dangerous levels of dietary toxicants. A set of abnormalities called fetal alcohol syndrome has been shown to appear in the children of women who consumed alcohol heavily during pregnancy. (Less is known about the risks of drinking alcohol in smaller amounts.) Practices such as pica and smoking may also affect the fetus, so pregnancy calls for an evaluation of many lifestyle factors besides nutritional ones.

■ The rapid growth of infants causes them to have the highest nutrient needs per unit of body weight of any age group, so the decision of what to feed a baby is an important matter. The immature gastrointestinal and urinary tracts of infants do not handle adult foods well for the first few months of life. Healthy full-term infants do have reserve supplies of some nutrients that can meet their needs during the time when milk is their only food.

■ Both breast feeding and bottle feeding have certain advantages. Breast milk is uniquely adapted to the infant's nutritional needs, and the colostrum contains factors that increase immunity to several infections. Both the composition and volume of milk produced can vary in response to the baby's demands. Formulas can provide nutritionally satisfactory substitutes for breast milk, and are available in several different varieties. Factors other than nutritional ones—such as cultural trends, psychological factors, convenience, economy, safety, and health of the mother—can also influence the decision of how to feed a baby.

■ Older infants need the nutrients that solid foods provide; such foods should be introduced when the baby is physically ready for them, as usually happens between four and six months of age. Iron-fortified cereals are often the first solid food, and can be followed by others introduced gradually. Commercially prepared baby foods are convenient and safe, though often more expensive than those prepared at home. Between seven and nine months of age, a baby is usually able to begin feeding him or herself, and to drink from a cup. At this stage of life (as at most others) it is probably best to provide appropriate food in response to the child's hunger and satiety messages. A reliable way to check on whether this provides enough nutrients is to keep track of the baby's height and weight, which can then be compared with population norms and the child's own past growth pattern.

REFERENCES

Alford, B.B., and M.L. Bogle. 1982. *Nutrition during the life cycle.* Englewood Cliffs, NJ: Prentice-Hall.

American Academy of Pediatrics. 1980. On the feeding of supplemental foods to infants. *Pediatrics* 65(no.6):1178–1181.

American Academy of Pediatrics. 1982. The promotion of breast feeding. *Pediatrics* 69(no.5):654–660.

American Academy of Pediatrics. 1983a. The use of whole cow's milk in infancy. *Pediatrics* 72(no.2):253–255.

American Academy of Pediatrics. 1983b. The transfer of drugs and other chemicals into human breast milk. *Pediatrics* 72(no.3):375–383.

American Academy of Pediatrics. 1983c. Soy protein formulas: Recommendations for use in infant feeding. *Pediatrics* 72(no.3):359–363.

American Medical Association. 1983. Fetal effects of maternal alcohol use. *Journal of the American Medical Association* 249(no.18):2517–2521.

Ansfield, E., and E. Lipper. 1983. Early contact, social support, and mother–infant bonding. *Pediatrics* 72(no.1):79–83.

Beal, V. 1984. An integrative point of view on current maternal–infant nutrition practices. *Journal of the American Dietetic Association* 84:527–528.

Berger, K.S. 1980. *The developing person*. New York: Worth Publishers.

Dobbing, J. 1984. Infant nutrition and later achievement. *Nutrition Reviews* 42(no.1):1–7.

Dwyer, J. 1979. Vegetarianism. *Contemporary Nutrition* 4(no.6).

Filer, L.J., F.S. Mattson, and S.J. Fomon. 1969. Triglyceride configuration and fat absorption by the human infant. *Journal of Nutrition* 99:293.

Fomon, S.J. 1974. *Infant nutrition*. Philadelphia: W.B. Saunders Co.

Food and Nutrition Service. 1981. *"What shall I feed my baby?" A month-by-month guide*. Program aid no. 1281. Washington, DC: U.S. Department of Agriculture.

Hackman, E., I. Emanuel, G. vanBelle, and J. Daling. 1983. Maternal birth weight and subsequent pregnancy outcome. *Journal of the American Medical Association* 250(no.5):2016–2019.

Harris, C.S., S.P. Baker, G.A. Smith, and R.M. Harris. 1984. Childhood asphyxiation by food: A national analysis and overview. *Journal of the American Medical Association* 251:2231–2235.

Hendershot, G.E. 1980. Trends in breast feeding. *Advance Data*, no. 59. Washington, DC: National Center for Health Statistics.

Hicks, L.E., A.L. Rose, and J. Takenaka. 1982. Cognitive and health measures following early nutritional supplementation: A sibling study. *American Journal of Public Health* 72(no.10):1110–1118.

Holmes, G.E., K.M. Hassanien, and H.C. Miller. 1983. Factors associated with infections among breast fed babies and babies fed proprietary milks. *Pediatrics* 72(no.3):300–306.

Hurley, L.S. 1980. *Developmental nutrition*. Englewood Cliffs, NJ: Prentice-Hall.

Lecos, C. 1980. Caution light on caffeine. *FDA Consumer*, October, 1980:6–9.

Linn, S., S.C. Schoenbaum, R.R. Monson, B. Rosner, P.G. Stubblefield, K.J. Ryan. 1982. No association between coffee consumption and adverse outcomes of pregnancy. *New England Journal of Medicine* 306:141–145.

Little, R.E., and A.P. Streissguth. 1981. Effects of alcohol on the fetus: Impact and prevention. *Canadian Medical Association Journal* 125:159.

Little, R.E., A.P. Streissguth, H.M. Barr, and C.S. Herman. 1980. Decreased birth weight in infants of alcoholic women who abstained during pregnancy. *Journal of Pediatrics* 96:974–977.

National Center for Health Statistics. 1977. *NCHS growth curves for children, birth–18 years, United States*. DHEW Publication No.(PHS)78-1650. Washington, DC: Department of Health, Education, and Welfare.

National Research Council. 1970. *Maternal nutrition and the course of pregnancy*. Washington, DC: National Academy of Sciences.

National Research Council, 1980. *Recommended dietary allowances*. Washington, DC: National Academy of Sciences.

Nutrition Foundation. 1980. Morbidity in breast fed and artificially fed infants. *Nutrition Reviews* 38(no.3):114–115.

Public Health Service. 1979. *Healthy people: The surgeon general's report on health promotion and disease prevention*, DHEW(PHS)Publication No.79-55071. Washington, DC: U.S. Department of Health, Education, and Welfare.

Rogan, W.J., A. Bagniewska, and T. Damstra. 1980. Pollutants in breast milk. *New England Journal of Medicine* 302(no.26):1450–1453.

Satter, E. 1983. *Child of mine: Feeding with love and good sense*. Palo Alto, CA: Bull Publishing Company.

Winick, M. 1982. *Growing up healthy: A parent's guide to good nutrition*. New York: William Morrow & Co.

Wolman, P.G. 1984. Feeding practices in infancy and prevalence of obesity in preschool children. *Journal of the American Dietetic Association* 84:436–438.

Worthington-Roberts, B.S., J. Vermeersch, and S. Rodwell-Williams. 1981. *Nutrition in pregnancy and lactation*. St. Louis: The C.V. Mosby Co.

Wright, J.T., I.G. Barrison, I.G. Lewis, K.D. MacRae, E.J. Waterson, P.J. Toplis, M.G. Gordon, N.F. Morris, and I.M. Murray-Lyon. 1983. Alcohol consumption, pregnancy and low birth weight. *Lancet* 1(no.8326):663–664.

Young, H.B., A.E. Buckley, B. Hamza, and C. Mandarano. 1982. Milk and lactation: Some social and developmental correlates among 1000 infants. *Pediatrics* 69(no.2):169–195.

17

Nutrition for Growing: Children and Adolescents

IN THIS CHAPTER: Food Intake for Children through the Elementary School Years Is Related to Many Changing Factors ▪ Another Growth Spurt and Increased Independence Influence Teen Needs and Eating

Change and more change—that's the hallmark of the growing years. Taking the first steps at about one year; developing thought processes and language during the preschool years; finding an identity within the wider society during the teens. Such changes make these first two decades of life very dynamic and exciting. At the same time, these years are also potentially very frustrating and filled with conflict, as the child and the caregivers repeatedly adjust to new circumstances.

Eating behaviors often reflect these changes. For example, fluctuations in appetite roughly parallel growth and plateaus in growth. Changes in food preferences may reflect an increasing self-awareness. And new eating styles may well be a consequence of the influences of peers, advertising, and increasing independence and mobility.

When conflicts over eating occur between children and their caregivers, the issue is usually one of control: who will make the decisions regarding what, how much, and when (or how often) to eat. Although the matter of how much to eat should be determined by the child from the beginning, he or she should gradually take on the other decisions as well. Of course the rate at which a child assumes responsibility for various aspects of eating has to be worked out individually, depending both on the child's needs and capabilities, and on the family's situation.

How can the adults in a child's life—in their roles as older brothers or sisters, parents, teachers, coaches, health care providers, neighbors—help the child cope with these changes? An important starting point is to become informed about what is normal during these transitional times. Such information can help you assist a child in developing sound eating habits that will last throughout life. This is the most important influence a caregiver can have on a child's nutrition during these years.

Food Intake for Children through the Elementary School Years Is Related to Many Changing Factors

Food and eating are closely interwoven with a child's development. Of course, foods provide energy and nutrients the body needs for physical growth, development, and activity. But foods and meals are also an important part of the socialization process through which feelings and behavior patterns are formed.

Influences on Needs and Intake

Let's first look at how changes in the body affect its need for nutrients.

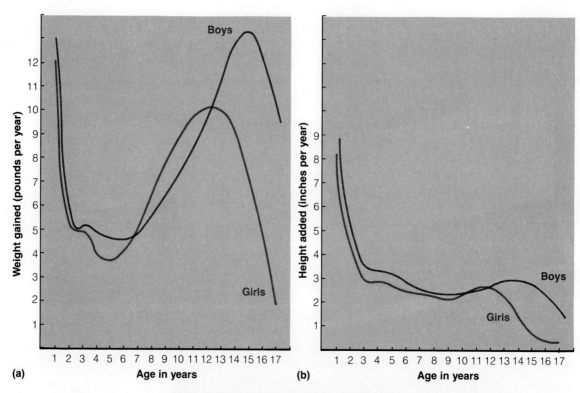

Figure 17.1 (a) Average gains in weight for girls and boys. (b) Average additions to height for girls and boys. (Data source: National Research Council. 1980. *Recommended Dietary Allowances*. Washington, DC: National Academy of Sciences.)

Physical Development and Activity. A growing child undergoes complex physical and emotional changes, the most obvious of which is growth. During the prenatal period and the first year after birth, growth takes place at a very rapid pace, but during early childhood (ages 1–9) the overall rate of growth is much slower. Figure 17.1 shows average gains in weight and height for girls and boys.

During these years, body tissues and organs also continue to develop (Figure 17.2). For example, the gastrointestinal tract matures so that it can handle complex foods. Gastric secretions and most enzymes are present at nearly adult levels by the end of the first year, making it feasible for the young child to consume a wide variety of foods. The presence of eight molar teeth by about two years of age and four permanent molars around age 6 allow a child to break apart meats and other chewy foods.

The nutrient content of the diet is very important during these years, because in addition to meeting immediate needs, nutrients must be stored in preparation for the accelerated growth that will take place during adolescence.

The food intake of young children is extremely variable, with peaks and valleys in appetite. Before and during a period of rapid growth, a child

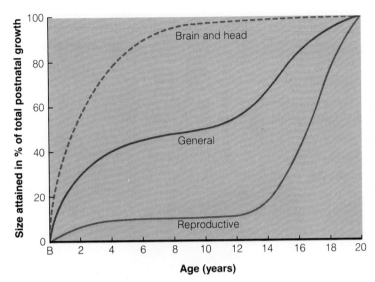

Figure 17.2 Growth of various systems. (Adapted from Scammon, R.E. 1927. The measurement of the body in childhood. In *The Measurement of Man* by J.A. Harris, C.M. Jackson, and R.E. Scammon. Minneapolis, MN: University of Minnesota Press.)

may seem like an eating machine, but during the periods of slow growth, it sometimes seems that he or she cannot possibly be eating enough to stay alive. In general, the appetite of children during their first year of life is regarded as excellent or good by over 80% of parents. However, between the ages of 3 and 4, less than 20% of parents rate their children's appetites that way. By the time their children are age 7, though, over half of parents again think of their children's appetites as excellent or good (Beal, 1957). It may help parents who worry about their child's lagging appetite to know that such fluctuation is normal and is usually not a danger sign.

Another fact for caregivers of young children to keep in mind is that the amount of food a child eats will not be strictly proportional to his or her weight. For example, a 30-pound toddler does not need twice as many kcalories as she did when she weighed 15 pounds. Her energy needs *per unit of body weight* actually decrease as her growth rate slows down. Of course, the *total* number of kcalories she needs per day still increases as she gets older, but not at a dramatic rate.

Children's energy needs are also partly determined by activity levels. Because physical activity varies greatly among children, some need more food than others, even when they are the same size. Other factors, as discussed in Chapter 5 (on energy), also play a role.

Coordination. Physical development in children generally takes place from trunk to extremities (arms and legs), and from head to toe. Large muscles develop before smaller muscles, so coordination and control over fine movements tend to follow increases in size and strength (Berger, 1980).

Fine motor skills and physical coordination improve throughout childhood. These changes enable a three-year-old child to manipulate a fork and spoon quite well at mealtime, and later to use a knife for spreading and cutting. As these skills develop, it is a good idea to encourage the child to practice them at mealtimes. This builds confidence. Many parents find

Helping to prepare food. When a child gets involved in food preparation, it can improve her or his acceptance of those foods.

this a good time to begin involving children in food preparation as well. Peeling an orange or stirring the batter for a batch of muffins can be engrossing new challenges for a child. It can also give him more interest in trying the finished product, and can sometimes mean the difference between acceptance and rejection of a food.

Psychosocial Development. Mental changes also occur during childhood. Throughout the growth years, the child is building his own self-image and gradually establishing his independence from his parents. The process of gaining independence can truly be a struggle, since it often conflicts with the need to be, at least in part, cared for by adults. This is especially true for preschoolers. A four-year-old may resist any parental efforts to help or control her ("Let *me* do it"), and then suddenly demand that her parents do everything for her ("Daddy, *you* put butter on my bread. I can't.")

Another food-related means of showing independence is food rejection. Refusing to eat certain foods is one way in which a child sometimes exercises control over his own behavior.

Children may also use their eating behavior to control others. For example, a child who senses his parents' concern over whether he eats his vegetables may learn that agreeing to eat them is a way of negotiating for things he wants. He may even go so far as to insist on a reward *before* eating them.

Emotions usually stabilize during the elementary school years. Maintaining a sense of humor and anticipating children's table behavior may help parents during these confrontations.

Environmental Factors. The average child in elementary school spends more time in front of a television set each year than he or she does in the classroom. The child watches about 20,000 television commercials each year, many of which promote foods that are high in sugar, salt, and/or fat (Goodman and Johnson, 1979).

For many children, TV and other media are a significant part of the process of nutrition socialization; that is, their values concerning food, and their concepts about what foods are appropriate to eat and when they should be eaten are partly determined by what they see on television (Way, 1983). Parents who watch TV with their children can help them understand that TV programs don't always show things as they are in real life, and that food commercials are designed to make them want a particular item whether or not it has any nutritional merit (Goodman and Johnson, 1979).

The type and amount of food available for the child is also influenced by a variety of family circumstances. The family's income and economic status influence a child's diet by limiting the types and amounts of food that can be purchased. Family structure and parents' employment also make a difference. Single-parent families and those in which both parents

---

SLICE OF LIFE:
(Some) Children's
Eating Practices

In her book *How to Eat Like a Child and Other Lessons in Not Being Grown Up,* Delia Ephron takes a tongue-in-cheek look at the mealtime antics of children. For example, she explains that this is how to eat spinach like a child:

> Divide into little piles. Rearrange into new piles. After five or six maneuvers, sit back and say you are full.

Children like to experiment with their food, and they frustrate their parents with awkward and unconventional eating methods such as this technique for eating spaghetti like a child:

> Wind too many strands on the fork and make sure at least two strands dangle down. Open your mouth wide and stuff in spaghetti; suck noisily to inhale the dangling strands. Clean plate, ask for seconds, and eat only half. When carrying your plate to the kitchen, hold it tilted so that the remaining spaghetti slides off and onto the floor.

Typical meals . . . then and now. Decades ago, most meals were major family social events: several generations gathered for home-prepared meals. Now, the average household size is much smaller, and families eat together less often. More food is eaten away from home or purchased as convenience items.

are employed outside the home often have different eating practices than the traditional family of several decades ago. In an earlier era, the mother usually made the food choices for all members of the household. Most meals were eaten by all family members together and were prepared by the mother from groceries she had selected. Lunch, the meal most often eaten away from home, was likely to have been packed by her. Except on rare occasions, family members had little opportunity to select what they were going to eat.

Of course, the current situation is dramatically different for many families, since over half of mothers with school-age children work outside

School can contribute to nutrition knowledge. Here, children interact with "Nutro," the nutrition robot, who appeared at schools through the Nutrition Education and Training Program.

the home. With fewer hours available for householding, parents prepare and serve fewer meals to the family; increasingly, family members (even young children) select their own meals. When parents are getting ready for work, everyone often chooses his or her own breakfast from what is in the cupboards and refrigerator. Some children do not even eat breakfast at home—the first meal of the day may be eaten at the babysitter's house, a day-care center, or at school.

For lunch, eating away from home (and family members selecting for themselves) is even more common. Lunches and snacks for young children are often provided by a babysitter or day-care facility, so there is less parental influence and interaction at these mealtimes. This may have either a positive or a negative effect on the child's diet, depending on the attitudes and actions of the caregivers.

A child in school or day care also experiences peer influences on his eating behavior. Johnnie may think that broccoli is a perfectly delicious food until he realizes that his friends say it's "yucky," or that one of his adult role models (a teacher or Uncle Howard or a hero from a comic book) doesn't like it (Birch et al., 1980).

Single parents and families in which both parents work utilize convenience foods and fast-food restaurants more often than the general public does (Sheridan and McPherrin, 1981). Research shows that people who eat one of the day's meals away from home tend to have lower intakes of some nutrients (Bunch, 1984).

A child may also be influenced by what is taught about nutrition in the classroom. However, the quantity and quality of nutrition education offered varies substantially from one location and time to another.

Recommended Nutrient Intakes for Children through the Elementary School Years

The recommended intakes of nutrients for children according to age and sex are shown in the 1980 RDA table. Figure 17.3 shows how the RDAs for various ages compare to the adult male RDA. In general, the older the child, the higher the nutrient intake recommendations. These increases reflect the demands of maintaining a larger body plus furnishing raw materials for further growth.

Nutritional Status of American Children through Elementary School Years

Do children get the nutrients they need? Compared with children in other parts of the world, children in North America do not exhibit many nutritional deficiencies, although the intake of few nutrients is of concern. Generally speaking, American children are more likely to be *over*nourished than *under*nourished (Snyderman, 1980). This discussion of the nutritional status of children through the elementary school years covers both forms of malnutrition.

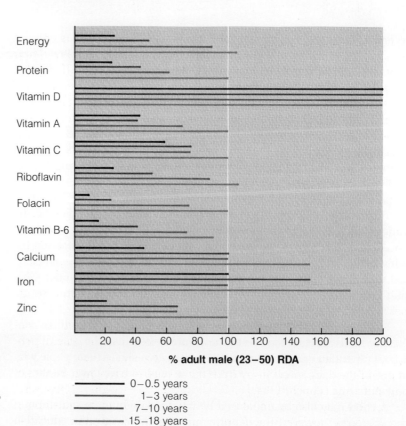

Figure 17.3 RDAs in childhood and adolescence. (Data source: National Research Council. 1980. *Recommended Dietary Allowances*. Washington, DC: National Academy of Sciences.)

Obesity. Depending on the criteria used to define and measure obesity, 3–20% of American children have been categorized as obese (Alford and Bogle, 1982; Knittle, 1972). This is of concern because even in childhood, overfatness has both physiological and psychological penalties (see Chapter 10). A child who is substantially overweight should be taken to a physician for a thorough evaluation. The method of treatment should, ideally, be based on the cause of the obesity if it can be determined. Another promising approach is to involve the public schools and/or parents in treatment programs for groups of obese children (Brownell, 1984).

Sometimes inactivity is the problem. When this is the case, the most logical and satisfactory intervention is encouraging more physical activity. Some obese children have learned to eat for comfort or as a self-reward. In this case, it is useful to help the child consider alternative gratifications to substitute for some of the eating (National Research Council, 1980).

For other obese children, overeating may be due to a disturbance of the mechanisms that control hunger and satiety. Imposing strict diets on these children or forcing them to ignore true feelings of hunger will cause ongoing frustration and resentment. In these instances, it is usually best to encourage increased exercise; make sure a variety of interesting, low-kcalorie food is available for meals and snacks; and avoid using food as a reward (Satter, 1983). These children also need support in accepting the fact that they may naturally have a somewhat higher body weight than many of their peers.

The question of whether obesity in childhood necessarily predisposes a person to overweight for life does not have a simple, clear-cut answer. Not all fat children become fat adults, and not all fat adults were fat as children; data do suggest, however, that a fat child has a greater chance of becoming a fat adult than a normal-weight child has. In one study, 36% of infants who were obese during the first six months of life (that is, had weights above the 90th percentile) were overweight as adults, while only 14% of normal-weight babies became fat adults (Charney et al., 1976).

This raises a related question: which is responsible for the development of overweight—heredity or environment? Some experts believe that a child inherits the tendency to have a particular number of adipose cells (Winick, 1982). A larger-than-average number of fat cells could lead to a higher-than-average natural weight. (Recall the theory discussed in Chapter 10 that once fat cells are formed, they are permanent, although they may temporarily change in size.) Other experts are not satisfied with this theory, and continue to look for other possible explanations (Vobecky et al., 1983).

To try to clarify the matter, data have been collected to measure the relationship between overweight parents and overweight children. One study showed that when a child had two overweight parents, his own chances of being overweight were 80%; with one overweight parent, the likelihood dropped to 40%; and children with no overweight parents were obese in only 7% of the cases (Himes, 1979). Of course, these statistics do not speak to the heredity vs. environment question, since either factor—

Frontier

or both together—could be operating when parents and their biological children live in the same household.

For that reason, the effect of parental fatness on biological vs. adopted children has been studied. It has been found that children, whether biological or adopted, who are living in a household with overweight parents reflect that overweight condition (Garn, 1977). This suggests that environmental influences can override inherited determinants of body fatness.

It seems likely, then, that genetic factors have a strong lifelong influence on whether a person will have little, average, or large amounts of body fat. Environmental factors also play an important role, primarily by exaggerating or interfering with this legacy.

Anemia. Iron deficiency anemia is a fairly common problem. It is most prevalent in children from one to three years of age (Figure 17.4), especially among Black children, children from large households, and children whose parents (heads of households) have low educational levels. Anemia is less common in preschoolers who were breast-fed in infancy (National Center for Health Statistics, 1982). [These data were collected in the Health and Nutrition Examination Survey (HANES), a comprehensive, periodic study done by the United States government. It includes biochemical and dietary studies of people of all economic levels, ages, and geographical regions. HANES I was conducted from 1971–1974 and involved over 20,000 subjects; HANES II data were collected from 1976–1980 on a similar number.]

Some factors associated with anemia in children are pica and low levels of dietary iron. Low iron intakes may in some cases result from drinking excessive amounts of milk, which may decrease consumption of needed iron-containing foods.

Health and Nutrition Examination Survey (HANES)—a comprehensive, periodic, federally managed study of the American population's health and nutritional status

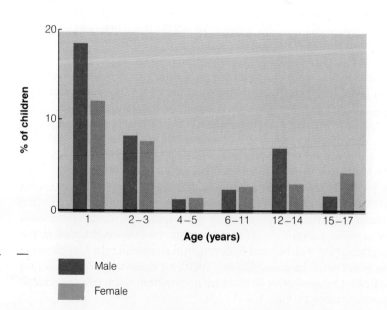

Figure 17.4 Prevalence of anemia as indicated by low hemoglobin levels, United States, 1971–1974. (Source: National Center for Health Statistics. 1982. *Diet and Iron Status, a study of relationships: United States, 1971–1974.* DHHS Publication No. (DHS)83-1679. Hyattsville, MD: U.S. Department of Health and Human Services.)

Table 17.1 Nutrients for Which Average Intakes Were Below the 1980 RDA for American Children

Age	Pro-tein	Calcium	Iron	Mag-nesium	Phos-phorus	Vita-min A	Thia-min	Ribo-flavin	Niacin	Vitamin B-6	Vita-min B-12	Vita-min C
<1												
1–2			less than 70%									
3–5		80–89%	70–79%	90–99%						90–99%		
6–8				90–99%						90–99%		

The shaded boxes show the average levels of intake for nutrients consumed in less quantity than their RDAs. Blank boxes mean that average nutrient intakes were at the RDA levels or better.
Adapted from Science and Education Administration, 1980. *Food and nutrient intakes of individuals in 1 day in the United States, Spring, 1977.* National food consumption preliminary report no. 2. Washington, DC: U.S. Department of Agriculture.

Dental Decay. Dental caries are another significant problem in children. As discussed in Chapter 6, tooth decay is most likely to occur in susceptible teeth in the presence of fermentable carbohydrate, acid-producing bacteria, and time. Important factors in the control of dental caries are adequate fluoride intake (from water or appropriate supplements) or topical application; restricted intake of fermentable carbohydrates such as sticky sweet snacks; and adequate dental hygiene to remove carbohydrates, acid, and bacteria.

Various studies contain data showing the status of dental health in the United States. One of these is the Ten State Nutrition Survey, conducted from 1968–1970 on over 40,000 people; it was unique in trying to focus on Americans with low incomes. The survey included dietary intake studies, physical exams, anthropometric measurements, and/or biochemical data. This study showed that the average American child had nine decayed, missing, or filled teeth by age 17. A decrease of 32% in caries incidence was achieved during the decade before 1981, as reported in the National Caries Prevalence Survey of school children ages 5–17 (National Institutes of Health, 1981). Fluoridation is likely to have been responsible for much of this improvement, but it probably should not be given sole credit (Leveille and Coccodrilli, 1982).

Ten State Nutrition Survey— nutritional survey (1968–1970) designed to focus on Americans with lower incomes

General Malnutrition. In dietary surveys, low intakes of calcium, iron, magnesium, and vitamin B-6 have been reported for children from ages 1 to 5. Table 17.1 shows the nutrients whose average intakes by children in various age groups were below the RDA (National Center for Health Statistics, 1977). Despite these surveys, biochemical evidence of severe general malnutrition in infants and preschool children in the United States is rare. When such malnutrition does occur, it is usually the result of a metabolic disease (such as cystic fibrosis) or severe dietary restriction (such as a Zen macrobiotic diet).

Children who have been severely malnourished in infancy experience growth deficits. Usually children who have been nutritionally deprived have also lacked social stimulation; therefore experts are not sure to what extent each influences poor growth. Some growth deficit may be partly made up for in early childhood; how much can be corrected depends on the age at which adequate nutrition is provided, and the length and severity of the previous inadequacy. Similarly, the intellectual impairment that results from malnutrition in early childhood may be partly or mostly restored when nutrition improves, if it takes place soon enough and if it ia accompanied by adequate social stimulation (Cravioto, 1981).

Recently, physicians have noted that some preteen children, especially girls, are so afraid of becoming fat that they restrict their food intake to very low levels. Over a period of time, this can interfere with linear growth and sexual maturation even if such children do not progress to the extreme disorder of anorexia nervosa (see Chapter 11). The problem emphasizes the need for children to develop good eating habits and establish realistic expectations of themselves and their bodies (Pugliese et al., 1983).

Recommendations for Feeding Children

The SANE guide recommends the types and amounts of food that should be the basis of children's diets (see Table 2.3). Note that these recommendations are not extremely different from those made for healthy adults. It is as important to emphasize a wide variety of high-nutrient-density foods during childhood as it is at all other ages.

Food rejection. A strong dislike for certain foods is not uncommon among young children. It may be a challenge for parents to encourage children gently to try and accept new foods, without being heavy-handed about it.

Selection of Foods. Children like familiar foods. For this reason, their meals should largely consist of foods they know and accept. (However, the whims of a finicky eater should not be allowed to seriously disrupt the variety of foods enjoyed by the rest of the family.)

Since studies show that familiarity is a prime determinant of food acceptance in children, it is important to expose young children gradually to an expanding assortment of nutritious foods; in this way, more and more foods *become* familiar. Although they may not accept some foods on the first few occasions—such as certain vegetables, strongly flavored items, and chewy meats—the new foods should be offered again at a later time and with a positive attitude. Beyond giving a child encouragement to join the "One Bite Club," caregivers should not force or beg a child to eat a particular food, no matter how nutritious it is.

Sometimes special attention to a new food may encourage a child to try it. Cutting sandwiches into interesting shapes, or decorating the food or telling a story about it may overcome an initial resistance to new foods.

Food Jags. Sometimes children like a food so much that they want it to be the mainstay of every meal. Nutritious though it may be, peanut butter for breakfast, lunch, and dinner cannot be accepted as a balanced diet. Thankfully, children themselves usually limit a food jag so parents do not have to make an issue of it unless it persists for more than a couple of weeks.

Amounts to Eat. The portions of most foods offered to a child should be smaller than those for adults. For preschoolers, one tablespoon per year of age of fruits or vegetables is a reasonable rule of thumb. For example, a serving of cooked carrots for a four-year-old is approximately one-quarter cup, rather than the half cup serving suggested for adults.

Servings of grain products should be adjusted according to relative body size: a one-year-old may be satisfied with half a piece of toast at a meal, whereas a three-year-old might prefer whole slices. Milk can be offered in servings nearly as large as for adults—not surprising, when you consider that it was the child's entire diet earlier. Meats and alternates should be offered to preschoolers in serving sizes about half those appropriate for adults.

In the final analysis, the child's sense of hunger and satiety must be the determining factor in the amount of food consumed. Attempts to limit the intake of a hungry child or to force a child who is feeling full to clean his plate may train him to override the messages his body gives about food intake regulation. Carried to the extreme, this could set the stage for later eating disorders.

Snacks. The timing and frequency of eating occasions are usually jointly determined by parents and children. For young children, regular family meals often need to be supplemented with snacks because the small stomach capacity of young children does not allow them to meet their needs in three meals per day. The 1977–1978 Nationwide Food Consumption Survey, a U.S. Department of Agriculture study done every ten years and involving almost 10,000 Americans of all ages, geographical regions, and economic levels, showed that 59–70% of American children eat one or more snacks each day. Children who snack get approximately 18% of their daily kcaloric intake from this source.

It is especially important that children's snacks be foods of high nutritional quality because children have relatively high nutrient needs and therefore have less leeway for low nutrient density foods. Table 17.2 gives an indication of the relative merits of common snack foods.

Nationwide Food Consumption Survey—A periodic USDA study of American food consumption patterns

Supplements. Many parents believe that their children should take supplements to make up for their poor eating habits. A multivitamin and mineral supplement at RDA levels can be useful for making up minor deficits, but should not be counted on to correct major dietary flaws. As a source of nutrients, supplements are an inferior second choice to a well-balanced diet. Of course, if a qualified health care provider diagnoses a medical condition (such as a malabsorptive disease), and recommends appropriate supplements, the advice should be followed.

Vegetarian Eating Style. The diets of lacto and lacto–ovo vegetarians can provide adequate amounts of nutrients for most children when they are carefully planned. Milk, cheese, eggs, and legumes usually can provide the protein, vitamins, and minerals that are provided by meat in the omnivore diet.

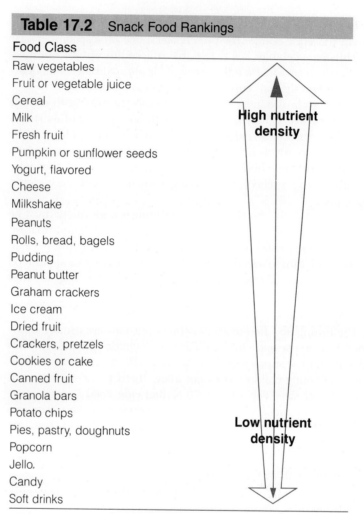

Table 17.2 Snack Food Rankings

Food Class

Raw vegetables
Fruit or vegetable juice
Cereal
Milk
Fresh fruit
Pumpkin or sunflower seeds
Yogurt, flavored
Cheese
Milkshake
Peanuts
Rolls, bread, bagels
Pudding
Peanut butter
Graham crackers
Ice cream
Dried fruit
Crackers, pretzels
Cookies or cake
Canned fruit
Granola bars
Potato chips
Pies, pastry, doughnuts
Popcorn
Jello.
Candy
Soft drinks

Data from Gillespie, A. 1983. Assessing snacking behavior of children. *Ecology of Food and Nutrition* 13:167–172.

However, strict vegetarian (vegan) diets are not recommended for preschool children because these diets make it difficult to provide adequate protein, vitamins, minerals, and energy for normal growth (Dwyer et al., 1980). One problem is that a large volume of food must be eaten to get the recommended amounts of nutrients. An additional problem is that the bioavailability of minerals from plant sources is relatively low. However, older children can usually thrive on properly planned vegan diets. Their growth should be monitored carefully, nevertheless, as a check for dietary adequacy.

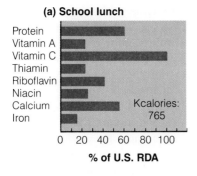

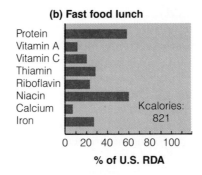

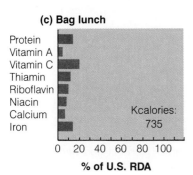

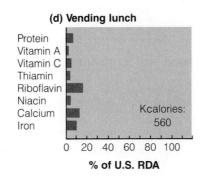

Figure 17.5 Nutrient and kcalorie profiles of various lunches. (a) Profile of a typical National School Lunch Program lunch of a turkey and cheese sandwich, celery sticks, cranberry sauce, fried potatoes, mixed fruit, whole milk, million dollar cookie (b) Profile of a typical fast-food lunch of a quarter-pound hamburger, fries, cola beverage (c) Profile of a typical bag lunch of a bologna sandwich, cookies, sweetened fruit drink (d) Profile of a typical vending machine lunch of potato chips, chocolate candy bar, soda (Courtesy National Dairy Council).

Monitoring Growth

When children are allowed to eat according to their own inner hunger and satiety signals, adult caregivers often look for reassurance that the children are getting the right amount of food. Continuing to keep a growth chart for a preschool or elementary school child can help provide this reassurance.

School Lunch

Some children, depending on circumstances at their schools, have several lunch options on school days. They may have access to the National School Lunch Program, buy lunch from vending machines or at fast-food restaurants, or bring it from home. Which is best?

According to a study by the U.S. Department of Agriculture's Consumer Nutrition Center and the University of North Carolina, the lunches from the National School Lunch Program were superior to other options in nutrient content (Figure 17.5). Children ages 6–11 in school lunch programs were found to consume 70% more vitamin A, 6% more energy, and 19–21% more calcium, iron, and vitamins B-6 and C than those who ate other kinds of lunches. The positive impact of the school lunch program was even greater for low-income children (Akin et al., 1983).

The high nutritional quality of meals served in the National School Lunch program is no accident: the meals are intended to provide about a

National School Lunch Program—federally funded and managed program that offers school lunches for children

third of the RDAs for protein, vitamins, minerals, and energy. This is not to say that the National School Lunch Program is the only possible nutritious choice: the other lunches could be improved by making some substitutions. The typical fast-food lunch (quarter-pound hamburger, fries, cola beverage) has many strengths, but would be improved by replacing the cola beverage with milk. A typical sack lunch (bologna sandwich, cookies, sweetened fruit drink) could be improved by substituting fruit for the drink and purchasing milk at school. It is more difficult to suggest how to improve the vending machine lunch because the items stocked are so variable.

Another attractive feature of school lunch is that it is often significantly less expensive than the other types of lunches, since USDA partly subsidizes it.

Food and Behavior Issues

A number of theories appearing in the popular literature attempt to link a child's diet and behavior. Most of these theories originate with self-proclaimed experts, and have not been proved in scientifically controlled studies. Some are even money-making schemes for sellers of dietary products promoted to cure behavioral problems (Herbert and Barrett, 1981).

Emotional/Behavioral Problems Related to Sugar? Some popular articles have claimed that refined sugars cause behavioral and emotional problems in children. The authors of such articles often suggest that parents should put their children on "natural" or "sugar-free" diets.

Let's examine this recommendation by looking at some facts and some evidence. When high-carbohydrate foods are eaten alone—whether the food is sucrose or any other readily digestible carbohydrates—digestion and absorption are relatively rapid, and blood sugar rises. This stimulates the pancreas to secrete extra insulin, the action of which causes glucose to move from the bloodstream into the body's cells, and brings about a decrease in blood sugar, generally still within the normal range. These physiological changes may be accompanied by some perceived energy differences, but do not normally involve major mood changes. On the other hand, people who have reactive hypoglycemia (a rare condition described in Chapter 6 in which blood glucose drops to abnormally low levels after eating carbohydrates), may experience anxiety along with the physical symptoms of this condition (American Medical Association et al., 1973).

Some uninformed individuals have tried to make a connection between the possible emotional effect of carbohydrate ingestion in people with hypoglycemia, and the effects of carbohydrates on children's emotions and behavior. They use theories and anecdotal reports to support their claims, rather than evidence from scientific double-blind studies (Gray and Gray, 1983).

When well-controlled studies have been conducted to determine the relationship between sugar consumption and behavior, the association has usually been found to be very weak (Rapoport and Kruesi, 1983). In one study, sugars actually had a calming influence. However, a study involving psychiatrically ill children showed an increase in total physical movement in association with sugar consumption. Given the current scarcity of good scientific data, it is premature to draw conclusions about the effects of sugar on behavior (Rapoport and Kruesi, 1983).

Hyperactivity Related to Other Food Components? Another popular theory linking food and behavior was published in 1973 by the late Dr. Benjamin Feingold, an allergist with the Kaiser-Permanente medical system in California. Among his patients were children with hyperactivity (also called hyperkinetic syndrome or attention deficit disorder). Children with this condition are more physically active, fidgety, excitable, impulsive, and distractable, and have shorter attention spans, lower tolerance for frustration, and more difficulties in learning than most children of their age. (These children are nonetheless of normal or above normal intelligence.)

According to his theory, certain food additives and salicylates (which are naturally occurring chemicals in many fruits and vegetables, and also comprise the drug aspirin) are responsible for these behaviors. Dr. Feingold reported that 50–70% of hyperactive children improved when they were placed on a diet free of foods containing salicylates and artificial flavors and colors (some of which are chemically related to salicylates) (1975).

This diet received so much publicity that several studies were conducted to determine whether such a relationship does exist. In 1982, a conference was held at the National Institutes of Health to review the literature and develop a consensus statement. After examining the evidence, the panel concluded:

> While differences and inadequacies in the design of the controlled trials make analysis difficult, these studies did indicate a limited positive association between the defined diets, and a decrease in hyperactivity. . . . Such decreases involved only a small proportion of patients; furthermore, the decreases in hyperactivity were not observed consistently. . . . (National Institutes of Health, 1982).

Therefore, if the Feingold diet really works, it does so for only a very small number of children, and then the results are inconsistent.

Some experts believe that there is no harm in trying to treat this problem with special diets, but others say that organizing the lives of a child and his family around a special diet is not recommended. Blaming behavior on an outside influence can decrease the child's sense of mastery over his own impulses and adversely affect his personality development.

School Performance Related to Eating Breakfast? Studies have been done to ascertain whether skipping breakfast affects the quality of children's schoolwork. It seems to. Investigators have shown that skipping breakfast impaired children's late morning problem-solving performance on a test that involved matching familiar figures (Pollitt et al., 1981). Another study showed poorer performance in arithmetic and in continuous performance tasks on days when breakfast had not been eaten (Rapoport and Kruesi, 1983).

hyperactivity—condition occurring in some children who tend to be more physically active, excitable, and distractable than their peers

salicylates—chemical compounds that occur naturally in some foods and that comprise aspirin

Another Growth Spurt and Increased Independence Influence Teen Needs and Eating

The adolescent years are unique in many ways. During this time, teenagers make a concerted effort to separate themselves from younger children and their parents by identifying with a "teen culture" that looks different and that acts and functions differently. Along with these lifestyle changes, eating habits also change during the teen years.

Influences on Needs and Intake

The adolescent years are a period of increased nutritional vulnerability because a dramatic increase in the rate of growth usually occurs at the very time when other factors tend to compromise nutrient intake.

Growth. According to data collected by the 1980 RDA committee, the average American girl adds more than 10 inches in height and 40–50 pounds in body weight during the five adolescent years of greatest growth, from ages 10 through 14 (see Figure 17.1). The average adolescent boy experiences his greatest growth from ages 12 through 16, during which time he is likely to add approximately 12 inches in height and 50–60 pounds in weight (see Figure 17.1).

As many junior-high school students have observed with dismay, the growth spurt in girls generally occurs two years earlier than it does in boys, although there is tremendous individual variation. In fact, the age at which puberty begins and growth spurts occur in teens is so variable that growth charts based on age are of limited value for teenagers. Some health care providers who work with adolescents find it more useful to evaluate growth in relation to sexual maturation rather than chronological age.

Another generalization is that the gains in weight are much more marked than the increases in height. At the end of the growth spurt, teens weigh 65% more than they did at the beginning, and have gained 15% in height. Weight gain in girls is attributable to increases in blood volume, muscle mass, and adipose tissue. Boys have greater increases in blood volume and muscle mass than girls, and actually become leaner during adolescence (Brasel, 1982) (Figure 17.6).

The increased blood volume and muscle mass raise the requirement for iron (for hemoglobin and myoglobin). Although girls add less of these materials than boys, they have a high need for iron to replace what is lost in menstrual flow.

There is some evidence that nutritional status affects the age of puberty. Young women from Western cultures, who are generally better nourished, usually begin to menstruate at an earlier age than women in less developed countries. Also, girls who have minimal levels of body fatness—such as athletes and ballet dancers—have been reported to begin menstruating later or to menstruate less often than other young women who have a greater percentage of body fat (Mann, 1981).

Psychosocial Development. During the teen years, children not only grow bigger, stronger, and more mature physically, but they also develop mental characteristics that are not common in younger children. Emotional volatility often replaces the more easy-going disposition of the elementary school years. The tendency to reject traditions in the search for their own identity can lead to some bizarre eating habits (National Dairy Council, 1981). In some teens, eating disorders such as anorexia nervosa may be caused by fear of the physical and social consequences of maturing, or by a sense of ineffectiveness (see Chapter 11).

Appearance. At no time in most people's lives is physical appearance of greater concern than during adolescence. Many teenage boys tend to desire a strong, muscular look, and a great majority of girls wish to be thinner than they are. The strength of these common concerns is such that fad diets and special body-shaping products have great appeal to many teens. Such "quick fix" approaches are less beneficial in the long run, however, than modifying long-term lifestyle practices to include a balanced diet and regular exercise.

Acne. The hormonal changes that trigger the onset of puberty are also largely responsible for acne, a common teenage problem that affects about 85% of teens and young adults to some degree (Burton et al., 1971).

Acne begins with the excessive secretion of sebum, an oily substance that lubricates the skin. This fosters the proliferation of bacteria that cause inflammation in ducts and glands beneath the skin. Anxiety, lack of sleep, and hormonal fluctuations during the menstrual cycle of women can aggravate the condition.

Scientific studies have not found creams, ointments, cleansing solutions, or abrasive treatments to be successful cures for acne (Hochman,

acne—skin condition especially common during adolescence; caused by proliferation of bacteria that produce inflammation in ducts and glands beneath the skin

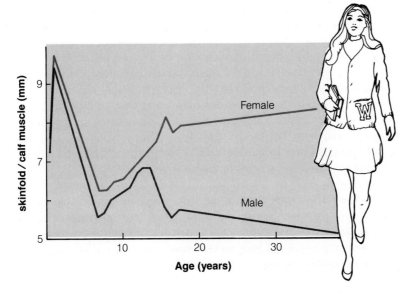

Figure 17.6 Fat accumulation between childhood and adolescence. Data from skinfold thicknesses in the calf indicate that the deposit of fat during adolescence varies greatly according to sex. (Adapted from Valadian, I., and D. Porter. 1977. *Physical growth and development from conception to maturity: A programmed text.* Boston: Little, Brown. © 1977 Little, Brown.)

1980). However, since some individuals experience limited improvement from one or more of these measures, people with acne often want to try them. They should check with a dermatologist about the skin care products they are considering to be sure no risk is associated with their use.

Similarly, these people may try avoiding foods such as chocolate, seafood, nuts, fatty foods in general, pork, and cola beverages, but usually this abstention brings about no significant improvement (Michaelsson, 1981). However, since certain food restrictions have been known to help some people, physicians may suggest this approach, making sure that the diet is nutritionally adequate at the same time. Alcoholic beverages in large amounts worsen acne (Michaelsson, 1981), so their intake should be limited. Fortunately, whether acne is treated or not, spontaneous improvement occurs in almost all cases before the end of the teen years.

For people with cystic acne, a severe form of the disease in which large abcesses cause pits and scars, help is now available. A synthetic form of vitamin A technically known as 13-cis-retinoic acid has been proved helpful in many of the most serious cases. This drug is not as toxic as other forms of vitamin A, but it can produce side effects including elevated levels of blood lipids, reduction of normal body secretions, and possible birth defects in animals. For these reasons, it is available by prescription only, and its use should be carefully monitored by a physician (American Academy of Pediatrics, 1983; Perry and McEvoy, 1983).

13-cis-retinoic acid—synthetic form of vitamin A that has been helpful in treating some serious cases of acne

Physical Performance. Physical performance is another common motivator of adolescent eating behavior. Many teens try to boost their athletic capabilities by using food supplements or eating good luck foods before an athletic event. The degree to which such approaches are useful or not (or dangerous or not) varies considerably.

Some regimens that become popular, although they have no physiological benefit, may contribute to the athlete's psychological preparation. Still others may actually be very dangerous—such as the fasting or restricting of fluids that some wrestlers practice in order to "make weight." In their "Position Stand on Weight Loss in Wrestlers," the American College of Sports Medicine points out the risks of such practices: a reduction in muscular strength; a decrease in endurance; lower blood volume; a reduction in cardiac functioning during submaximal work conditions; lower oxygen consumption, especially with food restriction; an impairment of body heat regulatory processes; decrease in kidney function; a depletion of liver glycogen stores; and an increase in the amount of electrolytes being lost from the body (American College of Sports Medicine, 1976). Such effects could not only jeopardize athletic performance, but could interfere with normal growth and development as well.

Environmental Factors. During the teen years, factors outside the home have a much greater impact on food habits and nutrition beliefs than those in the home. Peer pressure is at its peak during these years. Coaches and other adult role models can also have a significant influence on adolescents' nutrition beliefs and food habits.

Outside activities such as jobs and school functions keep teens away from home and may make family meals a rare occurrence. Even the dinner meal, which is usually eaten together by younger families, may be disrupted during the teen years, if schedules for teenagers' after-school activities and part-time jobs do not mesh with the rest of the family's program. Fast foods and vending machines may become a major source of meals and snacks. Skipping breakfast is common among adolescents, especially girls (National Dairy Council, 1981).

Smoking and the use of alcohol and other drugs often begin in the teen years. According to the Surgeon General's 1979 report on health promotion and disease prevention, 20–25% of adolescents are problem drinkers and are intoxicated at least once a month. Over 20% regularly smoke cigarettes, and about 10% use marijuana regularly (Public Health Service, 1979). Thirty-three percent of high school seniors had tried stimulant drugs, 29% had tried tranquilizers, and 18% had tried cocaine in 1982 (National Institute on Drug Abuse, 1982).

Alcohol can interfere with nutrient absorption and utilization, in addition to providing empty kcalories that displace nutritious foods. Because nutrient needs are high during the teen years, alcohol-induced nutrient shortages cause the classical ill effects of alcohol to be accentuated among teenagers. (These effects are discussed in Chapter 18.) Another serious concern regarding alcohol consumption is that approximately 50% of fatal automobile accidents involve a driver who is intoxicated. Smoking and the use of other drugs are less closely related to nutritional status, but are nonetheless damaging to health.

Despite all the factors that tend to separate the teen from his or her family, there is still some degree of interdependence, including in the nutrition realm. In some families, teen-aged children participate in routine food-related tasks such as food preparation and grocery shopping. In a study done in 1982 by the Food Marketing Institute and *CO-ED* magazine, over 42% of the teenagers surveyed were shopping periodically for their families.

Recommendations for Teen Diets

The SANE guide suggests which foods teenagers should emphasize. The minimum recommendations for teens are similar to those for adults, except that more milk—four servings—should be consumed daily (Table 2.3).

Because of the prevalence of anemia among teenagers, it is particularly important for teens to include meats in their diets as a source of heme iron, and to maximize the bioavailability of iron from plant sources. They can enhance bioavailability by including foods high in vitamin C or small amounts of meat with the plant sources of iron (see Chapter 13).

The frequency of meals and snacks, the amount of food consumed, and the types of food included in those meals and snacks are now mostly determined by the teens themselves; there is little parental control over eating. At this time, the major parental influence on diet has already occurred—the habits parents helped shape earlier in their children.

Nutritional Status of American Teens

Teenagers who have low nutrient intakes are more likely to be found among racial minorities and females.

Low Nutrient Intakes. The nutrients most likely to be deficient in the diets of teenage girls are iron, calcium, magnesium, and vitamin B-6 (Table 17.3). The diets of teenage boys appear to be somewhat better, although when their intakes fall short of the RDA, they are deficient in the same nutrients as girls. Eating one of the day's meals away from home significantly decreases the intake of calcium, iron, vitamin C, and thiamin for people aged 13–21 (Bunch, 1984).

Teenage girls on weight-reduction diets were reported to have the poorest quality diets of any group studied in the Nationwide Food Consumption Survey. Similarly, girls aged 11–16 had the poorest diets of any groups studied in the Ten State Nutrition Survey.

Other nutrients such as zinc and folacin have been reported to be present at low levels in teen diets (Greger et al., 1978; Bailey et al., 1981), but the significance of these findings is uncertain because the data are too sketchy for estimating accurately requirements and intakes of these nutrients. Folacin status is thought to be a potential problem for adolescents who have poor diets: the increased requirement for this nutrient during periods of rapid growth is difficult to meet without a generous intake of fruits and vegetables.

Table 17.3 Nutrients for Which Average Intakes Were Below the 1980 RDA for American Teenagers

	Age	Protein	Calcium	Iron	Magnesium	Phosphorus	Vitamin A	Thiamin	Riboflavin	Niacin	Vitamin B-6	Vitamin B-12	Vitamin C
Males	9–11		90–99%		80–89%						90–99%		
	12–14		90–99%	80–89%	80–89%						90–99%		
	15–18		90–99%	90–99%	70–79%						90–99%		
	19–22				80–89%						80–89%		
Females	9–11		80–89%	90–99%	80–89%						80–89%		
	12–14		70–79%	less than 70%	70–79%	90–99%					70–79%		
	15–18		less than 70%	less than 70%	70–79%	90–99%					less than 70%		
	19–22		70–79%	less than 70%	less than 70%		90–99%	90–99%			less than 70%		

The shaded squares show the average levels of intake for nutrients consumed in less quantity than their RDAs. Blank squares mean that average nutrient intakes were at the RDA levels or better.

Adapted from Science and Education Administration. 1980. *Food and nutrient intakes of individuals in 1 day in the United States, Spring, 1977.* National food consumption preliminary report no. 2. Washington, DC: U.S. Department of Agriculture.

Anemia. Anemia is a common problem among teenagers, as it is for younger children. Figure 17.4 (see page 466) presents HANES data showing that low hemoglobin levels were more prevalent in 12- to 14-year-old boys than girls; but in the later teen years, more girls were anemic than boys (Public Health Service, 1982). Blacks (especially males) were anemic more frequently than whites.

There was little correlation between the incidence of anemia, as indicated by low hemoglobin levels, and dietary iron in the HANES survey data. Therefore, other factors such as iron absorption and utilization, growth rates, and menstrual losses also are important in determining iron status.

Teenage Pregnancy

One of every five infants born in the United States has a teenage mother. The proportion of babies born to mothers who are 18 years old or younger has increased from 17% in 1966 to 20% in 1980 (Hollingsworth and Kreutner, 1980). Within the teenage population, there have also been some shifts in pregnancy rates. For older teens, the rate of pregnancy among teenagers has decreased; it is highest for 15- to 17-year-old girls. And each year, about 300,000 girls under 15 become pregnant (Public Health Service, 1979); the number of babies born to girls of this age has been rising (American Academy of Pediatrics, 1979).

Pregnancy in teenagers is a situation with sociological, medical, and nutritional consequences. Sociological difficulties common in early pregnancy include interrupted and incomplete education, poverty and welfare dependence, social disapproval, unstable families, and child abuse and neglect (Hollingsworth and Kreutner, 1980; American Academy of Pediatrics, 1979). Since most teen births occur out of wedlock (Public Health Service, 1979), another disruptive factor is the lack of emotional and financial support from the baby's father. Many pregnant girls experience an alienation from family and friends that can be emotionally devastating.

The medical consequences of pregnancy include more low-birth-weight babies, babies with respiratory problems, maternal preeclampsia (drastic fluid retention and elevated blood pressure), difficult deliveries due to small pelvic size, and higher maternal and fetal death rates. These problems are especially prevalent for pregnancies that occur within two years of menarche, when the mother may have poor body stores of nutrients (National Dairy Council, 1981). Some of these problems may be related to smoking, drug abuse, or inadequate medical care, as well as to the age and nutritional status of the mother. Teenage pregnancies are often considered high-risk situations and adequate nutrition and prenatal care are of the utmost importance.

menarche—the onset of menstruation

Recommended Food Intake. A pregnant teenager, like a pregnant adult, needs a good diet to meet her own needs and those of the fetus. As with all pregnancies, nutritional status prior to conception is very important. If her own reserves have been depleted by fad diets and long-term intake

Table 17.4 SANE Guide for the Pregnant Teenager (Nonpregnant teen and pregnant adult standards are included for comparison.)

	Include at least this many servings daily		
	Nonpregnant teen	Pregnant teen	Pregnant adult
Fruits and vegetables			
Vitamin A-rich	1	1	1
Vitamin C-rich	1	2	2
Others to make a group total of . . .	4	5	5
Grain products (preferably whole grain; otherwise enriched or fortified)	4	4 or more	4 or more
Milk and milk products	4	5	4
Meats and alternates	2	3	3

of foods low in nutrient density, the likelihood of a young mother delivering a healthy full-term baby may be reduced.

The RDAs for pregnant teens are higher than those for their nonpregnant counterparts. Supplements of iron and folacin or a multivitamin and mineral supplement are often recommended to bring intake of these nutrients up to satisfactory levels.

The recommended weight gain of 22–28 pounds during pregnancy is extremely important for pregnant teens. The extra 300 kcalories over the girl's prepregnancy needs should be obtained from foods high in nutrient density.

Table 17.4 compares the SANE guide recommendations for the pregnant teenager with those for other groups. Note that compared with the nonpregnant teen, the pregnant teenager should consume more food from all the groups. Compared with the adult pregnant woman, the pregnant teen needs more milk.

Special Programs. Pregnant teenagers can benefit from programs available from public and private agencies. Many school districts operate special classes in parenting, nutrition, infant care, and similar topics of concern to young mothers. These programs are often known as "SAM" (School-Age Maternity) or "SAP" (School-Age Parent) programs; many include services such as day-care assistance to help the young mother complete her high school courses and earn a diploma.

The March of Dimes provides information and counseling in health and nutrition for prospective parents, and often provides referral to other agencies when special assistance is needed. The WIC program (Supplemental Food Program for Women, Infants and Children) provides many services: nutrition education, prenatal health monitoring, medical referral for special problems, and food supplements. The program is designed to serve women and young children in high-risk categories, which includes pregnant teenagers. These types of services are available throughout most of the United States, and have proved to be successful in reducing the rate of low-birth-weight infants (Kennedy et al., 1982).

SUMMARY

■ The most important influence that caregivers can have on a child's nutrition during the growing years is to assist him or her in developing sound eating habits. This challenge demands patience, a sense of humor, and some knowledge about what is normal during these transitional times.

■ The food intake of young children is extremely variable and is not strictly proportional to their weight. As children's motor skills and coordination improve, they should be encouraged to participate in food preparation. Children often assert themselves by rejecting certain foods or using their eating behavior as a negotiating tool. Advertising, family circumstances, and peer influence all contribute to a child's nutrition socialization. Anticipating a child's behavior and the many influences on it can help put this issue in perspective.

■ Compared with children in other parts of the world, children in North America do not have many nutritional deficiencies; in general, they are more likely to be *over*nourished than *under*nourished. Obesity is a common problem for children as well as adults, and there is some debate about whether childhood obesity predisposes an individual to a lifelong weight problem. (It is thought that environmental factors play an important role here.) Iron deficiency anemia is another fairly common childhood nutritional problem, as are dental caries.

■ Recommended diets for children are similar in many ways to those for adults, and should include a wide variety of high-nutrient-density foods. Since children tend to like familiar foods more than unfamiliar ones, it is important to expose them to an increasing assortment of foods that can *become* familiar. As at other ages, the child's sense of hunger and satiety should determine the amount of food consumed. Keeping a growth chart for a child can help provide reassurance that he or she is eating enough.

■ Many popular articles have attempted to link a child's diet and behavior, although no meaningful scientific evidence supports such claims. The association between sugar consumption and behavior in normal children is very weak. Some hyperactive children, thought by a few investigators to be acting out under the influence of certain food additives and salicylates, have responded inconsistently to special diets; there is no evidence that this problem has a nutritional "cure" in most cases.

■ The dramatic growth of the adolescent years produces high nutrient demands at the very time when many other factors seem to affect nutrition adversely. Intense preoccupation with physical appearance can inspire strange eating habits (or, in extreme cases, eating disorders). Acne afflicts many teens, who sometimes try to deal with it by restricting certain foods. The desire to improve athletic performance also motivates adolescent eating behavior, as do peer pressure, the time demands of outside activities, and the use of alcohol and other drugs.

■ The diets of teenage boys appear to be slightly better than those of girls; teenage girls on weight reduction diets tend to be less well nourished than almost any other North American population group. Many teens have low intakes of certain nutrients, with iron deficiency anemia being common.

■ Teenage pregnancies present many medical and nutritional problems for both the mother and the baby, and are often considered high-risk situations. nutritional status both before and after conception is very important to the baby's health. Many public and private agencies sponsor programs to counsel teenage mothers about health, nutrition, and child care, and to allow them to finish school.

REFERENCES

Akin, J.S., J.S. Bass, D.K. Guilkey, P.S. Haines, and B.M. Popkin. 1983. Evaluating school meals. *The Community Nutritionist* 2(no.1):4–7.

Alford, B.B., and M.L. Bogle. 1982. *Nutrition during the life cycle.* Englewood Cliffs, NJ: Prentice-Hall, Inc.

American Academy of Pediatrics, Committee on Adolescence. 1979. Statement on teenage pregnancy. *Pediatrics* 63(no.5):795–797.

American Academy of Pediatrics, Committee on Drugs. 1983. New therapy for severe cystic acne. *Pediatrics* 72(no.2):258–259.

American College of Sports Medicine. 1976. Position stand on weight loss in wrestlers. *Medicine and Science in Sports and Exercise* 8(no.2):xi–xiii.

American Medical Association, American Diabetes Association, the Endocrine Society. 1973. Statement on hypoglycemia. *Journal of the American Medical Association* 223:682.

Bailey, L., P. Wagner, J. Christakis, C. Davis, H. Appledorf, J. Ginsburg, E. Dorsey, and J. Dinning. 1981. Folacin and iron status and hematological findings in adolescence. In *Proceedings of the Florida Symposium on Microsciences:* 113–119. Gainesville, FL: University of Florida.

Beal, V.A. 1957. On the acceptance of solid foods and other food patterns of infants and children. *Pediatrics* 20:448–456.

Berger, K.S. 1980. *The developing person.* New York: Worth Publishers.

Birch, L.L., S.I. Zimmerman, and H. Hind. 1980. The influence of social affective context on the formation of children's food preferences. *Child Development* 51:856–861.

Brasel, J.A. 1982. *Changes in body composition during adolescence.* In *Adolescent nutrition,* ed. M. Winick. New York: John Wiley and Sons.

Brownell, K.D. 1984. New developments in the treatment of obese children and adolescents. In *Eating and its disorders,* eds. A.J. Stunkard and E. Stellar. New York: Raven Press.

Bunch, K.L. 1984. Food away from home and the quality of the diet. *National Food Review* 25: 14–16.

Burton, J.S., W.J. Cunliffe, I. Stafford, and S. Shuster. 1971. The prevalence of acne vulgaris in adolescence. *British Journal of Dermatology* 85:119–126.

Charney, M., H.C. Goodman, M. McBride, B. Lyon, and R. Pratt. 1976. Childhood antecedents of adult obesity: Do chubby infants become obese adults? *New England Journal of Medicine* 195:6–9.

Cravioto, J. 1981. Nutrition, stimulation, mental development and learning. *Nutrition Today* 16(no.5):4–15.

Dwyer, J.T., E.M. Andrew, I. Valadian, and R.B. Reed. 1980. Size, obesity and leanness in vegetarian preschool children. *Journal of the American Dietetic Association* 77:434–439.

Ephron, Delia. 1978. *How to eat like a child and other lessons in not being grown up.* New York: Viking Press.

Garn, S.M. 1977. Effect of parental fatness levels on the fatness of biological and adoptive children. *Ecology of Food and Nutrition* 7:91–93.

Gillespie, A. 1983. Assessing snacking behavior of children. *Ecology of Food and Nutrition* 13: 167–172.

Goodman, I.F., and N.E. Johnson. 1979. *TV ads: Another dimension to children's eating behavior.* Madison, WI: University of Wisconsin Cooperative Extension Service Bulletin No. B7790809.

Gray, G.E., and L.K. Gray. 1983. Diet and juvenile delinquency. *Nutrition Today* 18(no.3):14–22.

Greger, J.L., M.M. Higgins, R.P. Abernathy, A. Kirksey, M.B. DeCorso, and P. Baligar. 1978. Nutritional status of adolescent girls in regard to zinc, copper, and iron. *American Journal of Clinical Nutrition* 31:269–275.

Herbert, V., and S. Barrett. 1981. *Vitamins and health foods: The great American hustle.* Philadelphia, PA: G.F. Stickley Co.

Himes, J.H. 1979. Infant feeding practices and obesity. *Journal of the American Dietetic Association* 75:122–125.

Hochman, H. 1980. Is eating hazardous to your skin? *Environmental Nutrition* 3(no.4):1–2.

Hollingsworth, D.R., and A.K.K. Kreutner. 1980. Sounding board: Teenage pregnancy-—solutions are evolving. *New England Journal of Medicine* 303(no.9):516–518.

Kennedy, E.T., S. Gershoff, R. Reed, and J.E. Austin. 1982. Evaluation of the effect of WIC supplemental feeding on birth weight. *Journal of the American Dietetic Association* 80:220–227.

Knittle, J.L. 1972. Obesity in childhood: A problem in adipose tissue cellular development. *Journal of Pediatrics* 81:1048–1059.

Leveille, G.A., and G.D. Coccodrilli. 1982. Cariogenicity of foods: Current concepts. *Food Technology* 36(no.9):93–98.

Mann, G.V. 1981. Menstrual effects of athletic training. In *Medicine and Sport*, eds. J. Borms, M. Hebbelinck, and A. Venerando. New York: Karger.

Michaelsson, G. 1981. Diet and acne. *Nutrition Reviews* 39(no.2):104–106.

National Center for Health Statistics. 1982. Diet and iron status, a study of relationships: United States, 1971–4. DHHS Publication No. (PHS)83-1679. Hyattsville, MD: U.S. Department of Health and Human Services.

National Dairy Council. 1980. *Lunch comparison cards*. Rosemont, IL: National Dairy Council.

National Dairy Council. 1981. Nutritional concerns during adolescence. *Dairy Council Digest* 52(no.2):7–11.

National Institute on Drug Abuse. 1982. Teenagers try drugs. *The Capital Times*, September 19, 1983, Madison, WI.

National Institutes of Health. 1981. *The prevalence of dental caries in United States children*. The national dental caries prevalence survey 1979–80. U.S. Department of Health and Human Services Publication No. 82-2245. Washington, DC: National Institutes of Health.

National Institutes of Health. 1982. *Defined diets and childhood hyperactivity*. National Institutes of Health consensus development conference summary. Volume 4, No.3. Bethesda, MD: National Institutes of Health.

National Research Council. 1980. *Recommended dietary allowances*. Washington, DC: National Academy of Sciences.

Perry, M.D. and G.K. McEvoy. 1983. Isotretinoin: New therapy for severe acne. *Clinical Pharmacy* 2(1):12–19.

Pollitt, E., R.L. Leibel, and D. Greenfield. 1981. Brief fasting, stress, and cognition in children. *American Journal of Clinical Nutrition* 34:1526–1533.

Public Health Service. 1978. *Health status of children: A review of surveys 1963–72*. DHEW Publication No. (HSA)78-5744. Rockville, MD: Health Services Administration.

Public Health Service. 1979. *Healthy people: The surgeon general's report on health promotion and disease prevention*. U.S.D.H.E.W. Publication No. (PHS)79-55071. Washington, DC.

Public Health Service. 1982. *Food for the teenager during and after pregnancy*. DHSS Publication Number (HRSA)82-5106. Rockville, MD: Public Health Service.

Pugliese, M., F. Lifshitz, G. Grad, P. Fort, and M. Marks-Katz. 1983. Fear of obesity: A cause of short stature and delayed puberty. *New England Journal of Medicine* 309:513–517.

Rapoport, J.L., and M.J.P. Kruesi. 1983. Behavior and nutrition: A minireview. *Contemporary Nutrition* 8(no.10). Minneapolis, MN: General Mills, Inc.

Satter, E. 1983. *Child of mine: Feeding with love and good sense*. Palo Alto, CA: Bull Publishing Co.

Scammon, R.E. 1927. The measurement of the body in childhood. In *The measurement of man*, by J.J. Harris, C.M. Jackson, and R.E. Scammon. Minneapolis, MN: University of Minnesota Press.

Science and Education Administration. 1980. *Food and nutrient intakes of individuals in 1 day in the United States, Spring, 1977*. National food consumption survey preliminary report no.2. Washington, DC: U.S. Department of Agriculture.

Sheridan, M.J., and G. McPherrin. 1981. *Fast food and the American diet*. Summit, NJ: American Council on Science and Health.

Snyderman, S.E. 1980. Nutrition in infancy and adolescence. In *Modern nutrition in health and disease*, eds. R.S. Goodhart and M.E. Shils. Philadelphia: Lea and Febiger.

Valadian, I., and D. Porter. 1977. *Physical growth and development from conception to maturity: A programmed text*. Boston: Little, Brown.

Vobecky, J.S., J. Vobecky, D. Shapcott, and P. Demers. 1983. Nutrient intake patterns and nutritional status with regard to relative weight in early infancy. *American Journal of Clinical Nutrition* 38:730–738.

Way, W.L. 1983. Food related behaviors on prime-time television. *Journal of Nutrition Education* 15:105–109.

Winick, M. 1982. *Growing up healthy: A parents' guide to good nutrition.* New York: William Morrow and Co.

18

Nutritional Needs and Challenges for Adults

IN THIS CHAPTER: Changes in Health Status and Nutritional Needs Take Place along a Continuum ▪ Drugs Can Interfere with Nutrition ▪ Alcohol Influences Nutrition and Health ▪ Dietary Recommendations for Adults Promote Health Maintenance ▪ Specific Programs Help Meet Nutritional Needs of Special Groups

The popular press makes some exciting claims about what nutrition can do for adults. One popular book on sports nutrition claims that a certain diet plus supplements can keep adult athletes at peak performance levels for ten years longer than most professionals have previously found possible. Another book claims that changing the diets of criminals can bring them around to socially acceptable behavior. Still other literature suggests that arthritis, the uncomfortable joint condition that affects most of us to some degree as we age, can be cured by the right diet.

Do these claims hold up when they are examined scientifically? Unfortunately, as with most promises that sound too good to be true, such claims *overextend* what nutrition is now known to be able to deliver. Although particular nutritional practices definitely can help an athlete perform at his or her best at a certain event, currently there is no evidence that nutritional practices can keep most athletes at the height of their careers until age 40. Such claims are in the realm of wishful thinking. On the matter of diet and criminal behavior, no well-designed scientific studies support the claims made by these enthusiasts, and it is highly unlikely that a particular eating style can undo antisocial behaviors. As far as arthritis is concerned, there is no cure to be found in the kitchen, although overweight arthritic people may become more comfortable if they lose some surplus fat.

What responsible statements can be made about the role of nutrition during the adult years, when the years of physical growth are over? Nutrients still perform their basic functions of providing energy, regulating body reactions, and contributing to structure. All tissues—even fully grown, apparently stable body structures such as bone—are dynamic: a regular exchange of their components occurs between the tissue and its biochemical environment. Small portions break down and are subsequently reconstructed from other metabolites and/or raw materials from the diet. Therefore people need to continue to include the building materials as well as the energy nutrients and regulators in their diets.

As we get older, the body's rate of cell reconstruction is unable to keep pace with degradation. This results in a gradual loss of tissue and organ function, the process we call aging. (Although some authors use the term *aging* to refer to all age-related changes that occur from birth to death, we are using it in this chapter to refer to the gradual degeneration that takes place during the adult years.)

People want to know how they can slow down tissue degradation and/or speed up reconstruction. *Most scientists believe that the overriding influences on aging are genetically determined, but that longstanding habits of nutrition and exercise probably modify longevity and health within those inherited limits.* In this chapter we will present the best substantiated ideas about the effects of nutrition on aging.

aging—gradual loss of tissue and organ function over time

Changes in Health Status and Nutritional Needs Take Place Along a Continuum

Aging gradually affects cells, tissues, organs, systems, and their functions throughout the body over many years. The rate and sequence of these changes varies greatly from one individual to another. Therefore, although we often arbitrarily assign age 21 as the official beginning of "adulthood," 40 as the start of "middle age," and 65 as the year in which a person becomes "elderly," the physiological changes of aging are neither that abrupt nor that uniform: they spread themselves over years at a rate that varies with the individual.

Physical Changes Observed during Aging

The average ages at which various physiological changes occur are shown in Figure 18.1. From age 30 to age 75, various functions decrease by from less than 10% to more than 50%. Overall, the most influential change is probably the decrease in lean body mass, and the concurrent decrease in energy need.

Other changes have more specific effects on nutrition. With aging, many changes occur in the gastrointestinal tract. Loss of teeth, decreased production of saliva, and a declining number of taste buds occur during aging and may change food preferences. People with missing teeth or ill-fitting dentures may avoid chewy, crunchy, or hard foods. Declining taste sensitivity may cause some adults to favor more highly seasoned and strongly

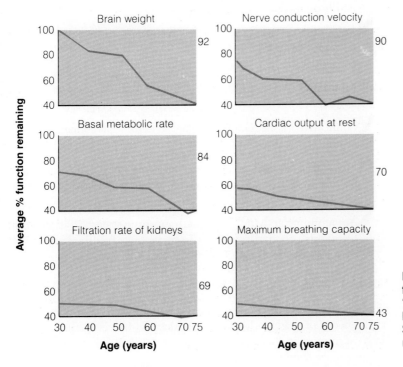

Figure 18.1 Loss of organ function with age. (From "Growing Old" by Alexander Leaf. Copyright © 1973 by Scientific American, Inc. All rights reserved.

flavored foods. Changing taste perceptions may lead some adults to comment sadly that food "doesn't taste as good as it used to."

Gastric secretions of acid and enzymes decrease with age, so digestion and absorption become less efficient. The reduction of stomach acid may make dietary iron less absorbable. Decreased production of intrinsic factor impairs the absorption of vitamin B-12. A decrease in the amount of bile secreted by the liver may make fat absorption less efficient in older people. With age, muscles in the lower gastrointestinal tract become weaker and peristalsis slows, so constipation may become a problem. Renal function decreases with age so that electrolyte and water balance are more difficult to maintain. This effect is more pronounced during periods of physical stress, such as during illness.

There are indirect effects of aging on nutrition as well. For example, if eyesight eventually deteriorates seriously, a person may have to stop driving a car and rely on less frequent trips to the store; this may influence how much fresh food he or she consumes. Or visual problems may make recipes too hard to read and a person may forego making favorite foods, which may lead to a general disinterest in eating.

Theories Concerning Age-related Changes

For several decades, scientists have theorized about what might be occurring at the cellular level to cause the obvious changes of aging. Although no one theory is completely satisfactory, each of the following hypotheses has its plausible aspects:

- **Programmed cell death**   The DNA in each cell puts a time limit on its life span (Roe, 1983a).

- **Maximum cell division**   Each cell can divide only a limited number of times, after which it becomes incapable of repairing itself and consequently dies (Baserga, 1977).

- **Mutation**   Outside influences such as radiation cause changes in DNA that interfere with cell replacement and repair (Watkin, 1980).

- **Connective tissue changes**   The structure of connective tissue is modified, resulting in less flexibility and resilience (Balazs, 1977).

- **Free radical damage**   Active chemicals called free radicals alter membrane structure, which allows permanent damage to cells (Roe, 1983a).

- **Autoimmune activity**   A person's immune system loses its ability to distinguish foreign materials from its own healthy body cells, and therefore destroys both (Rowe, 1978).

Nutrient Needs during Adulthood

More research has been done on the nutritional needs of young adults than on the needs of the elderly. In the last decade, however, there has been a surge of interest in this area; more research results on nutrition for older adults will be available soon.

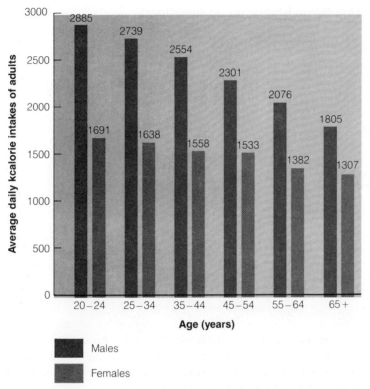

Figure 18.2 Average daily kcalorie intakes of adults.
(Data source: National Center for Health Statistics. 1977. *Dietary intake findings: United States, 1971–74*. Data from the National Health Survey, Series 11, No. 202. DHEW Publication No. (HRA)77-1647. Hyattsville, MD: Public Health Service.)

Energy. A study of healthy men showed that total energy usage declined annually, beginning in the 20s, by about 12 or 13 kcalories per day. Of this amount, approximately 5 kcalories per day were accounted for by falling basal metabolic rate, and the remainder were attributable to declining physical activity levels (McGandy et al., 1966). In keeping with this decrease in usage, total intake of kcalories also declines with age in men and women (Figure 18.2). The RDA for energy for people aged 51–75 is only 90% of that for a young adult, and the energy RDA for people over age 75 is only 75–80% of the young adult's RDA (National Research Council, 1980).

Other Nutrients. As mentioned, there are many gaps in our knowledge about the effect of age on most nutrient requirements. Much of the research that has been done to establish recommended nutrient intakes has involved young adults; many of the RDA figures for older adults have been estimated from these data.

Older adults may actually need some nutrients in higher amounts. They may require these higher amounts because their bodies have become less efficient in absorbing and metabolizing food due to the natural changes of the aging process; because certain diseases raise the need for some nutrients; and because some routinely used medications interfere with nutrition. Some studies have demonstrated an increased need for protein, for example (Watkin, 1980), and higher intakes are suggested for some other nutrients including calcium and zinc (Heaney et al., 1982; Sandstead et al., 1982). More research is needed to clarify the specific nutrient needs of the elderly.

Nutritional Status during Adulthood

How do adult diets compare with the RDAs? Just as energy intake declines with age, so do the intakes of most vitamins and minerals. Calcium, magnesium and vitamin B-6 were reported to be particularly low in the average diets of adults included in the Nationwide Food Consumption Survey. For women in their reproductive years, iron was also low; however, since women need less iron when menstruation stops (menopause), inadequate intakes of this nutrient are not as frequent in elderly women.

menopause—the termination of menstruation and reproductive capacity

Tables 18.1 and 18.2 show which nutrients tend to be consumed in less than RDA amounts by men and women of various ages. Although mean intakes of calcium, iron, magnesium, and vitamin B-6 are below standards in the diets of many adults, mean intakes were at RDA levels or better for protein, phosphorus, riboflavin, niacin, and vitamins B-12 and C.

There have been other surveys. In the 1971–1974 Health and Nutrition Examination Survey (HANES) data, Caucasians tended to have higher intakes of energy and nutrients than Blacks (National Center for Health Statistics, 1979). Females had more intakes below standard than males had. Although dietary surveys identify inadequate intakes of certain nutrients, obvious external signs of deficiency are not commonly seen (National Dairy Council, 1983). Biochemical measurements, however, show iron and vitamins B-6 and A as the most likely to be below standard.

Milk drinking declines markedly among older people, especially women, because some regard milk as a food for children and because some experience lactose intolerance. This is reflected in low calcium intakes. The intake of meat also declines with age (Science and Education Administration, 1980); this helps explain the low levels of zinc and vitamin B-6 seen in some studies. Declining zinc intakes are thought to compromise wound healing and immune function (Sandstead et al., 1982).

Diseases in Which Nutrition May Play a Role

Several health problems that have a nutritional aspect are fairly common in adulthood. Although these problems can occur at virtually any age, their incidence is generally higher among older adults. These conditions are usually also influenced by genetic and other environmental factors than diet, and may take many decades to develop. This is a key concept: the effects of nutrition and other lifestyle practices on health status are *cumulative*.

Obesity. From the discussion in Chapter 10, you know that obesity is a common nutritional problem during adulthood. According to the skinfold data collected during the 1971–1974 HANES, approximately 5% of men and 7% of women in the United States are severely obese (Figure 18.3). The prevalence of obesity increases with age for women until the mid-fifties, but men do not show this age-related trend (Abraham and Johnson, 1980). The problem is of particular concern since obesity can worsen several chronic diseases including hypertension, diabetes, and arthritis.

Table 18.1 Nutrients for Which Average Intakes Were Below the 1980 RDA for American Men

Age	Pro-tein	Calcium	Iron	Mag-nesium	Phos-phorus	Vita-min A	Thia-min	Ribo-flavin	Niacin	Vitamin B-6	Vitamin B-12	Vita-min C
19–22				80–89%						80–89%		
23–34				80–89%						80–89%		
35–50		90–99%		80–89%						70–79%		
51–64		80–89%		80–89%						70–79%		
65–74		90–99%		80–89%						70–79%		
75 and over		80–89%		70–79%						less than 70%		

The shaded squares show the average levels of intake for nutrients consumed in less quantity than their RDAs. Blank squares mean that average nutrient intakes were at the RDA levels or better.
Adapted from Science and Education Administration. 1980. *Food and nutrient intakes of individuals in 1 day in the United States, Spring, 1977.* Nationwide food consumption survey report no. 2. Washington, DC: U.S. Department of Agriculture.

Table 18.2 Nutrients for Which Average Intakes Were Below the 1980 RDA for American Women

Age	Pro-tein	Calcium	Iron	Mag-nesium	Phos-phorus	Vita-min A	Thia-min	Ribo-flavin	Niacin	Vitamin B-6	Vitamin B-12	Vita-min C
19–22		70–79%	less than 70%	less than 70%		90–99%	90–99%			less than 70%		
23–34		70–79%	less than 70%	70–79%			90–99%			less than 70%		
35–50		less than 70%	less than 70%	70–79%						less than 70%		
51–64		less than 70%		70–79%						less than 70%		
65–74		70–79%		70–79%						less than 70%		
75 and over		70–79%		70–79%						less than 70%	90–99%	

The shaded squares show the average levels of intake for nutrients consumed in less quantity than their RDAs. Blank squares mean that average nutrient intakes were at the RDA levels or better.
Adapted from Science and Education Administration. 1980. *Food and nutrient intakes of individuals in 1 day in the United States, Spring, 1977.* Nationwide food consumption survey report no. 2. Washington, DC: U.S. Department of Agriculture.

Figure 18.3 Percentage of adults who were severely obese according to skinfold thickness measures from the HANES survey. (Source: Abraham, S., and C.L. Johnson. 1980. Prevalence of severe obesity in adults in the U.S. *American Journal of Clinical Nutrition* 33:364–369.)

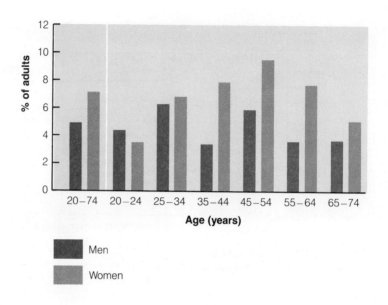

Hypertension. Blood pressure tends to increase with age in many, but not all, adults. For most people, systolic pressure (the upper number in a blood pressure reading, which represents pressure in arterial walls during heart contraction) rises faster than diastolic pressure (the lower number, which represents pressure between beats) during the aging process.

Body fatness is the most important nutritional variable associated with high blood pressure. Other variables such as dietary sodium, potassium, calcium, phosphorus, and alcohol have inconsistent relationships with blood pressure measurements, according to the 1971–1974 HANES data (National Center for Health Statistics, 1983). The relationship between mineral intake and blood pressure is an active area of current research, as discussed in Chapter 13 (on minerals).

Atherosclerosis. Recall our earlier discussion of atherosclerosis in Chapter 7 and elsewhere (see capsule). In brief: when blood vessels become narrowed and inflexible due to the accumulation of atherosclerotic plaque, heart attack or stroke can result. Atherosclerosis is so common in Americans that it is the leading cause of death in adults. In some situations, diet can affect risk factors for atherosclerosis such as high blood cholesterol and hypertension.

Cancer. The second most frequent cause of death for adults in the United States is cancer. As a prevention strategy, the Committee on Diet, Nutrition, and Cancer (1982) and the American Cancer Society suggest that Americans limit the fat in their diets to 30% of kcalories; include fruits, vegetables, and whole grains; limit intake of cured meats; and consume little if any alcohol. (Some experts debate these points, as we have mentioned elsewhere.)

Diabetes. The most common form of diabetes is the adult onset non–insulin-dependent type (see Chapter 6), which is associated with overweight in about 75% of adults who have it. Usually the most effective treatment is the reduction of body fat (Roe, 1983a).

Diverticular Disease. As Chapter 6 also discussed, diverticular disease occurs when the walls of the intestine develop balloonlike outpouchings (diverticula). It is theorized that these are created when pressure builds up in the intestine, which may occur when a person chronically consumes a low-fiber diet. This may explain why the condition is more common in North America than in areas of the world where high fiber-diets are the norm.

Arthritis. Arthritis is characterized by the distortion of joint surfaces due to degeneration or mineral deposits (Weimer, 1982). There are many types of arthritis, the causes of which have not been clearly defined. *Osteoarthritis* is the form very common among the elderly; *rheumatoid arthritis* is more likely to occur in younger adults, but is not as common. Dietary changes and supplements have not usually proved to be effective treatments in controlled studies (Hecht, 1980), except that weight loss in overweight osteoarthritics often relieves pain in weight-bearing joints.

Gout is a type of arthritis that has been thought to have a closer relationship to diet. In this condition, crystals of uric acid (a breakdown product of certain protein components) form in the joints, causing periods of pain during motion. In the past, foods containing chemicals from which larger amounts of uric acid are produced were limited in the diet. However, we now know that the body can produce uric acid precursors from fragments of any of the macronutrients. Even for gout, then, diet is not the primary cause or treatment method: genetic factors are probably the major cause, and drug therapies are the most effective treatment (Krause and Mahan, 1979).

Osteoporosis. We mentioned earlier that bones are slowly and continuously degraded and reconstructed throughout life. When breakdown is greater than rebuilding, a situation that probably begins in the middle 30s, especially in women, there is a gradual decrease in bone size and density. As the condition progresses, bones gradually weaken and become brittle. There is no obvious sign that this is happening unless a bone fracture or compression of the spinal vertebrae occur.

Four factors have been hypothetically related to such bone loss: lack of exercise, low levels of calcium and/or high levels of phosphorus in the diet, chronic alcohol use, and low levels of the hormone estrogen in women after menopause. The importance of each of these factors is somewhat controversial.

Researchers have studied whether the condition is forestalled or improved with frequent and vigorous exercise, generous intake of calcium, intakes of recommended amounts of vitamin D, little or no use of alcohol, and/or estrogen therapy after menopause. The studies have shown that these practices sometimes help slow the progress of the condition, but do

arthritis—painful condition resulting from the distortion of joint surfaces due to degeneration or mineral deposits

not reverse or prevent it (Heaney et al., 1982; Recker, 1983; Worthington-Roberts, 1981). For whatever help it might provide, some physicians routinely recommend a daily calcium intake of 1200–1500 mg (as opposed to the 1980 RDA of 800 mg) and exercise programs for all female patients over age 35.

Meanwhile, research on this complex problem continues.

periodontal disease—degeneration of the gum and bone tissues supporting the teeth

Periodontal Disease. Periodontal disease involves degeneration of the tissues supporting the teeth, including gum tissue and the bony arches in which the teeth are situated.

Periodontal disease is responsible for tooth loss in about 35 million people in the United States (Lutwak, 1976). It is important to our discussion of adult nutrition for two main reasons: first, the bone loss has been hypothetically related to diet (as in osteoporosis), and second, the deterioration of the bony arches makes it difficult to fit dentures properly. This results in chewing problems that make meats and some high-fiber foods less appealing.

The origin of periodontal disease is not known, although its initiation and progression correlate with the presence of bacterial plaque. Nutritionally, a diet deficient in vitamin C for several months can lead to symptoms of periodontal problems (Randolph and Dennison, 1981). Since vitamin C nutriture is not a problem for most people in North America, good dental hygiene is a primary recommendation for avoiding or controlling this problem.

Nervous System Changes. Although most cases of brain and nervous system dysfunction that occur as people age are primarily attributable to natural and gradual degeneration, or to such causes as stroke or Alzheimer's disease, nutritional deficiencies can produce nervous system symptoms in the elderly, as they can in people of any age.

If vitamin deficiencies cause nervous system problems, an increased intake of the vitamins will improve the nervous system condition. However, such poor vitamin status is not common among the elderly (Iber et al., 1982). There is no evidence that the gradual mental deterioration that occurs as a natural consequence of aging can be prevented or delayed through diet or supplements.

The Impact of Nutrition on Length of Life

The search for a way to live longer is as ancient as the quest for the Fountain of Youth. Periodically we hear stories of people in remote places like the mountains of Soviet Georgia, Pakistan, or Ecuador who achieve a vigorous old age. Some people have suggested that the diets of these cultures may be responsible for the people's longevity.

life span—potential oldest age to which an animal can survive

life expectancy—average length of life for a given group of animals

Each species of animal including humans has a maximum life span, which is the *potential oldest age* to which members of the species may survive. Life span appears to be set genetically and is therefore unlikely to be influenced by nutrition (Harper, 1982). Life expectancy, on the other hand, is the *average length of life* statistically shown for a given group of

Diet and longevity. Claims have been made that in certain isolated regions of the world many people live to extraordinary ages. Investigation casts doubt on whether these people are as old as first thought, and on the theory that their diets may have been responsible. The Russian men pictured are from a district legendary for its inhabitants' longevity: these five men claim that their ages total over 600.

animals. Longevity is the length of time actually lived by an individual member of a species. It has been suggested that nutrition may have a role in these latter areas.

longevity—length of time an individual animal actually lives

Animal Studies about Longevity. A number of animal studies have shown that feeding young animals a diet extremely inadequate in energy (approximately half the amount needed for full growth) increased the average age to which the animals lived (Harper, 1982).

Despite the fact that many underfed rats outlived their better fed peers, underfeeding had distinct drawbacks. Severely restricted animals had increased infant mortality, growth and developmental defects, greater susceptibility to bacterial and parasitic diseases, and fewer tumors overall but proportionately more malignant ones. On these physical bases alone, severe energy restriction would not be recommended as a means of lengthening life in humans (Ross, 1976). Beyond the physical effects, there would be severe negative psychological consequences as well. Furthermore, there is no proof that humans would react like rats.

Human Epidemiological Studies about Longevity. Regions in which a high proportion of the inhabitants are claimed to live to a very old age have been studied in an attempt to determine what factors might account for the people's longevity. In such regions of Russia, Pakistan, and Ecuador, several cultural characteristics were proposed to account for individuals' apparent long and vigorous lives: the nature of their diets, use (or nonuse) of alcohol and tobacco, exercise habits, mountainous altitude, air quality, and the positive attitude of the societies toward the elderly.

As early dietary information was published, many people in our culture hoped that consumption of foods indigenous to these areas would prolong their own lives. This led to an increase in the popularity of yogurt, certain exotic fruits and juices, and other products. However, when dietary comparisons were made among these particular cultures, no nutritional uniformity was apparent. Researchers began to look at other factors for explanations of longevity.

Further doubt was cast on the early theories when a research team in Vilcabamba, Ecuador, discovered that many people older than 65 routinely exaggerated their ages (Harper, 1982), sometimes by as much as 20 to 40 years. This practice was socially acceptable in a culture where village elders were esteemed in proportion to their ages (*Nutrition Today Staff*, 1978).

Studies demonstrated that the life expectancy of Vilcabambans was actually the same as for other Ecuadorans, that is, approximately 15% lower than for Americans. In addition, the higher concentration of elderly people in this village was explained by the fact that many of them had gravitated there for the sake of sociability with others of their own age, and younger people had left.

Thus the initial excitement regarding a provable association between diet and human longevity collapsed. Neither these investigations nor any other scientifically valid studies have ever shown that supplements or special foods will prolong human life more than a balanced diet of ordinary foods (Harper, 1982).

All of that notwithstanding, researchers in Vilcabamba noted that the older adults there enjoyed apparent good health: they were not overweight and had hypertension only rarely, and they had lower than usual blood cholesterol values, lower heart rates, and fewer fractures from osteoporosis (Mazess, 1978). It will take much careful research to learn what factors in this culture influenced these health characteristics.

Psychosocial Influences and Suggested Relationships to Nutrition

Adult nutrition is affected not only by physiological factors, but by some psychosocial conditions as well.

Sense of Self-Responsibility. As mentioned elsewhere in this text, in recent years more people have realized that they themselves, through their lifestyle choices, have a large responsibility for their own health. The health care system has promoted this thinking by increasing its emphasis on identifying health risk factors and educating people about how to minimize them.

Because nutrition has been recognized as one of the lifestyle factors with an important role, both men and women have taken new interest in the food they eat and how it is prepared. This situation has also led people to try foods from other cultures, some of which make excellent contributions to a healthy diet.

Psychological Stress. During the adult years, a person typically experiences many changes in personal and social life. In the younger adult years, psychological pressure is generated as people educate and establish themselves in a chosen field. Marrying (or not marrying), having children, and caring for aging parents are other stresses that are likely to be encountered during adulthood. Finally, realizing that one's physical and/or mental functions are declining can cause considerable stress. Pressure can be positive if it offers challenge and opportunity for self-actualization; it can be negative if individuals do not have the resources with which to manage it.

Although nutrient needs change somewhat in response to certain physical stresses, little scientific information suggests that nutritional consequences or effective treatments exist for mental and emotional stress. Therefore, there is no basis for recommending unusual diets or nutritional supplements for people dealing with the psychological ups and downs of everyday life.

However, some people undergoing stress may become careless about consuming a normally nutritious diet. An exploratory study showed that adults in dysfunctional families—those in which a high level of conflict and attempts to organize and control all members' activities were evident—had less adequate nutrient intakes than adults in families without those stresses (Kintner et al., 1981).

Poverty. Poverty reduces people's ability to obtain an adequate diet. The Ten State Nutrition Survey found that the lower the income level of a family, the poorer its nutrient intakes were likely to be. This is of consid-

Interest in nutrition and food preparation. Interest in cooking—particularly gourmet cooking—has enjoyed a renaissance in recent years. This interest has paralleled increased consciousness regarding self-responsibility for health among some adults.

erable concern because the proportion of people affected is substantial, particularly among the elderly: in 1980, almost 16% of the American population over age 65 had incomes below the poverty index. The poverty rate was even higher for females and Blacks (Weimer, 1982). The effects of poverty on nutrition are often compounded by inadequate education and health care.

Nutritional Quackery. People who are attempting to cope with difficult problems—whether of physical or psychosocial origin—may be vulnerable to the pitches of quacks who make appealing but unsubstantiated claims that their nutrition products can offer simple solutions. Because these "solutions" seem uncomplicated and guaranteed, people may succumb to the claims, paying high prices for unnecessary or worthless products. Unfortunately, the people who buy such products are often those whose financial resources are already limited. An additional penalty of using such products to solve health problems is that people then usually delay seeking competent medical advice.

If you are aware of the techniques and claims quacks use to market their products, you may better protect yourself from them. Victor Herbert and Stephen Barrett, who have studied nutritional quackery, list activities the nutrition quack is likely to be involved in (1982):

- Suggesting that most people are poorly nourished

- Claiming that most disease is due to faulty diet, which can be remedied by the product he or she sells

- Claiming that poor eating habits can be *totally* compensated for by taking vitamin and/or mineral supplements

- Recommending that everybody take vitamin and mineral supplements or eat health foods

- Claiming that natural vitamins are better than synthetic ones

- Trying to sell you a "vitamin" that isn't

- Telling you that the use of chemical fertilizers results in less-nourishing food

- Claiming that modern processing methods and storage remove all nutritive value from our food

- Claiming that all additives and preservatives are poisons

- Warning that sugar is a deadly poison

- Telling you it is easy to lose weight

- Promising quick, dramatic, miraculous cures

- Using anecdotes and testimonials as the only support for his or her claims

- Claiming that the medical establishment refuses to acknowledge these "truths" (the quack's) because doctors would lose business as a result of nutritional cures.

Drugs Can Interfere with Nutrition

Drugs can influence nutrition by affecting appetite, decreasing the absorption of nutrients, interfering with nutrient metabolism, and/or affecting excretion. People who are most at nutritional risk for experiencing negative effects of drugs are individuals who use certain medicines for long periods of time, those who take several kinds of drugs at the same time (whether prescription or over-the-counter types), and persons who have marginal nutritional status to begin with.

People of any age may need medications from time to time, but older adults are more likely to develop chronic conditions that require ongoing treatment with drugs. Therefore the elderly are generally more likely to experience negative effects from nutrient/drug interactions than people in other age groups.

Commonly Used Drugs That Can Interfere with Nutrition

Many drugs affect nutrient utilization. Examples of commonly used drugs with nutritional consequences are aspirin, oral contraceptives, laxatives, diuretics, and antacids.

Aspirin. Aspirin is one of the medicines used most frequently in America by people of all ages. It has a wide range of uses. Many older people are chronic users of high doses of aspirin because its antiinflammatory and pain-relieving properties make it helpful in treating arthritis.

Aspirin use causes a small amount of blood (and therefore iron) loss via the gastrointestinal tract (Roe, 1983a). Aspirin can also interfere with folacin nutriture. People who routinely use aspirin should emphasize sources of these nutrients in their diets.

Oral Contraceptives. Many oral contraceptives influence the body's metabolism of nutrients to some extent. According to the 1980 RDA committee, 15% to 20% of women who take oral contraceptives develop biochemical evidence of vitamin B-6 deficiency. This is occasionally accompanied by mental depression, high blood glucose levels, and/or general malaise. These symptoms may be reversed when vitamin supplements are given.

These findings were based mainly on the use of oral contraceptives that are no longer manufactured. Since the currently produced forms are not as concentrated as some of the earlier versions, their nutritional impact may also be lessened. More studies will be needed to determine this (Roe, 1983b).

Most women who take oral contraceptives have approximately the same requirement for vitamins and minerals as those who are not taking them. Therefore, routine supplementation is not indicated (National Research Council, 1980).

Laxatives. Because constipation becomes more common with age, many elderly people use laxatives frequently. This practice can have negative effects on nutrition. Repeated use of certain types of laxatives can cause calcium and potassium depletion (Roe, 1983a). Mineral oil should not be used as a laxative, since it prevents the absorption of fat-soluble vitamins (Roe, 1983a). Losses of vitamin D and minerals could be especially damaging to people with osteoporosis (Winick, 1981). A dietary alternative with fewer potential problems is to increase the fiber and fluid content of the diet. Adequate exercise can also help.

Diuretics. Diuretics cause the kidneys to excrete increased amounts of sodium and water. People who suffer from edema (accumulation of water in the tissues) or hypertension may become chronic users of diuretics.

Many diuretics cause potassium to be excreted along with the sodium and water, which can lead to severe electrolyte imbalance. For this reason, people taking certain diuretics are advised to eat several good sources of potassium daily or take potassium supplements. People who regularly use diuretics may also become depleted in other minerals such as calcium, magnesium, and zinc (Roe, 1983a).

Antacids. Even though older people generally have decreased levels of stomach acid, they often take antacids to treat indigestion or stomach discomfort (Roe, 1983a). Certain antacids contain aluminum or magnesium hydroxide, which combine with phosphorus in the gut to form salts that cannot be absorbed. Chronic use of these antacids may eventually result in the loss of phosphorus from bone, possibly hastening the course of bone disease (Winick, 1981).

Other Drugs. Anticonvulsants, which are taken by people prone to epileptic seizures, increase requirements for vitamin D and folacin (Lehmann, 1981). Several drugs including levodopa (a medicine used to treat Parkinson's disease), isoniazid (a drug for tuberculosis), and hydralazine (a drug for hypertension) cause vitamin B-6 depletion (Roe, 1983a).

Vitamin and Mineral Supplements. Nutrient supplements taken in megadoses can have druglike effects. As we mentioned in Chapters 12 and 13, high intakes of some nutrients can interfere with the absorption and utilization of other nutrients. The competition between zinc and copper is an example of how high intakes of one nutrient can depress absorption and increase requirements for another.

The Effect of Nutrients on Drugs

Nutrients can also affect drug utilization. The timing of meals and the levels of certain food components including protein, alcohol, dietary fiber, and methylxanthines can have strong effects on drug absorption and metabolism.

For example, the absorption of the antibiotic tetracycline can be *blocked* by calcium from milk, but milk *improves* the absorption of erythromycin ethylsuccinate, another type of antibiotic (Roe, 1983a). Excessive consumption of foods high in vitamin K (found in liver and green leafy vegetables, for example) can hinder the effectiveness of some anticoagulant drugs. People taking certain antidepressant drugs need to avoid aged and fermented foods because interactions between particular components of these foods, the drug, and body substances can result in dangerously high blood pressure.

Guidelines for People Who Take Drugs

To avoid undesirable food/drug interactions, consumers should:

- Follow instructions on over-the-counter remedies and package inserts with prescription drugs.

- Follow the doctor's orders regarding amount and timing of taking medications, and what foods and beverages to avoid or include when taking drugs. If your doctor neglects to mention nutrient/drug interactions, ask. If you are likely to want to consume alcoholic beverages during the course of drug therapy, ask whether your drug is one of the many that calls for avoidance of alcohol.

- Eat a nutritionally balanced diet from a variety of foods.

Alcohol Influences Nutrition and Health

Although the alcohol in alcoholic beverages has one characteristic of a nutrient—it provides energy at 7 kcalories per gram—it is primarily categorized as a drug. It influences health both by affecting nutrition and by producing direct toxic effects on the body.

The consumption of alcoholic beverages is widespread. An estimated one in three American adults drinks regularly (once a week or more); another one in three drinks occasionally (less than once a week); and the other one does not drink. This means that there are over 100 million adult drinkers in the United States (National Council on Alcoholism, 1972).

As mentioned in Chapter 17, many younger people also consume alcohol. Over 25% of those in grades 10–12 are said to drink at least once per month (National Council on Alcoholism, 1972).

Sources of Alcohol

Beers and ales, wines, and liquors are the common sources of alcohol. Although they differ in the percentage of alcohol they contain, a standard sized serving of any one of them puts approximately half an ounce of absolute alcohol into the consumer:

Beverage	Serving Size	% alcohol by weight
Beer	12–18 oz.	3–6%
Wine	4–5 oz.	12–14%
Hard liquor	1–1½ oz	40–50%

The consumption of alcohol affects the body within minutes; if ingested regularly in large amounts over a period of years, it will also have serious long-range effects on health.

Short-Term Effects of Alcohol Consumption

Alcohol needs no digestion. It is a simple molecule that is readily absorbed and circulated through the body in the bloodstream. Like some other drugs, it can be absorbed from the stomach; whatever passes into the small intestine is readily absorbed from there. Although its own entry into the body is uncomplicated, it can disturb the digestion and absorption of foods; and, particularly after heavy drinking, diarrhea can occur (Roe, 1979).

The body's normal reaction is to try to get rid of alcohol. The kidneys and the lungs excrete predictable percentages of it, which explains why the "breathalizer" test can provide a measure of alcohol in the body. The liver begins to detoxify alcohol as quickly as it circulates through. In most people, it takes the liver 1 to 1½ hours to change the alcohol from one drink into harmless metabolites.

The body uses alcohol as an energy source. Alcohol also alters the metabolism of carbohydrates, fats, and proteins. One consequence of this is that the blood sugar level of a person who has consumed alcoholic beverages may drop to low levels (Shaw and Lieber, 1980).

Alcohol has an anaesthetic (depressant) effect on the nervous system. First, judgment is impaired and inhibitions are reduced, allowing for feelings of euphoria and relaxation. With greater consumption, muscular coordination, reflexes, and speech are impaired. At even higher intakes, the hindbrain is affected: senses are dulled, and stupor results. Unconsciousness and death can follow if the part of the brain that controls vital functions is sufficiently depressed. For any given individual in a particular instance, the effects of alcohol depend on body size (lean body mass), the time frame within which the alcohol was drunk, other foods or beverages that were consumed, and drinking history.

Alcohol intake has an effect on food consumption. A small amount of alcohol usually stimulates the appetite (Roe, 1979) and fosters social interaction. For this reason, an increasing number of hospitals and nursing homes in the United States are serving a small amount of wine or beer before meals (McDonald, 1981). On the other hand, a large amount of alcohol depresses appetite (Roe, 1979). When alcoholic beverages displace food, nutrient intakes are likely to be low since alcoholic beverages are poor sources of nutrients themselves. Figure 18.4 shows this interplay between drink and food.

Strategies for Preventing Short-Term Problems from Alcohol

People can *moderate* (not eliminate) the effects of alcohol in several simple ways. If you expect to have several drinks during a social event but do not want to experience effects beyond those of mild euphoria and relaxation,

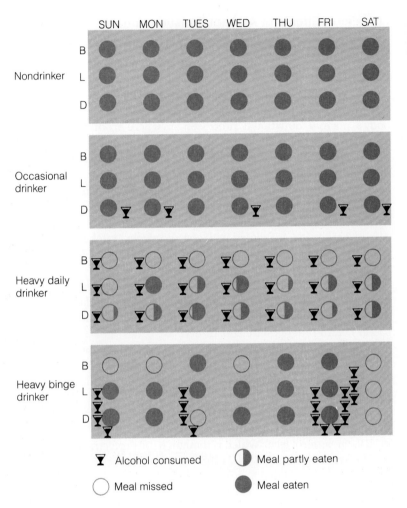

Figure 18.4 Relationship between drinking and meal consumption. Occasional drinking does not interfere with eating. However, at high levels of alcohol intake, people tend to eat poor meals or miss them entirely. (Adapted from Roe, D.A. 1979. Alcohol and the diet. Westport, CT: AVI Publishing Company.)

you can employ these methods to help delay and thus reduce the impact of the drinks.

First, eat something before you start drinking. The presence of any food in the stomach delays the absorption of alcohol; sources of carbohydrate and milk have been found particularly helpful (Roe, 1979).

Second, pace your consumption so that you are not drinking faster than the rate at which your liver can detoxify the alcohol. If you limit your intake to one drink per $1\frac{1}{2}$ hours, you are not likely to become seriously impaired. If you are thirsty and want to drink more than that, alternate alcoholic beverages with nonalcoholic beverages. If you are the host or hostess, be sure that you provide an acceptable nonalcoholic alternative to your guests.

Be aware that there is no way to hasten anybody's detoxification of alcohol once it has been overconsumed: neither cold showers, nor coffee, nor exercise, nor sleep can substantially speed up the process. In this case, ounces of prevention may be worth hours of cure.

Long-Term Effects of Alcohol Consumption

Consumption of excessive amounts of alcohol regularly over a period of many years is likely to have direct toxic effects and possibly produce nutritional inadequacies as well. The nutrient inadequacies most often seen in chronic consumers of alcohol are in thiamin, folacin, niacin, and vitamin B-6 (Halsted, 1976). These inadequacies result from interruptions in the body's normal nutritional processes anywhere from ingestion through excretion.

Health problems attributable to chronic alcohol consumption are liver diseases, anemias or bone marrow abnormalities (Shaw and Lieber, 1980), heart problems, nervous system diseases (Roe, 1979), skin problems (Stone, 1978), fetal alcohol syndrome, and cancer of the alimentary canal and liver.

Liver diseases associated with chronic alcohol intake have been shown to be the result of direct toxic effects rather than nutrient deficiencies. In the first phase, fat accumulates in the liver (fatty liver) due to many alcohol-induced changes in the metabolism of energy nutrients and fat mobilization. The second phase is alcoholic hepatitis—inflammation of the liver. Both of these conditions can be reversed if alcohol is avoided and sound health practices are substituted.

cirrhosis—scarring of the liver by fibrous deposits that interfere with its function; an irreversible condition

Cirrhosis, an irreversible condition, occurs when fibrous deposits scar the liver, interfering with its function. Since the liver is the primary site for many metabolic reactions, its progressive destruction by cirrhosis can be eventually fatal.

One effect of alcohol ingestion that may be more positive is that inactive people who consume one or two drinks per day experience a rise in HDL cholesterol level, which is thought to be protective against coronary heart disease (Hartung et al., 1983). However, others have suggested that this rise may represent a toxic effect on the liver from alcohol consumption (Barrett-Connor and Suarez, 1982).

Dietary Recommendations for Adults Promote Health Maintenance

Adults of all ages can best get the nutrients they need for repair of body tissues and maintenance of health and life by eating a variety of foods from the four basic food groups (Kohrs, 1982), as we have suggested in the SANE guide. For daily intake, the following are recommended: a minimum of four servings of fruits and vegetables including vitamin A and C sources; four servings of whole grain, enriched, or fortified grain products; two servings of milk and milk products; and two servings of meats and alternates.

Since the recommended intake of nutrients during adulthood remains stable while the need for energy decreases, adults should gradually reduce their intake of limited extras such as concentrated sugars, fats, and alcohol.

Adults benefit from emphasizing foods that are good sources of dietary fiber, which aids fecal elimination. In other words, it is better to consume solid fruits and vegetables than juice, and it is preferable to use whole grain products than refined grains. For the sake of both bowel and kidney function, water intake should continue to be 2–3 liters per day throughout adulthood. The water can come from both beverages and foods.

Some nutrition researchers promote increasing the intake of good sources of calcium during adult years in an attempt to moderate the bone losses of osteoporosis. Although the effectiveness of this practice is not guaranteed, adults (especially women) may find it helpful to take in more than two servings of milk and milk products daily.

Adults who believe that reducing their intake of fat, sugar, and salt will help them prevent or delay certain diseases such as heart disease or cancer can adjust their selections from the food groups accordingly. In the SANE guide (Figures 2.4–2.9), the rulers for fat, sugar, and salt under each food group are useful for identifying foods high in these constituents. Risk factors are more amenable to change if people do not wait to modify their diets until they are middle aged. In any case, there are no guarantees that a particular diet will prevent these multifactorial diseases.

Adults who are rearing children get double mileage out of practicing reasonable food habits: they benefit themselves, and they serve as healthy examples for their children.

People who routinely take medications will be advised by their health care providers whether a special diet or (occasionally) nutritional supplements are needed to compensate for any negative effects of drug/nutrient interactions.

People who have diseases that are partly treated by dietary modification should discuss the necessary changes with a qualified health care provider, preferably a registered dietitian.

Specific Programs Help Meet
Nutritional Needs of Special Groups

Various programs have been designed to help different subgroups of the population meet their nutritional needs.

Industry Health Maintenance Programs

Many firms have instituted health maintenance programs for their workers, which may include exercise facilities, nutrition counseling, and stress reduction education. It is claimed that such programs are cost effective because less work time is lost due to illness, and/or because productivity is increased due to employee satisfaction. In some instances, the company food service also makes a special effort to provide foods that follow the recommendations of the Dietary Guidelines.

Food Stamps for the Poor

The federal government funds a program that helps the impoverished to obtain an adequate diet. The USDA issues food stamps that people in low-income households can use to purchase food at any approved grocery store.

Lifestyle promotion in the workplace. An increasing number of employers are providing facilities in which their workers can exercise, get nutritious meals, and learn about stress reduction. Such programs can benefit both employees and employers.

The value of the food stamps issued depends on the income and size of the family.

Nutrition Program for Older Americans

The Nutrition Program for Older Americans, which is known as Title III and is administered by the Department of Health and Human Services, provides to people over 60 community-based noon meals at a nominal fee that is often optional. The largest component of this program is the congregate meals served at senior citizen centers, churches, schools, and other locations. These meals are designed to provide one-third of the RDAs; health and welfare counseling and nutrition education are also provided regularly (Roe, 1983a). Another benefit to the participants is the regular social interaction.

For the elderly who cannot leave their homes, local organizations help them meet their nutritional needs in various ways. Often using a combination of federal and local funds, some deliver ready-to-eat meals; others

Congregate meals for the elderly. The Nutrition Program for Older Americans provides a nutritious meal and a social opportunity for many mobile people.

Meals on wheels. Home-delivered meals can enable some people to continue to live independently.

supply frozen dinners; and others provide grocery service to people in their homes.

Programs for the elderly may include more people in the future, since it is projected that the number of Americans aged 65 and over will double between 1980 and 2020. By 2030, the elderly are likely to constitute 20% of the American population (National Dairy Council, 1983).

We conclude this chapter—and the book—by reemphasizing that nutrition plays a continuous role during the life cycle: at all stages, nutrients provide energy, regulate body processes, and maintain tissues that are continually being restructured. Therefore, at any one phase of the life cycle, nutrition meets current needs and also influences future health.

At the same time, it is important not to overstate what nutrients can accomplish: in the development of diseases, nutrition is usually just one of the relevant factors. To quote R.S. Rivlin, who summarized a conference on nutrition and aging: "Good nutrition cannot provide a guarantee against disease, and cannot give 'super health'; the most that one can realistically hope for at present is that nutrition in combination with other measures will increase disease-free lifetime, improve the quality of life, and delay the emergence of specific diseases" (1982).

SUMMARY

■ Aging is the gradual loss of tissue and organ function that occurs when the body's rate of cell replacement is unable to keep pace with the rate of cell death. There are several theories about what may cause the cellular changes involved in the aging process. Although most scientists believe that the major influences on aging are genetically determined, lifelong habits of nutrition and exercise can modify health and longevity within those inherited limits. The changes associated with aging take place gradually, and their rate and sequence vary in different individuals. The nutrition-related effects include a decreased need for energy, and less efficient digestion and absorption of nutrients. More research will help to clarify the specific nutrient needs of the elderly in the light of these changes.

■ Although dietary surveys have identified inadequate intakes of certain nutrients among adults, obvious external signs of deficiency are rare. Currently there is considerable scientific debate about the importance of nutrition and the development and treatment of several health problems that are fairly common in adulthood, such as obesity, hypertension, atherosclerosis, cancer, diabetes, diverticular disease, arthritis, osteoporosis, periodontal disease. More research is needed.

■ Every species of animal including humans has a maximum life span, which appears to be set genetically. Life expectancy is the statistical average length of life for a given group of animals, and longevity is the length of time an individual actually lives. Nutrition may play a role in determining life expectancy and longevity, although no scientifically valid studies have ever shown that supplements or special foods will prolong human life more than an ordinary, well balanced diet.

■ Adult nutrition is affected not only by physiological factors, but also psychosocial ones including a sense of self-responsibility, stress, poverty, and nutritional quackery. It is important to be able to recognize the techniques used by people who try to sell ineffective products, such as claiming that most diseases have dietary cures, and promising quick or dramatic solutions to complex problems.

■ Drugs can influence nutrition by affecting appetite, decreasing the absorption of nutrients, interfering with their metabolism, and/or affecting their excretion. Individuals who use any drug for a long period of time, or who use several drugs in combination, are at greatest nutritional risk. Examples of commonly used drugs that can have nutritional consequences are aspirin, oral contraceptives, laxatives, diuretics, and antacids. Nutrients can also affect drug utilization. Nutrient-drug interactions can be minimized by eating a balanced diet and carefully following the instructions for use of medications.

■ Alcohol is a widely used drug that can influence health both by affecting nutrition and by producing direct toxic effects on the body. People who use alcohol heavily over long periods of time are much more likely to suffer health problems including liver diseases such as cirrhosis, heart problems, and various types of cancer.

■ Adults of all ages can best get the nutrients they need by eating a variety of foods from the four basic food groups, and gradually reducing their intake of low nutrient density foods.

■ Several programs including industry health maintenance plans, Food Stamps for the poor, and the Nutrition Program for Older Americans have been designed to help different population groups meet their nutritional needs.

■ The role of nutrition during the life cycle involves a continuum; nutrition at any one stage meets current needs and also influences the body at later stages. At the same time, it is important not to expect more of nutrition than it can deliver. It *is* realistic to hope that good nutrition in combination with other sound lifestyle habits will minimize or delay some diseases, and improve the quality of life.

REFERENCES

Abraham, S., and C.L. Johnson. 1980. Prevalence of severe obesity in adults in the U.S. *American Journal of Clinical Nutrition* 33:364–369.

Balazs, E.A. 1977. Intracellular matrix of connective tissue. In *Handbook of the biology of aging*, eds. C.E. Finch and L. Hayflick. New York: Van Nostrand Reinhold Co.

Barrett-Connor, E., and L. Suarez. 1982. A community study of alcohol and other factors associated with the distribution of high density lipoprotein cholesterol in older vs. younger men. *American Journal of Epidemiology* 115:888–893.

Baserga, R.L. 1977. Cell division and the cell cycle. In *Handbook of the biology of aging*, eds. C.E. Finch and L. Hayflick. New York: Van Nostrand Reinhold Co.

Committee on Diet, Nutrition, and Cancer. 1982. *Diet, nutrition, and cancer.* Washington, DC: National Academy Press.

Halsted, C.H. 1976. Nutritional implications of alcohol. In *Present knowledge of nutrition*, eds. D.M. Hegsted, C.O. Chichester, W.J. Darby, K.W. McNutt, R.M. Stalvey, and E.H. Stotz. New York: The Nutrition Foundation.

Harper, A.E. 1982. Nutrition, aging and longevity. *American Journal of Clinical Nutrition* 36:737–749.

Hartung, G.H., J.P. Foreyt, R.E. Mitchell, J.G. Mitchell, R.S. Reeves, and A.M. Gotto, Jr. 1983. Effect of alcohol intake on high-density lipoprotein cholesterol levels in runners and inactive men. *Journal of the American Medical Association* 249:747–750.

Heaney, R.P., J.C. Gallagher, C.C. Johnson, R. Neer, A.M. Parfitt, and G.D. Whedon. 1982. Calcium nutrition and bone health in the elderly. *American Journal of Clinical Nutrition* 36:986–1013.

Hecht, A. 1980. Hocus-pocus as applied to arthritis. *FDA Consumer* 14(no. 7):24–30.

Herbert, V., and S. Barrett. 1981. *Vitamins and "health foods:" The great American hustle.* Philadelphia: The George F. Stickley Company.

Iber, F.L., J.P. Blass, M. Brin, and C.M. Leevy. 1982. Thiamin in the elderly—Relation to alcoholism and to neurological degenerative disease. *American Journal of Clinical Nutrition* 26:1067–1082.

Kintner, M., P.G. Boss, and N. Johnson. 1981. The relationship between dysfunctional family environments and family member food intake. *Journal of Marriage and the Family* 43:633–641.

Kohrs, M.B. 1982. A rational diet for the elderly. *American Journal of Clinical Nutrition* 36:796–802 (Supplement).

Krause, M.V., and L.K. Mahan. 1979. *Food, nutrition, and diet therapy.* Philadelphia: W.B. Saunders Company.

Leaf, A. 1973. Growing old. *Scientific American* 229 (no. 3):45–52.

Lehmann, P. 1981. *Food and drug interactions.* Health and Human Services Publication No. (FDA)81-3070. Rockville, MD: Food and Drug Administration.

Lutwak, L. 1976. Periodontal disease. In *Nutrition and aging*, ed. M. Winick. New York: John Wiley and Sons.

Mazess, R.B. 1978. Health and longevity in Vilcabamba, Ecuador. *Journal of the American Medical Association* 240:1981.

McDonald, J. 1981. Mixing alcohol with nutrition. *The Professional Nutritionist* 13(no.3):3–6.

McGandy, R.B., C.H. Barrows, A. Spanias, A. Meredith, J.L. Stone, and A.H. Norris. 1966. Nutrient intakes and energy expenditure in men of different ages. *Journal of Gerontology* 21:581–587.

National Center for Health Statistics. 1979. *Caloric and selected nutrient values for persons 1–74 years of age: First health and nutrition examination survey, United States, 1971–74*. Vital and health statistics series 11, no. 209. DHEW Publication No.(PHS)79-1657. Hyattsville, MD: Public Health Service.

National Center for Health Statistics. 1983 *Dietary intake and cardiovascular risk factors*, Part I. Blood pressure correlates: United States, 1971–74. Data from the National Health Survey, Series 11, No.226, DHHS Publication No.(PHS)83-1676. Hyattsville, MD: U.S. Department of Health and Human Services.

National Center for Health Statistics. 1977. *Dietary intake findings: United States, 1971–74*. Data from the National Health Survey, Series 11, No.202. DHEW Publication No.(HRA)77-1647. Hyattsville, MD: Public Health Service.

National Council on Alcoholism. 1972. *The modern approach to alcoholism*. Burlington, IA: The National Research Bureau, Inc.

National Dairy Council. 1983. Nutrition and the elderly. *Dairy Council Digest* 54(no.4):19–24.

National Research Council, National Academy of Sciences (NAS). 1980. *Recommended Dietary Allowances*. Washington, DC: NAS.

Nutrition Today staff. 1978. Paradise lost. *Nutrition Today* 13(no.3):6–9.

Randolph, P.M., and Dennison, C.I. 1981. *Diet, nutrition, and dentistry*. St. Louis: The C.V. Mosby Company.

Recker, R.R. 1983. Osteoporosis. *Contemporary Nutrition* 8(no.5). Minneapolis, MN: General Mills, Inc.

Rivlin, R.S. 1982. Summary and concluding statement: Evidence relating selected vitamins and minerals to health and disease in the elderly population in the United States. *American Journal of Clinical Nutrition* 36:1083–1086 (Supplement).

Roe, D.A. 1979. *Alcohol and the diet*. Westport, CT: AVI Publishing Company, Inc.

Roe, D.A. 1983a. *Geriatric nutrition*. Englewood Cliffs, NJ: Prentice-Hall, Inc.

Roe, D.A. 1983b. Drug-nutrient interactions: Update on animal models and research strategy. Nutritional Sciences Seminar, University of Wisconsin-Madison (WI), September 21, 1983.

Ross, M.H. 1976. Nutrition and longevity in experimental animals. In *Nutrition and aging*, ed. M. Winick. New York: John Wiley and Sons.

Rowe, D. 1978. Aging—a jewel in the mosaic of life. *Journal of the American Dietetic Association* 72:478–486.

Sandstead, H.H., L.K. Henricksen, J.L. Greger, A.S. Prasad, and R.A. Good. 1982. Zinc nutriture in the elderly in relation to taste acuity. *American Journal of Clinical Nutrition* 36:1046–1056.

Science and Education Administration. 1980. *Food and nutrient intakes of individuals in 1 day in the United States, Spring, 1977*. Nationwide food consumption survey report no.2. Washington, DC: U.S. Department of Agriculture.

Shaw, S., and C.S. Lieber. 1980. Nutrition and alcoholism. In *Modern nutrition in health and disease*, eds. R.S. Goodhart and M.E. Shils. Philadelphia: Lea and Febiger.

Stone, O.J. 1978. Alcohol malnutrition and skin infections. *Nutrition Today* 13(no.6):6–10,27–30.

Watkin, D.M. 1980. Nutrition for the aging and the aged. In *Modern nutrition in health and disease*, eds. R.S. Goodhart and M.E. Shils. Philadelphia: Lea and Febiger.

Weimer, J.P. 1982. The nutritional status of the elderly. *National Food Review* 19:7–10.

Winick, M. 1981. Drug-nutrition interaction in the elderly. *Nutrition and Health* 3(no.6):1–6.

Worthington-Roberts, B.S. 1981. The fat-soluble vitamins A and D. In *Contemporary developments in nutrition*, ed. B.S. Worthington-Roberts. St. Louis: The C.V. Mosby Co.

APPENDICES

Appendix A Estimated Safe and Adequate Daily Dietary Intakes of Selected Vitamins and Minerals[a]

| | Age (years) | Vitamins | | |
		Vitamin K (μg)	Biotin (μg)	Pantothenic acid (mg)
Infants	0–0.5	12	35	2
	0.5–1	10–20	50	3
Children and adolescents	1–3	15–30	65	3
	4–6	20–40	85	3–4
	7–10	30–60	120	4–5
	11+	50–100	100–200	4–7
Adults		70–140	100–200	4–7

| | Age (years) | Trace Elements[b] | | | | | |
		Copper (mg)	Manganese (mg)	Fluoride (mg)	Chromium (mg)	Selenium (mg)	Molybdenum (mg)
Infants	0–0.5	0.5–0.7	0.5–0.7	0.1–0.5	0.01–0.04	0.01–0.04	0.03–0.06
	0.5–1	0.7–1.0	0.7–1.0	0.2–1.0	0.02–0.06	0.02–0.06	0.04–0.08
Children and adolescents	1–3	1.0–1.5	1.0–1.5	0.5–1.5	0.02–0.08	0.02–0.08	0.05–0.1
	4–6	1.5–2.0	1.5–2.0	1.0–2.5	0.03–0.12	0.03–0.12	0.06–0.15
	7–10	2.0–2.5	2.0–3.0	1.5–2.5	0.05–0.2	0.05–0.2	0.10–0.3
	11+	2.0–3.0	2.5–5.0	1.5–2.5	0.05–0.2	0.05–0.2	0.15–0.5
Adults		2.0–3.0	2.5–5.0	1.5–4.0	0.05–0.2	0.05–0.2	0.15–0.5

| | Age (years) | Electrolytes | | |
		Sodium (mg)	Potassium (mg)	Chloride (mg)
Infants	0–0.5	115–350	350–925	275–700
	0.5–1	250–750	425–1275	400–1200
Children and adolescents	1–3	325–975	550–1650	500–1500
	4–6	450–1350	775–2325	700–2100
	7–10	600–1800	1000–3000	925–2775
	11+	900–2700	1525–4575	1400–4200
Adults		1100–3300	1875–5625	1700–5100

[a] Because there is less information on which to base allowances, these figures are not given in the main table of RDA and are provided here in the form of ranges of recommended intakes.

[b] Since the toxic levels for many trace elements may be only several times usual intakes, the upper levels for the trace elements given in this table should not be habitually exceeded.

Reproduced from "Recommended Dietary Allowances" 9th edition, 1980, with the permission of the National Academy Press, Washington, D.C.

Appendix B Summary Examples of Recommended Nutrient Intakes for Canadians[a,b] (1982)

Age	Sex	Average weight (kg)	Average energy needs (kcal/day)[c]	Protein (g/day)[d]	Vitamin A (RE/day)[e]	Vitamin D (µg/day)[f]	Vitamin E (mg/day)[g]
					Fat-soluble vitamins		
Months							
0–2	Both	4.5	500	11[i]	400	10	3
3–5	Both	7.0	700	14[i]	400	10	3
6–8	Both	8.5	800	16[i]	400	10	3
9–11	Both	9.5	950	18	400	10	3
Years							
1	Both	11	1100	18	400	10	3
2–3	Both	14	1300	20	400	5	4
4–6	Both	18	1800	25	500	5	5
7–9	M	25	2200	31	700	2.5	7
	F	25	1900	29	700	2.5	6
10–12	M	34	2500	38	800	2.5	8
	F	36	2200	39	800	2.5	7
13–15	M	50	2800	49	900	2.5	9
	F	48	2200	43	800	2.5	7
16–18	M	62	3200	54	1000	2.5	10
	F	53	2100	47	800	2.5	7
19–24	M	71	3000	57	1000	2.5	10
	F	58	2100	41	800	2.5	7
25–49	M	74	2700	57	1000	2.5	9
	F	59	1900	41	800	2.5	6
50–74	M	73	2300	57	1000	2.5	7
	F	63	1800	41	800	2.5	6
75+	M	69	2000	57	1000	2.5	6
	F	64	1500	41	800	2.5	5
Pregnancy (additional)							
1st Trimester				15	100	2.5	2
2nd Trimester				20	100	2.5	2
3rd Trimester				25	100	2.5	2
Lactation (additional)				20	400	2.5	3

[a] Recommended intakes of energy and of certain nutrients are not listed in this table because of the nature of the variables upon which they are based. The figures for energy are estimates of average requirements for expected patterns of activity. For nutrients not shown, the following amounts are recommended: thiamin, 0.4 mg/1000 kcal (0.48 mg/5000 kJ); riboflavin, 0.5 mg/1000 kcal (0.6 mg/5000 kJ); niacin, 7.2 NE/1000 kcal (8.6 NE/5000 kJ); vitamin B_6, 15µg, as pyridoxine, per gram of protein; phosphorus, same as calcium.

[b] Recommended intakes during periods of growth are taken as appropriate for individuals representative of the mid-point in each age group. All recommended intakes are designed to cover individual variations in essentially all of a healthy population subsisting upon a variety of common foods available in Canada.

[c] Requirements can be expected to vary within a range of ± 30%.

[d] The primary units are grams per kilogram of body weight. The figures shown here are only examples .

[e] One retinol equivalent (RE) corresponds to the biological activity of 1 µg of retinol, 6 µg of β-carotene or 12 µg of other carotenes.

Appendix B continued

Water-soluble vitamins			Minerals				
Vitamin C (mg/day)	Folacin (μg/day)[h]	Vitamin B-12 (μg/day)	Calcium (mg/day)	Magnesium (mg/day)	Iron (mg/day)	Iodine (μg/day)	Zinc (mg/day)
20	50	0.3	350	30	0.4[j]	25	2[k]
20	50	0.3	350	40	5	35	3
20	50	0.3	400	45	7	40	3
20	55	0.3	400	50	7	45	3
20	65	0.3	500	55	6	55	4
20	80	0.4	500	65	6	65	4
25	90	0.5	600	90	6	85	5
35	125	0.8	700	110	7	110	6
30	125	0.8	700	110	7	95	6
40	170	1.0	900	150	10	125	7
40	170	1.0	1000	160	10	110	7
50	160	1.5	1100	220	12	160	9
45	160	1.5	800	190	13	160	8
55	190	1.9	900	240	10	160	9
45	160	1.9	700	220	14	160	8
60	210	2.0	800	240	8	160	9
45	165	2.0	700	190	14	160	8
60	210	2.0	800	240	8	160	9
45	165	2.0	700	190	14[l]	160	8
60	210	2.0	800	240	8	160	9
45	165	2.0	800	190	7	160	8
60	210	2.0	800	240	8	160	9
45	165	2.0	800	190	7	160	8
0	305	1.0	500	15	6	25	0
20	305	1.0	500	20	6	25	1
20	305	1.0	500	25	6	25	2
30	120	0.5	500	80	0	50	6

[f] Expressed as cholecalciferol or ergocalciferol.

[g] Expressed as d-α-tocopherol equivalents, relative to which β- and γ-tocopherol and α-tocotrienol have activities of 0.5, 0.1 and 0.3 respectively.

[h] Expressed as total folate.

[i] Assumption that the protein is from breast milk or is of the same biological value as that of breast milk and that between 3 and 9 months adjustment for the quality of the protein is made.

[j] It is assumed that breast milk is the source of iron up to 2 months of age.

[k] Based on the assumption that breast milk is the source of zinc for the first 2 months.

[l] After the menopause the recommended intake is 7 mg/day.

Source: Bureau of Nutritional Sciences, Food Directorate, Health Protection Branch, Ottawa. Reproduced by permission of the Minister of Supply and Services Canada.

B

Appendix B continued

Canada's Food Guide (1983)

Variety. Choose different kinds of foods from within each group in appropriate numbers of servings and portion sizes.

Energy balance. Needs vary with age, sex, and activity. Balance energy intake from foods with energy output from physical activity to control weight. Foods selected according to the Guide can supply 1000–1400 kilocalories. For additional energy, increase the number and size of servings from the various food groups and/or add other foods.

Moderation. Select and prepare foods with limited amounts of fat, sugar and salt. If alcohol is consumed, use limited amounts.

Food group	Recommended number of servings (adults)	Some examples of one serving
Milk and milk products	2[a]	1 cup milk; ¾ cup yogurt; 1½ oz cheddar or process cheese
Meat, fish, poultry, and alternates	2	2–3 oz cooked lean meat, fish, poultry, or liver; 4 T peanut butter; 1 cup cooked dried peas, beans, or lentils; ½ cup nuts or seeds; 2 oz cheddar cheese; ½ cup cottage cheese; 2 eggs
Breads and cereals[b]	3–5	1 slice bread; ½ cup cooked cereal; ¾ cup ready-to-eat cereal; 1 roll or muffin; ½–¾ cup cooked rice, macaroni, spaghetti or noodles; ½ hamburger or wiener bun
Fruits and vegatables	4–5[c]	½ cup vegetables or fruits—fresh, frozen, or canned; ½ cup juice—fresh, frozen, or canned; 1 medium-sized potato, carrot, tomato, peach, apple, orange, or banana

[a] For children up to 11 years, 2–3 servings; adolescents, 3–4 servings; pregnant and nursing women, 3–4 servings.
[b] Whole grain or enriched. Whole grain products are recommended.
[c] Include at least two vegetables. Choose a variety of both vegetables and fruits—cooked, raw, or their juices. Include yellow, green, or green leafy vegetables.
Source: Minister of National Health and Welfare, Ottawa. Reproduced by permission of the Minister of Supply and Services Canada.

Appendix C   Measurements Used in Nutrition

In the science of nutrition, metric units are usually used to describe levels of nutrients. This system offers the simplicity of dealing in multiples of ten. Since the metric system is not yet widely used in the United States, we have provided conversion factors for the commonly used metric units and U.S. measures.

Metric Prefixes

Prefix	Abbreviation	Value
micro-	μ	one-millionth
milli-	m	one-thousandth
centi-	c	one-hundredth
deci-	d	one-tenth
deka-	da	ten
hecto-	h	one hundred
kilo-	k	one thousand

Metric and U.S. Equivalents

Metric unit	U.S. equivalent
Mass and weight	
1 microgram (μg)	0.00000004 ounce (oz)
1 milligram (mg)	0.00004 ounce
1 gram (g)	0.04 ounce
28.35 grams[a]	1 ounce
1 kilogram (kg)	2.2 pounds (lb)
0.454 kilogram	1 pound
Liquid capacity	
1 milliliter (ml)	0.035 fluid ounce
29.6 milliliters	1 fluid ounce
1 liter (l)	1.06 quarts (qt)
0.946 liter	1 fluid quart
Heat	
1 kilojoule	0.239 kilocalorie (kcal)
4.18 kilojoules	1 kilocalorie

[a]This is commonly rounded to 30 grams/ounce, except for calculations in which considerable exactness is required.

U.S. household measurements and equivalents

1 quart = 4 cups (c)

1 cup = 8 fluid ounces = 16 tablespoons (T)

1 T = 3 teaspoons (t)

1 t = 5 grams dry weight (such as sugar or salt)

D

Appendix D   Reliable Sources of Nutrition Information

Semitechnical periodicals

These materials contain reviews that are suitable for people without a strong science background. Most of them are available by subscription, except those indicated with an asterisk (*), which are available to health and education professionals on request.

California Council against Health Fraud Newsletter
A monthly newsletter. Contains information concerning health misinformation, faddism, and fraud.
CCAHF
Box 1276
Loma Linda, CA 92354

*Contemporary Nutrition
A monthly newsletter. Contains one referenced nutrition review topic by recognized expert per issue.
General Mills, Inc., Production Manager
P.O. Box 1112, Dept. 65
Minneapolis, MN 55440

Dairy Council Digest
A bimonthly newsletter. Contains one referenced nutrition review topic per issue.
National Dairy Council
6300 North River Road
Rosemont, IL 60018

*Dietetic Currents
A bimonthly newsletter. Contains one referenced nutrition review topic by recognized expert per issue.
Ross Laboratories
Director of Professional Services
625 Cleveland Avenue
Columbus, OH 43216

Environmental Nutrition
A newsletter published ten times per year. Contains reviews of current issues, books, and a readers' forum.
52 Riverside Drive, Suite 15A
New York, NY 10024

FDA Consumer
A monthly magazine. Contains articles on concerns and actions of the FDA.
Superintendent of Documents
General Printing Office
Washington, DC 20402

*Food and Nutrition News
A newsletter published five times per year. Contains one referenced article by recognized expert per issue; other features.
National Livestock and Meat Board
444 North Michigan Avenue
Chicago, IL 60611

Harvard Medical School Health Letter
A monthly newsletter. Contains information on a variety of health topics including nutrition.
Department of Continuing Education
25 Shattuck Street
Boston, MA 02115

Tufts University Diet and Nutrition Letter
A monthly newsletter. Contains reviews of current issues and books; questions and answers.
P.O. Box 2465
Boulder, CO 80322

Respected professional journals

Although this listing includes the journals that are most likely to carry original nutrition research, many other journals occasionally do also. Several of these journals feature technical review articles.

American Journal of Clinical Nutrition
American Society for Clinical Nutrition
9650 Rockville Pike
Bethesda, MD 20814

American Journal of Public Health
American Public Health Association
1015 Fifteenth Street, N.W.
Washington, DC 20005

Food and Chemical Toxicology

British Industrial Research Association
Maxwell House, Fairview Park
Elmsford, NY 10523

Food Technology

Institute of Food Technologists
Suite 2120
211 North LaSalle Street
Chicago, IL 60601

Gastroenterology

American Gastroenterology Association
Elsevier Publishing Co., Inc.
52 Vanderbilt Avenue
New York, NY 10017

Journal of the American Dietetic Association

American Dietetic Association
430 North Michigan Avenue
Chicago, IL 60611

Journal of the American Medical Association

American Medical Association
535 North Dearborn Street
Chicago, IL 60610

Journal of Applied Physiology

American Physiological Society
9650 Rockville Pike
Bethesda, MD 20814

Journal of Nutrition

American Institute of Nutrition
9650 Rockville Pike
Bethesda, MD 20814

Journal of Nutrition Education

Society for Nutrition Education
1736 Franklin Street
Oakland, CA 94612

Lancet (British)

Little, Brown, and Company
34 Beacon Street
Boston, MA 02106

Medicine and Science in Sports and Exercise

American College of Sports Medicine
1 Virginia Avenue, Suite 340
Indianapolis, IN 46204

Nature (British)

MacMillan Journals
Subscription Department
P.O. Box 1018
Manasquan, NJ 08736

New England Journal of Medicine

Massachusetts Medical Society
10 Shattuck Street
Boston, MA 02115

Nutrition Reviews

The Nutrition Foundation, Inc.
888 17th Street, N.W., Suite 300
Washington, DC 20006

Nutrition Today

P.O. Box 1829
Annapolis, MD 21404

Pediatric Research

International Pediatric Research Foundation, Inc.
428 East Preston Street
Baltimore, MD 21202

Pediatrics

American Academy of Pediatrics
P.O. Box 1034
Evanston, IL 60204

Science

American Association for the Advancement of Science
1515 Massachusetts Avenue, N.W.
Washington, DC 20005

Professional and service organizations

These are organizations that publish various nutrition-related materials but do not publish any of the journals just listed.

American Cancer Society

777 Third Avenue
New York, NY 10017

American Council on Science and Health

1995 Broadway
New York, NY 10023

continued

D

American Dental Association

211 East Chicago Avenue
Chicago, IL 60611

American Geriatrics Society

10 Columbus Circle
New York, NY 10010

American Heart Association

7320 Greenville Avenue
Dallas, TX 75231

American Home Economics Association

5010 Massachusetts Avenue, N.W.
Washington, DC 20036

Food and Nutrition Board

National Research Council, National Academy of
Sciences
2101 Constitution Avenue, N.W.
Washington, DC 20418

March of Dimes Birth Defects Foundation

1275 Mamaroneck Avenue
White Plains, NY 10605

National Nutrition Consortium, Inc.

1635 P Street, N.W., Suite #1
Washington, DC 20036

Office of Cancer Communications

National Cancer Institute
Bldg. 31, Room 10A18
9000 Rockville Pike
Bethesda, MD 20205

Federal government resources

These agencies will furnish lists of their nutrition-related government publications.

Consumer Information Center

U.S. General Services Administration
Pueblo, CO 81009

Food and Nutrition Information and Education Resources Center

National Library of Congress
Beltsville, MD 20705

Local resources

These are people whom you can contact in your own geographical area who are familiar with science-based nutrition information.

Cooperative extension agents

in county extension offices

Dietitians

in clinical positions in local hospitals or nursing homes

Home economists

employed in business (supermarkets, utilities, food processing companies, and so on)

Nutrition faculty

affiliated with a reputable department of nutritional science

Nutritionists

in city, county, or state public health departments

Appendix E Table of Food Composition—Common Foods (Values pertain to edible portions unless indicated otherwise.)

Food	Approximate Measure	Weight (g)	Water (%)	Food energy (kcal)	Protein (g)	Fat (g)	Saturated (total) (g)	Unsaturated Oleic (g)	Linoleic (g)	Carbohydrate (g)	Calcium (mg)	Phosphorous (mg)	Iron (mg)	Potassium (mg)	Vitamin A value (IU)	Thiamin (mg)	Riboflavin (mg)	Niacin (mg)	Ascorbic Acid (mg)
Alfalfa sprouts, raw	1 cup	105	93	27	3	tr	nd	nd	nd	3	23	57	0.8	63	16	0.07	0.13	0.4	8
Almonds, shelled:																			
Chopped (about 130 almonds)	1 cup	130	5	775	24	70	5.6	47.7	12.8	25	304	655	6.1	1,005	0	0.31	1.20	4.6	tr
Slivered, not pressed down (about 115 almonds)	1 cup	115	5	690	21	62	5.0	42.2	11.3	22	269	580	5.4	889	0	0.28	1.06	4.0	tr
Apples, raw, unpeeled, without cores:																			
2¾-in. diameter (about 3 per lb with cores)	1 apple	138	84	80	tr	1	*	*	*	20	10	14	0.4	152	120	0.04	0.03	0.1	6
3¼-in. diameter (about 2 per lb with cores)	1 apple	212	84	125	tr	1	nd	nd	nd	31	15	21	0.6	233	190	0.06	0.04	0.2	8
Apple, baked with 2 tbsp sugar	1 apple	150	nd	188	tr	1	*	*	*	46	10	15	0.5	165	140	0.04	0.03	0.2	5
Apple juice, bottled or canned	1 cup	248	88	120	tr	tr	*	*	*	30	15	22	1.5	250	*	0.02	0.05	0.2	2†
Applesauce, canned:																			
Sweetened	1 cup	255	76	230	1	tr	*	*	*	61	10	13	1.3	166	100	0.05	0.03	0.1	3†
Unsweetened	1 cup	244	89	100	tr	tr	*	*	*	26	10	12	1.2	190	100	0.05	0.02	0.1	2†
Apricots:																			
Raw, without pits (about 12 per lb with pits)	3 apricots	107	85	55	1	tr	*	*	*	14	18	25	0.5	301	2,890	0.03	0.04	0.6	11
Canned in heavy syrup (halves and syrup)	1 cup	258	77	220	2	tr	*	*	*	57	28	39	0.8	604	4,490	0.05	0.05	1.0	10
Dried:																			
Uncooked (28 large or 37 medium halves per cup)	1 cup	130	25	340	7	1	*	*	*	86	87	140	7.2	1,273	14,170	0.01	0.21	4.3	16
Cooked, unsweetened, fruit and liquid	1 cup	250	76	215	4	1	*	*	*	54	55	88	4.5	795	7,500	0.01	0.13	2.5	8
Apricot nectar, canned	1 cup	251	85	145	1	tr	*	*	*	37	23	30	0.5	379	2,380	0.03	0.03	0.5	36
Asparagus, green:																			
Cooked, drained:																			
Cuts and tips, 1½- to 2-in. lengths:																			
From raw	1 cup	145	94	30	3	tr	*	*	*	5	30	73	0.9	265	1,310	0.23	0.26	2.0	38
From frozen	1 cup	180	93	40	6	tr	*	*	*	6	40	115	2.2	396	1,530	0.25	0.23	1.8	41
Spears, ½-in. diameter at base:																			
From raw	4 spears	60	94	10	1	tr	*	*	*	2	13	30	0.4	110	540	0.10	0.11	0.8	16
From frozen	4 spears	60	92	15	2	tr	*	*	*	2	13	40	0.7	143	470	0.10	0.08	0.7	16
Canned, spears, ½-in. diameter at base	4 spears	80	93	15	2	tr	*	*	*	3	15	42	1.5	133	640	0.05	0.08	0.6	12
Avocados, raw, whole, without skins and seeds:																			
California, mid- and late-winter (with skin and seed, 3⅛-in. diameter; weight: 10 oz)	1 avocado	216	74	370	5	37	5.5	22.0	3.7	13	22	91	1.3	1,303	630	0.24	0.43	3.5	30
Florida, late summer and fall (with skin and seed, 3⅝-in. diameter; weight: 1 lb)	1 avocado	304	78	390	4	33	6.7	15.7	5.3	27	30	128	1.8	1,836	880	0.33	0.61	4.9	43
Bacon (20 slices per lb, raw), broiled or fried, crisp	2 slices	15	8	85	4	8	2.5	3.7	0.7	tr	2	34	0.5	35	0	0.08	0.05	0.8	*

Appendix E continued

Food	Approximate Measure	Weight (g)	Water (%)	Food energy (kcal)	Protein (g)	Fat (g)	Fatty acids Saturated (total) (g)	Unsaturated Oleic (g)	Linoleic (g)	Carbohydrate (g)	Calcium (mg)	Phosphorous (mg)	Iron (mg)	Potassium (mg)	Vitamin A value (IU)	Thiamin (mg)	Riboflavin (mg)	Niacin (mg)	Ascorbic Acid (mg)
Bagel, 3-in. diameter:																			
Egg	1 bagel	55	32	165	6	2	0.5	0.9	0.8	28	9	43	1.2	41	30	0.14	0.10	1.2	0
Water	1 bagel	55	29	165	6	1	0.2	0.4	0.6	30	8	41	1.2	42	0	0.15	0.11	1.4	0
Baking powders for home use:																			
Sodium aluminum sulfate:																			
With monocalcium phosphate monohydrate	1 tsp	3.0	2	5	tr	tr	0	0	0	1	58	87	*	5	0	0	0	0	0
With monocalcium phosphate monohydrate, calcium sulfate	1 tsp	2.9	1	5	tr	tr	0	0	0	1	183	45	*	*	0	0	0	0	0
Straight phosphate	1 tsp	3.8	2	5	tr	tr	0	0	0	1	239	359	*	6	0	0	0	0	0
Low sodium	1 tsp	4.3	2	5	tr	tr	0	0	0	2	207	314	*	471	0	0	0	0	0
Banana without peel (about 2.6 per lb with peel)	1 banana	119	76	100	1	tr	*	*	*	26	10	31	0.8	440	230	0.06	0.07	0.8	12
Banana flakes	1 tbsp	6	3	20	tr	tr	*	*	*	5	2	6	0.2	92	50	0.01	0.01	0.2	tr
Barbecue sauce	1 cup	250	81	230	4	17	2.2	4.3	10.0	20	53	50	2.0	435	900	0.03	0.03	0.8	13
Barley, pearled, light, uncooked	1 cup	200	11	700	16	2	0.3	0.2	0.8	158	32	378	4.0	320	0	0.24	0.10	6.2	0
Bean sprouts (mung):																			
Raw	1 cup	105	89	35	4	tr	*	*	*	7	20	67	1.4	234	20	0.14	0.14	0.8	20
Cooked, drained	1 cup	125	91	35	4	tr	*	*	*	7	21	60	1.1	195	30	0.11	0.13	0.9	8
Beans:																			
Lima, immature seeds, frozen, Cooked, drained:																			
Thick-seeded types (Fordhooks)	1 cup	170	74	170	10	tr	*	*	*	32	34	153	2.9	724	390	0.12	0.09	1.7	29
Thin-seeded types (baby limas)	1 cup	180	69	210	13	tr	*	*	*	40	63	227	4.7	709	400	0.16	0.09	2.2	22
Snap:																			
Green:																			
Cooked, drained:																			
From raw (cuts and French style)	1 cup	125	92	30	2	tr	*	*	*	7	63	46	0.8	189	680	0.09	0.11	0.6	15
From frozen:																			
Cuts	1 cup	135	92	35	2	tr	*	*	*	8	54	43	0.9	205	780	0.09	0.12	0.5	7
French style	1 cup	130	92	35	2	tr	*	*	*	8	49	39	1.2	177	690	0.08	0.10	0.4	9
Canned, drained solids (cuts)	1 cup	135	92	30	2	tr	*	*	*	7	61	34	2.0	128	630	0.04	0.07	0.4	5
Yellow or wax:																			
Cooked, drained:																			
From raw (cuts and French style)	1 cup	125	93	30	2	tr	*	*	*	6	63	46	0.8	189	290	0.09	0.11	0.6	16
From frozen (cuts)	1 cup	135	92	35	2	tr	*	*	*	8	47	42	0.9	221	140	0.09	0.11	0.5	8
Canned, drained solids (cuts)	1 cup	135	92	30	2	tr	*	*	*	7	61	34	2.0	128	140	0.04	0.07	0.4	7
Beans, baked, with pork & molasses, canned	½ cup	125	nd	188	8	5.9	nd	nd	nd	26	79	142	2.9	nd	nd	0.08	0.05	0.6	nd
Beans, dry:																			
Common varieties as Great Northern, navy, and others:																			
Cooked, drained:																			
Great Northern	1 cup	180	69	210	14	1	*	*	*	38	90	266	4.9	749	0	0.25	0.13	1.3	0
Pea (navy)	1 cup	190	69	225	15	1	*	*	*	40	95	281	5.1	790	0	0.27	0.13	1.3	0
Canned, solids and liquid:																			
White with—																			
Frankfurters (sliced)	1 cup	255	71	365	19	18	*	*	*	32	94	303	4.8	668	330	0.18	0.15	3.3	tr

E

Food	Measure	Weight (g)	Water (%)	Food energy (cal)	Protein (g)	Fat (g)	Saturated (g)	Oleic (g)	Linoleic (g)	Carbohydrate (g)	Calcium (mg)	Phosphorus (mg)	Iron (mg)	Potassium (mg)	Vitamin A (IU)	Thiamin (mg)	Riboflavin (mg)	Niacin (mg)	Ascorbic acid (mg)
Pork and tomato sauce	1 cup	255	71	310	16	7	2.4	2.8	0.6	48	138	235	4.6	536	330	0.20	0.08	1.5	5
Pork and sweet sauce	1 cup	255	66	385	16	12	4.3	5.0	1.1	54	161	291	5.9	*	*	0.15	0.10	1.3	*
Red kidney	1 cup	255	76	230	15	1	*	*	*	42	74	278	4.6	673	10	0.13	0.10	1.5	*
Lima, cooked, drained	1 cup	190	64	260	16	1	*	*	*	49	55	293	5.9	1,163	*	0.25	0.11	1.3	*
Beef,‡ cooked:																			
Cuts braised, simmered or pot roasted:																			
Lean and fat (piece, 2½ by 2½ by ¾ in.)	3 oz	85	53	245	23	16	6.8	6.5	0.4	0	10	114	2.9	184	30	0.04	0.18	3.6	*
Lean only	2.5 oz	72	62	140	22	5	2.1	1.8	0.2	0	10	108	2.7	176	10	0.04	0.17	3.3	*
Ground beef, broiled:																			
Lean with 10% fat	3 oz or patty 3 by ⅝ in.	85	60	185	23	10	4.0	3.9	0.3	0	10	196	3.0	261	20	0.08	0.20	5.1	*
Lean with 21% fat	2.9 oz or patty 3 by ⅝ in.	82	54	235	20	17	7.0	6.7	0.4	0	9	159	2.6	221	30	0.07	0.17	4.4	*
Roast, oven cooked, no liquid added:																			
Relatively fat, such as rib:																			
Lean and fat (2 pieces, 4⅛ by 2¼ by ¼ in.)	3 oz	85	40	375	17	33	14.0	13.6	0.8	0	8	158	2.2	189	70	0.05	0.13	3.1	*
Lean only	1.8 oz	51	57	125	14	7	3.0	2.5	0.3	0	6	131	1.8	161	10	0.04	0.11	2.6	*
Relatively lean, such as heel of round:																			
Lean and fat (2 pieces, 4⅛ by 2¼ by ¼ in.)	3 oz	85	62	165	25	7	2.8	2.7	0.2	0	11	208	3.2	279	10	0.06	0.19	4.5	*
Lean only	2.8 oz	78	65	125	24	3	1.2	1.0	0.1	0	10	199	3.0	268	tr	0.06	0.18	4.3	*
Steak:																			
Relatively fat—sirloin, broiled:																			
Lean and fat (piece, 2½ by 2½ by ¾ in.)	3 oz	85	44	330	20	27	11.3	11.1	0.6	0	9	162	2.5	220	50	0.05	0.15	4.0	*
Lean only	2.0 oz	56	59	115	18	4	1.8	1.6	0.2	0	7	146	2.2	202	10	0.05	0.14	3.6	*
Relatively lean—round, braised:																			
Lean and fat (piece, 4⅛ by 2¼ by ½ in.)	3 oz	85	55	220	24	13	5.5	5.2	0.4	0	10	213	3.0	272	20	0.07	0.19	4.8	*
Lean only	2.4 oz	68	61	130	21	4	1.7	1.5	0.2	0	9	182	2.5	238	10	0.05	0.16	4.1	*
Beef, canned:																			
Corned beef	3 oz	85	59	185	22	10	4.9	4.5	0.2	0	17	90	3.7		*	0.01	0.20	2.9	*
Corned beef hash	1 cup	220	67	400	19	25	11.9	10.9	0.5	24	29	147	4.4	440	*	0.02	0.20	4.6	*
Beef, dried, chipped	2½-oz jar	71	48	145	24	4	2.1	2.0	0.1	0	14	287	3.6	142	*	0.05	0.23	2.7	0
Beef and vegetable stew	1 cup	245	82	220	16	11	4.9	4.5	0.2	15	29	184	2.9	613	2,400	0.15	0.17	4.7	17
Beef potpie (home recipe), baked† (piece, ⅓ of 9-in. diameter pie)	1 piece	210	55	515	21	30	7.9	12.8	6.7	39	29	149	3.8	334	1,720	0.30	0.30	5.5	6
Beets:																			
Cooked, drained, peeled:																			
Whole beets, 2-in. diameter	2 beets	100	91	30	1	tr	*	*	*	7	14	23	0.5	208	20	0.03	0.04	0.3	6
Diced or sliced	1 cup	170	91	55	2	tr	*	*	*	12	24	39	0.9	354	30	0.05	0.07	0.5	10
Canned, drained solids:																			
Whole beets, small	1 cup	160	89	60	2	tr	*	*	*	14	30	29	1.1	267	30	0.02	0.05	0.2	5
Diced or sliced	1 cup	170	89	65	2	tr	*	*	*	15	32	31	1.2	284	30	0.02	0.05	0.2	5
Beet greens, leaves and stems, cooked, drained	1 cup	145	94	25	2	tr	*	*	*	5	144	36	2.8	481	7,400	0.10	0.22	0.4	22
Beverages, alcoholic:																			
Beer	12 fl oz	360	92	150	1	0	0	0	0	14	18	108	tr	90	*	0.01	0.11	2.2	*
Gin, rum, vodka, whisky:																			
80-proof	1½-fl oz jigger	42	67	95	*	0	0	0	0	tr	*	*	*	1	*	*	*	*	*

Appendix E continued

Food	Approximate Measure	Weight (g)	Water (%)	Food energy (kcal)	Protein (g)	Fat (g)	Saturated (total) (g)	Unsaturated Oleic (g)	Linoleic (g)	Carbohydrate (g)	Calcium (mg)	Phosphorous (mg)	Iron (mg)	Potassium (mg)	Vitamin A value (IU)	Thiamin (mg)	Riboflavin (mg)	Niacin (mg)	Ascorbic Acid (mg)
86-proof	1½-fl oz jigger	42	64	105	*	*	0	0	0	tr	*	*	*	1	*	*	*	*	*
90-proof	1½-fl oz jigger	42	62	110	*	*	0	0	0	tr	*	*	*	1	*	*	*	*	*
Wines:																			
Dessert	3½-fl oz glass	103	77	140	tr	0	0	0	0	8	8	10	*	77	*	0.01	0.02	0.2	*
Table	3½-fl oz glass	102	86	85	tr	0	0	0	0	4	9	10	0.4	94	*	tr	0.01	0.1	*
Beverages, nonalcoholic:																			
Carbonated soft drinks, artificially sweetened	12 fl oz	355	100	*	0	0	0	0	0	*	*	*	*	*	0	0	0	0	0
Carbonated water	12 fl oz	366	92	115	0	0	0	0	0	29	*	*	*	*	0	0	0	0	0
Cola type	12 fl oz	369	90	145	0	0	0	0	0	37	*	*	*	*	0	0	0	0	0
Fruit ades/drinks, powder plus water (Tang)	1 cup	270	nd	177	tr	1	nd	nd	nd	42	0	140	0.1	3	2,718	0.01	0	0	164
Fruit flavored sodas and Tom Collins mixer	12 fl oz	372	88	170	0	0	0	0	0	45	*	*	*	*	0	0	0	0	0
Ginger ale	12 fl oz	366	92	115	0	0	0	0	0	29	*	*	*	0	0	0	0	0	0
Noncarbonated soft drinks, powder plus water (Kool-aid)	1 cup	240	nd	100	0	0	0	0	0	25	1	18	0	1	150	0	0	0	10
Root beer	12 fl oz	370	90	150	0	0	0	0	0	39	*	*	*	0	0	0	0	0	0
Biscuits, baking powder, 2-in. diameter (enriched flour, vegetable shortening):																			
From home recipe	1 biscuit	28	27	105	2	5	1.2	2.0	1.2	13	34	49	0.4	33	tr	0.08	0.08	0.7	tr
From mix	1 biscuit	28	29	90	2	3	0.6	1.1	0.7	15	19	65	0.6	32	tr	0.09	0.08	0.8	tr
Biscuits, refrigerator, from canned dough	1 average	35	nd	97	3	2	nd	nd	nd	16	19	174	0.6	23	nd	0.09	0.06	0.7	0
Blackberries, raw	1 cup	144	85	85	2	1	*	*	*	19	46	27	1.3	245	290	0.04	0.06	0.6	30
Blackeye peas, dry, cooked (with residual cooking liquid)	1 cup	250	80	190	13	1	*	*	*	35	43	238	3.3	573	30	0.40	0.10	1.0	*
Blackeye peas, immature seeds, cooked and drained:																			
From raw	1 cup	165	72	180	13	1	*	*	*	30	40	241	3.5	625	580	0.50	0.18	2.3	28
From frozen	1 cup	170	66	220	15	1	*	*	*	40	43	286	4.8	573	290	0.68	0.19	2.4	15
Blueberries, raw	1 cup	145	83	90	1	1	*	*	*	22	22	19	1.5	117	150	0.04	0.09	0.7	20
Brazil nuts, shelled (6–8 large kernels)	1 oz	28	5	185	4	19	4.8	6.2	7.1	3	53	196	1.0	203	tr	0.27	0.03	0.5	*
Breads:																			
Banana	1 slice	49	nd	134	2	4	nd	nd	nd	23	8	30	0.4	nd	273	0.06	0.06	0.5	0
Boston brown bread, canned, slice 3¼ by ½ in.§	1 slice	45	45	95	2	1	0.1	0.2	0.2	21	41	72	0.9	131	0⁺	0.06	0.04	0.7	0
Cinnamon	1 slice	25	nd	68	2	1	nd	nd	nd	13	21	24	0.6	26	1	0.06	0.05	0.6	0
Cracked-wheat bread (¾ enriched wheat flour, ¼ cracked wheat):§																			
Loaf, 1 lb	1 loaf	454	35	1,195	39	10	2.2	3.0	3.9	236	399	581	9.5	608	tr	1.52	1.13	14.4	tr
Slice (18 per loaf)	1 slice	25	35	65	2	1	0.1	0.2	0.2	13	22	32	0.5	34	tr	0.08	0.06	0.8	tr

Food	Measure																		
French or vienna bread, enriched:[§]																			
Loaf: 1 lb	1 loaf	454	31	1,315	41	14	3.2	4.7	4.6	251	195	386	10.0	408	tr	1.80	1.10	15.0	tr
Slice: French (5 by 2½ by 1 in)	1 slice	35	31	100	3	1	0.2	0.4	0.4	19	15	30	0.8	32	tr	0.14	0.08	1.2	tr
Vienna (4¾ by 4 by ½ in.)	1 slice	25	31	75	2	1	0.2	0.3	0.3	14	11	21	0.6	23	tr	0.10	0.06	0.8	tr
High fiber (Fresh Horizon, dark)	1 slice	29	nd	54	3	1	nd	nd	nd	10	51	nd	0.9	nd	0	0.12	0.07	1.0	0
Italian bread, enriched:																			
Loaf, 1 lb	1 loaf	454	32	1,250	41	4	0.6	0.3	1.5	256	77	349	10.0	336	0	1.80	1.10	15.0	0
Slice, 4½ bt 3¼ by ¾ in.	1 slice	30	32	85	3	tr	tr	tr	0.1	17	5	23	0.7	22	0	0.12	0.07	1.0	0
Multigrain (Roman Meal)[§]	1 slice	23	nd	56	3	1	nd	nd	nd	11	24	nd	0.7	nd	0	0.09	0.07	0.8	0
Raisin bread, enriched:[§]																			
Loaf, 1 lb	1 loaf	454	35	1,190	30	13	3.0	4.7	3.9	243	322	395	10.0	1,057	tr	1.70	1.07	10.7	tr
Slice (18 per loaf)	1 slice	25	35	65	2	1	0.2	0.3	0.2	13	18	22	0.6	58	tr	0.09	0.06	0.6	tr
Rye:																			
American, light (⅔ enriched wheat flour, ⅓ rye flour):																			
Loaf, 1 lb	1 loaf	454	36	1,100	41	5	0.7	0.5	2.2	236	340	667	9.1	658	0	1.35	0.98	12.9	0
Slice (4¾ by 3¾ by ⁷⁄₁₆ in.)	1 slice	25	36	60	2	tr	tr	tr	0.1	13	19	37	0.5	36	0	0.07	0.05	0.7	0
Pumpernickel (⅔ rye flour, ⅓ enriched wheat flour):																			
Loaf, 1 lb	1 loaf	454	34	1,115	41	5	0.7	0.5	2.4	241	381	1,039	11.8	2,059	0	1.30	0.93	8.5	0
Slice (5 by 4 by ⅜ in.)	1 slice	32	34	80	3	tr	0.1	tr	0.2	17	27	73	0.8	145	0	0.09	0.07	0.6	0
Wheat germ (Pepperidge Farms)	1 slice	32	nd	79	4	tr	nd	nd	nd	14	30	81	1.1	78	nd	0.09	0.06	0.8	nd
White bread, enriched:[§]																			
Soft-crumb type:																			
Loaf, 1 lb	1 loaf	454	36	1,225	39	15	3.4	5.3	4.6	229	381	440	11.3	476	tr	1.80	1.10	15.0	tr
Slice (18 per loaf)	1 slice	25	36	70	2	1	0.2	0.3	0.3	13	21	24	0.6	26	tr	0.10	0.06	0.8	tr
Slice, toasted	1 slice	22	25	70	2	1	0.2	0.3	0.3	13	21	24	0.6	26	tr	0.08	0.06	0.8	tr
Slice (22 per loaf)	1 slice	20	36	55	2	1	0.2	0.2	0.2	10	17	19	0.5	21	tr	0.8	0.5	0.7	tr
Slice, toasted	1 slice	17	25	55	2	1	0.2	0.2	0.2	10	17	19	0.5	21	tr	0.6	0.5	0.7	tr
Loaf, 1½ lb	1 loaf	680	36	1,835	59	22	5.2	7.9	6.9	343	571	660	17.0	714	tr	2.70	1.65	22.5	tr
Slice (24 per loaf)	1 slice	28	36	75	2	1	0.2	0.3	0.3	14	24	27	0.7	29	tr	0.11	0.07	0.9	tr
Slice, toasted	1 slice	24	25	75	2	1	0.2	0.3	0.3	14	24	27	0.7	29	tr	0.09	0.07	0.9	tr
Slice (28 per loaf)	1 slice	24	36	65	2	1	0.2	0.3	0.3	12	20	23	0.6	25	tr	0.10	0.06	0.8	tr
Slice, toasted	1 slice	21	25	65	2	1	0.2	0.3	0.3	12	20	23	0.6	25	tr	0.08	0.06	0.8	tr
Cubes	1 cup	30	36	80	3	1	0.3	0.3	0.3	15	25	29	0.8	32	tr	0.12	0.07	1.0	tr
Crumbs	1 cup	45	36	120	4	1	0.5	0.5	0.5	23	38	44	1.1	47	tr	0.18	0.11	1.5	tr
Firm-crumb type:																			
Loaf, 1 lb	1 loaf	454	35	1,245	41	17	3.9	5.9	5.2	228	435	463	11.3	549	tr	1.80	1.10	15.0	tr
Slice (20 per loaf)	1 slice	23	35	65	2	1	0.2	0.3	0.3	12	22	23	0.6	28	tr	0.09	0.06	0.8	tr
Slice, toasted	1 slice	20	24	65	2	1	0.2	0.3	0.3	12	22	23	0.6	28	tr	0.07	0.06	0.8	tr
Loaf, 2 lb	1 loaf	907	35	2,495	82	34	7.7	11.8	10.4	455	871	925	22.7	1,097	tr	3.60	2.20	30.0	tr
Slice (34 per loaf)	1 slice	27	35	75	2	1	0.2	0.3	0.3	14	26	28	0.7	33	tr	0.11	0.06	0.9	tr
Slice, toasted	1 slice	23	24	75	2	1	0.2	0.3	0.3	14	26	28	0.7	33	tr	0.09	0.06	0.9	tr
White bread, not enriched	1 slice	23	35	62	2	1	0.2	0.3	0.3	12	19	22	0.2	24	tr	0.02	0.02	0.2	tr
Whole-wheat bread:																			
Soft-crumb type:[§]																			
Loaf, 1 lb	1 loaf	454	36	1,095	41	12	2.2	2.9	4.2	224	381	1,152	13.6	1,161	tr	1.37	0.45	12.7	tr
Slice (16 per loaf)	1 slice	28	36	65	3	1	0.1	0.2	0.2	14	24	72	0.8	72	tr	0.09	0.03	0.8	tr
Slice, toasted	1 slice	24	24	65	3	1	0.1	0.2	0.2	14	24	71	0.8	72	tr	0.07	0.03	0.8	tr
Firm-crumb type:[§]																			
Loaf, 1 lb	1 loaf	454	36	1,100	48	14	2.5	3.3	4.9	216	449	1,034	13.6	1,238	tr	1.17	0.54	12.7	tr
Slice (18 per loaf)	1 slice	25	36	60	3	1	0.1	0.2	0.3	12	25	57	0.8	68	tr	0.06	0.03	0.7	tr
Slice, toasted	1 slice	21	24	60	3	1	0.1	0.2	0.3	12	25	57	0.8	68	tr	0.05	0.03	0.7	tr
Breadcrumbs (enriched):[§]																			
Dry, grated	1 cup	100	7	390	13	5	1.0	1.6	1.4	73	122	141	3.6	152	tr	0.35	0.35	4.8	tr

Appendix E continued

Food	Approximate Measure	Weight (g)	Water (%)	Food energy (kcal)	Protein (g)	Fat (g)	Fatty acids Saturated (total) (g)	Unsaturated Oleic (g)	Linoleic (g)	Carbohydrate (g)	Calcium (mg)	Phosphorous (mg)	Iron (mg)	Potassium (mg)	Vitamin A value (IU)	Thiamin (mg)	Riboflavin (mg)	Niacin (mg)	Ascorbic Acid (mg)
Breakfast cereals:																			
Hot type, cooked:																			
Corn (hominy) grits, degermed:																			
Enriched	1 cup	245	87	125	3	tr	tr	tr	0.1	27	2	25	0.7	27	tr†	0.10	0.07	1.0	0
Unenriched	1 cup	245	87	125	3	tr	tr	tr	0.1	27	2	25	0.2	27	tr†	0.05	0.02	0.5	0
Farina, quick-cooking, enriched	1 cup	245	89	105	3	tr	tr	tr	0.1	22	147	113†	†	25	0	0.12	0.07	1.0	0
Oatmeal or rolled oats	1 cup	240	87	130	5	2	0.4	0.8	0.9	23	22	137	1.4	146	0	0.19	0.05	0.2	0
Rice	1 cup	245	88	123	2	tr	nd	nd	nd	27	5	32	1.7	tr	0	0.15	0.02	2.0	0
Wheat, rolled	1 cup	240	80	180	5	1	*	*	*	41	19	182	1.7	202	0	0.17	0.07	2.2	0
Wheat, whole-meal	1 cup	245	88	110	4	1	*	*	*	23	17	127	1.2	118	0	0.15	0.05	1.5	0
Ready-to-eat:																			
Bran flakes (40% bran), added sugar, salt, iron, vitamins	1 cup	35	3	105	4	1	*	*	*	28	19	125	5.6	137	1,540	0.46	0.52	6.2	0
Bran flakes with raisins, added sugar, salt, iron, vitamins	1 cup	50	7	145	4	1	*	*	*	40	28	146	7.9	154	2,200†	†	†	†	0
Cheerios	1 cup	25	nd	97	4	2	nd	nd	nd	18	35	115	4.0	83	1102	0.33	0.38	4.4	13
Corn flakes:																			
Plain, added sugar, salt, iron, vitamins	1 cup	25	4	95	2	tr	*	*	*	21	†	9	†	30	†	†	†	†	13†
Sugar-coated, added salt, iron, vitamins	1 cup	40	2	155	2	tr	*	*	*	37	1	10	†	27	1,760	0.53	0.50	7.1	21†
Corn, oat flour, puffed, added sugar, salt, iron, vitamins	1 cup	20	4	80	2	1	*	*	*	16	4	18	5.7	*	880	0.26	0.30	3.5	11
Corn, shredded, added sugar, salt, iron, thiamin, niacin	1 oz	25	3	95	2	tr	*	nd	nd	22	1	10	0.6	*	0	0.33	0.05	4.4	13
Granola (oat) (Nature Valley)	1 oz	28	nd	128	3	4	nd	nd	nd	20	nd	nd	nd	nd	nd	nd	nd	5.0	nd
Grapenuts (wheat)	1 oz	28	nd	100	4	tr	*	nd	nd	23	10	17	0.5	75	1,235	0.37	0.42	5.0	0
Oats, puffed, added sugar, salt, minerals, vitamins	1 cup	25	3	100	3	1	*	*	*	19	44	102	4.0	*	1,100	0.33	0.38	4.4	13
Rice, puffed:																			
Plain, added iron, thiamin, niacin	1 cup	15	4	60	1	tr	*	*	*	13	3	14	0.3	15	0	0.07	0.01	0.7	0
Presweetened, added salt, iron, vitamins	1 cup	28	3	115	1	0	*	*	*	26	3	14	†	43	1,240†	†	†	†	15†
Sugar Smacks (wheat)	1 cup	28	nd	109	2	tr	nd	nd	nd	24	5	40	1.8	45	1235	0.37	0.42	4.9	15
Wheat flakes, added sugar, salt, iron, vitamins	1 cup	30	4	105	3	tr	*	*	*	24	12	83	4.8	81	1,320	0.40	0.45	5.3	16
Wheat, puffed:																			
Plain, added iron, thiamin, niacin	1 cup	15	3	55	2	tr	*	*	*	12	4	48	0.6	51	0	0.08	0.03	1.2	0
Presweetened, added salt, iron, vitamins	1 cup	38	3	140	3	tr	*	*	*	33	7	52	†	63	1,680	0.50	0.57	6.7	20†
Wheat, shredded, plain	1 oblong biscuit or ½ cup spoon-size biscuits	25	7	90	2	1	*	*	*	20	11	97	0.9	87	0	0.06	0.03	1.1	0
Wheat germ, without salt and sugar, toasted	1 tbsp.	6	4	25	2	1	*	*	*	3	3	70	0.5	57	10	0.11	0.05	0.3	1

E

Food	Measure																		
Broccoli, cooked, drained:																			
From raw:																			
Stalk, medium size	1 stalk	180	91	45	6	1	*	*	*	8	158	112	1.4	481	4,500	0.16	0.36	1.4	162
Stalks cut into ½-in. pieces	1 cup	155	91	40	5	tr	*	*	*	7	136	96	1.2	414	3,880	0.14	0.31	1.2	140
From frozen:																			
Stalk, 4½ to 5 in. long	1 stalk	30	91	10	1	tr	*	*	*	1	12	17	0.2	66	570	0.02	0.03	0.2	22
Chopped	1 cup	185	92	50	5	1	*	*	*	9	100	104	1.3	392	4,810	0.11	0.22	0.9	105
Brussels sprouts, cooked, drained:																			
From raw, 7–8 sprouts (1¼- to 1½-in. diam.)	1 cup	155	88	55	7	1	*	*	*	10	50	112	1.7	423	810	0.12	0.22	1.2	135
From frozen	1 cup	155	89	50	5	tr	*	*	*	10	33	95	1.2	457	880	0.12	0.16	0.9	126
Buckwheat flour, light, sifted	1 cup	98	12	340	6	1	0.2	0.4	0.4	78	11	86	1.0	314	0	0.08	0.04	0.4	0
Bulgar, canned, seasoned	1 cup	135	56	245	8	4	*	*	*	44	27	263	1.9	151	0	0.08	0.05	4.1	0
Burrito, bean	1 average	169	nd	350	15	11	nd	nd	nd	48	208	200	1.2	479	nd	nd	nd	nd	nd
Butter:																			
Regular (1 brick or 4 sticks per lb):																			
Stick (½ cup)	Stick (½ cup)	113	16	815	1	92	57.3	23.1	2.1	tr	27	26	0.2	29	3,470	0.01	0.04	tr	0
Tablespoon (about ⅛ stick)	1 tbsp.	14	16	100	tr	12	7.2	2.9	0.3	tr	3	3	tr	4	430	tr	tr	tr	0
Pat (1 in. square, ⅓ in. high; 90 per lb.)	1 pat	5	16	35	tr	4	2.5	1.0	0.1	tr	1	1	tr	1	150	tr	tr	tr	0
Whipped (6 sticks or two 8-oz containers per lb.):																			
Stick (½ cup)	1 stick	76	16	540	1	61	38.2	15.4	1.4	tr	18	17	0.1	20	2,310	tr	0.03	tr	0
Tablespoon (about ⅛ stick)	1 tbsp.	9	16	65	tr	8	4.7	1.9	0.2	tr	2	2	tr	2	290	tr	tr	tr	0
Pat (1¼ in. square, ⅓ in. high; 120 per lb.)	1 pat	4	16	25	tr	3	1.9	0.8	0.1	tr	1	1	tr	1	120	0	tr	tr	0
Cabbage:																			
Common varieties:																			
Raw:																			
Coarsely shredded or sliced	1 cup	70	92	15	1	tr	*	*	*	4	34	20	0.3	163	90	0.04	0.04	0.2	33
Finely shredded or chopped	1 cup	90	92	20	1	tr	*	*	*	5	44	26	0.4	210	120	0.05	0.05	0.3	42
Cooked, drained	1 cup	145	94	30	2	tr	*	*	*	6	64	29	0.4	236	190	0.06	0.06	0.4	48
Red, raw, coarsely shredded or sliced	1 cup	70	90	20	1	tr	*	*	*	5	29	25	0.6	188	30	0.06	0.04	0.3	43
Savoy, raw, coarsely shredded or sliced	1 cup	70	92	15	2	tr	*	*	*	3	47	38	0.6	188	140	0.04	0.06	0.2	39
Cabbage, celery (also called petsai or wongbok), raw, 1-in. pieces	1 cup	75	95	10	1	tr	*	*	*	2	32	30	0.5	190	110	0.04	0.03	0.5	18
Cabbage, white mustard (also called bokchoy or pakchoy), cooked, drained	1 cup	170	95	25	2	tr	*	*	*	4	252	56	1.0	364	5,270	0.07	0.14	1.2	26
Cakes made from cake mixes with enriched flour:[§]																			
Angelfood:																			
Whole cake (9¾-in. diameter tube cake)	1 cake	635	34	1,645	36	1	*	*	*	377	603	756	2.5	381	0	0.37	0.95	3.6	0
Piece, 1/12 of cake	1 piece	53	34	135	3	tr	*	*	*	32	50	63	0.2	32	0	0.03	0.08	0.3	0
Coffeecake:																			
Whole cake (7¾ by 5⅝ by 1¼ in.)	1 cake	430	30	1,385	27	41	11.7	16.3	8.8	225	262	748	6.9	469	690	0.82	0.91	7.7	1
Piece, 1/6 of cake	1 piece	72	30	230	5	7	2.0	2.7	1.5	38	44	125	1.2	78	120	0.14	0.15	1.3	tr
Cupcakes, made with egg, milk, 2½-in. diameter:																			
Without icing	1 cupcake	25	26	90	1	3	0.8	1.2	0.7	14	40	59	0.3	21	40	0.05	0.05	0.4	tr
With chocolate icing[Δ]	1 cupcake	36	22	130	2	5	2.0	1.6	0.6	21	47	71	0.4	42	60	0.05	0.06	0.4	tr

E

Appendix E continued

Food	Approximate Measure	Weight (g)	Water (%)	Food energy (kcal)	Protein (g)	Fat (g)	Saturated (total) (g)	Oleic (g)	Linoleic (g)	Carbohydrate (g)	Calcium (mg)	Phosphorous (mg)	Iron (mg)	Potassium (mg)	Vitamin A value (IU)	Thiamin (mg)	Riboflavin (mg)	Niacin (mg)	Ascorbic Acid (mg)
Devil's food (with chocolate icing)Δ																			
Whole, 2-layer cake (8- or 9-in. diameter)	1 cake	1,107	24	3,755	49	136	50.0	44.9	17.0	645	653	1,162	16.6	1,439	1,660	1.06	1.65	10.1	1
Piece, 1/16 of cake	1 piece	69	24	235	3	8	3.1	2.8	1.1	40	41	72	1.0	90	100	0.07	0.10	0.6	tr
Cupcake, 2½-in. diameter	1 cupcake	35	24	120	2	4	1.6	1.4	0.5	20	21	37	0.5	46	50	0.03	0.05	0.3	tr
Gingerbread:																			
Whole cake (8-in. square)	1 cake	570	37	1,575	18	39	9.7	16.6	10.0	291	513	570	8.6	1,562	tr	0.84	1.00	7.4	tr
Piece, 1/9 of cake	1 piece	63	37	175	2	4	1.1	1.8	1.1	32	57	63	0.9	173	tr	0.09	0.11	0.8	tr
White, 2 layer (with chocolate icing)Δ																			
Whole cake (8- or 9-in. diameter)	1 cake	1,140	21	4,000	44	122	48.2	46.4	20.0	716	1,129	2,041	11.4	1,322	680	1.50	1.77	12.5	2
Piece, 1/16 of cake	1 piece	71	21	250	3	8	3.0	2.9	1.2	45	70	127	0.7	82	40	0.09	0.11	0.8	tr
Yellow, 2 layer (with chocolate icing)Δ																			
Whole cake (8- or 9-in. diameter)	1 cake	1,108	26	3,735	45	125	47.8	47.8	20.3	638	1,008	2,017	12.2	1,208	1,550	1.24	1.67	10.6	2
Piece, 1/16 of cake	1 piece	69	26	235	3	8	3.0	3.0	1.3	40	63	126	0.8	75	100	0.08	0.10	0.7	tr
Cakes made from home recipes using enriched flour:§																			
Boston cream pie with custard filling:																			
Whole cake (8-in. diameter)	1 cake	825	35	2,490	41	78	23.0	30.1	15.2	412	553	833	8.2	734†	1,730	1.04	1.27	9.6	2
Piece, 1/12 of cake	1 piece	69	35	210	3	6	1.9	2.5	1.3	34	46	70	0.7	61†	140	0.09	0.11	0.8	tr
Fruitcake, dark:																			
Loaf, 1-lb (7½ by 2 by 1½ in.)	1 loaf	454	18	1,720	22	69	14.4	33.5	14.8	271	327	513	11.8	2,250	540	0.72	0.73	4.9	2
Slice, 1/30 of loaf	1 slice	15	18	55	1	2	0.5	1.1	0.5	9	11	17	0.4	74	20	0.02	0.02	0.2	tr
Plain, sheet cake:																			
Without icing:																			
Whole cake (9-in. square)	1 cake	777	25	2,830	35	108	29.5	44.4	23.9	434	497	793	8.5	614†	1,320	1.21	1.40	10.2	2
Piece, 1/9 of cake	1 piece	86	25	315	4	12	3.3	4.9	2.6	48	55	88	0.9	68†	150	0.13	0.15	1.1	tr
With uncooked white icing:Δ																			
Whole cake (9-in. square)	1 cake	1,096	21	4,020	37	129	42.2	49.5	24.4	694	548	822	8.2	669†	2,190	1.22	1.47	10.2	2
Piece, 1/9 of cake	1 piece	121	21	445	4	14	4.7	5.5	2.7	77	61	91	0.8	74†	240	0.14	0.16	1.1	tr
Pound:																			
Loaf, 8½ by 3½ by 3¼ in.	1 loaf	565	16	2,725	31	170	42.9	73.1	39.6	273	107	418	7.9	345	1,410	0.90	0.99	7.3	0
Slice, 1/17 of a loaf	1 slice	33	16	160	2	10	2.5	4.3	2.3	16	6	24	0.5	20	80	0.05	0.06	0.4	0
Spongecake:																			
Whole cake 9¾-in. diameter tube cake	1 cake	790	32	2,345	60	45	13.1	15.8	5.7	427	237	885	13.4	687	3,560	1.10	1.64	7.4	tr
Piece, 1/12 of cake	1 piece	66	32	195	5	4	1.1	1.3	0.5	36	20	74	1.1	57	300	0.09	0.14	0.6	tr
Cake Icings:																			
Boiled, white:																			
Plain	1 cup	94	18	295	1	0	0	0	0	75	2	2	tr	17	0	tr	0.03	tr	0
With coconut	1 cup	166	15	605	3	13	11.0	0.9	tr	124	10	50	0.8	277	0	0.02	0.07	0.3	0
Uncooked:																			
Chocolate made with milk and butter	1 cup	275	14	1,035	9	38	23.4	11.7	1.0	185	165	305	3.3	536	580	0.06	0.28	0.6	1

Cakes made from home recipes—continued

E

Food	Measure	Grams	Water	Food energy	Protein	Fat	Saturated	Oleic	Linoleic	Carbohydrate	Calcium	Phosphorus	Iron	Potassium	Vitamin A	Thiamin	Riboflavin	Niacin	Ascorbic acid
Creamy fudge from mix and water	1 cup	245	15	830	7	16	5.1	6.7	3.1	183	96	218	2.7	238	tr	0.05	0.20	0.7	tr
White	1 cup	319	11	1,200	2	21	12.7	5.1	0.5	260	48	38	tr	57	860	tr	0.06	tr	tr
Candy:																			
Caramels, plain or chocolate	1 oz	28	8	115	1	3	1.6	1.1	0.1	22	42	35	0.4	54	tr	0.01	0.05	0.1	tr
Chocolate: Milk, plain	1 oz	28	1	145	2	9	5.5	3.0	0.3	16	65	65	0.3	109	80	0.02	0.10	0.1	tr
Semisweet, small pieces (60 per oz)	1 cup or 6-oz pkg	170	1	860	7	61	36.2	19.8	1.7	97	51	255	4.4	553	30	0.02	0.14	0.9	0
Chocolate-coated peanuts	1 oz	28	1	160	5	12	4.0	4.7	2.1	11	33	84	0.4	143	tr	0.10	0.05	2.1	tr
Fondant, uncoated (mints, candy corn, other)	1 oz	28	8	105	tr	1	0.1	0.3	0.1	25	4	2	0.3	1	0	tr	tr	tr	0
Fudge, chocolate, plain	1 oz	28	8	115	1	3	1.3	1.4	0.6	21	22	24	0.3	42	tr	0.01	0.03	0.1	tr
Gum drops	1 oz	28	12	100	tr	tr	*	*	*	25	2	tr	0.1	1	0	0	0	tr	0
Hard	1 oz	28	1	110	0	tr	*	*	*	28	6	2	0.5	1	0	0	0	0	0
Marshmallows	1 oz	28	17	90	1	0	*	*	*	23	5	2	0.5	2	0	0	tr	tr	0
Carrots: Raw, without crowns and tips, scraped: Whole, 7½ by 1⅛ in. or strips, 2½ to 3 in. long	1 carrot or 18 strips	72	88	30	1	tr	*	*	*	7	27	26	0.5	246	7,930	0.04	0.04	0.4	6
Grated	1 cup	110	88	45	1	tr	*	*	*	11	41	40	0.8	375	12,100	0.07	0.06	0.7	9
Cooked (crosswise cuts), drained	1 cup	155	91	50	1	tr	*	*	*	11	51	48	0.9	344	16,280	0.08	0.08	0.8	9
Canned: Sliced, drained solids	1 cup	155	91	45	1	tr	*	*	*	10	47	34	1.1	186	23,250	0.03	0.05	0.6	3
Strained or junior (baby food)	1 oz (1¾ to 2 tbsp)	28	92	10	tr	tr	*	*	*	2	7	6	0.1	51	3,690	0.01	0.01	0.1	1
Cashew nuts, roasted in oil	1 cup	140	5	785	24	64	12.9	36.8	10.2	41	53	522	5.3	650	140	0.60	0.35	2.5	*
Cauliflower: Raw, chopped	1 cup	115	91	31	3	tr	*	*	*	6	29	64	1.3	339	70	0.13	0.12	0.8	90
Cooked, drained: From raw (flower buds)	1 cup	125	93	30	3	tr	*	*	*	5	26	53	0.9	258	80	0.11	0.10	0.8	69
From frozen (flowerets)	1 cup	180	94	30	3	tr	*	*	*	6	31	68	0.9	373	50	0.07	0.09	0.7	74
Celery, Pascal type, raw: Stalk, large outer, 8 by 1½ in. at root end	1 stalk	40	94	5	tr	tr	*	*	*	2	16	11	0.1	136	110	0.01	0.01	0.1	4
Pieces, diced	1 cup	120	94	20	1	tr	*	*	*	5	47	34	0.4	409	320	0.04	0.04	0.4	11
Cheese: Natural: Blue	1 oz	28	42	100	6	8	5.3	1.9	0.2	1	150	110	0.1	73	200	0.01	0.11	0.3	0
Camembert (3 wedges per 4-oz container)	1 wedge	38	52	115	8	9	5.8	2.2	0.2	tr	147	132	0.1	71	350	0.01	0.19	0.2	0
Cheddar: Cut pieces	1 oz	28	37	115	7	9	6.1	2.1	0.2	tr	204	145	0.2	28	300	0.01	0.11	tr	0
	1 cu in.	17.2	37	70	4	6	3.7	1.3	0.1	tr	124	88	0.1	17	180	tr	0.06	tr	0
Shredded	1 cup	113	37	455	28	37	24.2	8.5	0.7	1	815	579	0.8	111	1,200	0.03	0.42	0.1	0
Cottage (curd not pressed down): Creamed (cottage cheese, 4% fat): Large curd	1 cup	225	79	235	28	10	6.4	2.4	0.2	6	135	297	0.3	190	370	0.05	0.37	0.3	tr
Small curd	1 cup	210	79	220	26	9	6.0	2.2	0.2	6	126	277	0.3	177	340	0.04	0.34	0.3	tr
Low fat (2%)	1 cup	226	79	205	31	4	2.8	1.0	0.1	8	155	340	0.4	217	160	0.05	0.42	0.3	tr
Low fat (1%)	1 cup	226	82	165	28	2	1.5	0.5	0.1	6	138	302	0.3	193	80	0.05	0.37	0.3	tr
Uncreamed (cottage cheese dry curd, less than ½% fat)	1 cup	145	80	125	25	1	0.4	0.1	tr	3	46	151	0.3	47	40	0.04	0.21	0.2	0
Cream	1 oz	28	54	100	2	10	6.2	2.4	0.2	1	23	30	0.3	34	400	tr	0.06	tr	0

Appendix E continued

Food	Approximate Measure	Weight (g)	Water (%)	Food energy (kcal)	Protein (g)	Fat (g)	Saturated (total) (g)	Unsaturated Oleic (g)	Unsaturated Linoleic (g)	Carbohydrate (g)	Calcium (mg)	Phosphorous (mg)	Iron (mg)	Potassium (mg)	Vitamin A value (IU)	Thiamin (mg)	Riboflavin (mg)	Niacin (mg)	Ascorbic Acid (mg)
Mozzarella, made with:																			
Whole milk	1 oz	28	48	90	6	7	4.4	1.7	0.2	1	163	117	0.1	21	260	tr	0.08	tr	0
Part skim milk	1 oz	28	49	80	8	5	3.1	1.2	0.1	1	207	149	0.1	27	180	0.01	0.10	tr	0
Parmesan, grated:																			
Cup, not pressed down	1 cup	100	18	455	42	30	19.1	7.7	0.3	4	1,376	807	1.0	107	700	0.05	0.39	0.3	0
Tablespoon	1 tbsp	5	18	25	2	2	1.0	0.4	tr	tr	69	40	tr	5	40	tr	0.02	tr	0
Ounce	1 oz	28	18	130	12	9	5.4	2.2	0.1	1	390	229	0.3	30	200	0.01	0.11	0.1	0
Provolone	1 oz	28	41	100	7	8	4.8	1.7	0.1	1	214	141	0.1	39	230	0.01	0.09	tr	0
Ricotta, made with:																			
Whole milk	1 cup	246	72	430	28	32	20.4	7.1	0.7	7	509	389	0.9	257	1,210	0.03	0.48	0.3	0
Part skim milk	1 cup	246	74	340	28	19	12.1	4.7	0.5	13	669	449	1.1	308	1,060	0.05	0.46	0.2	0
Romano	1 oz	28	31	110	9	8	*	*	*	1	302	215	*	*	160	*	0.11	tr	0
Swiss	1 oz	28	37	105	8	8	5.0	1.7	0.2	1	272	171	tr	31	240	0.01	0.10	tr	0
Pasteurized process cheese:																			
American	1 oz	28	39	105	6	9	5.6	2.1	0.2	tr	174	211	0.1	46	340	0.01	0.10	tr	0
Swiss	1 oz	28	42	95	7	7	4.5	1.7	0.1	1	219	216	0.2	61	230	tr	0.08	tr	0
Pasteurized process cheese food, American	1 oz	28	43	95	6	7	4.4	1.7	0.1	2	163	130	0.2	79	260	0.01	0.13	tr	0
Pasteurized process cheese spread, American	1 oz	28	48	80	5	6	3.8	1.5	0.1	2	159	202	0.1	69	220	0.01	0.12	tr	0
Cheesecake, French (Sara Lee)	1 piece	85	nd	265	4	17.3	nd	nd	nd	23	51	46	0.9	65	277	0.03	0.10	0.2	tr
Cherries:																			
Sour (tart), red, pitted, canned, water pack	1 cup	244	88	105	2	tr	*	*	*	26	37	32	0.7	317	1,660	0.07	0.05	0.5	12
Sweet, raw, without pits and stems	10 cherries	68	80	45	1	tr	*	*	*	12	15	13	0.3	129	70	0.03	0.04	0.3	7
Chicken, cooked:																			
Breast, fried, bones removed, ½ breast (3.3 oz with bones)	2.8 oz.	79	58	160	26	5	1.4	1.8	1.1	1	9	218	1.3	*	70	0.04	0.17	11.6	*
Drumstick, fried, bones removed (2 oz with bones)	1.3 oz	38	55	90	12	4	1.1	1.3	0.9	tr	6	89	0.9	*	50	0.03	0.15	2.7	*
Half broiler, broiled, bones removed (10.4 oz with bones)	6.2 oz	176	71	240	42	7	2.2	2.5	1.3	0	16	355	3.0	483	160	0.09	0.34	15.5	3
Chicken, canned, boneless	3 oz	85	65	170	18	10	3.2	3.8	2.0	0	18	210	1.3	117	200	0.03	0.11	3.7	3
Chicken à la king, cooked (home recipe)	1 cup	245	68	470	27	34	2.7	14.3	3.3	12	127	358	2.5	404	1,130	0.10	0.42	5.4	12
Chicken and noodles, cooked (home recipe)	1 cup	240	71	365	22	18	5.9	7.1	3.5	26	26	247	2.2	149	430	0.05	0.17	4.3	tr
Chicken chow mein:																			
Canned	1 cup	250	89	95	7	tr	*	*	*	18	45	35	1.3	418	150	0.05	0.10	1.0	13
From home recipe	1 cup	250	78	255	31	10	2.4	3.4	3.1	10	58	293	2.5	473	280	0.08	0.23	4.3	10
Chicken potpie (home recipe), baked, piece (⅓ of 9-in. diameter pie)	1 piece	232	57	545	23	31	11.3	10.9	5.6	42	70	232	3.0	343	3,090	0.34	0.31	5.5	5
Chili con carne with beans, canned	1 cup	255	72	340	19	16	7.5	6.8	0.3	31	82	321	4.3	594	150	0.08	0.18	3.3	*
Chocolate:																			
Bitter or baking	1 oz	28	2	145	3	15	8.9	4.9	0.4	8	22	109	1.9	235	20	0.01	0.07	0.4	0

Food	Measure	Weight (g)	Water (%)	Food energy	Protein (g)	Fat (g)	Saturated	Oleic	Linoleic	Carbohydrate (g)	Calcium (mg)	Phosphorus (mg)	Iron (mg)	Potassium (mg)	Vitamin A (IU)	Thiamin (mg)	Riboflavin (mg)	Niacin (mg)	Ascorbic acid (mg)
Chocolate-flavored beverage powders (about 4 heaping tsp per oz):																			
With nonfat dry milk	1 oz	28	2	100	5	1	0.5	0.3	tr	20	167	155	0.5	227	10	0.04	0.21	0.2	1
Without milk	1 oz	28	1	100	1	1	0.4	0.2	tr	25	9	48	0.6	142	*	0.01	0.03	0.1	0
Chop suey with beef and pork (home recipe)	1 cup	250	75	300	26	17	8.5	6.2	0.7	13	60	248	4.8	425	600	0.28	0.38	5.0	33
Cocoa/hot chocolate, with whole milk	1 cup	250	*	218	9	9.1	*	*	*	26	298	270	0.8	480	318	0.10	0.44	0.4	2
Coconut meat, fresh:																			
Piece, about 2 by 2 by ½ in.	1 piece	45	51	155	2	16	14.0	0.9	0.3	4	6	43	0.8	115	0	0.02	0.01	0.2	1
Shredded or grated, not pressed down	1 cup	80	51	275	3	28	24.8	1.6	0.5	8	10	76	1.4	205	0	0.04	0.02	0.4	2
Coffee, made from ground	1 cup	236	*	2	0	0	*	*	*	1	7	7	0	2	0	0	0	1.2	0
Cole slaw, made with mayonnaise	1 cup	120	*	173	2	17	*	*	*	6	53	35	0.5	239	190	0.06	0.06	0.4	35
Collards, cooked, drained:																			
From raw (leaves without stems)	1 cup	190	90	65	7	1	*	*	*	10	357	99	1.5	498	14,820	0.21	0.38	2.3	144
From frozen (chopped)	1 cup	170	90	50	5	1	*	*	*	10	299	87	1.7	401	11,560	0.10	0.24	1.0	56
Cookies made with enriched flour (mostly commercial):[g]																			
Brownies with nuts:																			
Home-prepared, 1¾ by 1¾ by ⅞ in.:																			
From home recipe	1 brownie	20	10	95	1	6	1.5	3.0	1.2	10	8	30	0.4	38	40	0.04	0.03	0.2	tr
From commercial recipe	1 brownie	20	11	85	1	4	0.9	1.4	1.3	13	9	27	0.4	34	20	0.03	0.02	0.2	tr
Frozen (with chocolate icing[Δ]), 1½ by 1¾ by ⅞ in.	1 brownie	25	13	105	1	5	2.0	2.2	0.7	15	10	31	0.4	44	50	0.03	0.03	0.2	tr
Chocolate chip:																			
Commercial, 2¼-in. diameter, ⅜-in. thick	4 cookies	42	3	200	2	9	2.8	2.9	2.2	29	16	48	1.0	56	50	0.10	0.17	0.9	tr
From home recipe, 2⅓ in. diameter	4 cookies	40	3	205	2	12	3.5	4.5	2.9	24	14	40	0.8	47	40	0.06	0.06	0.5	tr
Fig bars, square (1⅝ by 1⅝ by ⅜ in.) or rectangular (1½ by 1¾ by ½ in.)	4 cookies	56	14	200	2	3	0.8	1.2	0.7	42	44	34	1.0	111	60	0.04	0.14	0.9	tr
Gingersnaps, 2-in. diameter, ¼ in. thick	4 cookies	28	3	90	2	2	0.7	1.0	0.6	22	20	13	0.7	129	20	0.08	0.06	0.7	0
Macaroons, 2¾-in. diameter, ¼ in. thick	2 cookies	38	4	180	2	9	*	*	*	25	10	32	0.3	176	0	0.02	0.06	0.2	0
Oatmeal with raisins, 2⅝-in. diameter, ¼ in. thick	4 cookies	52	3	235	3	8	2.0	3.3	2.0	38	11	53	1.4	192	30	0.15	0.10	1.0	tr
Peanut	4 cookies	48	nd	228	4	9.2	nd	nd	nd	32	20	56	0.4	84	96	0.04	0.04	1.2	tr
Plain, prepared from commercial chilled dough, 2½-in. diameter, ¼ in. thick	4 cookies	48	5	240	2	12	3.0	5.2	2.9	31	17	35	0.6	23	30	0.10	0.08	0.9	0
Sandwich type (chocolate or vanilla), 1¾-in. diameter, ⅜ in. thick	4 cookies	40	2	200	2	9	2.2	3.9	2.2	28	10	96	0.7	15	0	0.06	0.10	0.7	0
Vanilla wafers, 1¾-in. diameter, ¼-in. thick	10 cookies	40	3	185	2	6	*	*	*	30	16	25	0.6	29	50	0.10	0.09	0.8	0
Corn, sweet:																			
Cooked, drained:																			
From raw, ear 5 by 1¾ in.	1 ear	140	74	70	2	1	*	*	*	16	2	69	0.5	151	310††	0.09	0.08	1.1	7
From frozen:																			
Ear, 5 in. long	1 ear	229	73	120	4	1	*	*	*	27	4	121	1.0	291	440††	0.18	0.10	2.1	9
Kernels	1 cup	165	77	130	5	1	*	*	*	31	5	120	1.3	304	580††	0.15	0.10	2.5	8
Canned:																			
Cream style	1 cup	256	76	210	5	2	*	*	*	51	8	143	1.5	248	840††	0.08	0.13	2.6	13

Appendix E   continued

Food	Approximate Measure	Weight (g)	Water (%)	Food energy (kcal)	Protein (g)	Fat (g)	Fatty acids Saturated (total) (g)	Fatty acids Unsaturated Oleic (g)	Fatty acids Unsaturated Linoleic (g)	Carbohydrate (g)	Calcium (mg)	Phosphorous (mg)	Iron (mg)	Potassium (mg)	Vitamin A value (IU)	Thiamin (mg)	Riboflavin (mg)	Niacin (mg)	Ascorbic Acid (mg)
Whole kernel:																			
Vacuum pack	1 cup	210	76	175	5	1	*	*	*	43	6	153	1.1	204	740††	0.06	0.13	2.3	11
Wet pack, drained solids	1 cup	165	76	140	4	1	*	*	*	33	8	81	0.8	160	580††	0.05	0.08	1.5	7
Corn chips (Fritos)	1 oz	28	nd	154	2	10.4	nd	nd	nd	15	35	52	0.3	23	99	0.01	0.02	0.3	0
Cornmeal:																			
Whole-ground, unbolted, dry form	1 cup	122	12	435	11	5	0.5	1.0	2.5	90	24	312	2.9	346	620††	0.46	0.13	2.4	0
Bolted (nearly whole-grain), dry form	1 cup	122	12	440	11	4	0.5	0.9	2.1	91	21	272	2.2	303	590††	0.37	0.10	2.3	0
Degermed, enriched: Dry form	1 cup	138	12	500	11	2	0.2	0.4	0.9	108	8	137	4.0	166	610††	0.61	0.36	4.8	0
Cooked	1 cup	240	88	120	3	tr	tr	0.1	0.2	26	2	34	1.0	38	140††	0.14	0.10	1.2	0
Degermed, unenriched: Dry form	1 cup	138	12	500	11	2	0.2	0.4	0.9	108	8	137	1.5	166	610††	0.19	0.07	1.4	0
Cooked	1 cup	240	88	120	3	tr	tr	0.1	0.2	26	2	34	0.5	38	140††	0.05	0.02	0.2	0
Crackers§:																			
Graham, plain, 2½ in. square	2 crackers	14	6	55	1	1	0.3	0.5	0.3	10	6	21	0.5	55	0	0.02	0.08	0.5	0
Rye wafers, whole-grain, 1⅞ by 3½ in.	2 wafers	13	6	45	2	tr	*	*	*	10	7	50	0.5	78	0	0.04	0.03	0.2	0
Saltines, made with enriched flour	4 crackers or 1 packet	11	4	50	1	1	0.3	0.5	0.4	8	2	10	0.5	13	0	0.05	0.05	0.4	0
Cranberries, raw	1 cup	100	nd	46	tr	tr	nd	nd	nd	11	14	10	0.5	82	40	0.03	0.02	0.1	11
Cranberry juice cocktail, bottled, sweetened, Vitamin C added	1 cup	253	83	165	tr	tr	*	*	*	42	13	8	0.8	25	tr	0.03	0.03	0.1	81†
Cranberry sauce, sweetened, canned, strained	1 cup	277	62	405	tr	1	*	*	*	104	17	11	0.6	83	60	0.03	0.03	0.1	6
Cream, sweet:																			
Half-and-half (cream and milk)	1 cup	242	81	315	7	28	17.3	7.0	0.6	10	254	230	0.2	314	260	0.08	0.36	0.2	2
Half-and-half (cream and milk)	1 tbsp	15	81	20	tr	2	1.1	0.4	tr	1	16	14	tr	19	20	0.01	0.02	tr	tr
Light, coffee, or table	1 cup	240	74	470	6	46	28.8	11.7	1.0	9	231	192	0.1	292	1,730	0.08	0.36	0.1	2
Light, coffee, or table	1 tbsp	15	74	30	tr	3	1.8	0.7	0.1	1	14	12	tr	18	110	tr	0.02	tr	tr
Whipping, unwhipped (volume about double when whipped):																			
Light	1 cup	239	64	700	5	74	46.2	18.3	1.5	7	166	146	0.1	231	2,690	0.06	0.30	0.1	1
Light	1 tbsp	15	64	45	tr	5	2.9	1.1	0.1	tr	10	9	tr	15	170	tr	0.02	tr	tr
Heavy	1 cup	238	58	820	5	88	54.8	22.2	2.0	7	154	149	0.1	179	3,500	0.05	0.26	0.1	1
Heavy	1 tbsp	15	58	80	tr	6	3.5	1.4	0.1	tr	10	9	tr	11	220	tr	0.02	tr	tr
Whipped topping (pressurized)	1 cup	60	61	155	2	13	8.3	3.4	0.3	7	61	54	tr	88	550	0.02	0.04	tr	tr
Whipped topping (pressurized)	1 tbsp	3	61	10	tr	1	0.4	0.2	tr	tr	3	3	tr	4	30	tr	tr	tr	tr
Cream, sour	1 cup	230	71	495	7	48	30.0	12.1	1.1	10	268	195	0.1	331	1,820	0.08	0.34	0.2	2
Cream, sour	1 tbsp	12	71	25	tr	3	1.6	0.6	0.1	1	14	10	tr	17	90	tr	0.02	tr	tr
Cream products, imitation (made with vegetable fat): Sweet: Creamers:																			
Liquid (frozen)	1 cup	245	77	335	2	24	22.8	0.3	tr	28	23	157	0.1	467	220†	0	0	0.1	0
Liquid (frozen)	1 tbsp	15	77	20	tr	1	1.4	tr	0	2	1	10	tr	29	10†	0	0	tr	0
Powdered	1 cup	94	2	515	5	33	30.6	0.9	tr	52	21	397	0.1	763	190†	0	0.16†	0	0
Powdered	1 tsp	2	2	10	tr	1	0.7	tr	0	1	tr	8	tr	16	tr†	0	tr	0	0

Cream products, imitation—continued

E

Food, approximate measure	Grams	Water %	Food energy	Protein	Fat	Sat.	Oleic	Lino.	Carb.	Calcium	Phos.	Iron	Potassium	Vit. A	Thiamin	Ribo.	Niacin	Asc.
Whipped topping: Frozen, 1 cup	75	50	240	1	19	16.3	1.0	0.2	17	5	6	0.1	14	650†	0	0	0.0	0
1 tbsp	4	50	15	tr	1	0.9	0.1	tr	1	tr	tr	tr	1	30†	0	0	0.0	0
Powdered, made with whole milk, 1 cup	80	67	150	3	10	8.5	0.6	0.1	13	72	69	tr	121	290†	0.02	0.09	tr	1
1 tbsp	4	67	10	tr	tr	0.4	tr	tr	1	4	3	tr	6	10†	tr	tr	tr	tr
Pressurized, 1 cup	70	60	185	1	16	13.2	1.4	0.2	11	4	13	tr	13	330†	0	0	0	0
1 tbsp	4	60	10	tr	1	0.8	0.1	tr	1	tr	1	tr	1	20†	0	0	0	0
Sour dressing (imitation sour cream) made with nonfat dry milk, 1 cup	235	75	415	8	39	31.2	4.4	1.1	11	266	205	0.1	380	20†	0.09	0.38	0.2	2
1 tbsp	12	75	20	tr	2	1.6	0.2	0.1	1	14	10	tr	19	tr†	0.01	0.02	tr	tr
Cucumber slices, ⅛ in. thick (large, 2⅛ in diameter; small, 1¾ in. diameter): With peel, 6 large or 8 small slices	28	95	5	tr	tr	*	*	*	1	7	8	0.3	45	70	0.01	0.01	0.1	3
Without peel, 6½ large or 9 small pieces	28	96	5	tr	tr	*	*	*	1	5	5	0.1	45	tr	0.01	0.01	0.1	3
Custard, baked, 1 cup	265	77	305	14	15	6.8	5.4	0.7	29	297	310	1.1	387	930	0.11	0.50	0.3	1
Dandelion greens, cooked drained, 1 cup	105	90	35	2	1	*	*	*	7	147	44	1.9	244	12,290	0.14	0.17	*	19
Danish pastry (enriched flour) plain without fruit or nuts:§∇ Packaged ring, 12 oz, 1 ring	340	22	1,435	25	80	24.3	31.7	16.5	155	170	371	6.1	381	1,050	0.97	1.01	8.6	tr
Round piece, about 4¼ in. diameter by 1 in., 1 pastry	65	22	275	5	15	4.7	6.1	3.2	30	33	71	1.2	73	200	0.18	0.19	1.7	tr
Ounce, 1 oz	28	22	120	2	7	2.0	2.7	1.4	13	14	31	0.5	32	90	0.08	0.08	0.7	tr
Dates: Whole, without pits, 10 dates	80	23	220	2	tr	*	*	*	58	47	50	2.4	518	40	0.07	0.08	1.8	0
Chopped, 1 cup	178	23	490	4	1	*	*	*	130	105	112	5.3	1,153	90	0.16	0.18	3.9	0
Doughnuts, made with enriched flour:§ Cake type, plain, 2½-in. diameter, 1 in. high, 1 doughnut	25	24	100	1	5	1.2	2.0	1.1	13	10	48	0.4	23	20	0.05	0.05	0.4	tr
Yeast-leavened, glazed, 3¾-in. diameter, 1¼ in. high, 1 doughnut	50	26	205	3	11	3.3	5.8	3.3	22	16	33	0.6	34	25	0.10	0.10	0.8	0
Eggnog (commercial), 1 cup	254	74	340	10	19	11.3	5.0	0.6	34	330	278	0.5	420	890	0.09	0.48	0.3	4
Eggs, large (24 oz per dozen): Raw: Whole, without shell, 1 egg	50	75	80	6	6	1.7	2.0	0.6	1	28	90	1.0	65	260	0.04	0.15	tr	0
White, 1 white	33	88	15	3	tr	0	0	0	tr	4	4	tr	45	0	tr	0.09	tr	0
Yolk, 1 yolk	17	49	65	3	6	1.7	2.1	0.6	tr	26	86	0.9	15	310	0.04	0.07	tr	0
Cooked: Fried in butter, 1 egg	46	72	85	5	6	2.4	1.7	0.6	1	26	80	0.9	58	290	0.03	0.13	tr	0
Hard-cooked, shell removed, 1 egg	50	75	80	6	6	2.2	2.0	0.6	1	28	90	1.0	65	260	0.04	0.14	tr	0
Poached, 1 egg	50	74	80	6	6	1.7	2.0	0.6	1	28	90	1.0	65	260	0.04	0.13	tr	0
Scrambled (milk added) in butter; also omelet, 1 egg	64	76	95	6	7	2.8	2.3	0.6	1	47	97	0.9	85	310	0.04	0.16	tr	0
Endive, curly (including escarole), raw, small pieces, 1 cup	50	93	10	1	tr	*	*	*	2	41	27	0.9	147	1,650	0.04	0.07	0.3	5
English muffin, 1 muffin	57	nd	140	5	1	nd	nd	nd	27	96	76	1.9	103	0.30	0.14	0.13	2.2	0
Fats, cooking (vegetable shortenings), 1 cup	200	0	1,770	0	200	48.8	88.2	48.4	0	0	0	0	0	*	0	0	0	0
1 tbsp	13	0	110	0	13	3.2	5.7	3.1	0	0	0	0	0	*	0	0	0	0
Filberts (hazelnuts), chopped (about 60 kernels), 1 cup	115	6	730	14	72	5.1	55.2	7.3	19	240	388	3.9	810	*	0.53	*	1.0	tr
Fish and shellfish: Bluefish, baked with butter or margarine, 3 oz	85	68	135	22	4	*	*	*	0	25	244	0.6	*	40	0.09	0.08	1.6	*

Appendix E continued

Food	Approximate Measure	Weight (g)	Water (%)	Food energy (kcal)	Protein (g)	Fat (g)	Saturated (total) (g)	Unsaturated Oleic (g)	Linoleic (g)	Carbohydrate (g)	Calcium (mg)	Phosphorous (mg)	Iron (mg)	Potassium (mg)	Vitamin A value (IU)	Thiamin (mg)	Riboflavin (mg)	Niacin (mg)	Ascorbic Acid (mg)
Clams:																			
Raw, meat only	3 oz	85	82	65	11	1	*	*	*	2	59	138	5.2	154	90	0.08	0.15	1.1	8
Canned, solids and liquid	3 oz	85	86	45	7	1	0.2	tr	tr	2	47	116	3.5	119	*	0.01	0.09	0.9	*
Crabmeat (white or king), canned, not pressed down	1 cup	135	77	135	24	3	0.6	0.4	0.1	1	61	246	1.1	149	*	0.11	0.11	2.6	*
Fish sticks, breaded, cooked, frozen (stick, 4 by 1 by 1/2 in.)	1 fish stick or 1 oz	28	66	50	5	3	*	*	*	2	3	47	0.1	*	0	0.01	0.02	0.5	0
Haddock, breaded, fried[§]	3 oz	85	66	140	17	5	1.4	2.2	1.2	5	34	210	1.0	295	*	0.03	0.06	2.7	2
Ocean perch, breaded, fried[§]	1 fillet	85	59	195	16	11	2.7	4.4	2.3	6	28	192	1.1	242	*	0.10	0.10	1.6	*
Oysters, raw, meat only (13–19 medium Selects)	1 cup	240	85	160	20	4	1.3	0.2	0.1	8	226	343	13.2	290	740	0.34	0.43	6.0	*
Salmon, pink, canned, solids (includ. bone) and liquid	3 oz	85	71	120	17	5	0.9	0.8	0.1	0	167	243	0.7	307	60	0.03	0.16	6.8	*
Sardines, Atlantic canned in oil, drained solids	3 oz	85	62	175	20	9	3.0	2.5	0.5	0	372	424	2.5	502	190	0.02	0.17	4.6	*
Scallops, frozen, breaded, fried, reheated	6 scallops	90	60	175	16	8	*	*	*	9	*	*	*	*	*	*	*	*	*
Shad, baked with butter or margarine, bacon	3 oz	85	64	170	20	10	*	*	*	0	20	266	0.5	320	30	0.11	0.22	7.3	*
Shrimp:																			
Canned meat	3 oz	85	70	100	21	1	0.1	0.1	tr	1	98	244	2.6	104	50	0.01	0.03	1.5	*
French fried	3 oz	85	57	190	17	9	2.3	3.7	2.0	9	61	162	1.7	195	*	0.03	0.07	2.3	*
Tuna, canned in oil, drained solids	3 oz	85	61	170	24	7	1.7	1.7	0.7	0	7	199	1.6	*	70	0.04	0.10	10.1	*
Tuna salad	1 cup	205	70	350	30	22	4.3	6.3	6.7	7	41	291	2.7	*	590	0.08	0.23	10.3	2
Fruit cocktail, canned, in heavy syrup	1 cup	255	80	195	1	tr	*	*	*	50	23	31	1.0	411	360	0.05	0.03	1.0	5
Gelatin, dry	1.7g envelope	7	13	25	6	tr	0	0	0	0	*	*	*	*	*	*	*	*	*
Gelatin dessert:																			
prepared with gelatin dessert powder and water	1 cup	240	84	140	4	0	0	0	0	34	15	16	0.4	nd	260	0.03	0.03	0.2	11
With fruit	1/2 cup	125	nd	93	1	4	nd	nd	nd	14.4									
Grapefruit:																			
Raw, medium, 3¾-in diameter (about 1 lb 1 oz):																			
Pink or red	1/2 grapefruit with peel	241	89	50	1	tr	*	*	*	13	20	20	0.5	166	540	0.05	0.02	0.2	44
White	1/2 grapefruit with peel	241	89	45	1	tr	*	*	*	12	19	19	0.5	159	10	0.05	0.02	0.2	44
Canned, sections with syrup	1 cup	254	81	180	2	tr	*	*	*	45	33	36	0.8	343	30	0.08	0.05	0.5	76
Grapefruit juice:																			
Raw white	1 cup	246	90	95	1	tr	*	*	*	23	22	37	0.5	399	20	0.10	0.05	0.5	93
Canned, white:																			
Unsweetened	1 cup	247	89	100	1	tr	*	*	*	24	20	35	1.0	400	20	0.07	0.05	0.5	84
Sweetened	1 cup	250	86	135	1	tr	*	*	*	32	20	35	1.0	405	30	0.08	0.05	0.5	78
Frozen, concentrate, unsweetened:																			
Undiluted, 6-fl-oz can	1 can	207	62	300	4	1	*	*	*	72	70	124	0.8	1,250	60	0.29	0.12	1.4	286
Diluted with 3 parts water by volume	1 cup	247	89	100	1	tr	*	*	*	24	25	42	0.2	420	20	0.10	0.04	0.5	96

Food	Measure	Grams	Water (%)	Calories	Protein (g)	Fat (g)	Saturated (g)	Oleic (g)	Linoleic (g)	Carbohydrate (g)	Calcium (mg)	Phosphorus (mg)	Iron (mg)	Potassium (mg)	Vitamin A (IU)	Thiamin (mg)	Riboflavin (mg)	Niacin (mg)	Ascorbic acid (mg)
Dehydrated crystals, prepared with water (1 lb yields about 1 gal)	1 cup	247	90	100	1	tr	*	*	*	24	22	40	0.2	412	20	0.10	0.05	0.5	91
Grapes, European type (adherent skin), raw: Thompson seedless	10 grapes	50	81	35	tr	tr	*	*	*	9	6	10	0.2	87	50	0.03	0.02	0.2	2
Tokay and Emperor, with seeds	10 grapes	60	81	40	tr	tr	*	*	*	10	7	11	0.2	99	60	0.03	0.02	0.2	2
Grape juice: Canned or bottled	1 cup	253	83	165	1	tr	*	*	*	42	28	30	0.8	293	*	0.10	0.05	0.5	tr†
Frozen concentrate, sweetened, vitamin C added: Undiluted, 6-fl-oz can	1 can	216	53	395	1	tr	*	*	*	100	22	32	0.9	255	40	0.13	0.22	1.5	32†
Diluted with 3 parts water by volume	1 cup	250	86	135	1	tr	*	*	*	33	8	10	0.3	85	10	0.05	0.08	0.5	10†
Grape drink, canned, some vitamins added	1 cup	250	86	135	tr	tr	*	*	*	35	8	10	0.3	88	*	0.03†	0.03†	0.3	†
Heart, beef, lean, braised	3 oz	85	61	160	27	5	1.5	1.1	0.6	1	5	154	5.0	197	20	0.21	1.04	6.5	1
Honey, strained or extracted	1 tbsp	21	17	65	tr	0	0	0	0	17	1	1	0.1	11	0	tr	0.01	0.1	tr
Ice cream: Regular (about 11% fat): Hardened	½ gal	1,064	61	2,155	38	115	71.3	28.8	2.6	254	1,406	1,075	1.0	2,052	4,340	0.42	2.63	1.1	6
	1 cup	133	61	270	5	14	8.9	3.6	0.3	32	176	134	0.1	257	540	0.05	0.33	0.1	1
	3-fl-oz container	50	61	100	2	5	3.4	1.4	0.1	12	66	51	tr	96	200	0.02	0.12	0.1	tr
Soft serve (frozen custard)	1 cup	173	60	375	7	23	13.5	5.9	0.6	38	236	199	0.4	338	790	0.08	0.45	0.2	1
Rich (about 16% fat), hardened	½ gal	1,188	59	2,805	33	190	118.3	47.8	4.3	256	1,213	927	0.8	1,771	7,200	0.36	2.27	0.9	5
	1 cup	148	59	350	4	24	14.7	6.0	0.5	32	151	115	0.1	221	900	0.04	0.28	0.1	1
Ice milk: Hardened (about 4.3% fat)	½ gal	1,048	69	1,470	41	45	28.1	11.3	1.0	232	1,409	1,035	1.5	2,117	1,710	0.61	2.78	0.9	6
	1 cup	131	69	185	5	6	3.5	1.4	0.1	29	176	129	0.1	265	210	0.08	0.35	0.1	1
Soft serve (about 2.6% fat)	1 cup	175	70	225	8	5	2.9	1.2	0.1	38	274	202	0.3	412	180	0.12	0.54	0.2	1
Jams and preserves	1 tbsp	20	29	55	tr	tr	*	*	*	14	4	2	0.2	18	tr	tr	0.01	tr	tr
	1 packet	14	29	40	tr	tr	*	*	*	10	3	1	0.1	12	tr	tr	tr	tr	tr
Jellies	1 tbsp	18	29	50	tr	tr	*	*	*	13	4	1	0.3	14	tr	tr	0.01	tr	1
	1 packet	14	29	40	tr	tr	*	*	*	10	3	1	0.2	11	tr	tr	tr	tr	1
Kale, cooked, drained: From raw (leaves without stems and midribs)	1 cup	110	88	45	6	1	*	*	*	7	206	64	1.8	243	9,130	0.11	0.20	1.8	102
From frozen (leaf style)	1 cup	130	91	40	4	1	*	*	*	7	157	62	1.3	251	10,660	0.08	0.20	0.9	49
Lamb, cooked: Chop, rib (cut 3 per lb with bone), broiled: Lean and fat	3.1 oz	89	43	360	18	32	14.8	12.1	1.2	0	8	139	1.0	200	*	0.11	0.19	4.1	*
Lean only	2 oz	57	60	120	16	6	2.5	2.1	0.2	0	6	121	1.1	174	*	0.09	0.15	3.4	*
Leg, roasted: Lean and fat (2 pieces, 4⅛ by 2¼ by ¼ in.)	3 oz	85	54	235	22	16	7.3	6.0	0.6	0	9	177	1.4	241	*	0.13	0.23	4.7	*
Lean only	2.5 oz	71	62	130	20	5	2.1	1.8	0.2	0	9	169	1.4	227	*	0.12	0.21	4.4	*
Shoulder, roasted: Lean and fat (3 pieces, 2½ by 2½ by ¼ in.)	3 oz	85	50	285	18	23	10.8	8.8	0.9	0	9	146	1.0	206	*	0.11	0.20	4.0	*
Lean only	2.3 oz	64	61	130	17	6	3.6	2.3	0.2	0	8	140	1.0	193	*	0.10	0.18	3.7	*
Lard	1 cup	205	0	1,850	0	205	81.0	83.8	20.5	0	0	0	0	0	0	0	0	0	0
Lard	1 tbsp	13	0	115	0	13	5.1	5.3	1.3	0	0	0	0	0	0	0	0	0	0
Lasagna, frozen (Green Giant)	1 serving	200	nd	250	10	10	nd	nd	nd	24	184	202	2.6	584	1,552	0.10	0.34	3.2	12
Lemon, raw, size 165, without peel and seeds (about 4 per lb with peels and seeds)	1 lemon	74	90	20	1	tr	*	*	*	6	19	12	0.4	102	?	0.03	0.01	0.1	39

Appendix E continued

Food	Approximate Measure	Weight (g)	Water (%)	Food energy (kcal)	Protein (g)	Fat (g)	Fatty acids Saturated (total) (g)	Unsaturated Oleic (g)	Unsaturated Linoleic (g)	Carbohydrate (g)	Calcium (mg)	Phosphorous (mg)	Iron (mg)	Potassium (mg)	Vitamin A value (IU)	Thiamin (mg)	Riboflavin (mg)	Niacin (mg)	Ascorbic Acid (mg)
Lemon juice:																			
Raw	1 cup	244	91	60	1	tr	*	*	*	20	17	24	0.5	344	50	0.07	0.02	0.2	112
Canned, or bottled, unsweetened	1 cup	244	92	55	1	tr	*	*	*	19	17	24	0.5	344	50	0.07	0.02	0.2	102
Frozen, single strength, unsweetened, 6-fl-oz can	1 can	183	92	40	1	tr	*	*	*	13	13	16	0.5	258	40	0.05	0.02	0.2	81
Lemonade concentrate, frozen:																			
Undiluted, 6-fl-oz can	1 can	219	49	425	tr	tr	*	*	*	112	9	13	0.4	153	40	0.05	0.06	0.7	66
Diluted with 4⅓ parts water by volume	1 cup	248	89	105	tr	tr	*	*	*	28	2	3	0.1	40	10	0.01	0.02	0.2	17
Lentils, whole, cooked	1 cup	200	72	210	16	tr	*	*	*	39	50	238	4.2	498	40	0.14	0.12	1.2	0
Lettuce, raw:																			
Butterhead, as Boston types:																			
Head, 5-in. diameter	1 head	163	95	25	2	tr	*	*	*	4	57	42	3.3	430	1,580	0.10	0.10	0.5	13
Leaves	1 outer or 2 inner or 3 heart leaves	15	95	tr	tr	tr	*	*	*	tr	5	4	0.3	40	150	0.01	0.01	tr	1
Crisphead, as Iceberg:																			
Head, 6-in. diameter	1 head	539	96	70	5	1	*	*	*	16	108	118	2.7	943	1,780	0.32	0.32	1.6	32
Wedge, ¼ of head	1 wedge	135	96	20	1	tr	*	*	*	4	27	30	0.7	236	450	0.08	0.08	0.4	8
Pieces, chopped or shredded	1 cup	55	96	5	tr	tr	*	*	*	2	11	12	0.3	96	180	0.03	0.03	0.2	3
Looseleaf (bunching varieties including romaine or cos), chopped or shredded pieces	1 cup	55	94	10	1	tr	*	*	*	2	37	14	0.8	145	1,050	0.03	0.04	0.2	10
Limeade concentrate, frozen:																			
Undiluted, 6-fl-oz can	1 can	218	50	410	tr	tr	*	*	*	108	11	13	0.2	129	tr	0.02	0.02	0.2	26
Diluted with 4⅓ parts water by volume	1 cup	247	89	100	tr	tr	*	*	*	27	3	3	tr	32	tr	tr	tr	tr	6
Lime juice:																			
Raw	1 cup	246	90	65	1	tr	*	*	*	22	22	27	0.5	256	20	0.05	0.02	0.2	79
Canned, unsweetened	1 cup	246	90	65	1	tr	*	*	*	22	22	27	0.5	256	20	0.05	0.02	0.2	52
Limes	1 medium	100	nd	28	1	0.2	nd	nd	nd	10	33	18	0.6	102	10	0.03	0.03	0.2	37
Liver, beef, fried§§ (slice, 6½ by 2⅜ by ⅜ in.)	3 oz	85	56	195	22	9	2.5	3.5	0.9	5	9	405	7.5	323	45,390†	0.22	3.56	14.0	23
Macaroni, enriched, cooked (cut lengths, elbows, shells):																			
Firm stage (hot)	1 cup	130	64	190	7	1	*	*	*	39	14	85	1.4	103	0	0.23	0.13	1.8	0
Tender stage:																			
Cold macaroni	1 cup	105	73	115	4	tr	*	*	*	24	8	53	0.9	64	0	0.15	0.08	1.2	0
Hot macaroni	1 cup	140	73	155	5	1	*	*	*	32	11	70	1.3	85	0	0.20	0.11	1.5	0
Macaroni (enriched) and cheese:																			
Canned§	1 cup	240	80	230	9	10	4.2	3.1	1.4	26	199	182	1.0	139	260	0.12	0.24	1.0	tr
From home recipe (served hot)§§	1 cup	200	58	430	17	22	8.9	8.8	2.9	40	362	322	1.8	240	860	0.20	0.40	1.8	tr
Margarine:																			
Regular (1 brick or 4 sticks per lb):																			
Stick (½ cup)	1 stick	113	16	815	1	92	16.7	42.9	24.9	tr	27	26	0.2	29	3,750	0.01	0.04	tr	0
Tablespoon (about ⅛ stick)	1 tbsp	14	16	100	tr	12	2.1	5.3	3.1	tr	3	3	tr	4	470	tr	tr	tr	0
Pat (1 in. square, ⅓ in. high; 90 per lb)	1 pat	5	16	35	tr	4	0.7	1.9	1.1	tr	1	1	tr	1	170	tr	tr	tr	0
Soft, two 8-oz containers per lb	1 container	227	16	1,635	1	184	32.5	71.5	65.4	tr	53	52	0.4	59	7,500	0.01	0.08	0.1	0
	1 tbsp	14	16	100	tr	12	2.0	4.5	4.1	tr	3	3	tr	4	470	tr	tr	tr	0

E

Food and amount	Grams	Water (%)	Food energy	Protein	Fat	Sat.	Mono.	Poly.	Carb.	Calcium	Phosphorus	Iron	Potassium	Vit. A	Thiamin	Riboflavin	Niacin	Ascorbic acid
Whipped (6 sticks per lb): Stick (½ cup)	76	16	545	tr	61	11.2	28.7	16.7	tr	18	17	0.1	20	2,500	tr	0.03	tr	0
Tablespoon (about ⅛ stick)	9	16	70	tr	8	1.4	3.6	2.1	tr	2	2	tr	2	310†	tr	tr	tr	0
Meat loaf, homemade 3½ oz	100	nd	160	17	8	nd	nd	nd	5	38	162	2.3	374	179	0.07	0.19	8.0	2
Meat tenderizer (papain) (not seasoned) 1 tsp	5	nd	2	0	0	nd	nd	nd	1	372	16	tr	tr	nd	nd	nd	nd	nd
Milk: Fluid: Whole (3.3% fat) 1 cup	244	88	150	8	8	5.1	2.1	0.2	11	291	228	0.1	370	310	0.09	0.40	0.2	2
Lowfat (2%): No milk solids added 1 cup	244	89	120	8	5	2.9	1.2	0.1	12	297	232	0.1	377	500	0.01	0.40	0.2	2
Milk solids added: Label claim less than 10 g of protein per cup 1 cup	245	89	125	9	5	2.9	1.2	0.1	12	313	245	0.1	397	500	0.10	0.42	0.2	2
Label claim 10 or more grams of protein per cup (protein fortified) 1 cup	246	88	135	10	5	3.0	1.2	0.1	14	352	276	0.1	447	500	0.11	0.48	0.2	3
Lowfat (1%): No milk solids added 1 cup	244	90	100	8	3	1.6	0.7	0.1	12	300	235	0.1	381	500	0.10	0.41	0.2	2
Milk solids added: Label claim less than 10 g of protein per cup 1 cup	245	90	105	9	2	1.5	0.6	0.1	12	313	245	0.1	397	500	0.10	0.42	0.2	2
Label claim 10 or more grams of protein per cup (protein fortified) 1 cup	246	89	120	10	3	1.8	0.7	0.1	14	349	273	0.1	444	500	0.11	0.47	0.2	3
Nonfat (skim): No milk solids added 1 cup	245	91	85	8	tr	0.3	0.1	tr	12	302	247	0.1	406	500	0.09	0.34	0.2	2
Milk solids added: Label claim less than 10 g of protein per cup 1 cup	245	90	90	9	1	0.4	0.1	tr	12	316	255	0.1	418	500	0.10	0.43	0.2	2
Label claim 10 or more grams of protein per cup (protein fortified) 1 cup	246	89	100	10	1	0.4	0.1	tr	14	352	275	0.1	446	500	0.11	0.48	0.2	3
Buttermilk 1 cup	245	90	100	8	2	1.3	0.5	tr	12	285	219	0.1	371	80†	0.08	0.38	0.1	2
Canned: Evaporated, unsweetened: Whole milk 1 cup	252	74	340	17	19	11.6	5.3	0.4	25	657	510	0.5	764	610†	0.12	0.80	0.5	5
Skim milk 1 cup	255	79	200	19	1	0.3	0.1	tr	29	738	497	0.7	845	1,000†	0.11	0.79	0.4	3
Sweetened, condensed 1 cup	306	27	980	24	27	16.8	6.7	0.7	166	868	775	0.6	1,136	1,000†	0.28	1.27	0.6	8
Dried: Buttermilk 1 cup	120	3	465	41	7	4.3	1.7	0.2	59	1,421	1,119	0.4	1,910	260†	0.47	1.90	1.1	7
Nonfat instant: Envelope, net wt: 3.2 oz 1 envelope	91	4	325	32	1	0.4	0.1	tr	47	1,120	896	0.3	1,552	2,160†	0.38	1.59	0.8	5
Cup 1 cup	68	4	245	24	tr	0.3	0.1	tr	35	837	670	0.2	1,160	1,610†	0.28	1.19	0.6	4
Milk beverages: Chocolate milk (commercial): Regular 1 cup	250	82	210	8	8	5.3	2.2	0.2	26	280	251	0.6	417	300†	0.09	0.41	0.3	2
Lowfat (2%) 1 cup	250	84	180	8	5	3.1	1.3	0.1	26	284	254	0.6	422	500	0.10	0.42	0.3	2
Lowfat (1%) 1 cup	250	85	160	8	3	1.5	0.7	0.1	26	287	257	0.6	426	500	0.10	0.40	0.2	2
Malted milk, home-prepared with 1 cup of whole milk and 2 to 3 heaping tsp of malted milk powder (about ¾ oz): Chocolate 1 cup of milk plus ¾ oz of powder	265	81	235	9	9	5.5	*	*	29	304	265	0.5	500	330	0.14	0.43	0.7	2
Natural 1 cup of milk plus ¾ oz of powder	265	81	235	11	10	6.0	*	*	27	347	307	0.3	529	380	0.20	0.54	1.3	2

E

Appendix E continued

Food	Approximate Measure	Weight (g)	Water (%)	Food energy (kcal)	Protein (g)	Fat (g)	Fatty acids Saturated (total) (g)	Unsaturated Oleic (g)	Linoleic (g)	Carbohydrate (g)	Calcium (mg)	Phosphorous (mg)	Iron (mg)	Potassium (mg)	Vitamin A value (IU)	Thiamin (mg)	Riboflavin (mg)	Niacin (mg)	Ascorbic Acid (mg)
Shakes, thick:																			
Chocolate, container, net wt: 10.6 oz	1 container	300	72	355	9	8	5.0	2.0	0.2	63	396	378	0.9	672	260	0.14	0.67	0.4	0
Vanilla, container, net wt: 11 oz	1 container	313	74	350	12	9	5.9	2.4	0.2	56	457	361	0.3	572	360	0.09	0.61	0.5	0
Miso	3 tbsp	50	43	102	6	3	nd	nd	nd	14	34	71	1.8	79	0	0.03	0.07	0.7	0
Muffins made with enriched flour:																			
From home recipe:																			
Blueberry, 2⅜-in. diameter, 1½ in. high	1 muffin	40	39	110	3	4	1.1	1.4	0.7	17	34	53	0.6	46	90	0.09	0.10	0.7	tr
Bran	1 muffin	40	35	105	3	4	1.2	1.4	0.8	17	57	162	1.5	172	90	0.07	0.10	1.7	tr
Corn (enriched degermed yellow cornmeal and flour) 2⅜-in. diameter, 1½ in. high	1 muffin	40	33	125	3	4	1.2	1.6	0.9	19	42	68	0.7	54	120	0.10	0.10	0.7	tr
Plain, 3-in. diameter, 1½-in. high	1 muffin	40	38	120	3	4	1.0	1.7	1.0	17	42	60	0.6	50	40	0.09	0.12	0.9	tr
From enriched mix, egg, milk: Corn, yellow, 2⅜-in. diameter, 1½-in. high	1 muffin	40	30	130	3	4	1.2	1.7	0.9	20	96	152	0.6	44	100	0.08	0.09	0.7	tr
Mushrooms, raw, sliced or chopped	1 cup	70	90	20	2	tr	*	*	*	3	4	81	0.6	290	tr	0.07	0.32	2.9	2
Muskmelons, raw, with rind, without seed cavity:																			
Cantaloupe, orange-fleshed (with rind and seed cavity, 5-in. diameter, 2⅓ lb)	½ melon with rind	477	91	80	2	tr	*	*	*	20	38	44	1.1	682	9,240	0.11	0.08	1.6	90
Honeydew (with rind and seed cavity, 6½-in. diameter, 5¼ lb)	1/10 melon with rind	226	91	50	1	tr	*	*	*	11	21	24	0.6	374	60	0.06	0.04	0.9	34
Mustard, prepared, yellow	1 tsp or individual serving pouch or cup	5	80	5	tr	tr	*	*	*	tr	4	4	0.1	7	*	*	*	*	*
Mustard greens, without stems and midribs, cooked, drained	1 cup	140	93	30	3	1	*	*	*	6	193	45	2.5	308	8,120	0.11	0.20	0.8	67
Nectarines	2 medium	100	nd	64	1	tr	nd	nd	nd	17.1	4	24	0.5	294	1,650	nd	nd	nd	13
Noodles (egg noodles), enriched, cooked	1 cup	160	71	200	7	2	*	*	*	37	16	94	1.4	70	110	0.22	0.13	1.9	0
Noodles, chow mein, canned	1 cup	45	1	220	6	11	*	*	*	26	*	*	*	*	*	*	*	*	*
Oils, salad or cooking:																			
Corn	1 cup	218	0	1,925	0	218	27.7	53.6	125.1	0	0	0	0	0	*	0	0	0	0
	1 tbsp	14	0	120	0	14	1.7	3.3	7.8	0	0	0	0	0	*	0	0	0	0
Olive	1 cup	216	0	1,910	0	216	30.7	154.4	17.7	0	0	0	0	0	*	0	0	0	0
	1 tbsp	14	0	120	0	14	1.9	9.7	1.1	0	0	0	0	0	*	0	0	0	0
Peanut	1 cup	216	0	1,910	0	216	37.4	98.5	67.0	0	0	0	0	0	*	0	0	0	0
	1 tbsp	14	0	120	0	14	2.3	6.2	4.2	0	0	0	0	0	*	0	0	0	0
Safflower	1 cup	218	0	1,925	0	218	20.5	25.9	159.8	0	0	0	0	0	*	0	0	0	0
	1 tbsp	14	0	120	0	14	1.3	1.6	10.0	0	0	0	0	0	*	0	0	0	0
Soybean oil, hydrogenated (partially hardened)	1 cup	218	0	1,925	0	218	31.8	93.1	75.6	0	0	0	0	0	*	0	0	0	0
	1 tbsp	14	0	120	0	14	2.0	5.8	4.7	0	0	0	0	0	*	0	0	0	0

E

Soybean-cottonseed oil blend, hydrogenated	1 cup	218	0	1,925	0	218	38.2	63.0	99.6	0	0	0	0	0	*	0	0	0	0
	1 tbsp	14	0	120	0	14	2.4	3.9	6.2	0	0	0	0	0	*	0	0	0	0
Okra pods, 3 by ⅝ in., cooked	10 pods	106	91	30	2	tr	*	*	0.1	6	98	43	0.5	184	520	0.14	0.19	1.0	21
Olives, pickled, canned: Green	4 medium or 3 extra large or 2 giant	16	78	15	tr	2	0.2	1.2	0.1	tr	8	2	0.2	7	40	*	*	*	*
Ripe, Mission	3 small or 2 large	10	73	15	tr	2	0.2	1.2	0.1	tr	9	1	0.1	2	10	tr	tr	*	*
Onions, white: Mature: Raw: Chopped	1 cup	170	89	65	3	tr	*	*	*	15	46	61	0.9	267	tr	0.05	0.07	0.3	17
Sliced	1 cup	115	89	45	2	tr	*	*	*	10	31	41	0.6	181	tr	0.03	0.05	0.2	12
Cooked (whole or sliced), drained	1 cup	210	92	60	3	tr	*	*	*	14	50	61	0.8	231	tr	0.06	0.06	0.4	15
Young green, bulb (⅜-in. diameter) and white portion of top	6 onions	30	88	15	tr	tr	*	*	*	3	12	12	0.2	69	tr	0.02	0.01	0.1	8
Oranges, all commercial varieties, raw: Whole, 2⅝-in. diameter, without peel and seeds (about 2½ per lb with peel and seeds)	1 orange	131	86	65	1	tr	*	*	*	16	54	26	0.5	263	260	0.13	0.05	0.5	66
Sections without membranes	1 cup	180	86	90	2	tr	*	*	*	22	74	36	0.7	360	360	0.18	0.07	0.7	90
Orange juice: Raw, all varieties	1 cup	248	88	110	2	tr	*	*	*	26	27	42	0.5	496	500	0.22	0.07	1.0	124
Canned, unsweetened	1 cup	249	87	120	2	tr	*	*	*	28	25	45	1.0	496	500	0.17	0.05	0.7	100
Frozen concentrate: Undiluted, 6-fl-oz can	1 can	213	55	360	5	tr	*	*	*	87	75	126	0.9	1,500	1,620	0.68	0.11	2.8	360
Diluted with 3 parts water by volume	1 cup	249	87	120	2	tr	*	*	*	29	25	42	0.2	503	540	0.23	0.03	0.9	120
Dehydrated crystals, prepared with water (1 lb yields about 1 gal)	1 cup	248	88	115	1	tr	*	*	*	27	25	40	0.5	518	500	0.20	0.07	1.0	109
Orange and grapefruit juice: Frozen concentrate: Undiluted, 6-fl-oz can	1 can	210	59	330	4	1	*	*	*	78	61	99	0.8	1,308	800	0.48	0.06	2.3	302
Diluted with 3 parts water by volume	1 cup	248	88	110	1	tr	*	*	*	26	20	32	0.2	439	270	0.15	0.02	0.7	102
Pancakes (4-in. diameter): Buckwheat, made from mix (with buckwheat and enriched flours), egg and milk added	1 cake	27	58	55	2	2	0.8	0.9	0.4	6	59	91	0.4	66	60	0.04	0.05	0.2	tr
Plain: Made from home recipe using enriched flour	1 cake	27	50	60	2	2	0.5	0.8	0.5	9	27	38	0.4	33	30	0.06	0.07	0.5	tr
Made from mix with enriched flour, egg and milk added	1 cake	27	51	60	2	2	0.7	0.7	0.3	9	58	70	0.3	42	70	0.04	0.06	0.2	tr
Papayas, raw, ½-in. cubes	1 cup	140	89	55	1	tr	*	*	*	14	28	22	0.4	328	2,450	0.06	0.06	0.4	78
Parsley, raw, chopped	1 tbsp	4	85	tr	tr	tr	*	*	*	tr	7	2	0.2	25	300	tr	0.01	tr	6
Parsnips, cooked (diced or 2-in. lengths)	1 cup	155	82	100	2	1	*	*	*	23	70	96	0.9	587	50	0.11	0.12	0.2	16
Peaches: Raw: Whole, 2½-in. diameter, peeled, pitted (about 4 per lb with peels and pits)	1 peach	100	89	40	1	tr	*	*	*	10	9	19	0.5	202	1,330‡	0.02	0.05	1.0	7

Appendix E continued

Food	Approximate Measure	Weight (g)	Water (%)	Food energy (kcal)	Protein (g)	Fat (g)	Fatty acids			Carbohydrate (g)	Calcium (mg)	Phosphorous (mg)	Iron (mg)	Potassium (mg)	Vitamin A value (IU)	Thiamin (mg)	Riboflavin (mg)	Niacin (mg)	Ascorbic Acid (mg)
							Saturated (total) (g)	Unsaturated Oleic (g)	Unsaturated Linoleic (g)										
Sliced	1 cup	170	89	65	1	tr	*	*	*	16	15	32	0.9	343	2,260‡	0.03	0.09	1.7	12
Canned, yellow-fleshed, solids and liquid (halves or slices):																			
Syrup pack	1 cup	256	79	200	1	tr	*	*	*	51	10	31	0.8	333	1,100	0.03	0.05	1.5	8
Water pack	1 cup	244	91	75	1	tr	*	*	*	20	10	32	0.7	334	1,100	0.02	0.07	1.5	7
Dried:																			
Uncooked	1 cup	160	25	420	5	1	*	*	*	109	77	187	9.6	1,520	6,240	0.02	0.30	8.5	29
Cooked, unsweetened, halves and juice	1 cup	250	77	205	3	1	*	*	*	54	38	93	4.8	743	3,050	0.01	0.15	3.8	5
Frozen, sliced sweetened, Vitamin C added:																			
10-oz container	1 container	284	77	250	1	tr	*	*	*	64	11	37	1.4	352	1,850	0.03	0.11	2.0	116†
Cup	1 cup	250	77	220	1	tr	*	*	*	57	10	33	1.3	310	1,630	0.03	0.10	1.8	103†
Peanuts, roasted in oil, salted (whole, halves, chopped)	1 cup	144	2	840	37	72	13.7	33.0	20.7	27	107	577	3.0	971	*	0.46	0.19	24.8	0
Peanut butter	1 tbsp	16	2	95	4	8	1.5	3.7	2.3	3	9	61	0.3	100	*	0.02	0.02	2.4	0
Pears																			
Raw, with skin, cored:																			
Bartlett, 2½-in. diameter (about 2½ per lb with cores and stems)	1 pear	164	83	100	1	1	*	*	*	25	13	18	0.5	213	30	0.03	0.07	0.2	7
Bosc, 2½-in. diameter (about 3 per lb with cores and stems)	1 pear	141	83	85	1	1	*	*	*	22	11	16	0.4	83	30	0.03	0.06	0.1	6
D'Anjou, 3½-in. diameter (about 2 per lb with cores and stems)	1 pear	200	83	120	1	1	*	*	*	31	16	22	0.6	260	40	0.04	0.08	0.2	8
Canned, solids and liquid, syrup pack, heavy (halves or slices)	1 cup	255	80	195	1	1	*	*	*	50	13	18	0.5	214	10	0.03	0.05	0.3	3
Peas																			
Canned:																			
Whole, drained solids	1 cup	170	77	150	8	1	*	*	*	29	44	129	3.2	163	1,170	0.15	0.10	1.4	14
Strained (baby food)	1 oz (1¾ to 2 tbsp)	28	86	15	1	tr	*	*	*	3	3	18	0.3	28	140	0.02	0.03	0.3	3
Frozen, cooked, drained	1 cup	160	82	110	8	tr	*	*	*	19	30	138	3.0	216	960	0.43	0.14	2.7	21
Peas, split, dry, cooked	1 cup	200	70	230	16	1	*	*	*	42	22	178	3.4	592	80	0.30	0.18	1.8	*
Pecans, chopped or pieces (about 120 large halves)	1 cup	118	3	810	11	84	7.2	50.5	20.0	17	86	341	2.8	712	150	1.01	0.15	1.1	2
Peppers, hot, red, without seeds, dried (ground chili powder, added seasonings)	1 tsp	2	9	5	tr	tr	*	*	*	1	9	4	0.3	20	1,300	tr	0.02	0.2	tr
Peppers, sweet (about 5 per lb, whole), stem and seeds removed:																			
Raw	1 pod	74	93	15	1	tr	*	*	*	4	7	16	0.5	157	310	0.06	0.06	0.4	94
Cooked, boiled, drained	1 pod	73	95	15	1	tr	*	*	*	3	7	12	0.4	109	310	0.05	0.05	0.4	70
Pickles, cucumber: Dill, medium, whole, 3¾ in. long, 1¼-in. diameter	1 pickle	65	93	5	tr	tr	*	*	*	1	17	14	0.7	130	70	tr	0.01	tr	4

Fresh-pack, slices 1½-in. diameter, ¼ in. thick	2 slices	15	79	10	tr	tr	*	*	*	3	5	4	0.3	*	20	tr	tr	tr	1
Sweet, gherkin, small, whole, about 2½ in. long, ¾-in. diameter	1 pickle	15	61	20	tr	tr	*	*	*	5	2	2	0.2	*	10	tr	tr	tr	1
Relish, finely chopped, sweet	1 tbsp	15	63	20	tr	tr	*	*	*	5	3	2	0.1	*	*	*	*	*	*
Pies, piecrust made with enriched flour, vegetable shortening (9-in. diameter):																			
Apple:																			
Whole	1 pie	945	48	2,420	21	105	27.0	44.5	25.2	360	76	208	6.6	756	280	1.06	0.79	9.3	9
Sector, 1/7 of a pie	1 sector	135	48	345	3	15	3.9	6.4	3.6	51	11	30	0.9	108	40	0.15	0.11	1.3	2
Banana cream																			
Whole	1 pie	910	54	2,010	41	85	26.7	33.2	16.2	279	601	746	7.3	1,847	2,280	0.77	1.51	7.0	9
Sector, 1/7 of a pie	1 sector	130	54	285	6	12	3.8	4.7	2.3	40	86	107	1.0	264	330	0.11	0.22	1.0	1
Blueberry																			
Whole	1 pie	945	51	2,285	23	102	24.8	43.7	25.1	330	104	217	9.5	614	280	1.03	0.80	10.0	28
Sector, 1/7 of pie	1 sector	135	51	325	3	15	3.5	6.2	3.6	47	15	31	1.4	88	40	0.15	0.11	1.4	4
Cherry:																			
Whole	1 pie	945	47	2,465	25	107	28.2	45.0	25.3	363	132	236	6.6	992	4,160	1.09	0.84	9.8	tr
Sector, 1/7 of a pie	1 sector	135	47	350	4	15	4.0	6.4	3.6	52	19	34	0.9	142	590	0.16	0.12	1.4	tr
Custard:																			
Whole	1 pie	910	58	1,985	56	101	33.9	38.5	17.5	213	874	1,028	8.2	1,247	2,090	0.79	1.92	5.6	0
Sector, 1/7 of a pie	1 sector	130	58	285	8	14	4.8	5.5	2.5	30	125	147	1.2	178	300	0.11	0.27	0.8	0
Lemon meringue:																			
Whole	1 pie	840	47	2,140	31	86	26.1	33.8	16.4	317	118	412	6.7	420	1,430	0.61	0.84	5.2	25
Sector, 1/7 of a pie	1 sector	120	47	305	4	12	3.7	4.8	2.3	45	17	59	1.0	60	200	0.09	0.12	0.7	4
Mince:																			
Whole	1 pie	945	43	2,560	24	109	28.0	45.9	25.2	389	265	359	13.3	1,682	20	0.96	0.86	9.8	9
Sector, 1/7 of a pie	1 sector	135	43	365	3	16	4.0	6.6	3.6	56	38	51	1.9	240	tr	0.14	0.12	1.4	1
Peach																			
Whole	1 pie	945	48	2,410	24	101	24.8	43.7	25.1	361	95	274	8.5	1,408	6,900	1.04	0.97	14.0	28
Sector, 1/7 of a pie	1 sector	135	48	345	3	14	3.5	6.2	3.6	52	14	39	1.2	201	990	0.15	0.14	2.0	4
Pecan																			
Whole	1 pie	825	20	3,450	42	189	27.8	101.0	44.2	423	388	850	25.6	1,015	1,320	1.80	0.95	6.9	tr
Sector, 1/7 of a pie	1 sector	118	20	495	6	27	4.0	14.4	6.3	61	55	122	3.7	145	190	0.26	0.14	1.0	tr
Pumpkin:																			
Whole	1 pie	910	59	1,920	36	102	37.4	37.5	16.6	223	464	628	7.3	1,456	22,480	0.78	1.27	7.0	tr
Sector, 1/7 of a pie	1 sector	130	59	275	5	15	5.4	5.4	2.4	32	66	90	1.0	208	3,210	0.11	0.18	1.0	tr
Piecrust (home recipe made with enriched flour and vegetable shortening, baked	1 pie shell, 9-in. diameter	180	15	900	11	60	14.8	26.1	14.9	79	25	90	3.1	89	0	0.47	0.40	5.0	0
Piecrust mix with enriched flour and vegetable shortening, 10-oz pkg, prepared and baked	Piecrust for 2-crust pie, 9-in. diameter	320	19	1,485	20	93	22.7	39.7	23.4	141	131	272	6.1	179	0	1.07	0.79	9.9	0
Pineapple:																			
Raw, diced	1 cup	155	85	80	1	tr	*	*	*	21	26	12	0.8	226	110	0.14	0.05	0.3	26
Canned, heavy syrup pack, solids and liquid:																			
Crushed, chunks, tidbits	1 cup	255	80	190	1	tr	*	*	*	49	28	13	0.8	245	130	0.20	0.05	0.5	18
Slices and liquid:																			
Large	1 slice; 2¼ tbsp liquid	105	80	80	tr	tr	*	*	*	20	12	5	0.3	101	50	0.08	0.02	0.2	7
Medium	1 slice; 1¼ tbsp liquid	58	80	45	tr	tr	*	*	*	11	6	3	0.2	56	30	0.05	0.01	0.1	4

Appendix E continued

Food	Approximate Measure	Weight (g)	Water (%)	Food energy (kcal)	Pro-tein (g)	Fat (g)	Satu-rated (total) (g)	Unsaturated Oleic (g)	Unsaturated Lino-leic (g)	Carbo-hydrate (g)	Cal-cium (mg)	Phos-phor-ous (mg)	Iron (mg)	Potas-sium (mg)	Vita-min A value (IU)	Thia-min (mg)	Ribo-flavin (mg)	Niacin (mg)	Ascor-bic Acid (mg)
Pineapple juice, unsweetened, canned, vitamin C added	1 cup	250	86	140	1	tr	*	*	*	34	38	23	0.8	373	130	0.13	0.05	0.5	80†
Pizza (cheese) baked, 4¾-in. sector, ⅛ of 12-in. diameter enriched pie⁹	1 sector	60	45	145	6	4	1.7	1.5	0.6	22	86	89	1.1	67	230	0.16	0.18	1.6	4
Plums: Raw, without pits:																			
Japanese and hybrid (2⅛-in. diameter, about 6½ per lb with pits)	1 plum	66	87	30	tr	tr	*	*	*	8	8	12	0.3	112	160	0.02	0.02	0.3	4
Prune-type (1½-in. diameter, about 15 per lb with pits)	1 plum	28	79	20	tr	tr	*	*	*	6	3	5	0.1	48	80	0.01	0.01	0.1	1
Canned, heavy syrup pack (Italian prunes), with pits and liquid:																			
Cup	1 cup	272	77	215	1	tr	*	*	*	56	23	26	2.3	367	3,130	0.05	0.05	1.0	5
Portion	3 plums; 2¾ tbsp liquid	140	77	110	1	tr	*	*	*	29	12	13	1.2	189	1,610	0.03	0.03	0.5	3
Popcorn, popped:																			
Plain, large kernel	1 cup	6	4	25	1	tr	tr	0.1	0.2	5	1	17	0.2	*	*	*	0.01	0.1	0
With oil (coconut) and salt added, large kernel	1 cup	9	3	40	1	2	1.5	0.2	0.2	5	1	19	0.2	*	*	*	0.01	0.2	0
Sugar coated	1 cup	35	4	135	2	1	0.5	0.2	0.4	30	2	47	0.5	*	*	*	0.02	0.4	0
Popsicle, 3-fl-oz size	1 popsicle	95	80	70	0	0	0	0	0	18	0	*	tr	*	0	0	0	0	0
Pork, cured, cooked: Ham, light cure, lean and fat, roasted (2 pieces, 4⅛ by 2¼ by ¼ in.)	3 oz	85	54	245	18	19	6.8	7.9	1.7	0	8	146	2.2	199	0	0.40	0.15	3.1	*
Luncheon meat: Boiled ham, slice (8 per 8-oz pkg.)	1 oz	28	59	65	5	5	1.7	2.0	0.4	0	3	47	0.8	*	0	0.12	0.04	0.7	*
Canned, spiced or unspiced: Slice, approx. 3 by 2 by ½ in.	1 slice	60	55	175	9	15	5.4	6.7	1.0	1	5	65	1.3	133	0	0.19	0.13	1.8	*
Chop, loin (cut 3 per lb with bone), broiled:																			
Lean and fat	2.7 oz	78	42	305	19	25	8.9	10.4	2.2	0	9	209	2.7	216	0	0.75	0.22	1.5	*
Lean only	2 oz	56	53	150	17	9	3.1	3.6	0.8	0	7	181	2.2	192	0	0.63	0.18	3.8	*
Roast, oven cooked, no liquid added:																			
Lean and fat (piece, 2½ by 2½ by¾ in.)	3 oz	85	46	310	21	24	8.7	10.2	2.2	0	9	218	2.7	233	0	0.78	0.22	4.8	*
Lean only	2.4 oz	68	55	175	20	10	3.5	4.1	0.8	0	9	211	2.6	224	0	0.73	0.21	4.4	*
Shoulder cut, simmered:																			
Lean and fat (3 pieces 2½ by 2½ by ¼ in.)	3 oz	85	46	320	20	26	9.3	10.9	2.3	0	9	118	2.6	158	0	0.46	0.21	4.1	*
Lean only	2.2 oz	63	60	135	18	6	2.2	2.6	0.6	0	8	111	2.3	146	0	0.42	0.19	3.7	*
Potatoes, cooked: Baked, peeled after baking (about 2 per lb, raw)	1 potato	156	75	145	4	tr	*	*	*	33	14	101	1.1	782	tr	0.15	0.07	2.7	31
Boiled (about 3 per lb, raw): Peeled after boiling	1 potato	137	80	105	3	tr	*	*	*	23	10	72	0.8	556	tr	0.12	0.05	2.0	22

Food	Measure (approx.)	Grams	Water (%)	Food energy (cal)	Protein (g)	Fat (g)	Saturated (g)	Oleic (g)	Linoleic (g)	Carbohydrate (g)	Calcium (mg)	Phosphorus (mg)	Iron (mg)	Potassium (mg)	Vitamin A (IU)	Thiamin (mg)	Riboflavin (mg)	Niacin (mg)	Ascorbic acid (mg)
Peeled before boiling	1 potato	135	83	90	3	tr	*	*	*	20	8	57	0.7	385	tr	0.12	0.05	1.6	22
French-fried, strip, 2 to 3½ in. long: Prepared from raw	10 strips	50	45	139	2	7	1.7	1.2	3.3	18	8	56	0.7	427	tr	0.07	0.04	1.6	11
Frozen, oven heated	10 strips	50	53	110	2	4	1.1	0.8	2.1	17	5	43	0.9	326	tr	0.07	0.01	1.3	11
Hashed brown, prepared from frozen	1 cup	155	56	345	3	18	4.6	3.2	9.0	45	28	78	1.9	439	tr	0.11	0.03	1.6	12
Mashed, prepared from Raw: Milk added	1 cup	210	83	135	4	2	0.7	0.4	tr	27	50	103	0.8	548	40	0.17	0.11	2.1	21
Milk and butter added	1 cup	210	80	195	4	9	5.6	2.3	0.2	26	50	101	0.8	525	360	0.17	0.11	2.1	19
Dehydrated flakes (without milk), water, milk, butter, and salt added	1 cup	210	79	195	4	7	3.6	2.1	0.2	30	65	99	0.6	601	270	0.08	0.08	1.9	11
Scalloped	½ cup	122	nd	127	4	5	nd	nd	nd	18	66	90	0.5	399	195	0.07	0.11	1.2	13
Potato chips, 1¾ by 2½ in. oval cross section	10 chips	20	2	115	1	8	2.1	1.4	4.0	10	8	28	0.4	226	tr	0.04	0.01	1.0	3
Potato salad, made with cooked salad dressing	1 cup	250	76	250	7	7	2.0	2.7	1.3	41	80	160	1.5	798	350	0.20	0.18	2.8	28
Pretzels, made with enriched flour: Dutch, twisted, 2¾ by 2⅝ in.	1 pretzel	16	5	60	2	1	*	*	*	12	4	21	0.2	21	0	0.05	0.04	0.7	0
Thin, twisted, 3¼ by 2¼ by ¼ in.	10 pretzels	60	5	235	6	3	*	*	*	46	13	79	0.9	78	0	0.20	0.15	2.5	0
Stick, 2¼ in. long	10 pretzels	3	5	10	tr	tr	*	*	*	2	1	4	tr	4	0	0.01	0.01	0.1	0
Prunes, dried, "softenized," with pits: Uncooked	4 extra large or 5 large	49	28	110	1	tr	*	*	*	29	22	34	1.7	298	690	0.04	0.07	0.7	1
Cooked, unsweetened, all sizes, fruit and liquid	1 cup	250	66	255	2	1	*	*	*	67	51	79	3.8	695	1,590	0.07	0.15	1.5	2
Prune juice, canned or bottled	1 cup	256	80	195	1	tr	*	*	*	49	36	51	10.5	602	*	0.03	0.03	1.0	5
Puddings: From home recipe: Starch base: Chocolate	1 cup	260	66	385	8	12	7.6	3.3	0.3	67	250	255	1.3	445	390	0.05	0.36	0.3	1
Vanilla (blancmange)	1 cup	255	76	285	9	10	6.2	2.5	0.2	41	298	232	tr	352	410	0.08	0.41	0.3	2
Tapioca cream	1 cup	165	72	220	8	8	4.1	2.5	0.5	28	173	180	0.7	223	480	0.07	0.30	0.2	2
From mix (chocolate) and milk: Regular (cooked)	1 cup	260	70	320	9	8	4.3	2.6	0.2	59	265	247	0.8	354	340	0.05	0.39	0.3	2
Instant	1 cup	260	70	320	9	8	4.3	2.6	0.2	59	265	247	0.8	354	340	0.08	0.39	0.3	2
Pumpkin, canned	1 cup	245	90	80	2	1	*	*	*	19	61	64	1.0	588	15,680	0.07	0.12	1.5	12
Pumpkin and squash kernels, dry, hulled	1 cup	140	4	775	41	65	11.8	23.5	27.5	21	71	1,602	15.7	1,386	100	0.34	0.27	3.4	*
Radishes, raw (prepackaged) stem ends, rootlets cut off	4 radishes	18	95	5	tr	tr	*	*	*	1	5	6	0.2	58	tr	0.01	0.01	0.1	5
Raisins, seedless: Cup, not pressed down	1 cup	145	18	420	4	tr	*	*	*	112	90	146	5.1	1,106	30	0.16	0.12	0.7	1
Packet, ½ oz (1½ tbsp)	1 packet	14	18	40	tr	tr	*	*	*	11	9	14	0.5	107	tr	0.02	0.01	0.1	tr
Raspberries, red: Raw, capped, whole	1 cup	123	84	70	1	1	*	*	*	17	27	27	1.1	207	160	0.04	0.11	1.1	31
Frozen, sweetened, 10-oz container	1 container	284	74	280	2	1	*	*	*	70	37	48	1.7	284	200	0.06	0.17	1.7	60
Rhubarb, cooked, added sugar: From raw	1 cup	270	63	380	1	tr	*	*	*	97	211	41	1.6	548	220	0.05	0.14	0.8	16
From frozen, sweetened	1 cup	270	63	385	1	1	*	*	*	98	211	32	1.9	475	190	0.05	0.11	0.5	16
Rice, white, enriched: Instant, ready-to-serve, hot	1 cup	165	73	180	4	tr	tr	tr	tr	40	5	31	1.3	*	0	0.21	†	1.7	0

Appendix E continued

Food	Approximate Measure	Weight (g)	Water (%)	Food energy (kcal)	Protein (g)	Fat (g)	Fatty acids Saturated (total) (g)	Unsaturated Oleic (g)	Unsaturated Linoleic (g)	Carbohydrate (g)	Calcium (mg)	Phosphorous (mg)	Iron (mg)	Potassium (mg)	Vitamin A value (IU)	Thiamin (mg)	Riboflavin (mg)	Niacin (mg)	Ascorbic Acid (mg)
Long grain:																			
Raw	1 cup	185	12	670	12	1	0.2	0.2	0.2	149	44	174	5.4	170	0	0.81	0.06	6.5	0
Cooked, served hot	1 cup	205	73	225	4	tr	0.1	0.1	0.1	50	21	57	1.8	57	0	0.23	0.02	2.1	0
Parboiled:																			
Raw	1 cup	185	10	685	14	1	0.2	0.1	0.2	150	111	370	5.4	278	0	0.81	0.07	6.5	0
Cooked, served hot	1 cup	175	73	185	4	tr	0.1	0.1	0.1	41	33	100	1.4	75	0	0.19	0.02	2.1	0
Rolls, enriched:§ Commercial:																			
Brown-and-serve (12 per 12-oz pkg.), browned	1 roll	26	27	85	2	2	0.4	0.7	0.5	14	20	23	0.5	25	tr	0.10	0.06	0.9	tr
Cloverleaf or pan, 2½-in. diameter, 2 in. high	1 roll	28	31	85	2	2	0.4	0.6	0.4	15	21	24	0.5	27	tr	0.11	0.07	0.9	tr
Frankfurter and hamburger (8 per 11½-oz pkg.)	1 roll	40	31	120	3	2	0.5	0.8	0.6	21	30	34	0.8	38	tr	0.16	0.10	1.3	tr
Hard, 3¾-in. diameter, 2 in. high	1 roll	50	25	155	5	2	0.4	0.6	0.5	30	24	46	1.2	49	tr	0.20	0.12	1.7	tr
Hoagie or submarine, 11½ by 3 by 2½ in.	1 roll	135	31	390	12	4	0.9	1.4	1.4	75	58	115	3.0	122	tr	0.54	0.32	4.5	tr
From home recipe:																			
Cloverleaf, 2½-in. diameter, 2 in. high	1 roll	35	26	120	3	3	0.8	1.1	0.7	20	16	36	0.7	41	30	0.12	0.12	1.2	tr
Salad dressings: Commercial: Blue cheese:																			
Regular	1 tbsp	15	32	75	1	8	1.6	1.7	3.8	1	12	11	tr	6	30	tr	0.02	tr	tr
Low calorie (5 kcal per tsp)	1 tbsp	16	84	10	tr	1	0.5	0.3	tr	1	10	8	tr	5	30	tr	0.01	tr	tr
French:																			
Regular	1 tbsp	16	39	65	tr	6	1.1	1.3	3.2	3	2	2	0.1	13	*	*	*	*	*
Low calorie (5 kcal per tsp)	1 tbsp	16	77	15	tr	1	0.1	0.1	0.4	2	2	2	0.1	13	*	*	*	*	*
Italian:																			
Regular	1 tbsp	15	28	85	tr	9	1.6	1.9	4.7	1	2	1	tr	2	tr	tr	tr	tr	*
Low calorie (2 kcal per tsp)	1 tbsp	15	90	10	tr	1	0.1	0.1	0.4	tr	tr	1	tr	2	tr	tr	tr	tr	*
Mayonnaise	1 tbsp	14	15	100	tr	11	2.0	2.4	5.6	tr	3	4	0.1	5	40	tr	0.01	tr	*
Mayonnaise type:																			
Regular	1 tbsp	15	41	65	tr	6	1.1	1.4	3.2	2	2	4	tr	1	30	tr	tr	tr	*
Low calorie (8 kcal per tsp)	1 tbsp	16	81	20	tr	2	0.4	0.4	1.0	2	3	4	tr	1	40	tr	tr	tr	*
Tartar sauce, regular	1 tbsp	14	34	75	tr	8	1.5	1.8	4.1	1	3	4	0.1	11	30	tr	tr	tr	tr
Thousand Island:																			
Regular	1 tbsp	16	32	80	tr	8	1.4	1.7	4.0	2	2	3	0.1	18	50	tr	tr	tr	*
Low calorie (10 kcal per tsp)	1 tbsp	15	68	25	tr	2	0.4	0.4	1.0	2	2	3	0.1	17	50	tr	tr	tr	*
From home recipe:																			
Cooked type§§	1 tbsp	16	68	25	1	2	0.5	0.6	0.3	2	14	15	0.1	19	80	0.01	0.03	tr	tr
Sauerkraut, canned, solids and liquid	1 cup	235	93	40	2	tr	*	*	*	9	85	42	1.2	329	120	0.07	0.09	0.5	33
Sausages:																			
Bologna, slice (8 per 8-oz pkg.)	1 slice	28	56	85	3	8	3.0	3.4	0.5	tr	2	36	0.5	65	*	0.05	0.06	0.7	*
Braunschweiger, slice (6 per 6-oz pkg.)	1 slice	28	53	90	4	8	2.6	3.4	0.8	1	3	69	1.7	*	1,850	0.05	0.41	2.3	*
Brown and serve (10–11 per 8-oz pkg.), browned	1 link	17	40	70	3	6	2.3	2.8	0.7	tr	*	*	*	*	*	*	*	tr	*

Food	Measure	Grams	Water (%)	Food energy (cal)	Protein (g)	Fat (g)	Saturated (g)	Oleic (g)	Linoleic (g)	Carbohydrate (g)	Calcium (mg)	Phosphorus (mg)	Iron (mg)	Potassium (mg)	Vitamin A (IU)	Thiamin (mg)	Riboflavin (mg)	Niacin (mg)	Ascorbic acid (mg)
Deviled ham, canned	1 tbsp	13	51	45	2	4	1.5	1.8	0.4	0	1	12	0.3	*	0	0.02	0.01	0.2	*
Frankfurter (8 per 1-lb pkg.), cooked (reheated)	1 frankfurter	56	57	170	7	15	5.6	6.5	1.2	1	3	57	0.8	*	*	0.08	0.11	1.4	*
Meat, potted (beef, chicken, turkey), canned	1 tbsp	13	61	30	2	2	*	*	*	0	*	*	*	*	*	tr	0.03	0.2	*
Pork link (16 per 1-lb pkg.), cooked	1 link	13	35	60	2	6	2.1	2.4	0.5	tr	1	21	0.3	35	0	0.10	0.04	0.5	*
Salami:																			
Dry type, slice (12 per 4-oz pkg.)	1 slice	10	30	45	2	4	1.6	1.6	0.1	tr	1	28	0.4	*	*	0.04	0.03	0.5	*
Cooked type, slice (8 per 8-oz pkg.)	1 slice	28	51	90	5	7	3.1	3.0	0.2	tr	3	57	0.7	*	*	0.07	0.07	1.2	*
Vienna sausage (7 per 4-oz can)	1 sausage	16	63	40	2	3	1.2	1.4	0.2	tr	1	24	0.3	*	*	0.01	0.02	0.4	*
Sherbet (about 2% fat)	1/2 gal	1,542	66	2,160	17	31	19.0	7.7	0.7	469	827	594	2.5	1,585	1,480	0.26	0.71	1.0	31
Soups:																			
Canned, condensed:																			
Prepared with equal volume of milk:																			
Cream of chicken	1 cup	245	85	180	7	10	4.2	3.6	1.3	15	172	152	0.5	260	610	0.05	0.27	0.7	2
Cream of mushroom	1 cup	245	83	215	7	14	5.4	2.9	4.6	16	191	169	0.5	279	250	0.05	0.34	0.7	1
Tomato	1 cup	250	84	175	7	6	3.4	1.7	1.0	23	168	155	0.8	418	1,200	0.10	0.25	1.3	15
Prepared with equal volume of water:																			
Bean with pork	1 cup	250	84	170	8	6	1.2	1.8	2.4	22	63	128	2.3	395	650	0.13	0.08	1.0	3
Beef broth, bouillon, consomme	1 cup	240	96	30	5	0	0	0	0	3	tr	31	0.5	130	tr	tr	0.02	1.2	*
Beef noodle	1 cup	240	93	65	4	3	0.6	0.7	0.8	7	7	48	1.0	77	50	0.05	0.07	1.0	tr
Clam chowder, Manhattan type (with tomatoes, without milk)	1 cup	245	92	80	2	2	0.5	0.4	1.3	12	34	47	1.0	184	880	0.02	0.02	1.0	*
Cream of chicken	1 cup	240	92	95	3	7	1.6	2.3	1.1	8	24	34	0.5	79	410	0.02	0.05	0.5	tr
Cream of mushroom	1 cup	240	90	135	2	10	2.6	1.7	4.5	10	41	50	0.5	98	70	0.02	0.12	0.7	tr
Minestrone	1 cup	245	90	105	5	3	0.7	0.9	1.3	14	37	59	1.0	314	2,350	0.07	0.05	1.0	*
Split pea	1 cup	245	85	145	9	3	1.1	1.2	0.4	21	29	149	1.5	270	440	0.25	0.15	1.5	1
Tomato	1 cup	245	91	90	2	2	0.5	0.5	1.0	16	15	34	0.7	230	1,000	0.05	0.05	1.2	12
Vegetable beef	1 cup	245	92	80	5	2	*	*	*	10	12	49	0.7	162	2,700	0.05	0.05	1.0	*
Vegetarian	1 cup	245	92	80	2	2	*	*	*	13	20	39	1.0	172	2,940	0.05	0.05	1.0	*
Dehydrated:																			
Bouillon cube, 1/2 in.	1 cube	4	4	5	1	tr	*	*	*	tr	*	*	*	4	*	*	*	*	*
Mixes:																			
Unprepared:																			
Onion	1 1/2-oz pkg.	43	3	150	6	5	1.1	2.3	1.0	23	42	49	0.6	238	30	0.05	0.03	0.3	6
Prepared with water:																			
Chicken noodle	1 cup	240	95	55	2	1	*	*	*	8	7	19	0.2	19	50	0.07	0.05	0.5	tr
Onion	1 cup	240	96	35	1	1	*	*	*	6	10	12	0.2	58	tr	tr	tr	tr	2
Tomato vegetable with noodles	1 cup	240	93	65	1	1	*	*	*	12	7	19	0.2	29	480	0.05	0.02	0.5	5
Soy milk (unfortified)	1 cup	240	91	90	6	4	nd	nd	nd	4	20	104	1.2	8	0	0.56	1.20	0.4	0
Soy sauce	1 tbsp	18	nd	11	1	0	nd	nd	nd	2	3	32	0.4	54	0	0.01	0.02	0.5	0
Spaghetti, enriched, cooked:																			
Firm stage, "al dente," served hot	1 cup	130	64	190	7	1	*	*	*	39	14	85	1.4	103	0	0.23	0.13	1.8	0
Tender stage, served hot	1 cup	140	73	155	5	1	*	*	*	32	11	70	1.3	85	0	0.20	0.11	1.5	0
Spaghetti (enriched) in tomato sauce with cheese:																			
From home recipe	1 cup	250	77	260	9	9	2.0	5.4	0.7	37	80	135	2.3	408	1,080	0.25	0.18	2.3	13
Canned	1 cup	250	80	190	6	2	0.5	0.3	0.4	39	40	88	2.8	303	930	0.35	0.28	4.5	10
Spaghetti (enriched) with meat balls and tomato sauce:																			
From home recipe	1 cup	248	70	330	19	12	3.3	6.3	0.9	39	124	236	3.7	665	1,590	0.25	0.30	4.0	22

Appendix E continued

Food	Approximate Measure	Weight (g)	Water (%)	Food energy (kcal)	Protein (g)	Fat (g)	Fatty acids Saturated (total) (g)	Unsaturated Oleic (g)	Linoleic (g)	Carbohydrate (g)	Calcium (mg)	Phosphorous (mg)	Iron (mg)	Potassium (mg)	Vitamin A value (IU)	Thiamin (mg)	Riboflavin (mg)	Niacin (mg)	Ascorbic Acid (mg)
Canned	1 cup	250	78	260	12	10	2.2	3.3	3.9	29	53	113	3.3	245	1,000	0.15	0.18	2.3	5
Spinach:																			
Raw, chopped	1 cup	55	91	15	2	tr	*	*	*	2	51	28	1.7	259	4,460	0.06	0.11	0.3	28
Cooked, drained:																			
From raw	1 cup	180	92	40	5	1	*	*	*	6	167	68	4.0	583	14,580	0.13	0.25	0.9	50
From frozen:																			
Chopped	1 cup	205	92	45	6	1	*	*	*	8	232	90	4.3	683	16,200	0.14	0.31	0.8	39
Leaf	1 cup	190	92	45	6	1	*	*	*	7	200	84	4.8	688	15,390	0.15	0.27	1.0	53
Canned, drained solids	1 cup	205	91	50	6	1	*	*	*	7	242	53	5.3	513	16,400	0.04	0.25	0.6	29
Squash, cooked:																			
Summer (all varieties), diced, drained	1 cup	210	96	30	2	tr	*	*	*	7	53	53	0.8	296	820	0.11	0.17	1.7	21
Winter (all varieties), baked, mashed	1 cup	205	81	130	4	1	*	*	*	32	57	98	1.6	945	8,610	0.10	0.27	1.4	27
Strawberries:																			
Raw, whole berries, capped	1 cup	149	90	55	1	1	*	*	*	13	31	31	1.5	244	90	0.04	0.10	0.9	88
Frozen, sweetened:																			
Sliced, 10-oz container	1 container	284	71	310	1	1	*	*	*	79	40	48	2.0	318	90	0.06	0.17	1.4	151
Whole, 1-lb container (about 1¾ cups)	1 container	454	76	415	2	1	*	*	*	107	59	73	2.7	472	140	0.09	0.27	2.3	249
Sugars:																			
Brown, pressed down	1 cup	220	2	820	0	0	0	0	0	212	187	42	7.5	757	0	0.02	0.07	0.4	0
White:																			
Granulated	1 cup	200	1	770	0	0	0	0	0	199	0	0	0.2	6	0	0	0	0	0
	1 tbsp	12	1	45	0	0	0	0	0	12	0	0	tr	tr	0	0	0	0	0
	1 packet	6	1	23	0	0	0	0	0	6	0	0	tr	tr	0	0	0	0	0
Powdered, sifted, spooned into cup	1 cup	100	1	385	0	0	0	0	0	100	0	0	0.1	3	0	0	0	0	0
Sunflower seeds, dry, hulled	1 cup	145	5	810	35	69	8.2	13.7	43.2	29	174	1,214	10.3	1,334	70	2.84	0.33	7.8	*
Sweet potatoes:																			
Cooked (raw, 5 by 2 in.; about 2½ per lb):																			
Baked in skin, peeled	1 potato	114	64	160	2	1	*	*	*	37	46	66	1.0	342	9,230	0.10	0.08	0.8	25
Boiled in skin, peeled	1 potato	151	71	170	3	1	*	*	*	40	48	71	1.1	367	11,940	0.14	0.09	0.9	26
Candied, 2½- by 2-in. piece	1 piece	105	60	175	1	3	2.0	0.8	0.1	36	39	45	0.9	200	6,620	0.06	0.04	0.4	11
Canned:																			
Solid pack (mashed)	1 cup	255	72	275	5	1	*	*	*	63	64	105	2.0	510	19,890	0.13	0.10	1.5	36
Vacuum pack, piece 2¾ by 1 in.	1 piece	40	72	45	1	tr	*	*	*	10	10	16	0.3	80	3,120	0.02	0.02	0.2	6
Syrups:																			
Chocolate-flavored syrup or topping: Thin type	1 fl oz or 2 tbsp	38	32	90	1	1	0.5	0.3	tr	24	6	35	0.6	106	tr	0.01	0.03	0.2	0
Fudge type	1 fl oz or 2 tbsp	38	25	125	2	5	3.1	1.6	0.1	20	48	60	0.5	107	60	0.02	0.08	0.2	tr
Molasses, cane:																			
Light (first extraction)	1 tbsp	20	24	50	*	*	*	*	*	13	33	9	0.9	183	*	0.01	0.01	tr	*
Blackstrap (third extraction)	1 tbsp	20	24	45	*	*	*	*	*	11	137	17	3.2	585	*	0.02	0.04	0.4	*
Sorghum	1 tbsp	21	23	55	*	*	*	*	*	14	35	5	2.6	*	*	*	0.02	tr	*

Table blends, chiefly corn, light and dark	1 tbsp	21	24	60	0	0	0	0	0	15	9	3	0.8	1	0	0	0	0	0
Tahini	1 tbsp	21	3	135	4	12	nd	nd	nd	3	21	177	1.8	87	0	0.12	0.06	0.9	0
Tangerine, raw, 2⅜-in. diameter, size 176, without peel (about 4 per lb with peels and seeds)	1 tangerine	86	87	40	1	tr	*	*	*	10	34	15	0.3	108	360	0.05	0.02	0.1	27
Tangerine juice, canned, sweetened	1 cup	249	87	125	1	tr	*	*	*	30	44	35	0.5	440	1,040	0.15	0.05	0.2	54
Tea, made from instant	1 cup	240	nd	5	0	0	nd	nd	nd	1.0	17	0	0	60	0	0	0.02	0	0
Teriyaki sauce	1 oz	30	nd	30	2	0	nd	nd	nd	5	7	46	0.5	68	0	0.01	0.02	0.4	0
Toaster pastries	1 pastry	50	12	200	3	6	*	*	*	36	54†	67†	1.9	74†	500	0.16	0.17	2.1	†
Tofu, soy cheese, soybean curd	3½ oz	100	nd	72	8	4	nd	nd	nd	2	128	126	1.9	42	0	0.06	0.08	0.1	0
Tomatoes:																			
Raw, 2⅗-in. diameter (3 per 12-oz pkg.)	1 tomato	135	94	25	1	tr	*	*	*	6	16	33	0.6	300	1,110	0.07	0.05	0.9	28
Canned, solids and liquid	1 cup	241	94	50	2	tr	*	*	*	10	14†	45	1.2	523	2,170	0.12	0.07	1.7	41
Tomato catsup	1 cup	273	69	290	5	1	*	*	*	69	60	137	2.2	991	3,820	0.25	0.19	4.4	41
	1 tbsp	15	69	15	tr	tr	*	*	*	4	3	8	0.1	54	210	0.01	0.01	0.2	2
Tomato juice, canned:																			
Cup	1 cup	243	94	45	2	tr	*	*	*	10	17	44	2.2	552	1,940	0.12	0.07	1.9	39
Glass (6 fl oz)	1 glass	182	94	35	2	tr	*	*	*	8	13	33	1.6	413	1,460	0.09	0.05	1.5	29
Tortilla, flour	1 average	30	nd	95	3	2	nd	nd	nd	17	46	25	1.1	nd	2	0.01	0.08	1.0	tr
Turkey, roasted, flesh without skin:																			
Dark meat, piece, 2½ by 1⅝ by ¼ in.	4 pieces	85	61	175	26	7	2.1	1.5	1.5	0	*	*	2.0	338	*	0.03	0.20	3.6	*
Light meat, piece, 4 by 2 by ¼ in.	2 pieces	85	62	150	28	3	0.9	0.6	0.7	0	*	*	1.0	349	*	0.04	0.12	9.4	*
Light and dark meat:																			
Chopped or diced	1 cup	140	61	265	44	9	2.5	1.7	1.8	0	11	351	2.5	514	*	0.07	0.25	10.8	*
Pieces (1 slice white meat, 4 by 2 by ¼ in. with 2 slices dark meat, 2½ by 1⅝ by ¼ in.)	3 pieces	85	61	160	27	5	1.5	1.0	1.1	0	7	213	1.5	312	*	0.04	0.15	6.5	*
Turnips, cooked, diced	1 cup	155	94	35	1	tr	*	*	*	8	54	37	0.6	291	tr	0.06	0.08	0.5	34
Turnip greens, cooked, drained:																			
From raw (leaves and stems)	1 cup	145	94	30	3	tr	*	*	*	5	252	49	1.5	*	8,270	0.15	0.33	0.7	68
From frozen (chopped)	1 cup	165	93	40	4	tr	*	*	*	6	195	64	2.6	246	11,390	0.08	0.15	0.7	31
Veal, medium fat, cooked, bone removed:																			
Cutlet (4⅛ by 2¼ by ½ in.), braised or broiled	3 oz	85	60	185	23	9	4.0	3.4	0.4	0	9	196	2.7	258	*	0.06	0.21	4.6	*
Rib (2 pieces, 4⅛ by 2¼ by ¼ in.), roasted	3 oz	85	55	230	23	14	6.1	5.1	0.6	0	10	211	2.9	259	*	0.11	0.26	6.6	*
Vegetables, mixed, frozen, cooked	1 cup	182	83	115	6	1	*	*	*	24	46	115	2.4	348	9,010	0.22	0.13	2.0	15
Vinegar, cider	1 tbsp	15	2	tr	tr	0	0	0	0	1	1	1	0.1	15	*	*	*	*	*
Waffles, made with enriched flour, 7-in. diameter:§																			
From home recipe	1 waffle	75	41	210	7	7	2.3	2.8	1.4	28	85	130	1.3	109	250	0.17	0.23	1.4	tr
From mix, egg and milk added	1 waffle	75	42	205	7	8	2.8	2.9	1.2	27	179	257	1.0	146	170	0.14	0.22	0.9	tr
Walnuts:																			
Black:																			
Chopped or broken kernels	1 cup	125	3	785	26	74	6.3	13.3	45.7	19	tr	713	7.5	575	380	0.28	0.14	0.9	*
Ground (finely)	1 cup	80	3	500	16	47	4.0	8.5	29.2	12	tr	456	4.8	368	240	0.18	0.09	0.6	*
Persian or English, chopped (about 60 halves)	1 cup	120	4	780	18	77	8.4	11.8	42.2	19	119	456	3.7	540	40	0.40	0.16	1.1	2
Watermelon, raw, 4 by 8 in. wedge with rind and seeds (1⁄16 of 32⅔-lb melon, 10 by 16 in.)	1 wedge with rind and seeds	926	93	110	2	1	*	*	*	27	30	43	2.1	426	2,510	0.13	0.13	0.9	30

Appendix E continued

Food	Approximate Measure	Weight (g)	Water (%)	Food energy (kcal)	Protein (g)	Fat (g)	Fatty acids Saturated (total) (g)	Unsaturated Oleic (g)	Linoleic (g)	Carbohydrate (g)	Calcium (mg)	Phosphorous (mg)	Iron (mg)	Potassium (mg)	Vitamin A value (IU)	Thiamin (mg)	Riboflavin (mg)	Niacin (mg)	Ascorbic Acid (mg)
Wheat flours:																			
All-purpose or family flour, enriched:																			
Sifted, spooned	1 cup	115	12	420	12	1	0.2	0.1	0.5	88	18	100	3.3	109	0	0.74	0.46	6.1	0
Unsifted, spooned	1 cup	125	12	455	13	1	0.2	0.1	0.5	95	20	109	3.6	119	0	0.80	0.50	6.6	0
Cake or pastry flour, enriched, sifted, spooned	1 cup	96	12	350	7	1	0.1	0.1	0.3	76	16	70	2.8	91	0	0.61	0.38	5.1	0
Self-rising, enriched, unsifted, spooned	1 cup	125	12	440	12	1	0.2	0.1	0.5	93	331	583	3.6	*	0	0.80	0.50	6.6	0
Whole wheat, from hard wheats, stirred	1 cup	120	12	400	16	2	0.4	0.2	1.0	85	49	446	4.0	444	0	0.66	0.14	5.2	0
White sauce, medium, with enriched flour	1 cup	250	73	405	10	31	19.3	7.8	0.8	22	288	233	0.5	348	1,150	0.12	0.43	0.7	2
Yeast:																			
Baker's, dry, active	1 pkg	7	5	20	3	tr	*	*	*	3	3	90	1.1	140	tr	0.16	0.38	2.6	tr
Brewer's, dry	1 tbsp	8	5	25	3	tr	*	*	*	3	17	140	1.4	152	tr	1.25	0.34	3.0	tr
Yogurt:																			
With added milk solids: Made with lowfat milk:																			
Fruit-flavored[†]	1 container, net wt: 8 oz	227	75	230	10	3	1.8	0.6	0.1	42	343	269	0.2	439	120[†]	0.08	0.40	0.2	1
Plain	1 container, net wt: 8 oz	227	85	145	12	4	2.3	0.8	0.1	16	415	326	0.2	531	150[†]	0.10	0.49	0.3	2
Made with nonfat milk	1 container, net wt: 8 oz	227	85	125	13	tr	0.3	0.1	tr	17	452	355	0.2	579	20[†]	0.11	0.53	0.3	2
Without added milk solids: Made with whole milk	1 container, net wt: 8 oz	227	88	140	8	7	4.8	1.7	0.1	11	274	215	0.1	351	280	0.07	0.32	0.2	1

* Nutrient believed to be present in measurable amount, but data are not reliable.
nd No data available.
tr Present in trace amounts.
† Values vary according to season, ingredients, fortification, or other factors; check nutrition label if available.
‡ Outer layer of fat was removed to within approximately ½ inch of the lean.
§ Made with vegetable shortening.
Δ Made with butter.
†† Applies to yellow varieties; white varieties contain considerably less.
§§ Regular-type margarine used.

Most data drawn from: Science and Education Administration, 1981. *Nutritive value of foods*. Home and Garden Bulletin Number 72. Washington, DC: U.S. Government Printing Office. Some data drawn from: (1) Agricultural Research Service, United States Department of Agriculture, 1975. *Nutritive value of American foods in common units*. Agricultural Handbook No. 456. Washington, DC: U.S. Government Printing Office; (2) Pennington, J.A.T., and H.N. Church, 1980. *Food values of portions commonly used*. Philadelphia. J.B. Lippincott Company; (3) Truesdell, D.D., E.N. Whitney, and P.B. Acosta, 1984. Nutrients in vegetarian foods. *Journal of the American Dietetic Association 84:28—35.*

Appendix F Table of Food Composition—Fast Foods

	Weight (g)	Energy (kcal)	Protein (g)	Carbohydrate (g)	Fat (g)	Cholesterol (mg)	Vitamin A (IU)	Thiamin (mg)	Riboflavin (mg)	Niacin (mg)	Vitamin C (mg)	Calcium (mg)	Iron (mg)	Phosphorus (mg)	Sodium (mg)	Zinc (mg)
ARBY'S®																
Roast beef	140	350	22	32	15	45	X	0.30	0.34	5	X	80	3.6	nd	880	nd
Beef and cheese	168	450	27	36	22	55	X	0.38	0.43	6	X	200	4.5	nd	1220	nd
Super roast beef	263	620	30	61	28	85	X	0.53	0.43	7	X	100	5.4	nd	1420	nd
Junior roast beef	74	220	12	21	9	35	X	0.15	0.17	3	X	40	1.8	nd	530	nd
Ham & cheese	154	380	23	33	17	60	X	0.75	0.34	5	X	200	2.7	nd	1350	nd
Turkey deluxe	236	510	28	46	24	70	X	0.45	0.34	8	X	80	2.7	nd	1220	nd
Club sandwich	252	560	30	43	30	100	X	0.68	0.43	7	X	200	3.6	nd	1610	nd

Source: Consumer Affairs, Arby's Inc., Atlanta, Georgia. Nutritional analysis by Technological Resources, Camden, New Jersey.

	Weight (g)	Energy (kcal)	Protein (g)	Carbohydrate (g)	Fat (g)	Cholesterol (mg)	Vitamin A (IU)	Thiamin (mg)	Riboflavin (mg)	Niacin (mg)	Vitamin C (mg)	Calcium (mg)	Iron (mg)	Phosphorus (mg)	Sodium (mg)	Zinc (mg)
BURGER CHEF®																
Hamburger	91	244	11	29	9	27	114	0.17	0.16	2.7	1.2	45	2.0	106	nd	1.6
Cheeseburger	104	290	14	29	13	39	267	0.18	0.21	2.8	1.2	132	2.2	202	nd	1.9
Double cheeseburger	145	420	24	30	22	77	431	0.20	0.32	4.4	1.2	223	3.2	355	nd	3.6
Fish filet	179	547	21	46	31	43	400	0.23	0.22	2.7	1.0	145	2.2	302	nd	1.2
Super Shef® sandwich	252	563	29	44	30	105	754	0.31	0.40	6.0	9.3	205	4.5	377	nd	4.5
Big Shef® sandwich	186	569	23	38	36	81	279	0.26	0.31	4.7	1.0	152	3.6	280	nd	3.4
TOP Shef® sandwich	138	661	41	36	38	134	273	0.35	0.47	8.1	0	194	5.4	445	nd	5.9
Funmeal® feast	—	545	15	55	30	27	123	0.25	0.21	4.6	12.8	61	2.8	183	nd	1.6
Rancher® platter*	316	640	32	33	42	106	1750*	0.29	0.38	8.6	23.5	66	5.3	326	nd	5.6
Mariner® platter*	373	734	29	78	34	35	2069*	0.34	0.23	5.2	23.5	63	3.3	397	nd	1.2
French fries, small	68	250	2	20	19	0	0	0.07	0.04	1.7	11.5	9	0.7	62	nd	<0.1
French fries, large	85	351	3	28	26	0	0	0.10	0.06	2.4	16.2	13	0.9	86	nd	<0.1
Vanilla shake (12 oz)	336	380	13	60	10	40	387	0.10	0.66	0.5	0	497	0.3	392	nd	1.3
Chocolate shake (12 oz)	336	403	10	72	9	36	292	0.16	0.76	0.4	0	449	1.1	429	nd	1.6
Hot chocolate	—	198	8	23	8	30	288	0.93	0.39	0.3	2.1	271	0.7	245	nd	1.1

*Includes salad.
Source: Burger Chef Systems, Inc., Indianapolis, Indiana. Nutritional analysis from *Handbook No. 8*. Washington: US Dept of Agriculture.

	Weight (g)	Energy (kcal)	Protein (g)	Carbohydrate (g)	Fat (g)	Cholesterol (mg)	Vitamin A (IU)	Thiamin (mg)	Riboflavin (mg)	Niacin (mg)	Vitamin C (mg)	Calcium (mg)	Iron (mg)	Phosphorus (mg)	Sodium (mg)	Zinc (mg)
CHURCH'S FRIED CHICKEN®																
White chicken portion	100	327	21	10	23	nd	160	0.10	0.18	7.2	0.7	94	1.0	nd	498	nd
Dark chicken portion	100	305	22	7	21	nd	140	0.10	0.27	5.3	1.0	15	1.3	nd	475	nd

Source: Church's Fried Chicken, San Antonio, Texas. Nutritional analysis by Medallion Laboratories, Minneapolis, Minnesota.

	Weight (g)	Energy (kcal)	Protein (g)	Carbohydrate (g)	Fat (g)	Cholesterol (mg)	Vitamin A (IU)	Thiamin (mg)	Riboflavin (mg)	Niacin (mg)	Vitamin C (mg)	Calcium (mg)	Iron (mg)	Phosphorus (mg)	Sodium (mg)	Zinc (mg)
DAIRY QUEEN®																
Frozen dessert	113	180	5	27	6	20	100	0.09	0.17	X	X	150	X	100	nd	nd
DQ cone, small	71	110	3	18	3	10	100	0.03	0.14	X	X	100	X	60	nd	nd
DQ cone, regular	142	230	6	35	7	20	300	0.09	0.26	X	X	200	X	150	nd	nd
DQ cone, large	213	340	10	52	10	30	400	0.15	0.43	X	X	300	X	200	nd	nd
DQ dip cone, small	78	150	3	20	7	10	100	0.03	0.17	X	X	100	X	80	nd	nd
DQ dip cone, regular	156	300	7	40	13	20	300	0.09	0.34	X	X	200	0.4	150	nd	nd
DQ dip cone, large	234	450	10	58	20	30	400	0.12	0.51	X	X	300	0.4	200	nd	nd
DQ sundae, small	106	170	4	30	4	15	100	0.03	0.17	X	X	100	0.7	100	nd	nd

The letters "nd" indicate no data available; X = Less than 2% U.S. RDA; tr = trace.

continued

F

Appendix F continued

Dairy Queen—continued

	Weight (g)	Energy (kcal)	Protein (g)	Carbohydrate (g)	Fat (g)	Cholesterol (mg)	Vitamin A (IU)	Thiamin (mg)	Riboflavin (mg)	Niacin (mg)	Vitamin C (mg)	Calcium (mg)	Iron (mg)	Phosphorus (mg)	Sodium (mg)	Zinc (mg)
DQ sundae, regular	177	290	6	51	7	20	300	0.06	0.26	X	X	200	1.1	150	nd	nd
DQ sundae, large	248	400	9	71	9	30	400	0.09	0.43	0.4	X	300	1.8	250	nd	nd
DQ malt, small	241	340	10	51	11	30	400	0.06	0.34	0.4	2.4	300	1.8	200	nd	nd
DQ malt, regular	418	600	15	89	20	50	750	0.12	0.60	0.8	3.6	500	3.6	400	nd	nd
DQ malt, large	588	840	22	125	28	70	750	0.15	0.85	1.2	6	600	5.4	600	nd	nd
DQ float	397	330	6	59	8	20	100	0.12	0.17	X	X	200	X	200	nd	nd
DQ banana split	383	540	10	91	15	30	750	0.60	0.60	0.8	18	350	1.8	250	nd	nd
DQ parfait	284	460	10	81	11	30	400	0.12	0.43	0.4	X	300	1.8	250	nd	nd
DQ freeze	397	520	11	89	13	35	200	0.15	0.34	X	X	300	X	250	nd	nd
Mr. Misty® freeze	411	500	10	87	12	35	200	0.15	0.34	X	X	300	X	200	nd	nd
Mr. Misty® float	404	440	6	85	8	20	100	0.12	0.17	X	X	200	X	200	nd	nd
"Dilly"® bar	85	240	4	22	15	10	100	0.06	0.17	X	X	100	0.4	100	nd	nd
DQ sandwich	60	140	3	24	4	10	100	0.03	0.14	0.4	X	60	0.4	60	nd	nd
Mr. Misty Kiss®	89	70	0	17	0	0	X	X	X	X	X	X	X	X	nd	nd
Brazier® cheese dog	113	330	15	24	19	nd	nd	nd	0.18	3.3	nd	168	1.6	182	nd	1.9
Brazier® chili dog	128	330	13	25	20	nd	nd	0.15	0.23	3.9	11.0	86	2.0	139	939	1.8
Brazier® dog	99	273	11	23	15	nd	nd	0.12	0.15	2.6	11.0	75	1.5	104	868	1.4
Fish sandwich	170	400	20	41	17	nd	tr	0.15	0.26	3.0	tr	60	1.1	200	nd	0.3
Fish sandwich w/ch	177	440	24	39	21	nd	100	0.15	0.26	3.0	tr	150	0.4	250	nd	0.3
Super Brazier® dog	182	518	20	41	30	nd	tr	0.42	0.44	7.0	14.0	158	4.3	195	1552	2.8
Super Brazier® dog w/ch	203	593	26	43	36	nd	nd	0.43	0.48	8.1	14.0	297	4.4	312	1986	3.5
Super Brazier® chili dog	210	555	23	42	33	nd	nd	0.42	0.48	8.8	18.0	158	4.0	231	1640	2.8
Brazier® fries, small	71	200	2	25	10	nd	tr	0.06	tr	0.8	3.6	tr	0.4	100	nd	tr
Brazier® fries, large	113	320	3	40	16	nd	tr	0.09	0.03	1.2	4.8	tr	0.4	150	nd	0.3
Brazier® onion rings	85	300	6	33	17	nd	tr	0.09	tr	0.4	2.4	20	0.4	60	nd	0.3

Source: International Dairy Queen, Inc, Minneapolis, Minnesota. Nutritional analysis by Raltech Scientific Services, Inc (formerly WARF), Madison, Wisconsin. (Nutritional analysis not applicable in the state of Texas.)

JACK IN THE BOX®

	Weight (g)	Energy (kcal)	Protein (g)	Carbohydrate (g)	Fat (g)	Cholesterol (mg)	Vitamin A (IU)	Thiamin (mg)	Riboflavin (mg)	Niacin (mg)	Vitamin C (mg)	Calcium (mg)	Iron (mg)	Phosphorus (mg)	Sodium (mg)	Zinc (mg)
Hamburger	97	263	13	29	11	26	49	0.27	0.18	5.6	1.1	82	2.3	115	566	1.8
Cheeseburger	109	310	16	28	15	32	338	0.27	0.21	5.4	<1.1	172	2.6	194	877	2.3
Jumbo Jack® hamburger	246	551	28	45	29	80	246	0.47	0.34	11.6	3.7	134	4.5	261	1134	4.2
Jumbo Jack® hamburger w/ch	272	628	32	45	35	110	734	0.52	0.38	11.3	4.9	273	4.6	411	1666	4.8
Regular taco	83	189	8	15	11	22	356	0.07	0.08	1.8	<0.9	116	1.2	150	460	1.3
Super taco	146	285	12	20	17	37	599	0.10	0.12	2.8	1.6	196	1.9	235	968	2.1
Moby Jack® sandwich	141	455	17	38	26	56	240	0.30	0.21	4.5	1.4	167	1.7	263	837	1.1
Breakfast Jack® sandwich	121	301	18	28	13	182	442	0.41	0.47	5.1	3.4	177	2.5	310	1037	1.8
French fries	80	270	3	31	15	13	nd	0.12	0.02	1.9	3.7	19	0.7	88	128	0.3
Onion rings	85	351	5	32	23	24	nd	0.24	0.12	3.1	<1.2	26	1.4	69	318	0.4
Apple turnover	119	411	4	45	24	17	nd	0.23	0.12	2.5	<1.2	11	1.4	33	352	0.2
Vanilla shake*	317	317	10	57	6	26	nd	0.16	0.38	0.5	<3.2	349	0.2	312	229	1.0
Strawberry shake*	328	323	11	55	7	26	nd	0.16	0.46	0.6	<3.3	371	0.6	328	241	1.1

Item																
Chocolate shake*	322	322	11	55	7	26	nd	0.16	0.64	0.6	<3.2	348	0.7	328	270	1.1
Vanilla shake	314	342	10	54	9	36	440	0.16	0.47	0.5	3.5	349	0.4	318	263	1.0
Strawberry shake	328	380	11	63	10	33	426	0.16	0.62	0.5	<3.3	351	0.3	316	268	1.0
Chocolate shake	317	365	11	59	10	35	380	0.16	0.60	0.6	<3.2	350	1.2	332	294	1.2
Ham & cheese omelette	174	425	21	32	23	355	766	0.45	0.70	3.0	<1.7	260	4.0	397	975	2.3
Double cheese omelette	166	423	19	30	25	370	797	0.33	0.68	2.5	1.7	276	3.6	370	899	2.1
Ranchero style omelette	196	414	20	33	23	343	853	0.33	0.74	2.6	<2.0	278	3.8	372	1098	2.0
French toast	180	537	15	54	29	115	522	0.56	0.30	4.4	9.2	119	3.0	256	1130	1.8
Pancakes	232	626	16	79	27	87	488	0.63	0.44	4.6	<26.2	105	2.8	633	1670	1.9
Scrambled eggs	267	719	26	55	44	259	694	0.69	0.56	5.2	<12.8	257	5.0	483	1110	3.0

*Special formula for shakes sold in California, Arizona, Texas and Washington. Source: Jack-in-the-Box, Foodmaker, Inc, San Diego, California. Nutritional analysis by Raltech Scientific Services, Inc (formerly WARF), Madison, Wisconsin.

KENTUCKY FRIED CHICKEN®

Item																
Original Recipe® dinner*																
Wing & rib	322	603	30	48	32	133	25.5	0.22	0.19	10.0	36.6	nd	nd	nd	nd	nd
Wing & thigh	341	661	33	48	38	172	25.5	0.24	0.27	8.4	36.6	nd	nd	nd	nd	nd
Drum & thigh	346	643	35	46	35	180	25.5	0.25	0.32	8.5	36.6	nd	nd	nd	nd	nd
Extra crispy dinner*																
Wing & rib	349	755	33	60	43	132	25.5	0.31	0.29	10.4	36.6	nd	nd	nd	nd	nd
Wing & thigh	371	812	36	58	48	176	25.5	0.31	0.35	10.3	36.6	nd	nd	nd	nd	nd
Drum & thigh	376	765	38	55	44	183	25.5	0.32	0.38	10.4	36.6	nd	nd	nd	nd	nd
Mashed potatoes	85	64	2	12	1	0	<18	<0.01	0.02	0.8	4.9	nd	nd	nd	nd	nd
Gravy	14	23	0	1	2	0	<3	0.00	0.01	0.1	<0.2	nd	nd	nd	nd	nd
Cole slaw	91	122	1	13	8	7	nd	nd	nd	nd	nd	nd	nd	nd	nd	nd
Rolls	21	61	2	11	1	1	<5	0.10	0.04	1.0	0.3	nd	nd	nd	nd	nd
Corn (5.5-inch ear)	135	169	5	31	3	X	162	0.12	0.07	1.2	2.6	nd	nd	nd	nd	nd

*Includes two pieces of chicken, mashed potato and gravy, cole slaw, and roll.
Source: Kentucky Fried Chicken, Inc, Louisville, Kentucky. Nutritional analysis by Raltech Scientific Services, Inc (formerly WARF), Madison, Wisconsin.

LONG JOHN SILVER'S®

Item																
Fish w/batter (2 pc)	136	366	22	21	22	nd	nd	nd	nd	nd	nd	nd	nd	nd	nd	nd
Fish w/batter (3 pc)	207	549	32	32	32	nd	nd	nd	nd	nd	nd	nd	nd	nd	nd	nd
Treasure Chest®	143	506	30	32	33	nd	nd	nd	nd	nd	nd	nd	nd	nd	nd	nd
Chicken Planks® (4 pc)	166	457	27	35	23	nd	nd	nd	nd	nd	nd	nd	nd	nd	nd	nd
Peg Legs® w/batter (5 pc)	125	350	22	26	28	nd	nd	nd	nd	nd	nd	nd	nd	nd	nd	nd
Ocean scallops (6 pc)	120	283	11	30	13	nd	nd	nd	nd	nd	nd	nd	nd	nd	nd	nd
Shrimp w/batter (6 pc)	88	268	8	30	13	nd	nd	nd	nd	nd	nd	nd	nd	nd	nd	nd
Breaded oysters (6 pc)	156	441	13	53	19	nd	nd	nd	nd	nd	nd	nd	nd	nd	nd	nd
Breaded clams	142	617	18	61	34	nd	nd	nd	nd	nd	nd	nd	nd	nd	nd	nd
Fish sandwich	193	337	22	49	31	nd	nd	nd	nd	nd	nd	nd	nd	nd	nd	nd
French fries	85	288	4	33	16	nd	nd	nd	nd	nd	nd	nd	nd	nd	nd	nd
Cole slaw	113	138	1	16	8	nd	nd	nd	nd	nd	nd	nd	nd	nd	nd	nd
Corn on the cob (1 ear)	150	176	5	29	4	nd	nd	nd	nd	nd	nd	nd	nd	nd	nd	nd
Hushpuppies (3)	45	153	3	20	7	nd	nd	nd	nd	nd	nd	nd	nd	nd	nd	nd
Clam chowder (8 oz)	170	107	5	15	3	nd	nd	nd	nd	nd	nd	nd	nd	nd	nd	nd

Source: Long John Silver's Food Shoppes, Lexington, Kentucky. Nutritional analysis by L. V. Packett, PhD, The Department of Nutrition and Food Science, University of Kentucky.

The letters "nd" indicate no data available; X = Less than 2% U.S. RDA; tr = trace.

Appendix F continued

	Weight (g)	Energy (kcal)	Protein (g)	Carbohydrate (g)	Fat (g)	Cholesterol (mg)	Vitamin A (IU)	Thiamin (mg)	Riboflavin (mg)	Niacin (mg)	Vitamin C (mg)	Calcium (mg)	Iron (mg)	Phosphorus (mg)	Sodium (mg)	Zinc (mg)
McDONALD'S®																
Egg McMuffin®	138	327	19	31	15	229	97	0.47	0.44	3.8	<1.4	226	2.9	322	885	1.9
English muffin, buttered	63	186	5	30	5	13	164	0.28	0.49	2.6	0.8	117	1.5	74	318	0.5
Hotcakes w/butter & syrup	214	500	8	94	10	47	257	0.26	0.36	2.3	4.7	103	2.2	501	1070	0.7
Sausage (pork)	53	206	9	tr	19	43	<32	0.27	0.11	2.1	0.5	16	0.8	95	615	1.5
Scrambled eggs	98	180	13	3	13	349	652	0.08	0.47	0.2	1.2	61	2.5	264	205	1.7
Hashbrown potatoes	55	125	2	14	7	7	<14	0.06	<0.01	0.8	4.1	5	0.4	67	325	0.2
Big Mac®	204	563	26	41	33	86	530	0.39	0.37	6.5	2.2	157	4.0	314	1010	4.7
Cheeseburger	115	307	15	30	14	37	345	0.25	0.23	3.8	1.6	132	2.4	205	767	2.6
Hamburger	102	255	12	30	10	25	82	0.25	0.18	4.0	1.7	51	2.3	126	520	2.1
Quarter Pounder®	166	424	24	33	22	67	133	0.32	0.28	6.5	<1.7	63	4.1	249	735	5.1
Quarter Pounder® w/ch	194	524	30	32	31	96	660	0.31	0.37	7.4	2.7	219	4.3	382	1236	5.7
Filet-O-Fish®	139	432	14	37	25	47	42	0.26	0.20	2.6	<1.4	93	1.7	229	781	0.9
Regular fries	68	220	3	26	12	9	<17	0.12	0.02	2.3	12.5	9	0.6	101	109	0.3
Apple pie	85	253	2	29	14	12	<34	0.02	0.02	0.2	<0.8	14	0.6	27	398	0.2
Cherry pie	88	260	2	32	14	13	114	0.03	0.02	0.4	<0.8	12	0.6	27	427	0.2
McDonaldland® cookies	67	308	4	49	11	10	<27	0.23	0.23	2.9	0.9	12	1.5	74	358	0.3
Chocolate shake	291	383	10	66	9	30	349	0.12	0.44	0.5	<2.9	320	0.8	335	300	1.4
Strawberry shake	290	362	9	62	9	32	377	0.12	0.44	0.4	4.1	322	0.2	313	207	1.2
Vanilla shake	291	352	9	60	8	31	349	0.12	0.70	0.3	3.2	329	0.2	314	201	1.2
Hot fudge sundae	164	310	7	46	11	18	230	0.07	0.31	1.1	2.5	215	0.6	236	175	1.0
Caramel sundae	165	328	7	53	10	26	279	0.07	0.31	1.0	3.6	200	0.2	230	195	0.9
Strawberry sundae	164	289	7	46	9	20	230	0.07	0.30	1.0	2.8	174	0.4	80	96	0.8

Source: McDonald's Corporation, Oak Brook, Illinois. Nutritional analysis by Raltech Scientific Services, Inc. (formerly WARF), Madison, Wisconsin.

	Weight (g)	Energy (kcal)	Protein (g)	Carbohydrate (g)	Fat (g)	Cholesterol (mg)	Vitamin A (IU)	Thiamin (mg)	Riboflavin (mg)	Niacin (mg)	Vitamin C (mg)	Calcium (mg)	Iron (mg)	Phosphorus (mg)	Sodium (mg)	Zinc (mg)
TACO BELL®																
Bean burrito	166	343	11	48	12	nd	1657	0.37	0.22	2.2	15.2	98	2.8	173	272	nd
Beef burrito	184	466	30	37	21	nd	1675	0.30	0.39	7.0	15.2	83	4.6	288	327	nd
Beefy tostada	184	291	19	21	15	nd	3450	0.16	0.27	3.3	12.7	208	3.4	265	138	nd
Bellbeefer®	123	221	15	23	7	nd	2961	0.15	0.20	3.7	10.0	40	2.6	140	231	nd
Bellbeefer® w/ch	137	278	19	23	12	nd	3146	0.16	0.27	3.7	10.0	147	2.7	208	330	nd
Burrito Supreme®	225	457	21	43	22	nd	3462	0.33	0.35	4.7	16.0	121	3.8	245	367	nd
Combination burrito	175	404	21	43	16	nd	1666	0.34	0.31	4.6	15.2	91	3.7	230	300	nd
Enchirito®	207	454	25	42	21	nd	1178	0.31	0.37	4.7	9.5	259	3.8	338	1175	nd
Pintos 'n cheese	158	168	11	21	5	nd	3123	0.26	0.16	0.9	9.3	150	2.3	210	102	nd
Taco	83	186	15	14	8	nd	120	0.09	0.16	2.9	0.2	120	2.5	175	79	nd
Tostada	138	179	9	25	6	nd	3152	0.18	0.15	0.8	9.7	191	2.3	186	101	nd

Sources: 1) *Menu Item Portions.* San Antonio, Texas: Taco Bell Co, July 1976. 2) Adams CF: Nutritive value of American foods in common units, in *Handbook No. 456.* Washington: USDA Agricultural Research Service, November 1975. 3) Church EF, Church HN (eds): *Food Values of Portions Commonly Used,* ed 12. Philadelphia: JB Lippincott Co, 1975. 4) Valley Baptist Medical Center, Food Service Department: Descriptions of Mexican American Foods. Fort Atkinson, WI: NASCO.

WENDY'S®

Single hamburger	200	470	26	34	26	70	94	0.24	0.36	5.8	0.6	84	5.3	239	774	4.8
Double hamburger	285	670	44	34	40	125	128	0.43	0.54	10.6	1.5	138	8.2	364	980	8.4
Triple hamburger	360	850	65	33	51	205	220	0.47	0.68	14.7	2.0	104	10.7	525	1217	13.5
Single w/cheese	240	580	33	34	34	90	221	0.38	0.43	6.3	0.7	228	5.4	315	1085	5.5
Double w/cheese	325	800	50	41	48	155	439	0.49	0.75	11.4	2.3	177	10.2	489	1414	10.1
Triple w/cheese	400	1040	72	35	68	225	472	0.80	0.84	15.1	3.4	371	10.9	712	1848	14.3
Chili	250	230	19	21	8	25	1188	0.22	0.25	3.4	2.9	83	4.4	168	1065	3.7
French fries	120	330	5	41	16	5	40	0.14	0.07	3.0	6.4	16	1.2	196	112	0.5
Frosty	250	390	9	54	16	45	355	0.20	0.60	X	0.7	270	0.9	278	247	1.0

Source: Wendy's International, Inc, Dublin, Ohio. Nutritional analysis by Medallion Laboratories, Minneapolis, Minnesota.

BEVERAGES

Coffee*	180	2	tr	tr	tr	nd	0	0	tr	0.5	0	4	0.2	7	2	nd
Tea*	180	2	tr	nd	tr	nd	0	0	0.04	0.1	1	5	0.2	4	nd	nd
Orange juice	183	82	1	20	tr	nd	366	0.17	0.02	0.6	82.4	17	0.2	29	2	nd
Chocolate milk	250	213	9	28	9	nd	330	0.08	0.40	0.3	3.0	278	0.5	235	118	nd
Skim milk	245	88	9	13	tr	nd	10	0.09	0.44	0.2	2.0	296	0.1	233	127	nd
Whole milk	244	159	9	12	9	27	342	0.07	0.41	0.2	2.4	188	tr	227	122	nd
Coca-Cola®	246	96	0	24	0	nd	nd	nd	nd	nd	nd	nd	nd	40	20‡	nd
Fanta® ginger ale	244	84	0	21	0	nd	nd	nd	nd	nd	nd	nd	nd	0	30‡	nd
Fanta® grape	247	114	0	29	0	nd	nd	nd	nd	nd	nd	nd	nd	0	21‡	nd
Fanta® orange	248	117	0	30	0	nd	nd	nd	nd	nd	nd	nd	nd	0	21‡	nd
Fanta® root beer	246	103	0	27	0	nd	nd	nd	nd	nd	nd	nd	nd	0	23‡	nd
Mr. Pibb®	245	95	0	25	0	nd	nd	nd	nd	nd	nd	nd	nd	29	23‡	nd
Mr. Pibb® w/o sugar	236	1	0	tr	0	nd	nd	nd	nd	nd	nd	nd	nd	28	37‡	nd
Sprite®	245	95	0	24	0	nd	nd	nd	nd	nd	nd	nd	nd	0	42‡	nd
Sprite® w/o sugar	236	3	0	0	0	nd	nd	nd	nd	nd	nd	nd	nd	0	42‡	nd
Tab®	236	tr	0	tr	0	nd	nd	nd	nd	nd	nd	nd	nd	30	30‡	nd
Fresca®	236	2	0	0	0	nd	nd	nd	nd	nd	nd	nd	nd	0	38	nd

*6-oz serving; all other data are for 8-oz serving. ‡Value when bottling water with average sodium content (12 mg/8 oz) is used.
Sources: 1) Adams CF: Nutritive value of American foods in common units, in *Handbook No. 456*. Washington: USDA Agricultural Research Service, November 1975; 2) The Coca-Cola Company, Atlanta, Georgia, January 1977; 3) *American Hospital Formulary Service*. Washington, American Society of Hospital Pharmacists, Section 28:20, March 1978.

Reprinted with permission from Young EA, Brennan EH, Irving GL: Nutritional analysis of fast foods. *Dietetic Currents* 8:5-12, 1981. Published by Ross Laboratories, Columbus, Ohio 43216.

The letters "nd" indicate no data available; X = Less than 2% U.S. RDA; tr = trace.

Appendix G   Dietary Fiber Content of Foods*

Food**	Approximate measure	Dietary fiber (g)	Food**	Approximate measure	Dietary fiber (g)
Fruits			**Vegetables**		
Apple	1 med	3.2	Asparagus	4 spears	0.9
Apricots	3	2.4	Beans, baked	1 c	18.6
Banana	1 med	5.9	Green beans	1 c	3.5
Cherries	10	1.3	Broccoli tops	1 c	5.6
Cranberries	$\frac{1}{2}$ c	2.3	Brussels sprouts	1 c	6.5
Dates, dried	10	7.0	Cabbage, shredded	1 c	1.9
Figs, dried	2	18.5	Carrots	1 c	3.2
Grapes, green	20	1.1	Cauliflower	1 c	2.5
Mangoes	1	4.5	Celery	1 stalk	0.7
Cantaloupe	$\frac{1}{4}$ melon	2.5	Cucumber	6 slices	0.2
Honeydew	$\frac{1}{4}$ melon	2.7	Lettuce	1 c	0.8
Orange	1 med	4.5	Mushrooms	1 c	1.8
Peach	1 med	2.1	Onion	1 small	1.4
Pear	1 med	3.1	Peas	1 c	11.3
Pineapple, canned	1 c	2.2	Pepper, sweet	1 c	0.9
Pineapple, fresh	1 c	1.9	Potato, boiled	1 med	1.4
Plums	2	2.5	Spinach	1 c	3.5
Prunes, dried	4	5.2	Tomato	1 med	3.0
Raisins	$\frac{1}{2}$ c	5.4	**Breads and Cereals**		
Strawberries	1 c	3.3	White bread	1 slice	0.8
			Whole wheat bread	1 slice	2.4
			All-Bran	$\frac{1}{2}$ c	9.9
Nuts			Cornflakes	1 c	2.8
Almonds	10	3.6	Grape Nuts	1 c	5.3
Brazil nuts	10	5.4	Rice Krispies	1 c	1.4
Peanuts	$\frac{1}{2}$ c	5.7	Shredded Wheat	1 biscuit	3.0
Peanut butter	2 T	2.1	Special K	1 c	1.7

*Paul, A.A., and D.A.T. Southgate. *McCance and Widdowson's composition of foods*. London: Medical Research Council, 1978.
**All foods fresh unless stated otherwise.
Reprinted with permission from Slavin JL: Dietary fiber. *Dietetic Currents* 10:27-32, 1983. Published by Ross Laboratories, Columbus, Ohio 43216.

Appendix H   Cholesterol Content of Foods

Food	Approximate measure	Weight (g)	Cholesterol (mg)
Beef, oven-cooked:			
Lean cut, lean only	3 oz	85	56
Fatty cut, lean and fat	3 oz	85	70
Beef potpie	1 piece	210	42
Beef stew	1 cup	245	72
Butter	1 tbsp	14	31
Cakes:			
Pound[1]	1 slice	33	68
White, 2 layer with chocolate icing[2]	1 piece	71	3
Yellow, 2 layer with chocolate icing[1]	1 piece	69	36
Cheese:			
American	1 oz	28	27
Blue	1 oz	28	21
Camembert	1 oz	28	20
Cheddar	1 oz	28	30
Cottage:			
Creamed, 4% fat:			
Large curd	1 cup	225	34
Small curd	1 cup	210	31
Lowfat, 1% fat	1 cup	226	10
Uncreamed, dry curd, less than $\frac{1}{2}$% fat	1 cup	145	10
Cream	1 oz	28	31
Mozzarella, made with part skim milk	1 oz	28	16
Muenster	1 oz	28	27
Parmesan, grated	1 tbsp[2]	5	4
Ricotta, made with part skim milk	1 oz	28	9
Swiss	1 oz	28	26
Chicken à la king	1 cup	245	220
Chicken potpie	1 piece	232	56
Chili with beef	1 cup	255	28
Chocolate, milk (20% milk solids)[3]	1 oz	28	5
Coconut oil	1 tbsp	14	0
Coffee whitener:			
Liquid, frozen (contains coconut or palm kernel oil)	$\frac{1}{2}$ fl oz	15	0
Powdered (contains coconut or palm kernel oil)	1 tbsp	6	0
Cookies:			
Brownies, with chocolate icing[1]	1 brownie	25	13
Chocolate chip[4]	4 cookies	40	21
Vanilla wafers[4]	10 cookies	40	25
Corn oil	1 tbsp	14	0
Crackers:			
Graham	2 crackers	14	0
Saltines[5]	4 crackers	11	3
Cream, sour, cultured	1 tbsp	12	5
Cream, sweet:			
Half-and-half (cream and milk)	1 tbsp	15	6
Light, coffee, or table	1 tbsp	15	10
Heavy, whipping, unwhipped	1 tbsp	15	21
Cupcakes, with chocolate icing[1]	1 cupcake	36	15

Appendix H continued Food	Approximate measure	Weight (g)	Cholesterol (mg)
Dessert toppings (nondairy):			
Powdered, made with whole milk	1 tbsp	4	trace
Pressurized	1 tbsp	4	0
Doughnuts, cake type[4]	1 doughnut	25	10
Doughnuts, yeast-leavened[4]	1 doughnut	50	13
Eggnog	1 cup	254	149
Eggs, large:			
Hard cooked, shell removed	1 egg	50	274
Fried in butter	1 egg	46	246
Scrambled (milk added) in butter. Also omelet.	1 egg	64	248
Fish:			
Cooked:			
Flounder or sole (a lean fish) baked with lemon juice	3 oz	85	59
Salmon, red (a fatty fish) baked	3 oz	85	59
Canned:			
Salmon, pink, water pack, solids and liquid	3 oz	85	34
Sardines, Atlantic, oil pack, drained solids	3 oz	85	85
Tuna, chunk light, oil pack, drained solids	3 oz	85	55
Ice cream:			
Regular (about 10% fat)	1 cup	133	59
Rich (about 16% fat)	1 cup	148	88
Ice milk:			
Hardened (about 4.3% fat)	1 cup	131	18
Soft serve (about 2.6% fat)	1 cup	175	13
Lamb, loin chop:			
Lean only	3 oz	85	80
Lean and fat	3 oz	85	82
Lard	1 tbsp	13	12
Liver, beef, fried	3 oz	85	372
Margarine, regular (at least 80% fat):			
Stick:			
Corn oil	1 tbsp	14	0
Soybean oil	1 tbsp	14	0
Tub:			
Corn oil	1 tbsp	14	0
Soybean oil	1 tbsp	14	0
Spread (about 60% fat):			
Stick	1 tbsp	14	0
Tub	1 tbsp	14	0
Margarine, diet (about 40% fat), tub	1 tbsp	14	0
Mayonnaise	1 tbsp	14	8
Milk, fluid:			
Whole, 3.3% fat	1 cup	244	33
Lowfat, 2% fat	1 cup	245	18
Lowfat, 1% fat	1 cup	245	10
Nonfat, skim	1 cup	245	5
Buttermilk, cultured	1 cup	245	9
Milkshake, thick, vanilla	1 container	313	37
Olive oil	1 tbsp	14	0

H

Appendix H continued Food	Approximate measure	Weight (g)	Cholesterol (mg)
Palm kernel oil	1 tbsp	14	0
Palm oil	1 tbsp	14	0
Peanut butter	1 tbsp	16	0
Peanut oil	1 tbsp	14	0
Pizza with cheese[6]	1 sector	60	13
Pork:			
Ham, roasted	3 oz	85	80
Bacon, fried crisp	2 slices	13	11
Potatoes, french-fried (fried in edible tallow)[7]	10 strips	50	6
Poultry:			
Dark meat, fried	3 oz	85	82
Light meat, fried	3 oz	85	76
Safflower oil	1 tbsp	14	0
Sausages and cold cuts:			
Bologna (beef and pork)	1 slice	28	16
Braunschweiger	1 slice	28	44
Frankfurters (beef)	1 frank	57	27
Salami, cooked (beef and pork)	1 slice	28	18
Shellfish:			
Raw:			
Clams, unspecified	3 oz	85	42
Oysters, Eastern	3 oz	85	42
Canned:			
Crabmeat	3 oz	85	85
Shrimp, dry pack	3 oz	85	128
Sherbet (about 2% fat)	1 cup	193	14
Shortening (animal and vegetable fat)	1 tbsp	13	7
Shortening (vegetable)	1 tbsp	13	0
Soybean oil (partially hydrogenated)	1 tbsp	14	0
Soybean-cottonseed oil blend (partially hydrogenated)	1 tbsp	14	0
Sunflower oil	1 tbsp	14	0
Tallow, edible	1 tbsp	13	14
Veal cutlet (1 cutlet)	3 oz	85	86
Yogurt:			
With added milk solids:			
Made with lowfat milk	1 container	227	11
Made with nonfat milk	1 container	227	4
Without added milk solids, made with whole milk	1 container	227	29

[1]Major sources of cholesterol are eggs and butter.
[2]Major sources of cholesterol are milk and butter.
[3]Source of cholesterol is milk solids.
[4]Major source of cholesterol is eggs.
[5]Major source of cholesterol is animal shortening.
[6]Source of cholesterol is cheese.
[7]Source of cholesterol is tallow.

Adapted from Weihrauch, J.L. 1984. *Provisional table on the fatty acid and cholesterol content of selected foods.* Washington, DC: Data Research Branch, Consumer Nutrition Division, United States Department of Agriculture.

Appendix I Folacin Content of Foods
(Values pertain to edible portions.)

Food	Approximate measure	Total folacin (μg)
Almonds	1 c	136
Apples, raw	1 medium	13
Applesauce, sweetened	1 c	3
Apricots, dried	1 c	18
Asparagus, raw	1 c	86
Avocados, raw	$\frac{1}{2}$ medium	59
Bagel	1	13
Bananas, raw	1 medium	33
Barbecue sauce	1 tbsp	1
Beans, common, mature seeds		
White, canned, baked with tomato sauce	1 c	61
Red, cooked	1 c	68
Pinto, mature seeds, dry, cooked	1 c	112
Beans, Lima, mature seeds, cooked	1 c	82
Beans, Lima, frozen	1 c	50
Beans, snap		
Green		
Cooked, drained	1 c	50
Frozen	1 c	41
Yellow or wax, frozen	1 c	42
Bean sprouts, canned	1 c	12
Beef		
Separable lean, cooked	3 oz	3
Ground, cooked	3 oz	3
Beets, common, red, cooked	1 c	133
Beverages, alcoholic		
Beer	12 fl oz	20
Wines		
Dessert, sweet	3.5 fl oz	2
Table, red	3.5 fl oz	1
Table, white	3.5 fl oz	0
Biscuits, from mix	1 medium	2
Blueberries, raw	1 c	9
Brazil nuts, shelled	1 c	6
Bread		
Cornbread	$1\frac{1}{2}$ oz	4
French/Vienna	1 slice	10
Mixed grain	1 slice	18
Raisin	1 slice	10
Rye	1 slice	6
White	1 slice	10
Whole wheat	1 slice	16
Breakfast cereals, dry		
Farina	1 c	43
Oatmeal	1 c	42

Appendix I   continued

Food	Approximate measure	Total folacin (μg)
Breakfast cereals, ready-to-eat, not fortified with folacin		
Cornflakes	1 oz	3
Oats, with added wheat gluten	1 oz	6
Rice, puffed	1 oz	6
Wheat germ, toasted	1 oz	118
Wheat and malted barley granules	1 oz	15
Wheat, shredded	1 oz	14
Broccoli spears		
Raw	3 medium	244
Cooked	1 medium	101
Brussels sprouts, cooked	1 c (7–8 sprouts)	56
Butter	1 Tbsp	<0.5
Cabbage		
Common varieties		
Raw	1 c	59
Cooked	1 c	26
Red, raw	1 c	31
Cabbage, Chinese (also called celery cabbage or petsai), raw	1 c	62
Cakes		
Angel food	2 oz	5
Chocolate	2.5 oz	7
Chocolate with icing	1 slice (3 in. high; $2\frac{3}{8}$ in. arc)	6
Sponge	1 slice (3 in. high; $2\frac{1}{4}$ in. arc)	3
White	2.5 oz	4
Candy, milk chocolate, plain	1 oz	2
Carrots		
Raw	1 medium	19
Cooked	1 c	37
Cashew nuts, roasted	1 c	95
Cauliflower		
Raw	1 c	55
Cooked	1 c	42
Celery, raw	1 c	12
Cheeses, natural		
Cheddar	1 c shredded	20
Cheddar	1 oz	5
Cottage	1 c packed	29
Cream	3 oz pack	11
Cheese spread, pasteurized process	1 oz	2
Cheesecake, commercial	3 oz slice	15
Cherries, raw	1 c	9
Chicken, without skin		
Dark meat, cooked	3 oz	6
Light meat, cooked	3 oz	3
Chickpeas or garbanzos, mature seeds canned, drained	$3\frac{1}{2}$ oz	102

Appendix I continued Food	Approximate measure	Total folacin (μg)
Coconut, shredded	1 c	31
Collards, raw	1 c	56
Cookies		
Brownies with nuts/icing	1 square, 1 oz	3
Chocolate chip	1 cookie	1
Chocolate sandwich	1 cookie	<0.5
Oatmeal	1 cookie	2
Shortbread	1 cookie	1
Corn, sweet frozen	1 c	35
Cornmeal, degermed	1 c	29
Crackers		
Graham, sugar-honey	2 squares	2
Saltines	2 squares	1
Cranberries, raw	1 c	2
Cream, fluid		
Half-and-half	1 Tbsp	<0.5
Sour, cultured	1 Tbsp	1
Whipping, light	1 Tbsp	1
Cucumber, raw, pared	1 small	19
Dates, dried	10 dates	17
Doughnuts		
Cake type	1 doughnut	3
Yeast leavened	1 doughnut	8
Eggnog	$\frac{1}{2}$ c	1
Eggs		
Whole		
Raw	1 medium	29
Hard-cooked	1 medium	22
White, raw	1 medium	5
Yolk, raw	1 medium	23
Endive, raw	1 c	24
English muffins	1 whole	19
Figs, dried	1 large	2
Filberts (hazelnuts), shelled	1 c	97
Fish and shellfish		
Cod, frozen	3 oz	15
Crab, frozen	3 oz	17
Haddock, frozen	3 oz	8
Halibut, frozen	3 oz	10
Lobster, canned	3 oz	14
Ocean perch, frozen	3 oz	8
Salmon		
canned	3 oz	17
frozen	3 oz	22
Sardines, canned	1 fish	2
Scallops, frozen	3 oz	14
Shrimp		
canned	3 oz	13
frozen	3 oz	9

Appendix I continued Food	Approximate measure	Total folacin (μg)
Fish—continued		
Smelt, frozen	3 oz	14
Sole, frozen	3 oz	9
Tuna, canned	3 oz	13
Grapefruit, raw	$\frac{1}{2}$ medium	11
Grapefruit juice, fresh or frozen reconstituted	1 c	52
Grapes, red or white, raw	1 c	11
Grape juice, canned or frozen reconstituted	1 c	5
Ice cream, vanilla	1 c	3
Jam, strawberry	1 Tbsp	2
Kale, raw	1 c	66
Lamb, cooked	3 oz	3
Lemon, raw	1 medium	9
Lemonade	1 c	12
Lentils, mature seeds, dry	1 c	68
Lettuce, raw		
Leaf or head	1 c	20
Romaine	1 c	98
Limes, raw	1 lime	3
Liver		
Beef, lamb, or pork, cooked	3 oz	123
Chicken, cooked	3 oz	204
Macaroni, dry form	8-oz pkg.	27
Margarine	1 Tbsp	<0.5
Mayonnaise	1 Tbsp	<0.5
Milk, cow, fluid		
Whole, pasteurized	1 c	12
Evaporated	1 c	20
Muffins, bran	$1-1\frac{1}{2}$ oz	18
Mushrooms, raw	1 c	16
Muskmelon or cantaloupe	$\frac{1}{2}$ medium	82
Nectarines, raw	1 medium	7
Okra, raw	1 c	24
Onion, mature, dry, chopped	1 Tbsp	2
Onion, young green, raw		
Bulbs and white portion of top	1 Tbsp	2
Tops only (green portion), chopped	1 Tbsp	5
Oranges, raw	1 medium	65
Orange juice, fresh or frozen reconstituted	1 c	136
Pancakes, from mix	1, 4-in. diameter	3
Parsley, raw	1 Tbsp	5
Parsnips, raw	1 c	87
Peaches		
Raw	1 medium	8
Canned, heavy syrup, slices	$\frac{1}{2}$ c	3

Appendix I continued

Food	Approximate measure	Total folacin (μg)
Peanuts, roasted	1 c	153
Peanut butter	1 Tbsp	13
Pears		
Raw	1 medium	23
Canned, heavy syrup, slices	$\frac{1}{2}$ cup	1
Peas, green, frozen	1 c	77
Pecans, shelled	1 c	26
Peppers, sweet, immature, green, raw	1 medium	31
Pies		
Apple	$\frac{1}{6}$ of pie (9 inch)	6
Chocolate cream	$\frac{1}{6}$ of pie	14
Lemon meringue	$\frac{1}{6}$ of pie	14
Pineapple		
Raw	1 c	17
Canned, heavy syrup, chunks	$\frac{1}{2}$ c	6
Pizza		
Cheese	$\frac{1}{8}$ pie, $13\frac{3}{4}$-in. diameter	24
Sausage	$\frac{1}{8}$ pie, $13\frac{3}{4}$-in. diameter	23
Plums		
Raw	1 medium	3
Canned, heavy syrup	3 medium	3
Pork, separable lean		
Cooked	3 oz	4
Ham, smoked	3 oz	9
Potatoes, cooked		
French fried	10 pieces	11
Hashed brown	1 c	26
Mashed	1 c	21
Pretzels	10 sticks, small	<0.5
Prunes, dried, softenized, raw	1 medium	1
Pumpkin		
Raw	1 c	36
Cooked	1 c	47
Radishes, common, raw	4 small	9
Raisins, natural (unbleached), raw	1 c	6
Raspberries, frozen, sweetened	$\frac{1}{2}$ c	32
Rhubarb, raw	1 c	9
Rice		
Brown	1 c	30
White	1 c	18
Parboiled	1 c	20
Rolls		
Dinner	1 roll	11
French	1 roll	21
Hot dog/hamburger	1 roll	15
Sweet	1 roll	20

Appendix I continued Food	Approximate measure	Total folacin (μg)
Rutabagas		
Raw	1 c	38
Cooked, mashed	1 c	50
Sausages, cold cuts, and luncheon meats		
Boiled ham	1 slice (1 oz)	1
Bologna	1 slice (1 oz)	1
Frankfurters, unheated	1 (5-in. long, $\frac{3}{4}$-in. diameter)	2
Liverwurst	1 slice (1 oz)	8
Pork, spiced	1 slice (1 oz)	1
Soups, commercial, canned		
Asparagus, cream of	1 c	47
Beef broth	1 c	10
Clam chowder	1 c	18
Mushroom, cream of	1 c	7
Vegetable beef	1 c	15
Soybeans, mature, dry	1 c	359
Soybean products, fermented		
Natto	3.5 oz	126
Tempeh	3.5 oz	156
Soy sauce	1 Tbsp	5
Spaghetti, dry form	8-oz pkg.	27
Spinach		
Raw	1 c	106
Cooked	1 c	164
Squash, summer		
Raw	1 c	40
Frozen, cooked	1 c	21
Strawberries		
Raw	1 c	24
Frozen, sweetened	1 c	24
Sweet potatoes, cooked	1 medium	26
Tangerines, raw	1 medium	18
Tomatoes, raw	1 medium	53
Tomato catsup	1 Tbsp	1
Tomato juice, canned	1 c	63
Tortillas, corn	1	5
Turkey, without skin		
Dark meat, cooked	3 oz	6
Light meat, cooked	3 oz	4
Turnips, raw	1 c	26
Turnip greens, raw	1 c	52
TV dinners, frozen		
Beef with one vegetable	1 pkg.	13
Beef with two vegetables, soup, dessert	1 pkg.	55
Chicken, fried, with one vegetable	1 pkg.	25
Chicken, fried, with two vegetables, dessert	1 pkg.	57
Haddock with one vegetable	1 pkg.	49
Ham with two vegetables, dessert	1 pkg.	47

Appendix I continued Food	Approximate measure	Total folacin (μg)
TV dinner—continued		
Lasagna	10-oz portion	62
Pork with one vegetable, one fruit, dessert	1 pkg.	21
Poultry, Oriental style with rice, vegetables	1 pkg.	17
Shrimp, Oriental style with rice, vegetables	1 pkg.	50
Spaghetti with meatballs, one vegetable, dessert	1 pkg.	64
Turkey with one vegetable	1 pkg.	29
Veal, cooked	3 oz	3
Waffles		
Homemade	1, 2.5 oz	13
Frozen	1, 1.5 oz	<1
Walnuts, English, shelled	1 c	66
Watermelon, raw	1 wedge, 4-in. × 8-in.	34
Wheat, whole grain	1 oz	15
Wheat bran	1 oz	71
Wheat flour		
Whole	1 c	65
Patent		
Bread, sifted	1 c	29
All-purpose, sifted	1 c	24
Yeast, brewer's, debittered	1 Tbsp	313
Yogurt	1 c	27

Most data drawn from Perloff, B.P., and R.R. Butrum, 1977. Folacin in selected foods. *Journal of the American Dietetic Association* 70:161–172.

Some data drawn from (1) McQuitkin, C., and R.H. Matthews, 1981. *Provisional table on the nutrient content of bakery foods and related items.* Washington, DC: Nutrient Data Research Group, United States Department of Agriculture (USDA); (2) Cutrufelli, R., and R.H. Matthews, 1981. *Provisional table on nutrient content of beverages.* Washington, DC: Nutrient Data Research Group, USDA; (3) Gebhardt, S.E., R. Cutrufelli, and R.H. Matthews, 1981. *Provisional table on the nutrient content of canned, dried, and frozen fruit.* Washington, DC: Nutrient Data Research Group, USDA.

Appendix J   Vitamin B-6 and Vitamin B-12 Content of Foods

Food	Approximate Measure	B-6 (mg)	B-12 (μg)
Almonds, shelled, slivered	1 c	0.12	0
Apples, raw	1 medium	0.04	0
Apple juice	1 c	0.07	0
Applesauce, canned, sweetened	1 c	0.08	0
Apricots			
Raw	3 apricots	0.07	0
Canned, heavy syrup	1 c	0.14	0
Asparagus			
Canned, drained, green	1 c	0.08	0
Frozen	1 c	0.28	0
Avocado, raw	$\frac{1}{2}$ medium	0.45	0
Bacon, raw	2 slices	0.08	0.43
Bananas, raw	1 medium	0.61	0
Beans, common, mature, dry			
Red, raw	1 c	0.88	0
White, raw	1 c	1.06	0
Beans, lima, dry, canned	1 c	0.16	0
Beans, snap, canned, drained			
Green	1 c	0.05	0
Yellow	1 c	0.06	0
Beef			
Raw, lean, trimmed	3 oz	0.40	1.66
Corned, canned	3 oz	nd	1.70
Beef, dried, chipped	3 oz	nd	1.70
Beets, canned	1 c	0.09	0
Beverages, alcoholic			
Beer	12 oz	0.22	0
Wine	$3\frac{1}{2}$ oz	0.04	0
Blueberries, raw	1 c	0.10	0
Brazil nuts, shelled	1 oz	0.05	0
Breads			
Cracked wheat	1 slice (1 oz)	0.03	0
Rye, pumpernickel	1 slice (1 oz)	0.05	0
White	1 slice (1 oz)	0.01	trace
Whole wheat	1 slice (1 oz)	0.06	0
Breakfast cereals			
Cornmeal grits, dry	1 c	0.24	0
Oatmeal, dry	1 c	0.12	0
Breakfast cereals, ready-to-eat			
Bran flakes 100%	1 c	0.49	0
Bran flakes 40%	1 c	0.13	0
Corn flakes	1 c	0.02	0
Rice, puffed	1 c	0.01	0
Wheat			
Flakes	1 c	0.09	0
Puffed	1 c	0.03	0
Shredded	1 biscuit	0.06	0
Wheat germ	1 tbsp	0.07	0

Appendix J continued Food	Approximate Measure	B-6 (mg)	B-12 (μg)
Butter	1 tbsp	<0.01	trace
Cabbage, raw, green, coarse shred	1 c	0.12	0
Cake, commercial, plain	$3\frac{1}{4}$ oz	0.04	0
Carrots			
Raw	1 medium	0.11	0
Canned, drained	1 c	0.05	0
Celery, raw, diced	1 c	0.07	0
Cheese, natural			
Blue	1 oz	0.05	0.43
Camembert	1 oz	0.07	0.40
Cheddar	1 oz	0.02	0.31
Cottage	1 c	0.10	2.46
Cream	1 oz	0.02	0.07
Mozzarella	1 oz	0.02	0.31
Provolone	1 oz	0.03	0.38
Swiss	1 oz	0.02	0.55
Cheese food, processed, American	1 oz	0.04	0.20
Cherries, canned, sour (water pack)	1 c	0.09	0
Chicken			
Dark meat	3 oz	0.30	0.37
Light meat	3 oz	0.63	0.42
Chickpeas (garbanzos), dry, raw	1 c	1.08	0
Chili con carne with beans, canned	1 c	0.26	nd
Chocolate, baking	1 oz	0.01	0
Coconut, fresh meat	1 oz	0.01	0
Coffee, instant	1 c	trace	0
Corn, sweet, canned	1 c	0.42	0
Cornmeal, yellow/white	1 c	0.35	0
Crackers, saltines	4 crackers	<0.01	0
Cranberry sauce, canned	1 c	0.06	0
Cream, fluid, light whipping	1 tbsp	<0.01	0
Cucumbers, raw	$\frac{1}{2}$ large	0.01	0
Dates, chopped	1 c	0.27	0
Eggs			
Whole	1 egg	0.06	1.00
White	1 white	<0.01	0.03
Yolk	1 yolk	0.05	≃1.00
Filberts (hazelnuts), chopped	1 c	0.63	0
Fish and shellfish			
Clams, canned	3 oz	0.08	nd
Cod			
Raw	3 oz	0.21	0.74
Smoked	3 oz	0.20	1.29
Crab, cooked/canned	3 oz	0.28	9.20
Haddock, raw	3 oz	0.17	1.20
Halibut, raw	3 oz	0.40	0.92

Appendix J continued Food	Approximate Measure	B-6 (mg)	B-12 (μg)
Fish and shellfish—continued			
Lobster, raw	3 oz	nd	0.46
Ocean perch, raw	3 oz	0.21	0.92
Oysters, raw	3 oz	0.05	16.56
Salmon, canned	3 oz	0.28	6.34
Sardines, canned in oil	3 oz	0.17	9.20
Shrimp, canned	3 oz	0.06	nd
Trout, rainbow, raw	3 oz	0.63	4.60
Tuna, canned	3 oz	0.39	2.02
Fruit cocktail	1 c	0.08	0
Grapefruit, raw	$\frac{1}{2}$ medium	0.09	0
Grapefruit juice, canned/frozen	1 c	0.03	0
Grapes, raw	1 c	0.13	0
Grape juice, frozen	1 c	0.05	0
Honey	1 tbsp	<0.01	0
Jam	1 tbsp	<0.01	0
Lamb, raw	3 oz	0.25	1.98
Lard	1 tbsp	<0.01	0
Lemons, raw	1 lemon	0.06	0
Lemonade, from frozen concentrate	1 c	0.01	0
Lentils, dry, raw	1 c	1.20	0
Lettuce, raw	1 c	0.03	0
Liver			
Beef, raw	3 oz	0.77	73.60
Chicken, raw	3 oz	0.69	23.00
Macaroni, dry	1 c	0.07	0
Milk, cow			
Whole or skim	1 c	0.10	0.98
Canned, evaporated	1 c	0.12	0.39
Dry, skim	1 c	0.26	2.18
Molasses	1 tbsp	0.04	0
Mushrooms			
Raw	1 c	0.09	0
Canned	1 c	0.12	0
Muskmelons, raw			
Cantaloupe, diced	1 c	0.21	0
Honeydew, diced	1 c	0.13	0
Nectarines, raw	2 medium	0.02	0
Noodles, egg, dry	1 c	0.06	trace
Okra, raw	10 pods	0.08	0
Olives, ripe, canned	2 large	0.01	0
Onions, raw, chopped	1 c	0.22	0
Oranges, raw	1 medium	0.08	0
Orange juice			
Fresh/canned	1 c	0.09	0
From frozen concentrate	1 c	0.07	0

J

Appendix J continued Food	Approximate Measure	B-6 (mg)	B-12 (µg)
Parsley, raw	1 tbsp	<0.01	0
Peaches			
Raw	1 medium	0.02	0
Canned	1 c	0.05	0
Peanut butter	1 tbsp	0.05	0
Peanuts, roasted	1 c	0.58	0
Pears			
Raw	1 medium	0.03	0
Canned	1 c	0.04	0
Peas, canned	1 c	0.09	0
Pecans, chopped	1 c	0.22	0
Pickles, dill	1 medium	<0.01	0
Pineapple			
Raw, diced	1 c	0.14	0
Frozen/canned, chunks	1 c	0.19	0
Pineapple juice, canned	1 c	0.24	0
Plums, raw	1 medium	0.03	0
Popcorn, popped, no oil	1 c	0.01	0
Pork			
Raw, trimmed	3 oz	0.41	0.64
Cured, ham, canned	3 oz	0.33	nd
Potatoes			
Canned	1 c	0.26	0
Hash browns, frozen	1 c	0.17	0
French fries, frozen	10 strips	0.09	0
Potato chips	10 chips	0.04	0
Pretzels	10 small sticks	<0.01	trace
Prunes, dried	5 large	0.12	0
Pumpkin, canned	1 c	0.14	0
Pumpkin seeds, roasted	1 c	0.13	0
Radishes	4 radishes	0.01	0
Raisins, dark seedless	1 c	0.35	0
Raspberries, raw	1 c	0.07	0
Rhubarb, raw, without leaves	1 c	0.03	0
Rice			
Brown, raw	1 c	1.10	0
White, dry			
Regular	1 c	0.31	0
Parboiled	1 c	0.79	0
Rolls	1 roll	0.01	0
Sauerkraut, canned	1 c	0.31	0
Sausage/cold cuts, luncheon meats			
Bologna	1 slice (1 oz)	0.03	nd
Braunschweiger/liverwurst	1 slice (1 oz)	0.06	4.28
Frankfurters	1 frank (2 oz)	0.08	0.80
Pork sausage, raw	1 oz link	0.05	0.17
Salami	1 slice (1 oz)	0.04	0.43

Appendix J continued Food	Approximate Measure	B-6 (mg)	B-12 (µg)
Soups, canned, commercial, not diluted (10½ oz can)			
Barley	1 can	0.24	nd
Chicken noodle	1 can	0.17	nd
Chicken vegetable	1 can	0.14	nd
Tomato	1 can	0.14	nd
Soybean milk powder	1 oz	0.09	0
Spaghetti, dry	1 c	0.10	0
Spinach, raw, chopped	1 c	0.15	0
Squash, raw			
Summer	1 c	0.16	0
Winter	1 c	0.31	0
Strawberries, raw	1 c	0.08	0
Sunflower seeds, hulled	1 oz	0.38	0
Sweet potatoes, canned	1 c	0.19	0
Tangerine, raw	1 medium	0.06	0
Tomato			
Raw	1 medium	0.14	0
Canned	1 c	0.22	0
Tomato catsup	1 tbsp	0.02	0
Tomato juice, canned	1 c	0.47	0
Tomato paste, canned	1 c	0.95	0
Tortilla	1 average	0.02	0
Turnips, raw	1 c	0.12	0
Veal, raw, trimmed	3 oz	0.37	1.61
Walnuts, chopped	1 c	0.88	0
Watermelon, raw, cubed	1 c	0.14	0
Wheat flours			
All-purpose or family	1 c	0.07	0
Whole wheat	1 c	0.41	0
Yeast, baker's, dry	1 tbsp	0.14	0
Yogurt, plain	1 8-oz container	0.11	0.27

nd = No data available
Data adapted from Orr, M.L. 1969. *Pantothenic acid, vitamin B-6, and vitamin B-12 in foods*. Home Economics Research Report No. 36. Washington, DC: USDA.

J

Appendix K Sodium Content of Foods

Food	Approximate Measure	Sodium (mg)
Almonds:		
Salted, roasted	1 c	311
Unsalted, slivered	1 c	4
Apples:		
Raw or baked	1 apple	2
Frozen, slices	1 c	28
Dried, sulfured	8 oz	210
Apple cider or juice	1 c	5
Applesauce, canned:		
Sweetened	1 c	6
Unsweetened	1 c	5
With added salt	1 c	68
Apricots:		
Raw	3 apricots	1
Canned:		
Peeled	1 c	27
Unpeeled	1 c	10
Dried	1 c	12
Apricot nectar	1 c	9
Asparagus:		
Raw	1 spear	1
Frozen	4 spears	4
Canned		
Regular	4 spears	298
Low sodium	1 c	7
Avocado, raw	1 avocado	22
Bacon		
Cooked	2 slices	274
Canadian	1 slice	394
Bagel	1	67
Baking powder	1 tsp	339
Baking soda	1 tsp	821
Banana, raw	1 banana	2
Barbecue sauce	1 tbsp	130
Barley, pearled, cooked	1 c	6
Beans:		
Italian:		
Frozen	3 oz	4
Canned, regular	1 c	913
Lima:		
Cooked	1 c	2
Frozen	1 c	128
Canned, regular	1 c	456
Low sodium	1 c	7
Snap:		
Cooked	1 c	5
Frozen		
Regular	3 oz	3

Food	Approximate Measure	Sodium (mg)
Beans, snap—continued		
With almonds	3 oz	335
Canned:		
Regular	1 c	326
Low sodium	1 c	3
Beans, dried:		
Baked, canned:		
Boston style	1 c	606
With or without pork	1 c	928
Dry, cooked:		
Great Northern	1 c	5
Kidney	1 c	4
Kidney, canned	1 c	844
Bean sprouts, mung:		
Raw	1 c	5
Canned	1 c	71
Beef:		
Cooked, lean	3 oz	55
Corned:		
Cooked	3 oz	802
Canned	3 oz	893
Dried, chipped	1 oz	1219
Beef prepared main dishes:		
And macaroni:		
Frozen	6 oz	673
Canned	1 c	1185
Dinners, frozen:		
Beef	1 dinner	998
Meat loaf	1 dinner	1304
Sirloin, chopped	1 dinner	978
Swiss steak	1 dinner	682
Hash, corned beef, canned	1 c	1520
Pot pie:		
Home baked	1 pie	644
Frozen	1 pie	1093
Stew, canned	8 oz	980
Beets:		
Cooked	1 c	73
Canned:		
Sliced	1 c	479
Low sodium	1 c	110
Harvard	1 c	275
Pickled	1 c	330
Beet greens, cooked	1 c	110
Beverages		
Alcoholic:		
Beer	12 fl oz	25
Gin, rum, whisky	2 fl oz	1

Appendix K   continued

Food	Approximate Measure	Sodium (mg)
Wine:		
Red:		
Domestic	4 fl oz	12
Imported	4 fl oz	6
Sherry	4 fl oz	14
White:		
Domestic	4 fl oz	19
Imported	4 fl oz	2
Carbonated, non-alcoholic:		
Club soda	8 fl oz	39
Cola:		
Regular	8 fl oz	16
Low calorie	8 fl oz	21
Fruit-flavored:		
Regular	8 fl oz	34
Low calorie	8 fl oz	46
Ginger ale	8 fl oz	13
Root beer	8 fl oz	24
Fruit drinks, canned:		
Apple	8 fl oz	16
Grape	8 fl oz	1
Lemonade	8 fl oz	60
Orange	8 fl oz	77
Pineapple-grapefruit	8 fl oz	80
Fruit drinks, dehydrated, reconstituted:		
Sweetened:		
Lemonade	8 fl oz	50
Orange	8 fl oz	35
Other fruit	8 fl oz	0
Unsweetened, all flavors	8 fl oz	0
Instant breakfast drinks:		
Grape	8 fl oz	0
Citrus fruits	8 fl oz	14
Thirst quencher	8 fl oz.	140
Biscuits, baking powder:		
Regular flour	1 biscuit	175
Self-rising flour	1 biscuit	185
With milk from mix	1 biscuit	272
Low sodium	1 biscuit	1
Blackberries		
Raw	1 c	1
Canned	1 c	3
Blueberries:		
Raw	1 c	1
Canned	1 c	2
Brazil nuts, shelled	1 c	1

Food	Approximate Measure	Sodium (mg)
Bread:		
Boston brown	1 slice	120
Corn, homemade	1 oz	176
Cracked wheat	1 slice	148
Pita	1 loaf	132
Rye:		
Regular	1 slice	139
Pumpernickel	1 slice	182
Salt rising	1 slice	66
White:		
Regular	1 slice	114
Low sodium	1 slice	7
Whole wheat	1 slice	132
Breakfast cereals:		
Hot, cooked, in unsalted water:		
Corn (hominy) grits:		
Regular	$\frac{1}{3}$ c	1
Instant	$\frac{3}{4}$ c	354
Cream of Wheat:		
Regular	$\frac{3}{4}$ c	2
Instant	$\frac{3}{4}$ c	5
Quick	$\frac{3}{4}$ c	126
Mix 'n' Eat	$\frac{3}{4}$ c	350
Farina	$\frac{3}{4}$ c	1
Oatmeal:		
Regular or quick	$\frac{3}{4}$ c	1
Instant:		
No sodium added	$\frac{3}{4}$ c	1
Sodium added	$\frac{3}{4}$ c	283
With apples and cinnamon	$\frac{3}{4}$ c	220
Ready-to-eat:		
Bran cereals:		
All-Bran	$\frac{1}{3}$ c	160
40% Bran	$\frac{2}{3}$ c	251
Cheerios	$1\frac{1}{4}$ c	304
Corn cereals:		
Corn Chex	1 c	297
Corn flakes:		
Low sodium	$1\frac{1}{4}$ c	10
Regular	1 c	256
Sugar coated	$\frac{3}{4}$ c	274
Sugar Corn Pops	1 c	105
Granola:		
Regular	$\frac{1}{4}$ c	61
No sodium added	$\frac{1}{4}$ c	16

K

Appendix K continued Food	Approximate Measure	Sodium (mg)
Breakfast		
cereals—continued		
Kix	$1\frac{1}{2}$ c	261
Life	$\frac{2}{3}$ c	146
Product 19	$\frac{3}{4}$ c	175
Rice cereals:		
Low sodium	1 c	10
Puffed rice	2 c	2
Rice Chex	$1\frac{1}{8}$ c	238
Rice Krispies	1 c	340
Sugar coated	$\frac{7}{8}$ c	149
Special K	$1\frac{1}{4}$ c	265
Total	1 c	359
Trix	1 c	160
Wheat cereals:		
Puffed wheat	2 c	2
Sugar coated	1 c	46
Shredded wheat	1 biscuit	3
Wheat Chex	$\frac{2}{3}$ c	190
Wheaties	1 c	355
Wheat germ, toasted	$\frac{1}{4}$ c	1
Broccoli:		
Raw	1 stalk	23
Frozen:		
Cooked	1 c	35
With cheese sauce	3.3 oz	440
With hollandaise sauce	3.3 oz	115
Brussels sprouts:		
Raw	1 medium	1
Frozen:		
Cooked	1 c	15
In butter sauce	3.3 oz	421
Butter:		
Regular	1 tbsp	116
Unsalted	1 tbsp	2
Whipped	1 tbsp	74
Cabbage:		
Green:		
Raw	1 c	8
Cooked	1 c	16
Red, raw	1 c	18
Cakes, from mix:		
Angel food:		
Regular	$\frac{1}{12}$ cake	134
One step	$\frac{1}{12}$ cake	250
Devil's food	$\frac{1}{12}$ cake	402
Pound	$\frac{1}{12}$ cake	171
White	$\frac{1}{12}$ cake	238
Yellow	$\frac{1}{12}$ cake	242

Food	Approximate Measure	Sodium (mg)
Coffee cake:		
Almond	$\frac{1}{8}$ cake	167
Blueberry	$\frac{1}{8}$ cake	135
Honey nut	$\frac{1}{8}$ cake	110
Pecan	$\frac{1}{8}$ cake	172
Gingerbread	$\frac{1}{9}$ cake	65
Candy:		
Candy corn	1 oz	60
Caramel	1 oz	74
Chocolate:		
Bitter	1 oz	4
Milk	1 oz	28
Fudge, chocolate	1 oz	54
Gum drops	1 oz	10
Hard	1 oz	9
Jelly beans	1 oz	3
Licorice	1 oz	28
Marshmallows	1 oz	11
Mints, uncoated	1 oz	56
Peanut brittle	1 oz	145
Taffy	1 oz	88
Toffee bar, almond	1 oz	65
Carrots:		
Raw	1 carrot	34
Frozen:		
Cut or whole	3.3 oz	43
In butter sauce	3.3 oz	350
With brown sugar		
glaze	3.3 oz	500
Canned:		
Regular	1 c	386
Low sodium	1 c	58
Cashews:		
Roasted in oil	1 c	21
Dry roasted, salted	1 c	1200
Cauliflower:		
Raw	1 c	17
Cooked	1 c	13
Frozen:		
Cooked	1 c	18
With cheese sauce	3 oz	325
Celery, raw	1 stalk	25
Cheese:		
Natural:		
Blue	1 oz	396
Brick	1 oz	159
Brie	1 oz	178
Camembert	1 oz	239
Cheddar:		
Regular	1 oz	176
Low sodium	1 oz	6

K

Appendix K continued Food	Approximate Measure	Sodium (mg)
Cheese—continued		
Colby	1 oz	171
Cottage:		
Regular and lowfat	4 oz	457
Dry curd, unsalted	4 oz	14
Cream	1 oz	84
Edam	1 oz	274
Feta	1 oz	316
Gouda	1 oz	232
Gruyere	1 oz	95
Limburger	1 oz	227
Monterey	1 oz	152
Mozzarella, from:		
Whole milk	1 oz	106
Part skim milk	1 oz	132
Muenster	1 oz	178
Neufchatel	1 oz	113
Parmesan:		
Grated	1 oz	528
Hard	1 oz	454
Provolone	1 oz	248
Ricotta, made with:		
Whole milk	$\frac{1}{2}$ c	104
Part skim milk	$\frac{1}{2}$ c	155
Roquefort	1 oz	513
Swiss	1 oz	74
Tilsit	1 oz	213
Pasteurized processed cheese:		
American	1 oz	406
Low sodium	1 oz	2
Swiss	1 oz	388
Cheese food:		
American	1 oz	337
Swiss	1 oz	440
Cheese spread:		
American	1 oz	381
Cheesecake (Sara Lee)	1 slice	173
Cherries:		
Raw	1 c	1
Frozen	8 oz	3
Canned	1 c	10
Chicken, roasted:		
Breast with skin	$\frac{1}{2}$ breast	69
Drumstick with skin	1 drumstick	47
Products:		
Canned	1 5-oz can	714
Frankfurter	1 frankfurter	617
Chicken:		
And dumplings, frozen	12 oz	1506
And noodles, frozen	$\frac{3}{4}$ c	662

Food	Approximate Measure	Sodium (mg)
Chicken—continued		
Chow mein, home recipe	1 c	718
Dinner, frozen	1 dinner	1153
Potpie:		
Home recipe	1 pie	594
Frozen	1 pie	907
Chili con carne with beans, canned:		
Regular	1 c	1194
Low sodium	1 c	100
Cocoa mix, water added	8 fl oz	232
Coconut	2 tbsp	3
Coffee:		
Brewed	8 fl oz	2
Instant:		
Regular or decaf	8 fl oz	1
With flavorings	8 fl oz	124
Substitute	8 fl oz	3
Cole slaw	$\frac{1}{2}$ c	68
Collards:		
Cooked	1 c	24
Frozen	3 oz	41
Cookies:		
Brownies, iced	1 brownie	69
Chocolate chip	2 cookies	69
Fig bars	2 bars	96
Gingersnaps	4 cookies	161
Macaroons	2 cookies	14
Oatmeal:		
Plain	1 cookie	77
With chocolate chips	2 cookies	54
With raisins	2 cookies	55
Peanut butter	1 cookie	21
Sandwich type	2 cookies	96
Shortbread	4 cookies	116
Sugar	1 cookie	108
Sugar wafer	4 cookies	43
Vanilla wafer	6 cookies	53
Corn:		
Cooked	1 ear	1
Frozen	1 c	7
Canned:		
Cream style:		
Regular	1 c	671
Low sodium	1 c	5
Vacuum pack	1 c	577
Whole kernel:		
Regular	1 c	384
Low sodium	1 c	2
Corn chips	1 oz	231

K

Appendix K continued Food	Approximate Measure	Sodium (mg)
Crackers:		
Graham	1 cracker	48
Low sodium	1 cracker	1
Rye	1 cracker	70
Saltine	2 crackers	70
Whole wheat	1 cracker	30
Cranberry, raw	1 c	1
Cranberry juice cocktail	8 fl oz	4
Cranberry sauce	1 c	75
Cream, sweet:		
Fluid, all types	1 tbsp	6
Whipped	1 tbsp	4
Cream, sour, cultured	1 tbsp	6
Cream products, imitation:		
Sweet:		
Coffee whitener:		
Liquid	1 tbsp	12
Powdered	1 tbsp	12
Whipped Topping	1 tbsp	2
Sour, cultured	1 oz	29
Cucumber	7 slices	2
Custard, baked	1 c	209
Dandelion greens, cooked	1 c	46
Danish:		
Apple, frozen	1 roll	220
Cheese, frozen	1 roll	250
Cinnamon, frozen	1 roll	260
Orange, refrigerated dough	1 roll	329
Dates, dried	10 dates	1
Doughnut:		
Cake type	1 doughnut	160
Yeast leavened	1 doughnut	99
Eggs:		
Whole	1 egg	59
White	1 white	50
Yolk	1 yolk	9
Substitute, frozen	$\frac{1}{4}$ c	120
Enchiladas, beef	1 pkg	725
Endive, raw	1 c	7
English muffin	1 medium	293
Filberts (hazelnuts), chopped	1 c	2
Fish and shellfish:		
Clams, raw:		
Hard	3 oz	174
Soft	3 oz	30
Cod, broiled with butter	3 oz	93

Food	Approximate Measure	Sodium (mg)
Fish—continued		
Crab:		
Canned, drained	3 oz	425
Steamed	3 oz	314
Flounder (includes sole and other flat fish) baked with butter		
Haddock, breaded, fried	3 oz	201
Halibut, broiled with butter	3 oz	150
	3 oz	114
Herring, smoked	3 oz	5234
Lobster, boiled	3 oz	212
Mackerel, raw	3 oz	40
Ocean perch, fried	3 oz	128
Oysters:		
Fried	3 oz	174
Frozen	3 oz	323
Pollock, creamed	3 oz	94
Salmon:		
Broiled with butter	3 oz	99
Canned:		
Salt added:		
Pink	3 oz	443
Red	3 oz	329
Without salt added	3 oz	41
Sardines, canned:		
Drained	3 oz	552
In tomato sauce	3 oz	338
Scallops, steamed	3 oz	225
Shad, baked with butter	3 oz	66
Shrimp:		
Fried	3 oz	159
Canned	3 oz	1955
Tuna, canned:		
Light meat, chunk:		
Oil pack	3 oz	303
Water pack	3 oz	288
White meat (Albacore)		
Chunk low sodium	3 oz	34
Solid:		
Oil pack	3 oz	384
Water pack	3 oz	309
Fruit cocktail, canned	1 c	15
Gelatin dessert	$\frac{1}{2}$ c	55
Gelatin dessert with fruit	$\frac{1}{2}$ c	43
Grapefruit:		
Raw	$\frac{1}{2}$ grapefruit	1
Frozen, unsweetened	1 c	6
Canned, sweetened	1 c	4
Grapefruit juice:		
Canned	1 c	4
Frozen, diluted	1 c	5
Grapes, Thompson seedless	10 grapes	1

K

Appendix K continued Food	Approximate Measure	Sodium (mg)
Grape juice, bottled	1 c	8
Honey	2 tbsp	1
Ice cream:		
Chocolate	1 c	75
Custard, French	1 c	84
Strawberry	1 c	77
Vanilla:		
French, softserve	1 c	153
Hardened	1 c	112
Ice milk:		
Vanilla:		
Hardened	1 c	105
Soft serve	1 c	163
Jams and jellies:		
Jam:		
Regular	1 tbsp	2
Low calorie	1 tbsp	19
Jelly:		
Regular	1 tbsp	3
Low calorie	1 tbsp	21
Kale:		
Cooked	1 c	47
Frozen	3 oz	13
Lamb, cooked, lean	3 oz	58
Lasagna	1 serving	825
Lemon, raw	1 lemon	1
Lemon or lime juice:		
Canned	1 c	2
Frozen, diluted	1 c	4
Lentils, cooked	1 c	4
Lettuce	1 c	4
Liver:		
Calf, fried	1 oz	33
Pork, simmered	1 oz	14
Poultry, simmered	1 oz	16
Macaroni, cooked	1 c	2
Macaroni salad	$\frac{2}{3}$ c	676
Margarine:		
Regular	1 tbsp	140
Unsalted	1 tbsp	1
Meatloaf (homemade)	$3\frac{1}{2}$ oz	653
Meat tenderizer:		
Regular	1 tsp	1750
Low sodium	1 tsp	1
Milk:		
Fluid:		
Whole and lowfat	1 c	122
Whole, low sodium	1 c	6

Food	Approximate Measure	Sodium (mg)
Milk—continued		
Buttermilk, cultured:		
Salted		
Unsalted	1 c	257
Canned:	1 c	122
Evaporated, whole		
Sweetened,	1 c	266
condensed	1 c	389
Dry:		
Nonfat:		
Regular	$\frac{1}{2}$ c	322
Instantized	1 c	373
Buttermilk	$\frac{1}{2}$ c	310
Milk beverages:		
Chocolate	1 c	149
Cocoa, hot	1 c	123
Eggnog	1 c	138
Malted:		
Natural flavor	1 c	215
Chocolate flavor	1 c	168
Shakes, thick:		
Chocolate or vanilla	1 shake	317
MSG (monosodium glutamate)	1 tsp	492
Mushrooms:		
Raw	1 c	7
Canned, regular	2 oz	242
Muskmelon:		
Cantaloupe	$\frac{1}{2}$ melon	24
Casaba	$\frac{1}{5}$ melon	34
Honeydew	$\frac{1}{5}$ melon	28
Mustard, prepared	1 tsp	65
Mustard greens:		
Raw	1 c	11
Cooked	1 c	25
Frozen	3 oz	25
Nectarines, raw	1 nectarine	1
Noodles, cooked	1 c	2
Oil, vegetable, (includes corn, olive, and soybean)	1 tbsp	0
Okra, cooked	10 pods	2
Olives:		
Green	4 olives	323
Ripe, mission	3 olives	96
Onions:		
Mature, dry	1 medium	10
Green	2 medium	2
Flaked	1 tbsp	31

Appendix K continued Food	Approximate Measure	Sodium (mg)
Onions, processed:		
Powder	1 tsp	1
Salt	1 tsp	1620
Oranges, raw	1 orange	1
Orange juice:		
Canned	1 c	5
Frozen, diluted	1 c	5
Pancakes, from mix	1 pancake	152
Pancake mix	1 c	2036
Papaya, raw	1 papaya	8
Parsley, raw	1 tbsp	2
Parsnips, cooked	1 c	19
Peaches:		
Raw	1 peach	1
Frozen	1 c	10
Canned	1 c	15
Dried, uncooked	1 c	10
Peanuts:		
Dry roasted, salted	1 c	986
Roasted, salted	1 c	601
Unsalted	1 c	8
Peanut butter:		
Smooth or crunchy	1 tbsp	81
Low sodium	1 tbsp	1
Pears:		
Raw	1 pear	1
Canned	1 c	15
Dried	1 c	10
Peas:		
Blackeye, cooked	1 c	12
Split, cooked	1 c	5
Peas, green:		
Cooked	1 c	2
Frozen:		
Regular	3 oz	80
In butter sauce	3.3 oz	402
With mushrooms	3.3 oz	240
Canned:		
Regular	1 c	493
Low sodium	1 c	8
Pecans	1 c	1
Peppers:		
Hot, raw	1 pod	7
Sweet, raw or cooked	1 pod	9
Pickles:		
Bread and butter	2 slices	101
Dill	1 pickle	928
Relish, sweet	1 tbsp	124
Sweet	1 pickle	128

Food	Approximate Measure	Sodium (mg)
Pies, frozen:		
Apple	$\frac{1}{8}$ of pie	208
Banana cream	$\frac{1}{6}$ of pie	90
Bavarian cream:		
Chocolate	$\frac{1}{8}$ of pie	78
Lemon	$\frac{1}{8}$ of pie	71
Blueberry	$\frac{1}{8}$ of pie	163
Cherry	$\frac{1}{8}$ of pie	169
Chocolate cream	$\frac{1}{6}$ of pie	107
Coconut:		
Cream	$\frac{1}{6}$ of pie	104
Custard	$\frac{1}{8}$ of pie	194
Lemon cream	$\frac{1}{6}$ of pie	92
Mince	$\frac{1}{8}$ of pie	258
Peach	$\frac{1}{8}$ of pie	169
Pecan	$\frac{1}{8}$ of pie	241
Pumpkin	$\frac{1}{8}$ of pie	169
Strawberry cream	$\frac{1}{6}$ of pie	101
Pineapple:		
Raw	1 c	1
Canned	1 c	7
Pineapple juice	1 c	5
Pizza, cheese	$\frac{1}{4}$ pie	599
Pizza, frozen:		
With pepperoni	$\frac{1}{2}$ pie	813
With sausage	$\frac{1}{2}$ pie	967
Plums:		
Raw	1 plum	1
Canned	1 c	10
Popcorn:		
Caramel coated	1 c	262
Oil, salt	1 c	175
Plain	1 c	1
Pork:		
Fresh, cooked, lean	3 oz	59
Ham	3 oz	1114
Salt pork, raw	1 oz	399
Potatoes:		
Baked or boiled	1 medium	5
Frozen:		
French fried	10 strips	15
Salted	2.5 oz	270
Canned	1 c	753
Instant, reconstituted	1 c	485
Mashed, milk and salt	1 c	632
Au gratin	1 c	1095
Potato chips	10 chips	200

K

Appendix K continued Food	Approximate Measure	Sodium (mg)
Potato salad	$\frac{1}{2}$ c	625
Pretzels:		
Regular twist	1 pretzel	101
Small stick	3 sticks	17
Prunes:		
Cooked	1 c	8
Dried	5 large	2
Prune juice	1 c	5
Puddings		
Butterscotch:		
Regular, whole milk	$\frac{1}{2}$ c	245
Instant, whole milk	$\frac{1}{2}$ c	445
LoCal, skim milk	$\frac{1}{2}$ c	130
Ready-to-serve	1 can	290
Chocolate:		
Home recipe	$\frac{1}{2}$ c	73
Regular, whole milk	$\frac{1}{2}$ c	195
Instant, whole milk	$\frac{1}{2}$ c	470
LoCal, skim milk	$\frac{1}{2}$ c	80
Ready-to-serve	1 can	262
Vanilla:		
Home recipe	$\frac{1}{2}$ c	83
Regular, whole milk	$\frac{1}{2}$ c	200
Instant, whole milk	$\frac{1}{2}$ c	400
LoCal, skim milk	$\frac{1}{2}$ c	115
Ready-to-serve	1 can	279
Tapioca, cooked	$\frac{1}{2}$ c	130
Pumpkin, canned	1 c	12
Radish	4 small	2
Raisins, seedless	1 c	17
Raspberries:		
Raw	1 c	1
Frozen	1 pkg	3
Ravioli, canned	7.5 oz	1065
Rhubarb:		
Cooked, sugared	1 c	5
Frozen	1 c	5
Rice, cooked:		
Brown	1 c	10
White:		
Regular	1 c	6
Parboiled	1 c	4
Quick	1 c	13
Rolls:		
Brown and serve	1 roll	138
Refrigerated dough	1 roll	342

Food	Approximate Measure	Sodium (mg)
Salad dressing:		
Blue cheese	1 tbsp	153
French:		
Home recipe	1 tbsp	92
Bottled	1 tbsp	214
Dry mix, prepared	1 tbsp	253
Low sodium	1 tbsp	3
Italian:		
Bottled	1 tbsp	116
Dry mix, prepared	1 tbsp	172
Mayonnaise	1 tbsp	78
Russian	1 tbsp	133
Thousand Island:		
Regular	1 tbsp	109
Low calorie	1 tbsp	153
Salt	1 tsp	1938
Sauerkraut, canned	1 c	1554
Sausages, luncheon meats, and spreads:		
Beer salami, beef	1 slice	56
Bologna:		
Beef	1 slice	220
Beef and pork	1 slice	224
Bratwurst, cooked	1 oz	158
Braunschweiger	1 slice	324
Chicken spread	1 oz	115
Frankfurter	1 frankfurter	639
Ham:		
And cheese loaf	1 oz	381
Chopped	1 slice	288
Spread	1 oz	258
Kielbasa	1 slice	280
Knockwurst	1 link	687
Liver cheese	1 slice	245
Old-fashioned loaf	1 slice	275
Olive loaf	1 slice	312
Salami:		
Cooked:		
Beef	1 slice	255
Beef and pork	1 slice	234
Dry or hard, pork	1 slice	226
Sausage:		
Cooked:		
Pork	1 link	168
Pork and beef	1 patty	217
Smoked	1 link	264
Thuringer	1 slice	320
Tuna spread	1 oz	92
Turkey roll	1 oz	166
Vienna sausage	1 link	152
Sherbet, orange	1 c	89

K

Appendix K continued Food	Approximate Measure	Sodium (mg)
Syrup:		
Chocolate flavored:		
Thin	1 tbsp	10
Fudge	1 tbsp	17
Corn	1 tbsp	14
Maple:		
Regular	1 tbsp	1
Imitation	1 tbsp	20
Molasses, medium	1 tbsp	7
Soups:		
Beef broth, cube	1 c	1152
Beef noodle:		
Condensed		
with water	1 c	952
Dehydrated		
with water	1 c	1041
Chicken noodle:		
Condensed,		
with water	1 c	1107
Dehydrated,		
with water	1 c	1284
Chicken rice:		
Condensed,		
with water	1 c	814
Dehydrated,		
with water	1 c	980
Clam chowder,		
Manhattan,		
condensed,		
with water	1 c	1029
Clam chowder,		
New England,		
condensed:		
with water	1 c	914
with milk	1 c	992
Minestrone,		
Condensed,		
with water	1 c	911
Mushroom:		
Condensed,		
with water	1 c	1031
Condensed,		
with milk	1 c	1076
Dehydrated,		
with water	1 c	1019
Low sodium	1 c	27
Pea, green:		
Condensed,		
with water	1 c	987
Dehydrated,		
with water	1 c	1220
Tomato:		
Condensed,		
with water	1 c	872

Food	Approximate Measure	Sodium (mg)
Soup, tomato—continued		
Condensed,		
with milk	1 c	932
Dehydrated,		
with water	1 c	943
Low sodium	1 c	29
Vegetable:		
Condensed,		
with water	1 c	823
Dehydrated,		
with water	1 c	1146
Vegetable beef:		
Condensed,		
with water	1 c	957
Dehydrated,		
with water	1 c	1000
Low sodium	1 c	51
Soybeans:		
Cooked	1 c	4
Curd (tofu)	$\frac{1}{4}$ block	9
Fermented (miso):		
Red	$\frac{1}{4}$ c	3708
White	$\frac{1}{4}$ c	2126
Soy sauce	1 tbsp	1029
Spaghetti, cooked	1 c	2
Spaghetti, canned:		
And ground beef	7.5 oz	1054
And meatballs	7.5 oz	942
Sauce	4 oz	856
Spinach:		
Raw	1 c	49
Cooked	1 c	94
Frozen:		
Regular	3.3 oz	65
Creamed	3 oz	280
Canned:		
Regular	1 c	910
Low sodium	1 c	148
Squash:		
Summer:		
Cooked	1 c	5
Frozen, with curry	$\frac{1}{3}$ c	228
Canned, regular	1 c	785
Winter:		
Baked, mashed	1 c	2
Frozen	1 c	4
Strawberries:		
Raw	1 c	2
Frozen, sliced	1 c	6
Stuffing mix, cooked	1 c	1131
Sugar:		
Brown	1 c	66

K

Appendix K continued Food	Approximate Measure	Sodium (mg)
Sugar—continued		
Granulated	1 c	2
Powdered	1 c	1
Sweet potatoes:		
Baked or boiled in skin	1 potato	20
Canned:		
Regular	1 potato	48
Low sodium	1 serving	27
Candied	1 potato	42
Yam, white, raw	1 c	28
Sweet rolls:		
Apple crunch, frozen	1 roll	105
Caramel, frozen	1 roll	118
Taco	1 taco	401
Tangelo	1 tangelo	1
Tangerine	1 tangerine	1
Tangerine juice	1 c	2
Tea:		
Hot:		
Brewed	8 fl oz	1
Instant	8 fl oz	2
Iced:		
Canned	8 fl oz	9
Powdered, lemon flavored		
Sugar sweetened	8 fl oz	1
Low calorie	8 fl oz	15
Teriyaki sauce	1 tbsp	690
Toaster pastry:		
Apple, frosted	1 pastry	324
Blueberry, frosted	1 pastry	242
Cinnamon, frosted	1 pastry	326
Strawberry	1 pastry	238
Tomatoes:		
Raw	1 tomato	14
Cooked	1 c	10
Canned:		
Whole, regular	1 c	390
Stewed, regular	1 c	584
Low sodium	1 c	16
Tomato catsup:		
Regular	1 tbsp	156
Low sodium	1 tbsp	3
Tomato juice:		
Regular	1 c	878
Low sodium	1 c	9

Food	Approximate Measure	Sodium (mg)
Tomato paste	1 c	77
Tomato sauce	1 c	1498
Turkey, small, roasted:		
Breast with skin	$\frac{1}{2}$ breast	182
Leg with skin	1 leg	195
Turkey:		
Dinner, frozen	1 dinner	1228
Potpie:		
Home recipe	1 pie	620
Frozen	1 pie	1018
Turnip greens, cooked	1 c	17
Veal, cooked, lean	3 oz	69
Veal Parmigiana	7.5 oz	1825
Vegetable juice cocktail	1 c	887
Vegetables, mixed:		
Frozen	3.3 oz	45
Canned, regular	1 c	380
Vinegar	$\frac{1}{2}$ c	1
Waffle, frozen	1 waffle	275
Walnuts, English	1 c	3
Watermelon	$\frac{1}{16}$ melon	8
Worcestershire sauce	1 tbsp	206
Yeast, baker's, dry	1 pkg.	1
Yogurt:		
Plain:		
Regular	8 oz	105
Lowfat	8 oz	159
Skim milk	8 oz	174
With fruit	8 oz	133

Most data drawn from: Science and Education Administration in cooperation with Northeast Cooperative Extension Services. 1980. *The sodium content of your food*. Home and Garden Bulletin Number 233. Washington, DC: U.S. Government Printing Office.
Some data drawn from: (1) McQuitkin, C., and R.H. Matthews. 1981. *Provisional table on the nutrient content of bakery foods and related items*. Washington, DC: Nutrient Data Research Group, United States Department of Agriculture; and (2) Pennington, J.A.T., and H.N. Church. 1980. *Food values of portions commonly used*. Philadelphia: J.B. Lippincott Company.

K

Appendix L Zinc Content of Foods
(Values pertain to edible portions unless indicated otherwise.)

Food	Approximate measure	Zinc (mg)
Alfalfa sprouts, raw	1 c	0.7
Apples, raw	1 medium	0.1
Applesauce, unsweetened	1 c	0.3
Bananas, raw	1 medium	0.3
Beans, common, mature dry, boiled, drained	1 c	1.8
Beans, Lima, mature, dry, boiled, drained	1 c	1.7
Beans, snap, green		
Raw, cut into 1- to 2-in. lengths	1 c	0.4
Boiled, drained, cut and French style	1 c	0.4
Canned, drained solids	1 c	0.4
Beef, separable lean		
Cooked, dry heat	3 oz	4.9
Cooked, moist heat	3 oz	5.3
Beef, ground, cooked	3 oz	3.8
Beverages, carbonated, nonalcoholic		
12 fl. oz	1 bottle	tr
12 fl. oz	1 can	0.3
Breakfast cereals, cooked		
Cornmeal, white or yellow, degermed, cooked	1 c	0.3
Farina, regular, cooked	1 c	0.2
Oatmeal or rolled oats, cooked	1 c	1.2
Wheat cereal, cooked	1 c	1.2
Breakfast cereals, ready-to-eat		
Corn flakes	1 oz	0.1
Granola	1 oz	0.6
Oat cereal, puffed	1 oz	0.8
Rice cereal, ready-to-eat, Puffed or flakes	1 oz	0.4
Wheat cereals, ready-to-eat		
Bran flakes, 40%	1 oz	1.0
Flakes	1 oz	0.6
Germ, toasted	1 tbsp	0.9
Puffed	1 oz	0.7
Shredded	1 oz	0.8
Breads		
Rye	1 slice	0.4
White	1 slice	0.2
Whole wheat	1 slice	0.5
Butter	1 tbsp	tr
Cabbage, common		
Raw, shredded finely	1 c	0.3
Shredded, boiled, drained	1 c	0.6
Cake, white, without icing	1 piece (3 × 3 × 2 in.)	0.2
Carrots		
Raw	1 medium	0.3
Cooked or canned, drained solids	1 c	0.5

tr = present in trace amounts—in this case, less than 0.05 mg/serving.

Appendix L   continued

Food	Approximate measure	Zinc (mg)
Cheese, Cheddar type	1 slice	0.5
Chicken, broiler-fryer, cooked, dry heat		
Breast, cooked		
Meat only	$\frac{1}{2}$ breast	0.7
Meat and skin	$\frac{1}{2}$	0.9
Drumstick, thigh, back, meat only, cooked	3 oz	2.4
Drumstick		
Meat only	1	1.3
Meat and skin	1	1.4
Chickpeas or garbanzos, boiled, drained	1 c	2.0
Chocolate syrup, 1 fl oz	2 tbsp	0.3
Cocoa, dry powder	1 tbsp	0.3
Coffe		
Dry, instant	1 tbsp	tr
Fluid beverage, 6 fl oz	1 c	0.1
Cookies ($1\frac{3}{8} \times \frac{1}{4}$ in.)	10	0.1
Corn, sweet, yellow		
Boiled, drained	1 c	0.7
Canned, vacuum pack, solids and liquid	1 c	0.8
Corn chips	1 oz	0.4
Cowpeas (blackeye) boiled, drained	1 c	3.0
Crackers		
Graham ($2\frac{1}{2} \times 2\frac{1}{2}$ in.)	2	0.2
Saltines	10	0.1
Doughnuts ($3\frac{1}{4}$-in. diameter)	1	0.2
Eggs, fresh		
White	1 large	tr
Yolk	1 large	0.5
Whole	1 large	0.5
Fish and shellfish		
Clams		
Soft shell, cooked	3 oz	1.4
Hard shell, cooked	4 or 5 clams	1.0
Crabs, steamed, pieces	1 c	6.7
Fish, white varieties, flesh only		
Fillet, cooked	3 oz	0.9
Steak, cooked	3 oz	0.7
Lobster, cooked, cubed	1 c	3.1
Oysters		
Atlantic, frozen, solids and liquid, 12-fl-oz can	1 can	268.9
Pacific, frozen, solids and liquid, 12-fl-oz can	1 can	32.4
Salmon, canned, solids and liquid	1 c	2.1
Shrimp		
Boiled, peeled, deveined, 33/lb	6	1.7
Canned, drained, solids	1 c	2.7
Tuna fish, canned in oil, drained solids, can size 307 × 113, $6\frac{1}{2}$ oz	1 can	1.8

tr = present in trace amounts—in this case, less than 0.05 mg/serving.

L

Appendix L continued

Food	Approximate measure	Zinc (mg)
Heart, cooked, drained, diced		
Chicken	1 c	6.9
Turkey	1 c	7.0
Ice cream	1 c	0.6
Lamb, separable lean		
Cooked, dry heat	3 oz	3.7
Cooked, moist heat	3 oz	4.2
Lard	1 tbsp	tr
Lentils, mature, boiled, drained	1 c	2.0
Lettuce, head or leaf		
Approximately $\frac{1}{6}$ head	1 wedge	0.4
Loose leaf, chopped	1 c	0.2
Liver, cooked		
Beef	2 oz	2.9
Chicken, chopped	1 c	4.7
Macaroni, cooked tender	1 c	0.7
Margarine	1 tbsp	tr
Milk		
Fluid	1 c	0.9
Canned, evaporated	1 c	1.9
Dry, nonfat	1 c	3.1
Miso	3 tbsp	3.3
Oil, salad or cooking	1 c	0.4
Onions		
Mature, chopped	1 c	0.6
Young green, chopped	1 c	0.3
Oranges, raw ($2\frac{5}{8}$-in. diameter)	1	0.2
Orange juice		
Canned, unsweetened	1 c	0.2
Fresh or frozen	1 c	0.1
Peaches		
Raw, peeled ($2\frac{1}{2}$-in. diameter)	1 medium	0.2
Canned, drained slices	1 c	0.3
Peanuts, roasted	1 tbsp	0.3
Peanut butter	1 tbsp	0.5
Peas, green, immature		
Boiled, drained	1 c	1.2
Canned, drained solids	1 c	1.3
Peas, green dry mature, boiled, drained	1 c	2.1
Popcorn		
Unpopped	1 c	7.9
Popped		
Plain, large kernel	1 c	0.2
Oil and salt added	1 c	0.3
Pork, cooked, dry heat, separable lean trimmed	3 oz	3.2

Appendix L   continued

Food	Approximate measure	Zinc (mg)
Potatoes		
Pared before cooking, boiled, drained	1 medium	0.3
Boiled in skin, drained, pared	1 medium	0.4
Rice		
Brown, cooked	1 c	1.2
White, regular, long-grain, cooked	1 c	0.8
White, parboiled, cooked	1 c	0.6
White, precooked, quick, cooked	1 c	0.4
Rolls, hamburger ($3\frac{1}{2}$-in. diameter)	1	0.2
Salad dressing	1 tbsp	tr
Sausages and cold cuts		
Bologna, beef ($4\frac{1}{2}$-in. diameter), 1 oz	1 slice	0.5
Braunschweiger, 1 oz	1 slice	0.8
Frankfurters		
Made with beef, 10/lb	1	0.9
Made with beef and pork, 10/lb	1	0.7
Soymilk (unfortified)	$\frac{1}{2}$ c	0.2
Spinach		
Raw, chopped	1 c	0.5
Boiled, drained, canned	1 c	1.3
Sugar, white, granulated	1 c	0.1
Tahini	1 tsp	0.3
Tea, fluid beverage, 6 fl oz	1 c	tr
Tomatoes, ripe		
Raw ($2\frac{3}{5}$-in. diameter)	1 medium	0.2
Boiled	1 c	0.5
Canned, solids and liquid	1 c	0.5
Turkey, cooked, dry heat, meat only		
Light meat	3 oz	1.8
Dark meat	3 oz	3.7
Veal, separable lean		
Cooked, dry heat	3 oz	3.5
Cooked, moist heat	3 oz	3.6
Wheat flours		
Whole, stirred, spooned into cup	1 c	2.9
All-purpose, sifted, spooned into cup, standard granulation	1 c	0.8
Bread flour, sifted, spooned into cup, standard granulation	1 c	0.9
Cake flour, sifted, spooned into cup	1 c	0.3
Yeast, Brewer's, dry	1 tbsp	0.6

Most data drawn from: Murphy, E.W., B.W. Willis, and B.K. Watt. 1975. Provisional tables on the zinc content of foods. *Journal of the American Dietetic Association* 66:345–355.
Some data drawn from: Truesdell, D.D., E.N. Whitney, and P.B. Acosta. 1984. Nutrients in vegetarian foods. *Journal of the American Dietetic Association* 84:28–35.

tr = present in trace amounts—in this case, less than 0.05 mg/serving.

L

Appendix M   Additives in U.S. Foods

This list identifies the functions of a few of the over 2800 additives allowed in the U.S. food supply.

KEY

■ **Aid in processing or preparation**

● **Maintain product quality**

◆ **Maintain/improve nutritional quality**

▲ **Affect appeal characteristics**

stabil-thick-tex = stabilizers-thickeners-texturizers

leavening = leavening agents

pH control = pH control agents

mat-bleach-condit = maturing and bleaching agents, dough conditioners

anticaking = anticaking agents

A

Acetic acid	■ pH control
Acetone peroxide	■ mat-bleach-condit
Adipic acid	■ pH control
Ammonium alginate	■ stabil-thick-tex
Annatto extract	▲ color
Arabinogalactan	■ stabil-thick-tex
Ascorbic acid	◆ nutrient
	● preservative
	● antioxidant
Azodicarbonamide	■ mat-bleach-condit

B

Benzoic acid	● preservative
Benzoyl peroxide	■ mat-bleach-condit
Beta-apo-8′ carotenal	▲ color
Beta carotene	◆ nutrient
	▲ color
BHA (butylated hydroxyanisole)	● antioxidant
BHT (butylated hydroxytoluene)	● antioxidant
Butylparaben	● preservative

C

Calcium alginate	■ stabil-thick-tex
Calcium bromate	■ mat-bleach-condit
Calcium lactate	● preservative
Calcium phosphate	■ leavening
Calcium propionate	● preservative

Calcium silicate	■ anticaking
Calcium sorbate	● preservative
Canthaxanthin	▲ color
Caramel	▲ color
Carob bean gum	■ stabil-thick-tex
Carrageenan	■ emulsifier
	■ stabil-thick-tex
Carrot oil	▲ color
Cellulose	● stabil-thick-tex
Citric acid	● preservative
	● antioxidant
	■ pH control
Citrus Red No. 2	▲ color
Cochineal extract	▲ color
Corn endosperm	▲ color
Corn syrup	▲ sweetener

D

Dehydrated beets	▲ color
Dextrose	▲ sweetener
Diglycerides	■ emulsifier
Dioctyl sodium sulfosuccinate	■ emulsifier
Disodium guanylate	▲ flavor enhancer
Disodium inosinate	▲ flavor enhancer
Dried algae meal	▲ color

E

EDTA (ethylenediaminetetraacetic acid)	● antioxidant

F

FD&C Colors:	
Blue No. 1	▲ color
Red No. 3	▲ color
Red No. 40	▲ color
Yellow No. 5	▲ color
Fructose	▲ sweetener

G

Gelatin	■ stabil-thick-tex
Glucose	▲ sweetener
Glycerine	■ humectant
Glycerol monostearate	■ humectant
Grape skin extract	▲ color
Guar gum	■ stabil-thick-tex
Gum arabic	■ stabil-thick-tex
Gum ghatti	■ stabil-thick-tex

H

Heptylparaben	● preservative
Hydrogen peroxide	■ mat-bleach-condit
Hydrolyzed vegetable protein	▲ flavor enhancer

M

I

Invert sugar	▲ sweetener
Iodine	◆ nutrient
Iron	◆ nutrient
Iron-ammonium citrate	■ anticaking
Iron oxide	▲ color

K

Karaya gum	■ stabil-thick-tex

L

Lactic acid	■ pH control
	● preservative
Larch gum	■ stabil-thick-tex
Lecithin	■ emulsifier
Locust bean gum	■ stabil-thick-tex

M

Mannitol	▲ sweetener
	■ anticaking
	■ stabil-thick-tex
Methylparaben	● preservative
Modified food starch	■ stabil-thick-tex
Monoglycerides	■ emulsifer
MSG (monosodium glutamate)	▲ flavor enhancer

N

Niacinamide	◆ nutrient

P

Paprika (and oleoresin)	▲ flavor
	▲ color
Pectin	■ stabil-thick-tex
Phosphates	■ pH control
Phosphoric acid	■ pH control
Polysorbates	■ emulsifiers
Potassium alginate	■ stabil-thick-tex
Potassium bromate	■ mat-bleach-condit
Potassium iodide	◆ nutrient
Potassium propionate	● preservative
Potassium sorbate	● preservative
Propionic acid	● preservative
Propyl gallate	● antioxidant
Propylene glycol	■ stabil-thick-tex
	■ humectant
Propylparaben	● preservative

R

Riboflavin	◆ nutrient
	▲ color

M

S

Saccharin	▲ sweetener
Saffron	▲ color
Silicon dioxide	■ anticaking
Sodium acetate	■ pH control
Sodium alginate	■ stabil-thick-tex
Sodium aluminum sulfate	■ leavening
Sodium benzoate	● preservative
Sodium bicarbonate	■ leavening
Sodium calcium alginate	■ stabil-thick-tex
Sodium citrate	■ pH control
Sodium diacetate	● preservative
Sodium erythorbate	● preservative
Sodium nitrate	● preservative
Sodium nitrite	● preservative
Sodium propionate	● preservative
Sodium sorbate	● preservative
Sodium stearyl fumarate	■ mat-bleach-condit
Sorbic acid	● preservative
Sorbitan monostearate	■ emulsifier
Sorbitol	■ humectant
	▲ sweetener
Spices	▲ flavor
Sucrose (table sugar)	▲ sweetener

T

Tagetes (Aztec Marigold)	▲ color
Tartaric acid	■ pH control
TBHQ (tertiary butyl hydroquinone)	● antioxidant
Thiamine	♦ nutrient
Titanium dioxide	▲ color
Toasted, partially defatted cooked cottonseed flour	▲ color
Tocopherols (vitamin E)	♦ nutrient
	● antioxidant
Tragacanth gum	■ stabil-thick-tex
Turmeric (oleoresin)	▲ flavor
	▲ color

U

Ultramarine blue	▲ color

V

Vanilla, vanillin	▲ flavor
Vitamin A	♦ nutrient
Vitamin C (ascorbic acid)	♦ nutrient
	● preservative
	● antioxidant

Vitamin D (D$_2$, D$_3$)	◆	nutrient
Vitamin E (tocopherols)	◆	nutrient
Y		
Yeast-malt sprout extract	▲	flavor enhancer
Yellow prussiate of soda	■	anticaking

Adapted from Lehmann, P. 1979. More than you ever thought you would know about food additives. *FDA Consumer* reprint. Health and Human Services Publication No. (FDA) 79-2115.

M

Photo Credits

Index

Note: Bold number indicates term defined; t = table; f = figure.